Elayn Martin-Gay

Beginning & Intermediate Algebra

A Custom Edition for Anne Arundel Community College

Taken from:
Beginning & Intermediate Algebra, Fifth Edition
by Elayn Martin-Gay

Cover Art: Illustration by Kristen Kiley

Taken from:

Beginning & Intermediate Algebra, Fifth Edition
by Elayn Martin-Gay
Copyright © 2013, 2009, 2005, 2001, 1996 by Pearson Education, Inc.
Published by Prentice Higher Education
Upper Saddle River, New Jersey 07458

This special edition published in cooperation with Pearson Learning Solutions.

Pearson Learning Solutions, 501 Boylston Street, Suite 900, Boston, MA 02116
A Pearson Education Company
www.pearsoned.com

Printed in the United States of America

5 6 7 8 9 10 V0ZN 18 17 16 15 14

0002000010271674267

MM

ISBN 10: 1-256-83437-8
ISBN 13: 978-1-256-83437-3

This book is dedicated to students everywhere—and we should all be students. After all, is there anyone among us who really knows too much? Take that hint and continue to learn something new every day of your life.

Best of wishes from a fellow student: Elayn Martin-Gay

Contents

Student Resources

These resources, located in the back of the text, give you a variety of tools conveniently located in one place to help you succeed in math.

Study Skills Builders

Attitude and Study Tips:

1. Have You Decided to Complete This Course Successfully?
2. Tips for Studying for an Exam
3. What to Do the Day of an Exam
4. Are You Satisfied with Your Performance on a Particular Quiz or Exam?
5. How Are You Doing?
6. Are You Preparing for Your Final Exam?

Organizing Your Work:

7. Learning New Terms
8. Are You Organized?
9. Organizing a Notebook
10. How Are Your Homework Assignments Going?

MyMathLab and MathXL:

11. Tips for Turning in Your Homework on Time
12. Tips for Doing Your Homework Online
13. Organizing Your Work
14. Getting Help with Your Homework Assignments
15. Tips for Preparing for an Exam
16. How Well Do You Know the Resources Available to You in MyMathLab?

Additional Help Inside and Outside Your Textbook:

17. How Well Do You Know Your Textbook?
18. Are You Familiar with Your Textbook Supplements?
19. Are You Getting All the Mathematics Help That You Need?

The Bigger Picture–Study Guide Outline

Practice Final Exam

Answers to Selected Exercises

A New Tool to Help You Succeed

Introducing Martin-Gay's New Student Organizer

The new **Student Organizer** guides you through three important parts of studying effectively—note-taking, practice, and homework.

It is designed to help you organize your learning materials and develop the study habits you need to be successful. The Student Organizer includes:

- How to prepare for class
- Space to take class notes
- Step-by-step worked examples
- Your Turn exercises (modeled after the examples)
- Answers to the Your Turn exercises as well as worked-out solutions via references to the Martin-Gay text and videos
- Helpful hints and directions for completing homework assignments

A flexible design allows instructors to assign any or all parts of the Student Organizer.

The Student Organizer is available in a loose-leaf, notebook-ready format. It is also available for download in MyMathLab.

For more information, please go to

www.pearsonhighered.com/martingay

www.mypearsonstore.com

    (search Martin-Gay, Beginning & Intermediate Algebra, Fifth Edition)
your Martin-Gay MyMathLab® course

Martin-Gay Video Resources to Help You Succeed

Interactive DVD Lecture Series

Active Learning at Your Pace

Designed for use on your computer or DVD player, these interactive videos include a 15–20 minute lecture for every section in the text as well as Concept Checks, Study Skills Builders, and a Practice Final Exam.

Pop-ups
Take note of key concepts, terms, and definitions as pop-ups appear throughout each section.

Be careful: Combine like terms only.

CC ESP Menu   ◄ 6/8 ►

Exercises
Know how to do an exercise? Click the "next" arrow to skip ahead or the "back" arrow to review an exercise.

Progress Meter
Monitor your progress through the lecture and exercises at a glance.

Interactive Concept Checks
pose questions about key concepts and prompt you to click on an answer. Learn whether your answer is correct and view the full solution.

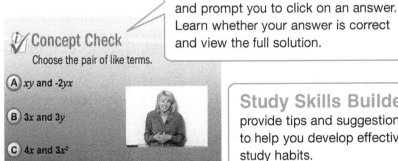

☑ Concept Check
Choose the pair of like terms.
(A) xy and $-2yx$
(B) $3x$ and $3y$
(C) $4x$ and $3x^2$
CC ESP Menu   ◄ ☑CC ►

Study Skills Builders
provide tips and suggestions to help you develop effective study habits.

Study Skills Builder
Doing your homework online
• Help Me Solve This
• View an Example
• Video 🎥
• Textbook Pages
CC ESP Menu   ◄ SSB ►

Chapter Test Prep Videos

Step-by-step solutions on video for all chapter test exercises from the text. Available via:

- Interactive DVD Lecture Series
- MyMathLab®
- You Tube™

English and Spanish Subtitles Available

AlgebraPrep Apps for the iPhone™ and iPod Touch®

Your 24/7 Algebra Tutor—Anytime, Anywhere!

Choose to take a Practice Test or a MiniTest (designed to take 10 minutes or less).

Practice Test exercises provide answer feedback to help you study and self-correct.

Step-by-step video solutions give you the guidance of an expert tutor whenever you need help.

Preface

Beginning & Intermediate Algebra, **Fifth Edition,** was written to provide a solid foundation in algebra for students who might not have previous experience in algebra. Specific care was taken to make sure students have the most up-to-date, relevant text preparation for their next mathematics course or for nonmathematical courses that require an understanding of algebraic fundamentals. I have tried to achieve this by writing a user-friendly text that is keyed to objectives and contains many worked-out examples. As suggested by AMATYC and the NCTM Standards (plus Addenda), real-life and real-data applications, data interpretation, conceptual understanding, problem solving, writing, cooperative learning, appropriate use of technology, mental mathematics, number sense, estimation, critical thinking, and geometric concepts are emphasized and integrated throughout the book.

The many factors that contributed to the success of the previous editions have been retained. In preparing the Fifth Edition, I considered comments and suggestions of colleagues, students, and many users of the prior edition throughout the country.

What's New in the Fifth Edition?

- **The Martin-Gay Program** has been revised and enhanced with a new design in the text and MyMathLab to actively encourage students to use the text, video program, and Student Organizer as an integrated learning system.

- **The Student Organizer** is designed by me to help students develop the study habits they need to be successful. This Organizer guides students through the three main components of studying effectively—note-taking, practice, and homework—and helps them develop the habits that will enable them to succeed in future courses. The Student Organizer can be packaged with the text in loose-leaf, notebook-ready format and is also available for download in MyMathLab.

- **New Vocabulary, Readiness & Video Check** questions have been added prior to every section exercise set. These exercises quickly check a student's understanding of new vocabulary words. The **readiness** exercises center on a student's understanding of a concept that is necessary in order to continue to the exercise set. **New video check questions for the Martin-Gay Interactive Lecture videos** are now included in every section for each learning objective. **These exercises are all available for assignment in MyMathLab** and are a great way to assess whether students have viewed and understood the key concepts presented in the videos.

- **The Interactive DVD Lecture Series,** featuring your text author (Elayn Martin-Gay), provides students with active learning at their own pace. The videos offer the following resources and more:

    A complete lecture for each section of the text highlights key examples and exercises from the text. New "pop-ups" reinforce key terms, definitions, and concepts.

    An interface with menu navigation features allows students to quickly find and focus on the examples and exercises they need to review.

    Interactive Concept Check exercises measure students' understanding of key concepts and common trouble spots.

    The Interactive DVD Lecture Series also includes the following resources for test prep:

    The Practice Final Exam helps students prepare for an end-of-course final. Students can watch full video solutions to each exercise.

The Chapter Test Prep Videos help students during their most teachable moment–when they are preparing for a test. This innovation provides step-by-step solutions for the Chapter Test exercises found at the end of each chapter in the text. The videos are captioned in English and Spanish. For the Fifth Edition, the chapter test prep videos are also available on YouTube™.

● **The Martin-Gay MyMathLab course** has been updated and revised to provide more exercise coverage, including assignable video check questions, and an expanded video program. There are section lecture videos for every section, students can also access at the specific objective level, and there are an increased number of watch clips at the exercise level to help students while doing homework in MathXL. Suggested homework assignments have been premade for assignment at the instructor's discretion.

● **New MyMathLab Ready to Go courses** (access code required) provide students with all the same great MyMathLab features that you're used to, but make it easier for instructors to get started. Each course includes preassigned homework and quizzes to make creating your course even simpler. Ask your Pearson representative about the details for this particular course or to see a copy of this course.

● **A new section** (12.4) devoted specifically to exponential growth and decay and applications has been added. This section includes the definition and examples of half-life.

● **The new Student Resources** section, located in the back of the text, gives students a variety of tools that are conveniently located in one place to help them achieve success in mathematics.

— **Study Skills Builders** give students tips and suggestions on successful study habits and help them take responsibility for their learning. Assignable exercises check students' progress in improving their skills.

— The **Bigger Picture—Study Guide Outline** covers key concepts of the course—simplifying expressions and solving equations and inequalities—to help students transition from thinking section-by-section to thinking about how the material they are learning fits into mathematics as a whole. This outline provides a model for students on how to organize and develop their own study guide.

— The **Practice Final Exam** helps students prepare for the end-of-the-course exam. Students can also watch the step-by-step solutions to all the Practice Final Exam exercises on the new Interactive DVD Lecture Series and in MyMathLab.

— The **Answers to Selected Exercises** section allows students to check their answers for all Practice exercises; odd-numbered Vocabulary, Readiness & Video Check exercises; odd-numbered section exercises; odd-numbered Chapter Review and Cumulative Review exercises; and all Integrated Review and Chapter Test exercises.

● **New guided application exercises** appear in many sections throughout the text, beginning with Section 2.4. These applications prompt students on how to set up the application and get started with the solution process. These guided exercises will help students prepare to solve application exercises on their own.

● **Enhanced emphasis on Study Skills** helps students develop good study habits and makes it more convenient for instructors to incorporate or assign study skills in their courses. The following changes have been made in the Fifth Edition:

Section 1.1, Tips for Success in Mathematics, has been updated to include helpful hints for doing homework online in MyMathLab. Exercises pertaining to doing homework online in MyMathLab are now included in the exercise set for 1.1.

The Study Skills Builders, formerly located at the end of select exercise sets, are now included in the new **Student Resources** section at the back of the book and are organized by topic for ease of assignment. This section now also includes new Study Skills Builders on doing homework online in MyMathLab.

- All exercise sets have been reviewed and updated to ensure that even- and odd-numbered exercises are paired.

Key Pedagogical Features

The following key features have been retained and/or updated for the Fifth Edition of the text:

Problem-Solving Process This is formally introduced in Chapter 2 with a four-step process that is integrated throughout the text. The four steps are **Understand, Translate, Solve,** and **Interpret.** The repeated use of these steps in a variety of examples shows their wide applicability. Reinforcing the steps can increase students' comfort level and confidence in tackling problems.

Exercise Sets Revised and Updated The exercise sets have been carefully examined and extensively revised. Special focus was placed on making sure that even- and odd-numbered exercises are paired.

Examples Detailed, step-by-step examples were added, deleted, replaced, or updated as needed. Many of these reflect real life. Additional instructional support is provided in the annotated examples.

Practice Exercises Throughout the text, each worked-out example has a parallel Practice Exercise. These invite students to be actively involved in the learning process. Students should try each Practice Exercise after finishing the corresponding example. Learning by doing will help students grasp ideas before moving on to other concepts. Answers to the Practice Exercises are provided in the back of the text.

Helpful Hints Helpful Hints contain practical advice on applying mathematical concepts. Strategically placed where students are most likely to need immediate reinforcement, Helpful Hints help students avoid common trouble areas and mistakes.

Concept Checks This feature allows students to gauge their grasp of an idea as it is being presented in the text. Concept Checks stress conceptual understanding at the point-of-use and help suppress misconceived notions before they start. Answers appear at the bottom of the page. Exercises related to Concept Checks are included in the exercise sets.

Mixed Practice Exercises Found in the section exercise sets, each requires students to determine the problem type and strategy needed to solve it just as they would need to do on a test.

Integrated Reviews A unique, mid-chapter exercise set that helps students assimilate new skills and concepts that they have learned separately over several sections. These reviews provide yet another opportunity for students to work with "mixed" exercises as they master the topics.

Vocabulary Check Provides an opportunity for students to become more familiar with the use of mathematical terms as they strengthen their verbal skills. These appear at the end of each chapter before the Chapter Highlights. Vocabulary, Readiness & Video Check exercises also provide vocabulary practice at the section level.

Chapter Highlights   Found at the end of every chapter, these contain key definitions and concepts with examples to help students understand and retain what they have learned and help them organize their notes and study for tests.

Chapter Review   The end of every chapter contains a comprehensive review of topics introduced in the chapter. The Chapter Review offers exercises keyed to every section in the chapter, as well as Mixed Review exercises that are not keyed to sections.

Chapter Test and Chapter Test Prep Video   The Chapter Test is structured to include those problems that involve common student errors. The **Chapter Test Prep Videos** give students instant access to a step-by-step video solution of each exercise in the Chapter Test.

Cumulative Review   Follows every chapter in the text (except Chapter 1). Each odd-numbered exercise contained in the Cumulative Review is an earlier worked example in the text that is referenced in the back of the book along with the answer.

Writing Exercises   ＼ These exercises occur in almost every exercise set and require students to provide a written response to explain concepts or justify their thinking.

Applications   Real-world and real-data applications have been thoroughly updated and many new applications are included. These exercises occur in almost every exercise set and show the relevance of mathematics and help students gradually, and continuously, develop their problem-solving skills.

Review and Preview Exercises   These exercises occur in each exercise set (except in Chapter 1) and are keyed to earlier sections. They review concepts learned earlier in the text that will be needed in the next section or chapter.

Exercise Set Resource Icons   Located at the opening of each exercise set, these icons remind students of the resources available for extra practice and support:

See Student Resources descriptions on page xviii for details on the individual resources available.

Exercise Icons   These icons facilitate the assignment of specialized exercises and let students know what resources can support them.

- ▶ Video icon: exercise worked on the Interactive DVD Lecture Series and in MyMathLab.
- △ Triangle icon: identifies exercises involving geometric concepts.
- ＼ Pencil icon: indicates a written response is needed.
- ▦ Calculator icon: optional exercises intended to be solved using a scientific or graphing calculator.

Optional: Graphing Calculator Exploration Boxes and Calculator Exercises   The optional Graphing Calculator Explorations provide keystrokes and exercises at appropriate points to give an opportunity for students to become familiar with these tools. Section exercises that are best completed by using a calculator are identified by ▦ for ease of assignment.

Student and Instructor Resources

STUDENT RESOURCES

Student Organizer Guides students through the 3 main components of studying effectively–note-taking, practice, and homework. The organizer includes before-class preparation exercises, note-taking pages in a 2-column format for use in class, and examples paired with exercises for practice for each section. It is 3-hole-punched. Also available in MyMathLab.	**Student Solutions Manual** Provides complete worked-out solutions to • the odd-numbered section exercises; all Practice Exercises; all exercises in the Integrated Reviews, Chapter Reviews, Chapter Tests, and Cumulative Reviews

Interactive DVD Lecture Series
 	
Provides students with active learning at their pace. The videos offer:
 	
  • A complete lecture for each text section. The interface allows easy navigation to examples and exercises students need to review.
  • Interactive Concept Check exercises
  • Study Skills Builders
  • Practice Final Exam
  • Chapter Test Prep Videos
	Chapter Test Prep Videos
	
	  • Step-by-step solutions to every exercise in each Chapter Practice Test.
	  • Available in MyMathLab® and on YouTube, and in the Interactive DVD Lecture Series.

INSTRUCTOR RESOURCES

Annotated Instructor's Edition
 	
Contains all the content found in the student edition, plus the following:
 	
  • Answers to exercises on the same text page
  • Answers to graphing exercises and all video exercises
  • Teaching Tips throughout the text placed at key points.
  • Classroom Examples in the margin paired to each example in the text.
	Instructor's Resource Manual with Tests and Mini-Lectures
	
	  • Mini-lectures for each text section
	  • Additional Practice worksheets for each section
	  • Several forms of test per chapter–free response and multiple choice
	  • Group activities
	  • Video key to the example number in the video questions and section exercises worked in the videos
	  • Answers to all items
	
	Instructor's Solutions Manual
	TestGen® (Available for download from the IRC)

	Online Resources **MyMathLab®** (access code required) **MathXL®** (access code required)

Acknowledgments

There are many people who helped me develop this text, and I will attempt to thank some of them here. Cindy Trimble and Carrie Green were *invaluable* for contributing to the overall accuracy of the text. Dawn Nuttall, Courtney Slade, and JoAnne Thomasson were *invaluable* for their many suggestions and contributions during the development and writing of this Fifth Edition. Debbie Meyer and Amanda Zagnoli of Integra-Chicago provided guidance throughout the production process.

A very special thank you goes to my editor, Mary Beckwith, for being there 24/7/365, as my students say. Last, my thanks to the staff at Pearson for all their support: Patty Bergin, Heather Scott, Michelle Renda, Chris Hoag, and Greg Tobin.

I would like to thank the following reviewers for their input and suggestions:

Sandi Athanassiou, *University of Missouri–Columbia*
Michelle Beerman, *Pasco-Hernandez Community College*
Monika Bender, *Central Texas College*
Bob Hervey, *Hillsborough Community College*
Michael Maltenfort, *Truman College*
Jorge Romero, *Hillsborough Community College*
Joseph Wakim, *Brevard Community College*
Flo Wilson, *Central Texas College*
Marie Caruso and students, *Middlesex Community College*

I would also like to thank the following dedicated group of instructors who participated in our focus groups, Martin-Gay Summits, and our design review for the series. Their feedback and insights have helped to strengthen this edition of the text. These instructors include:

Billie Anderson, *Tyler Junior College*
Joey Anderson, *Central Piedmont Community College*
Cedric Atkins, *Mott Community College*
Teri Barnes, *McLennan Community College*
Andrea Barnett, *Tri-County Technical College*
Lois Beardon, *Schoolcraft College*
Michelle Beerman, *Pasco-Hernandez Community College*
Laurel Berry, *Bryant & Stratton College*
John Beyers, *University of Maryland*
Jennifer Brahier, *Pensacola Junior College*
Bob Brown, *Community College of Baltimore County–Essex*
Lisa Brown, *Community College of Baltimore County–Essex*
NeKeith Brown, *Richland College*
Sue Brown, *Guilford Technical Community College*
Gail Burkett, *Palm Beach State College*
Cheryl Cantwell, *Seminole Community College*
Janie Chapman, *Spartanburg Community College*
Jackie Cohen, *Augusta State College*
Julie Dewan, *Mohawk Valley Community College*
Janice Ervin, *Central Piedmont Community College*
Karen Estes, *St. Petersburg College*
Richard Fielding, *Southwestern College*
Sonia Ford, *Midland College*
Julie Francavilla, *State College of Florida*
Cindy Gaddis, *Tyler Junior College*
Nita Graham, *St. Louis Community College*
Pauline Hall, *Iowa State College*
Elizabeth Hamman, *Cypress College*
Kathy Hoffmaster, *Thomas Nelson Community College*
Pat Hussey, *Triton College*
Dorothy Johnson, *Lorain County Community College*
Sonya Johnson, *Central Piedmont Community College*

Irene Jones, *Fullerton College*
Paul Jones, *University of Cincinnati*
Mike Kirby, *Tidewater Community College*
Kathy Kopelousos, *Lewis and Clark Community College*
Nancy Lange, *Inver Hills Community College*
Judy Langer, *Westchester Community College*
Lisa Lindloff, *McLennan Community College*
Sandy Lofstock, *St. Petersburg College*
Kathy Lovelle, *Westchester Community College*
Jamie Malek, *Florida State College*
Jean McArthur, *Joliet Junior College*
Kevin McCandless, *Evergreen Valley College*
Daniel Miller, *Niagara County Community College*
Marcia Molle, *Metropolitan Community College*
Carol Murphy, *San Diego Miramar College*
Charlotte Newsom, *Tidewater Community College*
Greg Nguyen, *Fullerton College*
Eric Ollila, *Jackson Community College*
Linda Padilla, *Joliet Junior College*
Rena Petrello, *Moorpark College*
Davidson Pierre, *State College of Florida*
Marilyn Platt, *Gaston College*
Susan Poss, *Spartanburg Community College*
Natalie Rivera, *Estrella Mountain Community College*
Judy Roane, *Pearl River Community College*
Claudinna Rowley, *Montgomery Community College, Rockville*
Ena Salter, *State College of Florida*
Carole Shapero, *Oakton Community College*
Janet Sibol, *Hillsborough Community College*
Anne Smallen, *Mohawk Valley Community College*
Mike Stack, *South Suburban College*
Barbara Stoner, *Reading Area Community College*
Jennifer Strehler, *Oakton Community College*
Ellen Stutes, *Louisiana State University Eunice*
Tanomo Taguchi, *Fullerton College*
Sam Tinsley, *Richland College*
Linda Tucker, *Rose State College*
MaryAnn Tuerk, *Elgin Community College*
Gwen Turbeville, *J. Sargeant Reynolds Community College*
Walter Wang, *Baruch College*
Leigh Ann Wheeler, *Greenville Technical Community College*
Jenny Wilson, *Tyler Junior College*
Valerie Wright, *Central Piedmont Community College*

A special thank you to those students who participated in our design review: Katherine Browne, Mike Bulfin, Nancy Canipe, Ashley Carpenter, Jeff Chojnachi, Roxanne Davis, Mike Dieter, Amy Dombrowski, Kay Herring, Todd Jaycox, Kaleena Levan, Matt Montgomery, Tony Plese, Abigail Polkinghorn, Harley Price, Eli Robinson, Avery Rosen, Robyn Schott, Cynthia Thomas, and Sherry Ward.

Elayn Martin-Gay

About the Author

Elayn Martin-Gay has taught mathematics at the University of New Orleans for more than 25 years. Her numerous teaching awards include the local University Alumni Association's Award for Excellence in Teaching, and Outstanding Developmental Educator at University of New Orleans, presented by the Louisiana Association of Developmental Educators.

Prior to writing textbooks, Elayn Martin-Gay developed an acclaimed series of lecture videos to support developmental mathematics students in their quest for success. These highly successful videos originally served as the foundation material for her texts. Today, the videos are specific to each book in the Martin-Gay series. The author has also created Chapter Test Prep Videos to help students during their most "teachable moment"—as they prepare for a test—along with Instructor-to-Instructor videos that provide teaching tips, hints, and suggestions for each developmental mathematics course, including basic mathematics, prealgebra, beginning algebra, and intermediate algebra. Her most recent innovations are the AlgebraPrep Apps for the iPhone and iPod Touch. These Apps embrace the different learning styles, schedules, and paces of students and provide them with quality math tutoring.

Elayn is the author of 12 published textbooks as well as interactive multimedia mathematics, all specializing in developmental mathematics courses. She has participated as an author across the broadest range of educational materials: textbooks, videos, tutorial software, and courseware. This provides the opportunity of various combinations for an integrated teaching and learning package that offers great consistency for the student.

Applications Index

Equations, Inequalities, and Problem Solving

Much of mathematics relates to deciding which statements are true and which are false. For example, the statement $x + 7 = 15$ is an equation stating that the sum $x + 7$ has the same value as 15. Is this statement true or false? It is false for some values of x and true for just one value of x, namely 8. Our purpose in this chapter is to learn ways of deciding which values make an equation or an inequality true.

Top 10 Countries by Number of Internet-Crime Complaints

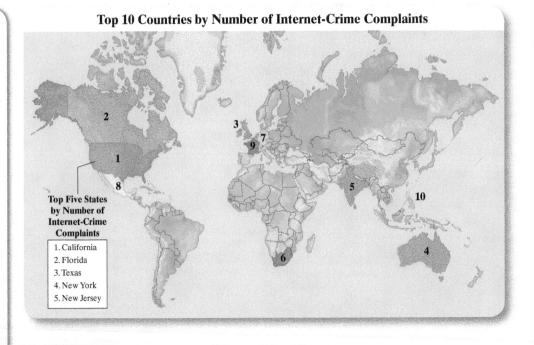

Top Five States by Number of Internet-Crime Complaints

1. California
2. Florida
3. Texas
4. New York
5. New Jersey

Internet Crime

The Internet Crime Complaint Center (IC3) is a joint operation between the FBI and the National White-Collar Crime Center. The IC3 receives and refers criminal complaints occurring on the Internet. Of course, nondelivery of merchandise or payment are the highest reported offenses.

In Section 2.6, Exercises 15 and 16, we analyze a bar graph on the yearly number of complaints received by the IC3.

Ages of Persons Filing Complaints

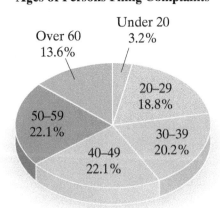

2.3 | Solving Linear Equations

OBJECTIVES

1 Apply a General Strategy for Solving a Linear Equation.

2 Solve Equations Containing Fractions.

3 Solve Equations Containing Decimals.

4 Recognize Identities and Equations with No Solution.

OBJECTIVE

1   Apply a General Strategy for Solving a Linear Equation

We now present a general strategy for solving linear equations. One new piece of strategy is a suggestion to "clear an equation of fractions" as a first step. Doing so makes the equation less tedious, since operating on integers is usually more convenient than operating on fractions.

Solving Linear Equations in One Variable

Step 1. Multiply on both sides by the LCD to clear the equation of fractions if they occur.

Step 2. Use the distributive property to remove parentheses if they occur.

Step 3. Simplify each side of the equation by combining like terms.

Step 4. Get all variable terms on one side and all numbers on the other side by using the addition property of equality.

Step 5. Get the variable alone by using the multiplication property of equality.

Step 6. Check the solution by substituting it into the original equation.

EXAMPLE 1   Solve: $4(2x - 3) + 7 = 3x + 5$

Solution   There are no fractions, so we begin with Step 2.

$$4(2x - 3) + 7 = 3x + 5$$

Step 2.	$8x - 12 + 7 = 3x + 5$	Apply the distributive property.
Step 3.	$8x - 5 = 3x + 5$	Combine like terms.

Step 4. Get all variable terms on the same side of the equation by subtracting $3x$ from both sides, then adding 5 to both sides.

$8x - 5 - 3x = 3x + 5 - 3x$	Subtract $3x$ from both sides.
$5x - 5 = 5$	Simplify.
$5x - 5 + 5 = 5 + 5$	Add 5 to both sides.
$5x = 10$	Simplify.

Step 5. Use the multiplication property of equality to get x alone.

$\dfrac{5x}{5} = \dfrac{10}{5}$	Divide both sides by 5.
$x = 2$	Simplify.

Step 6. Check.

> **Helpful Hint**
> When checking solutions, remember to use the original written equation.

$4(2x - 3) + 7 = 3x + 5$	Original equation
$4[2(2) - 3] + 7 \overset{?}{=} 3(2) + 5$	Replace x with 2.
$4(4 - 3) + 7 \overset{?}{=} 6 + 5$	
$4(1) + 7 \overset{?}{=} 11$	
$4 + 7 \overset{?}{=} 11$	
$11 = 11$	True

The solution is 2 or the solution set is $\{2\}$.   □

PRACTICE
1   Solve: $2(4a - 9) + 3 = 5a - 6$

EXAMPLE 2   Solve: $8(2 - t) = -5t$

Solution   First, we apply the distributive property.

$$8(2 - t) = -5t$$

Step 2.	$16 - 8t = -5t$	Use the distributive property.
Step 4.	$16 - 8t + 8t = -5t + 8t$	To get variable terms on one side, add $8t$ to both sides.
	$16 = 3t$	Combine like terms.
Step 5.	$\dfrac{16}{3} = \dfrac{3t}{3}$	Divide both sides by 3.
	$\dfrac{16}{3} = t$	Simplify.

Step 6. Check.

$8(2 - t) = -5t$	Original equation
$8\left(2 - \dfrac{16}{3}\right) \overset{?}{=} -5\left(\dfrac{16}{3}\right)$	Replace t with $\dfrac{16}{3}$.
$8\left(\dfrac{6}{3} - \dfrac{16}{3}\right) \overset{?}{=} -\dfrac{80}{3}$	The LCD is 3.

$$8\left(-\frac{10}{3}\right) \stackrel{?}{=} -\frac{80}{3} \quad \text{Subtract fractions.}$$

$$-\frac{80}{3} = -\frac{80}{3} \quad \text{True}$$

The solution is $\frac{16}{3}$.

PRACTICE
2   Solve: $7(x - 3) = -6x$

OBJECTIVE
2   **Solving Equations Containing Fractions**

If an equation contains fractions, we can clear the equation of fractions by multiplying both sides by the LCD of all denominators. By doing this, we avoid working with time-consuming fractions.

EXAMPLE 3   Solve: $\frac{x}{2} - 1 = \frac{2}{3}x - 3$

Solution   We begin by clearing fractions. To do this, we multiply both sides of the equation by the LCD of 2 and 3, which is 6.

$$\frac{x}{2} - 1 = \frac{2}{3}x - 3$$

Step 1. $6\left(\frac{x}{2} - 1\right) = 6\left(\frac{2}{3}x - 3\right)$ Multiply both sides by the LCD, 6.

Step 2. $6\left(\frac{x}{2}\right) - 6(1) = 6\left(\frac{2}{3}x\right) - 6(3)$ Apply the distributive property.

$$3x - 6 = 4x - 18 \quad \text{Simplify.}$$

> ▶ **Helpful Hint**
> Don't forget to multiply *each* term by the LCD.

There are no longer grouping symbols and no like terms on either side of the equation, so we continue with Step 4.

$$3x - 6 = 4x - 18$$

Step 4. $3x - 6 - 3x = 4x - 18 - 3x$ To get variable terms on one side, subtract $3x$ from both sides.

$$-6 = x - 18 \quad \text{Simplify.}$$

$$-6 + 18 = x - 18 + 18 \quad \text{Add 18 to both sides.}$$

$$12 = x \quad \text{Simplify.}$$

Step 5.   The variable is now alone, so there is no need to apply the multiplication property of equality.

Step 6.   Check.

$$\frac{x}{2} - 1 = \frac{2}{3}x - 3 \quad \text{Original equation}$$

$$\frac{12}{2} - 1 \stackrel{?}{=} \frac{2}{3} \cdot 12 - 3 \quad \text{Replace } x \text{ with 12.}$$

$$6 - 1 \stackrel{?}{=} 8 - 3 \quad \text{Simplify.}$$

$$5 = 5 \quad \text{True}$$

The solution is 12.

PRACTICE
3   Solve: $\frac{3}{5}x - 2 = \frac{2}{3}x - 1$

EXAMPLE 4   Solve: $\dfrac{2(a + 3)}{3} = 6a + 2$

Solution   We clear the equation of fractions first.

$$\frac{2(a + 3)}{3} = 6a + 2$$

Step 1. $3 \cdot \dfrac{2(a + 3)}{3} = 3(6a + 2)$ Clear the fraction by multiplying both sides by the LCD, 3.

$2(a + 3) = 3(6a + 2)$

Step 2.   Next, we use the distributive property and remove parentheses.

$2a + 6 = 18a + 6$ Apply the distributive property.

Step 4. $2a + 6 - 6 = 18a + 6 - 6$ Subtract 6 from both sides.

$2a = 18a$

$2a - 18a = 18a - 18a$ Subtract 18a from both sides.

$-16a = 0$

Step 5. $\dfrac{-16a}{-16} = \dfrac{0}{-16}$ Divide both sides by −16.

$a = 0$ Write the fraction in simplest form.

Step 6.   To check, replace a with 0 in the original equation. The solution is 0.   □

PRACTICE
4   Solve: $\dfrac{4(y + 3)}{3} = 5y - 7$

> ▶ **Helpful Hint**
> Remember: When solving an equation, it makes no difference on which side of the equation variable terms lie. Just make sure that constant terms lie on the other side.

OBJECTIVE
3   Solving Equations Containing Decimals

When solving a problem about money, you may need to solve an equation containing decimals. If you choose, you may multiply to clear the equation of decimals.

EXAMPLE 5   Solve: $0.25x + 0.10(x - 3) = 0.05(22)$

Solution   First we clear this equation of decimals by multiplying both sides of the equation by 100. Recall that multiplying a decimal number by 100 has the effect of moving the decimal point 2 places to the right.

$$0.25x + 0.10(x - 3) = 0.05(22)$$

> ▶ Helpful Hint
> By the distributive property, 0.10 is multiplied by x and −3. Thus to multiply each term here by 100, we only need to multiply 0.10 by 100.

Step 1. $0.25x + 0.10(x - 3) = 0.05(22)$ Multiply both sides by 100.

$25x + 10(x - 3) = 5(22)$

Step 2. $25x + 10x - 30 = 110$ Apply the distributive property.

Step 3. $35x - 30 = 110$ Combine like terms.

Step 4. $35x - 30 + 30 = 110 + 30$ Add 30 to both sides.

$35x = 140$ Combine like terms.

Step 5.
$$\frac{35x}{35} = \frac{140}{35}$$ Divide both sides by 35.

$$x = 4$$

Step 6. To check, replace x with 4 in the original equation. The solution is 4.   □

PRACTICE
5   Solve: $0.35x + 0.09(x + 4) = 0.03(12)$

OBJECTIVE
4   Recognizing Identities and Equations with No Solution

So far, each equation that we have solved has had a single solution. However, not every equation in one variable has a single solution. Some equations have no solution, while others have an infinite number of solutions. For example,

$$x + 5 = x + 7$$

has no solution since no matter which **real number** we replace x with, the equation is false.

real number + 5 = same real number + 7   **FALSE**

On the other hand,

$$x + 6 = x + 6$$

has infinitely many solutions since x can be replaced by any real number and the equation is always true.

real number + 6 = same real number + 6   **TRUE**

The equation $x + 6 = x + 6$ is called an **identity.** The next two examples illustrate special equations like these.

EXAMPLE 6   Solve: $-2(x - 5) + 10 = -3(x + 2) + x$

Solution

$$-2(x - 5) + 10 = -3(x + 2) + x$$
$$-2x + 10 + 10 = -3x - 6 + x$$ Apply the distributive property on both sides.
$$-2x + 20 = -2x - 6$$ Combine like terms.
$$-2x + 20 + 2x = -2x - 6 + 2x$$ Add $2x$ to both sides.
$$20 = -6$$ Combine like terms.

The final equation contains no variable terms, and there is no value for x that makes $20 = -6$ a true equation. We conclude that there is **no solution** to this equation. In set notation, we can indicate that there is no solution with the empty set, $\{ \ \}$, or use the empty set or null set symbol, $\varnothing$. In this chapter, we will simply write *no solution*.   □

PRACTICE
6   Solve: $4(x + 4) - x = 2(x + 11) + x$

EXAMPLE 7   Solve: $3(x - 4) = 3x - 12$

Solution

$$3(x - 4) = 3x - 12$$
$$3x - 12 = 3x - 12$$ Apply the distributive property.

The left side of the equation is now identical to the right side. Every real number may be substituted for x and a true statement will result. We arrive at the same conclusion if we continue.

$$3x - 12 = 3x - 12$$
$$3x - 12 + 12 = 3x - 12 + 12 \quad \text{Add 12 to both sides.}$$
$$3x = 3x \quad \text{Combine like terms.}$$
$$3x - 3x = 3x - 3x \quad \text{Subtract } 3x \text{ from both sides.}$$
$$0 = 0$$

Again, one side of the equation is identical to the other side. Thus, $3(x - 4) = 3x - 12$ is an **identity** and **all real numbers** are solutions. In set notation, this is $\{\text{all real numbers}\}$.

PRACTICE

7 Solve: $12x - 18 = 9(x - 2) + 3x$

 CONCEPT CHECK

Suppose you have simplified several equations and obtain the following results. What can you conclude about the solutions to the original equation?

a. $7 = 7$ **b.** $x = 0$ **c.** $7 = -4$

Graphing Calculator Explorations

Checking Equations

We can use a calculator to check possible solutions of equations. To do this, replace the variable by the possible solution and evaluate both sides of the equation separately.

Equation: $3x - 4 = 2(x + 6)$ *Solution: $x = 16$*

$$3x - 4 = 2(x + 6) \quad \text{Original equation}$$
$$3(16) - 4 \stackrel{?}{=} 2(16 + 6) \quad \text{Replace } x \text{ with 16.}$$

Now evaluate each side with your calculator.

Evaluate left side:

| 3 | × | 16 | − | 4 | = or ENTER   Display: 44   or $\begin{array}{l} 3*16 - 4 \\ \hspace{1.2cm} 44 \end{array}$

Evaluate right side:

| 2 | (| 16 | + | 6 |) | = or ENTER   Display: 44   or $\begin{array}{l} 2(16 + 6) \\ \hspace{1.2cm} 44 \end{array}$

Since the left side equals the right side, the solution checks.

Use a calculator to check the possible solutions to each equation.

1. $2x = 48 + 6x; \quad x = -12$ **2.** $-3x - 7 = 3x - 1; \quad x = -1$

3. $5x - 2.6 = 2(x + 0.8); \quad x = 4.4$ **4.** $-1.6x - 3.9 = -6.9x - 25.6; \quad x = 5$

5. $\dfrac{564x}{4} = 200x - 11(649); \quad x = 121$ **6.** $20(x - 39) = 5x - 432; \quad x = 23.2$

Answers to Concept Check:
a. Every real number is a solution.
b. The solution is 0.
c. There is no solution.

Vocabulary, Readiness & Video Check

Throughout algebra, it is important to be able to identify equations and expressions.

Remember,
- an equation contains an equal sign and
- an expression does not.

Also,
- we solve equations and
- we simplify or perform operations on expressions.

Identify each as an equation or an expression.

1. $x = -7$ _____

2. $x - 7$ _____

3. $4y - 6 + 9y + 1$ _____

4. $4y - 6 = 9y + 1$ _____

5. $\dfrac{1}{x} - \dfrac{x-1}{8}$ _____

6. $\dfrac{1}{x} - \dfrac{x-1}{8} = 6$ _____

7. $0.1x + 9 = 0.2x$ _____

8. $0.1x^2 + 9y - 0.2x^2$ _____

Martin-Gay Interactive Videos

See Video 2.3 🍎

Watch the section lecture video and answer the following questions.

OBJECTIVE 1

9. The general strategy for solving linear equations in one variable is discussed after ▭ Example 1. How many properties are mentioned in this strategy and what are they?

OBJECTIVE 2

10. In the first step for solving ▭ Example 2, both sides of the equation are being multiplied by the LCD. Why is the distributive property mentioned?

OBJECTIVE 3

11. In ▭ Example 3, why is the number of decimal places in each term of the equation important?

OBJECTIVE 4

12. Complete each statement based on ▭ Examples 4 and 5.

When solving an equation and all variable terms subtract out:

a. If you have a true statement, then the equation has _____ solution(s).

b. If you have a false statement, then the equation has _____ solution (s).

2.3   Exercise Set   MyMathLab®

Solve each equation. See Examples 1 and 2.

1. $-4y + 10 = -2(3y + 1)$

2. $-3x + 1 = -2(4x + 2)$

3. $15x - 8 = 10 + 9x$

4. $15x - 5 = 7 + 12x$

5. $-2(3x - 4) = 2x$

6. $-(5x - 10) = 5x$

▶ **7.** $5(2x - 1) - 2(3x) = 1$

8. $3(2 - 5x) + 4(6x) = 12$

9. $-6(x - 3) - 26 = -8$

10. $-4(n - 4) - 23 = -7$

11. $8 - 2(a + 1) = 9 + a$

12. $5 - 6(2 + b) = b - 14$

13. $4x + 3 = -3 + 2x + 14$

14. $6y - 8 = -6 + 3y + 13$

15. $-2y - 10 = 5y + 18$

16. $-7n + 5 = 8n - 10$

Solve each equation. See Examples 3 through 5.

17. $\dfrac{2}{3}x + \dfrac{4}{3} = -\dfrac{2}{3}$

18. $\dfrac{4}{5}x - \dfrac{8}{5} = -\dfrac{16}{5}$

19. $\dfrac{3}{4}x - \dfrac{1}{2} = 1$

20. $\dfrac{2}{9}x - \dfrac{1}{3} = 1$

▶ **21.** $0.50x + 0.15(70) = 35.5$

22. $0.40x + 0.06(30) = 9.8$

23. $\dfrac{2(x + 1)}{4} = 3x - 2$

24. $\dfrac{3(y + 3)}{5} = 2y + 6$

25. $x + \dfrac{7}{6} = 2x - \dfrac{7}{6}$

26. $\dfrac{5}{2}x - 1 = x + \dfrac{1}{4}$

27. $0.12(y - 6) + 0.06y = 0.08y - 0.70$

28. $0.60(z - 300) + 0.05z = 0.70z - 205$

Solve each equation. See Examples 6 and 7.

29. $4(3x + 2) = 12x + 8$

30. $14x + 7 = 7(2x + 1)$

31. $\dfrac{x}{4} + 1 = \dfrac{x}{4}$

32. $\dfrac{x}{3} - 2 = \dfrac{x}{3}$

33. $3x - 7 = 3(x + 1)$

34. $2(x - 5) = 2x + 10$

35. $-2(6x - 5) + 4 = -12x + 14$

36. $-5(4y - 3) + 2 = -20y + 17$

MIXED PRACTICE

Solve. See Examples 1 through 7.

37. $\dfrac{6(3 - z)}{5} = -z$

38. $\dfrac{4(5 - w)}{3} = -w$

39. $-3(2t - 5) + 2t = 5t - 4$

40. $-(4a - 7) - 5a = 10 + a$

41. $5y + 2(y - 6) = 4(y + 1) - 2$

42. $9x + 3(x - 4) = 10(x - 5) + 7$

43. $\dfrac{3(x - 5)}{2} = \dfrac{2(x + 5)}{3}$

44. $\dfrac{5(x - 1)}{4} = \dfrac{3(x + 1)}{2}$

45. $0.7x - 2.3 = 0.5$

46. $0.9x - 4.1 = 0.4$

▶ **47.** $5x - 5 = 2(x + 1) + 3x - 7$

48. $3(2x - 1) + 5 = 6x + 2$

49. $4(2n + 1) = 3(6n + 3) + 1$

50. $4(4y + 2) = 2(1 + 6y) + 8$

51. $x + \dfrac{5}{4} = \dfrac{3}{4}x$

52. $\dfrac{7}{8}x + \dfrac{1}{4} = \dfrac{3}{4}x$ ▶ **53.** $\dfrac{x}{2} - 1 = \dfrac{x}{5} + 2$

54. $\dfrac{x}{5} - 7 = \dfrac{x}{3} - 5$

▶ **55.** $2(x + 3) - 5 = 5x - 3(1 + x)$

56. $4(2 + x) + 1 = 7x - 3(x - 2)$

57. $0.06 - 0.01(x + 1) = -0.02(2 - x)$

58. $-0.01(5x + 4) = 0.04 - 0.01(x + 4)$

59. $\dfrac{9}{2} + \dfrac{5}{2}y = 2y - 4$

60. $3 - \dfrac{1}{2}x = 5x - 8$

61. $-2y - 10 = 5y + 18$

62. $7n + 5 = 10n - 10$

63. $0.6x - 0.1 = 0.5x + 0.2$

64. $0.2x - 0.1 = 0.6x - 2.1$

65. $0.02(6t - 3) = 0.12(t - 2) + 0.18$

66. $0.03(2m + 7) = 0.06(5 + m) - 0.09$

TRANSLATING

Write each phrase as an algebraic expression. Use x for the unknown number. See Section 2.1.

67. A number subtracted from -8

68. Three times a number

69. The sum of -3 and twice a number

70. The difference of 8 and twice a number

71. The product of 9 and the sum of a number and 20

72. The quotient of -12 and the difference of a number and 3

See Section 2.1.

73. A plot of land is in the shape of a triangle. If one side is x meters, a second side is $(2x - 3)$ meters, and a third side is $(3x - 5)$ meters, express the perimeter of the lot as a simplified expression in x.

See Section 2.2.

74. A portion of a board has length x feet. The other part has length $(7x - 9)$ feet. Express the total length of the board as a simplified expression in x.

CONCEPT EXTENSIONS

See the Concept Check in this section.

75. a. Solve: $x + 3 = x + 3$

 b. If you simplify an equation and get $0 = 0$, what can you conclude about the solution(s) of the original equation?

 c. On your own, construct an equation for which every real number is a solution.

76. a. Solve: $x + 3 = x + 5$

 b. If you simplify an equation and get $3 = 5$, what can you conclude about the solution(s) of the original equation?

 c. On your own, construct an equation that has no solution.

For Exercises 77 through 82, match each equation in the first column with its solution in the second column. Items in the second column may be used more than once.

77. $5x + 1 = 5x + 1$

78. $3x + 1 = 3x + 2$

79. $2x - 6x - 10 = -4x + 3 - 10$

80. $x - 11x - 3 = -10x - 1 - 2$

81. $9x - 20 = 8x - 20$

82. $-x + 15 = x + 15$

A. all real numbers

B. no solution

C. 0

83. Explain the difference between simplifying an expression and solving an equation.

84. On your own, write an expression and then an equation. Label each.

For Exercises 85 and 86, **a.** *Write an equation for perimeter.* **b.** *Solve the equation in part (a).* **c.** *Find the length of each side.*

85. The perimeter of a geometric figure is the sum of the lengths of its sides. The perimeter of the following pentagon (five-sided figure) is 28 centimeters.

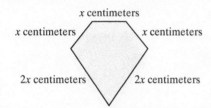

x centimeters

x centimeters x centimeters

$2x$ centimeters $2x$ centimeters

86. The perimeter of the following triangle is 35 meters.

$(2x + 1)$ meters

x meters

$(3x - 2)$ meters

Fill in the blanks with numbers of your choice so that each equation has the given solution. Note: Each blank may be replaced by a different number.

87. $x + \underline{\quad} = 2x - \underline{\quad}$; solution: 9

88. $-5x - \underline{\quad} = \underline{\quad}$; solution: 2

Solve.

89. $1000(7x - 10) = 50(412 + 100x)$

90. $1000(x + 40) = 100(16 + 7x)$

91. $0.035x + 5.112 = 0.010x + 5.107$

92. $0.127x - 2.685 = 0.027x - 2.38$

For Exercises 93 through 96, see the example below.

Example

Solve: $t(t + 4) = t^2 - 2t + 6$.

Solution
$$t(t + 4) = t^2 - 2t + 6$$
$$t^2 + 4t = t^2 - 2t + 6$$
$$t^2 + 4t - t^2 = t^2 - 2t + 6 - t^2$$
$$4t = -2t + 6$$
$$4t + 2t = -2t + 6 + 2t$$
$$6t = 6$$
$$t = 1$$

Solve each equation.

93. $x(x - 3) = x^2 + 5x + 7$

94. $t^2 - 6t = t(8 + t)$

95. $2z(z + 6) = 2z^2 + 12z - 8$

96. $y^2 - 4y + 10 = y(y - 5)$

Integrated Review   SOLVING LINEAR EQUATIONS

Sections 2.1–2.3

Solve. Feel free to use the steps given in Section 2.3.

1. $x - 10 = -4$

2. $y + 14 = -3$

3. $9y = 108$

4. $-3x = 78$

5. $-6x + 7 = 25$

6. $5y - 42 = -47$

7. $\frac{2}{3}x = 9$

8. $\frac{4}{5}z = 10$

9. $\frac{r}{-4} = -2$

10. $\frac{y}{-8} = 8$

11. $6 - 2x + 8 = 10$

12. $-5 - 6y + 6 = 19$

13. $2x - 7 = 2x - 27$

14. $3 + 8y = 8y - 2$

15. $-3a + 6 + 5a = 7a - 8a$

16. $4b - 8 - b = 10b - 3b$

17. $-\frac{2}{3}x = \frac{5}{9}$

18. $-\frac{3}{8}y = -\frac{1}{16}$

19. $10 = -6n + 16$

20. $-5 = -2m + 7$

21. $3(5c - 1) - 2 = 13c + 3$

22. $4(3t + 4) - 20 = 3 + 5t$

23. $\frac{2(z + 3)}{3} = 5 - z$

24. $\frac{3(w + 2)}{4} = 2w + 3$

25. $-2(2x - 5) = -3x + 7 - x + 3$

26. $-4(5x - 2) = -12x + 4 - 8x + 4$

27. $0.02(6t - 3) = 0.04(t - 2) + 0.02$

28. $0.03(m + 7) = 0.02(5 - m) + 0.03$

29. $-3y = \dfrac{4(y - 1)}{5}$

30. $-4x = \dfrac{5(1 - x)}{6}$

35. $\dfrac{1}{10}(3x - 7) = \dfrac{3}{10}x + 5$

31. $\dfrac{5}{3}x - \dfrac{7}{3} = x$

32. $\dfrac{7}{5}n + \dfrac{3}{5} = -n$

36. $\dfrac{1}{7}(2x - 5) = \dfrac{2}{7}x + 1$

33. $9(3x - 1) = -4 + 49$

34. $12(2x + 1) = -6 + 66$

37. $5 + 2(3x - 6) = -4(6x - 7)$

38. $3 + 5(2x - 4) = -7(5x + 2)$

2.4 An Introduction to Problem Solving

OBJECTIVES

Apply the steps for problem solving as we

1 Solve Problems Involving Direct Translations.

2 Solve Problems Involving Relationships Among Unknown Quantities.

3 Solve Problems Involving Consecutive Integers.

OBJECTIVE

1 Solving Direct Translation Problems

In previous sections, we practiced writing word phrases and sentences as algebraic expressions and equations to help prepare for problem solving. We now use these translations to help write equations that model a problem. The problem-solving steps given next may be helpful.

General Strategy for Problem Solving

1. UNDERSTAND the problem. During this step, become comfortable with the problem. Some ways of doing this are to:

   Read and reread the problem.

   Choose a variable to represent the unknown.

   Construct a drawing whenever possible.

   Propose a solution and check. Pay careful attention to how you check your proposed solution. This will help when writing an equation to model the problem.

2. TRANSLATE the problem into an equation.

3. SOLVE the equation.

4. INTERPRET the results: *Check* the proposed solution in the stated problem and state your conclusion.

Much of problem solving involves a direct translation from a sentence to an equation.

EXAMPLE 1 **Finding an Unknown Number**

Twice a number, added to seven, is the same as three subtracted from the number. Find the number.

Solution Translate the sentence into an equation and solve.

In words:	twice a number	added to	seven	is the same as	three subtracted from the number
	↓	↓	↓	↓	↓
Translate:	$2x$	$+$	7	$=$	$x - 3$

▶ **Helpful Hint**
Order matters when subtracting (and dividing), so be especially careful with these translations.

To solve, begin by subtracting x from both sides to get all variable terms on one side.

$$2x + 7 = x - 3$$

$$2x + 7 - x = x - 3 - x \quad \text{Subtract } x \text{ from both sides.}$$

$$x + 7 = -3 \quad \text{Combine like terms.}$$

$$x + 7 - 7 = -3 - 7 \quad \text{Subtract 7 from both sides.}$$

$$x = -10 \quad \text{Combine like terms.}$$

Check the solution in the problem as it was originally stated. To do so, replace "number" in the sentence with -10. Twice "-10" added to 7 is the same as 3 subtracted from "-10."

$$2(-10) + 7 = -10 - 3$$
$$-13 = -13$$

The unknown number is -10. □

PRACTICE

1   Three times a number, minus 6, is the same as two times a number, plus 3. Find the number.

> ▶ Helpful Hint
>
> When checking solutions, go back to the original stated problem, rather than to your equation, in case errors have been made in translating to an equation.

EXAMPLE 2   **Finding an Unknown Number**

Twice the sum of a number and 4 is the same as four times the number, decreased by 12. Find the number.

Solution

1. UNDERSTAND. Read and reread the problem. If we let

$$x = \text{the unknown number, then}$$

"the sum of a number and 4" translates to "$x + 4$" and "four times the number" translates to "$4x$."

2. TRANSLATE.

twice	the sum of a number and 4	is the same as	four times the number	decreased by	12
↓	↓	↓	↓	↓	↓
2	$(x + 4)$	$=$	$4x$	$-$	12

3. SOLVE.

$$2(x + 4) = 4x - 12$$
$$2x + 8 = 4x - 12 \qquad \text{Apply the distributive property.}$$
$$2x + 8 - 4x = 4x - 12 - 4x \quad \text{Subtract } 4x \text{ from both sides.}$$
$$-2x + 8 = -12$$
$$-2x + 8 - 8 = -12 - 8 \qquad \text{Subtract 8 from both sides.}$$
$$-2x = -20$$
$$\frac{-2x}{-2} = \frac{-20}{-2} \qquad \text{Divide both sides by } -2.$$
$$x = 10$$

4. INTERPRET.

Check: Check this solution in the problem as it was originally stated. To do so, replace "number" with 10. Twice the sum of "10" and 4 is 28, which is the same as 4 times "10" decreased by 12.

State: The number is 10. □

PRACTICE

2   Three times a number, decreased by 4, is the same as double the difference of the number and 1.

2 Solving Problems Involving Relationships Among Unknown Quantities

The next three examples have to do with relationships among unknown quantities.

EXAMPLE 3 Finding the Length of a Board

Balsa wood sticks are commonly used for building models (for example, bridge models). A 48-inch balsa wood stick is to be cut into two pieces so that the longer piece is 3 times the shorter. Find the length of each piece.

Solution

1. **UNDERSTAND** the problem. To do so, read and reread the problem. You may also want to propose a solution. For example, if 10 inches represents the length of the shorter piece, then $3(10) = 30$ inches is the length of the longer piece, since it is 3 times the length of the shorter piece. This guess gives a total stick length of 10 inches + 30 inches = 40 inches, too short. However, the purpose of proposing a solution is not to guess correctly but to help understand the problem better and how to model it.

   Since the length of the longer piece is given in terms of the length of the shorter piece, let's let

$$x = \text{length of shorter piece; then}$$
$$3x = \text{length of longer piece}$$

2. **TRANSLATE** the problem. First, we write the equation in words.

length of shorter piece	added to	length of longer piece	equals	total length of stick
↓	↓	↓	↓	↓
x	+	$3x$	=	48

3. **SOLVE.**

$$x + 3x = 48$$
$$4x = 48 \quad \text{Combine like terms.}$$
$$\frac{4x}{4} = \frac{48}{4} \quad \text{Divide both sides by 4.}$$
$$x = 12$$

4. **INTERPRET.**

Check: Check the solution in the stated problem. If the shorter piece of stick is 12 inches, the longer piece is $3 \cdot (12 \text{ inches}) = 36$ inches, and the sum of the two pieces is 12 inches + 36 inches = 48 inches.

State: The shorter piece of balsa wood is 12 inches, and the longer piece of balsa wood is 36 inches.

> ▶ **Helpful Hint**
> Make sure that units are included in your answer, if appropriate.

PRACTICE

3 A 45-inch board is to be cut into two pieces so that the longer piece is 4 times the shorter. Find the length of each piece.

EXAMPLE 4   **Finding the Number of Republican and Democratic Representatives**

The 112th Congress began on January 3, 2011, and had a total of 435 Democrat and Republican representatives. There were 49 fewer Democratic representatives than Republican. Find the number of representatives from each party. (*Source:* Wikipedia.com)

Solution:

1. UNDERSTAND the problem. Read and reread the problem. Let's suppose that there were 200 Republican representatives. Since there were 49 fewer Democrats than Republicans, there must have been $200 - 49 = 151$ Democrats. The total number of Republicans and Democrats was then $200 + 151 = 351$. This is incorrect since the total should be 435, but we now have a better understanding of the problem.

In general, if we let

$$x = \text{number of Republicans, then}$$
$$x - 49 = \text{number of Democrats}$$

2. TRANSLATE the problem. First, we write the equation in words.

number of Republicans	added to	number of Democrats	equals	435
↓	↓	↓	↓	↓
x	$+$	$(x - 49)$	$=$	435

3. SOLVE.

$$x + (x - 49) = 435$$
$$2x - 49 = 435 \qquad \text{Combine like terms.}$$
$$2x - 49 + 49 = 435 + 49 \qquad \text{Add 49 to both sides.}$$
$$2x = 484$$
$$\frac{2x}{2} = \frac{484}{2} \qquad \text{Divide both sides by 2.}$$
$$x = 242$$

4. INTERPRET.

Check: If there were 242 Republican representatives, then there were $242 - 49 = 193$ Democratic representatives. The total number of representatives was then $242 + 193 = 435$. The results check.

State: There were 242 Republican and 193 Democratic representatives at the beginning of the 112th Congress.

PRACTICE
4   In 2011, there were 9 fewer Democratic State Governors than Republican State Governors. Find the number of State Governors from each party. Rhode Island had an independent governor, so use a total of 49, representing the other 49 states. (*Source:* National Conference of State Legislatures).

△ **EXAMPLE 5**   **Finding Angle Measures**

If the two walls of the Vietnam Veterans Memorial in Washington, D.C., were connected, an isosceles triangle would be formed. The measure of the third angle is 97.5° more than the measure of either of the other two equal angles. Find the measure of the third angle. (*Source:* National Park Service)

Solution

1. UNDERSTAND. Read and reread the problem. We then draw a diagram (recall that an isosceles triangle has two angles with the same measure) and let

$$x = \text{degree measure of one angle}$$
$$x = \text{degree measure of the second equal angle}$$
$$x + 97.5 = \text{degree measure of the third angle}$$

2. TRANSLATE. Recall that the sum of the measures of the angles of a triangle equals 180.

measure of first angle		measure of second angle		measure of third angle		equals		180
↓		↓		↓		↓		↓
x	$+$	x	$+$	$(x + 97.5)$	$=$			180

3. SOLVE.

$$x + x + (x + 97.5) = 180$$
$$3x + 97.5 = 180 \qquad \text{Combine like terms.}$$
$$3x + 97.5 - 97.5 = 180 - 97.5 \quad \text{Subtract 97.5 from both sides.}$$
$$3x = 82.5$$
$$\frac{3x}{3} = \frac{82.5}{3} \qquad \text{Divide both sides by 3.}$$
$$x = 27.5$$

4. INTERPRET.

Check: If $x = 27.5$, then the measure of the third angle is $x + 97.5 = 125$. The sum of the angles is then $27.5 + 27.5 + 125 = 180$, the correct sum.

State: The third angle measures 125°.*

> PRACTICE
> **5**   The second angle of a triangle measures three times as large as the first. If the third angle measures 55° more than the first, find the measures of all three angles.

OBJECTIVE
3   Solving Consecutive Integer Problems

The next example has to do with consecutive integers. Recall what we have learned thus far about these integers.

	Example	*General Representation*
Consecutive Integers	11, 12, 13	Let x be an integer. x, $x + 1$, $x + 2$
Consecutive Even Integers	38, 40, 42	Let x be an even integer. x, $x + 2$, $x + 4$
Consecutive Odd Integers	57, 59, 61	Let x be an odd integer. x, $x + 2$, $x + 4$

---

*The two walls actually meet at an angle of 125 degrees 12 minutes. The measurement of 97.5° given in the problem is an approximation.

EXAMPLE 6   Some states have a single area code for the entire state. Two such states have area codes that are consecutive odd integers. If the sum of these integers is 1208, find the two area codes. (*Source:* North American Numbering Plan Administration)

Solution:

1. UNDERSTAND. Read and reread the problem. If we let

x = the first odd integer, then

$x + 2$ = the next odd integer

> **Helpful Hint**
> Remember, the 2 here means that odd integers are 2 units apart, for example, the odd integers 13 and 13 + 2 = 15.

2. TRANSLATE.

first odd integer	the sum of	next odd integer	is	1208
↓	↓	↓	↓	↓
x	$+$	$(x + 2)$	$=$	1208

3. SOLVE.

$$x + x + 2 = 1208$$
$$2x + 2 = 1208$$
$$2x + 2 - 2 = 1208 - 2$$
$$2x = 1206$$
$$\frac{2x}{2} = \frac{1206}{2}$$
$$x = 603$$

4. INTERPRET.

Check: If $x = 603$, then the next odd integer $x + 2 = 603 + 2 = 605$. Notice their sum, $603 + 605 = 1208$, as needed.

State: The area codes are 603 and 605.

Note: New Hampshire's area code is 603 and South Dakota's area code is 605.   ☐

PRACTICE
6   The sum of three consecutive even integers is 144. Find the integers.

Vocabulary, Readiness & Video Check

Fill in the table.

	A number		Operation 1		Operation 2
1.	A number: x	→	Double the number:	→	Double the number, decreased by 31:
2.	A number: x	→	Three times the number:	→	Three times the number, increased by 17:
3.	A number: x	→	The sum of the number and 5:	→	Twice the sum of the number and 5:
4.	A number: x	→	The difference of the number and 11:	→	Seven times the difference of a number and 11:
5.	A number: y	→	The difference of 20 and the number:	→	The difference of 20 and the number, divided by 3:
6.	A number: y	→	The sum of −10 and the number:	→	The sum of −10 and the number, divided by 9:

Martin-Gay Interactive Videos

Watch the section lecture video and answer the following questions.

OBJECTIVE 1

7. At the end of Example 1, where are you told is the best place to check the solution of an application problem?

OBJECTIVE 2

8. The solution of the equation for Example 3 is $x = 43$. Why is this not the solution to the application?

OBJECTIVE 3

9. What are two things that should be checked to make sure the solution of Example 4 is correct?

See Video 2.4

2.4 Exercise Set   MyMathLab®

TRANSLATING

Write each of the following as an equation. Then solve. See Examples 1 and 2.

1. The sum of six times a number, and 1, is equal to five times the number. Find the number.

2. The difference of three times a number, and 1, is the same as twice the number. Find the number.

3. Three times a number, minus 6, is equal to two times the number, plus 8. Find the number.

4. The sum of 4 times a number, and -2, is equal to the sum of 5 times the number, and -2. Find the number.

▶ **5.** Twice the difference of a number and 8 is equal to three times the sum of the number and 3. Find the number.

6. Five times the sum of a number and -1 is the same as 6 times the difference of the number and 5. Find the number.

7. Twice the sum of -2 and a number is the same as the number decreased by $\frac{1}{2}$. Find the number.

8. If the difference of a number and four is doubled, the result is $\frac{1}{4}$ less than the number. Find the number.

Solve. For Exercises 9 and 10, the solutions have been started for you. See Examples 3 through 5.

9. A 25-inch piece of steel is cut into three pieces so that the second piece is twice as long as the first piece, and the third piece is one inch more than five times the length of the first piece. Find the lengths of the pieces.

Start the solution:

1. UNDERSTAND the problem. Reread it as many times as needed.

2. TRANSLATE into an equation. (Fill in the blanks below.)

total length of steel	equals	length of first piece	plus	length of second piece	plus	length of third piece
↓	↓	↓	↓	↓	↓	↓
25	=	____	+	____	+	____

Finish with:

3. SOLVE and **4.** INTERPRET

10. A 46-foot piece of rope is cut into three pieces so that the second piece is three times as long as the first piece, and the third piece is two feet more than seven times the length of the first piece. Find the lengths of the pieces.

Start the solution:

1. UNDERSTAND the problem. Reread it as many times as needed.

2. TRANSLATE into an equation. (Fill in the blanks below.)

total length of rope	equals	length of first piece	plus	length of second piece	plus	length of third piece
↓	↓	↓	↓	↓	↓	↓
46	=	____	+	____	+	____

Finish with:

3. SOLVE and **4.** INTERPRET

11. A 40-inch board is to be cut into three pieces so that the second piece is twice as long as the first piece, and the third piece is 5 times as long as the first piece. If x represents the length of the first piece, find the lengths of all three pieces.

12. A 21-foot beam is to be cut into three pieces so that the second and the third piece are each 3 times the length of the first piece. If x represents the length of the shorter piece, find the lengths of all three pieces.

For Exercises 13 and 14, use each table to find the value of x. Then write a sentence to explain, in words, the meaning and the value of x. (Source: IHS Screen Digest)

13. The fastest growing type of movie screen in 2010 was 3D.

Type of Screen	Number of Screens
3D	x
Non-3D	23,873 more than x
Total screens	39,547

14. The majority of movie screens in the United States in 2010 were located at sites with five or more screens.

Type of Site	Number of Screens
Smaller (1–4 screens)	x
Larger (5 or more screens)	22,857 more than x
Total screens	39,547

15. The flag of Equatorial Guinea contains an isosceles triangle. (Recall that an isosceles triangle contains two angles with the same measure.) If the measure of the third angle of the triangle is 30° more than twice the measure of either of the other two angles, find the measure of each angle of the triangle. (*Hint:* Recall that the sum of the measures of the angles of a triangle is 180°.)

16. The flag of Brazil contains a parallelogram. One angle of the parallelogram is 15° less than twice the measure of the angle next to it. Find the measure of each angle of the parallelogram. (*Hint:* Recall that opposite angles of a parallelogram have the same measure and that the sum of the measures of the angles is 360°.)

Solve. See Example 6. For Exercises 17 through 24, fill in the table. Most of the first row has been completed for you.

	First Integer →	Next Integers	→	Indicated Sum
17. Three consecutive integers:	Integer: x	$x + 1$	$x + 2$	Sum of the three consecutive integers, simplified:
18. Three consecutive integers:	Integer: x			Sum of the second and third consecutive integers, simplified:
19. Three consecutive even integers:	Even integer: x			Sum of the first and third even consecutive integers, simplified:
20. Three consecutive odd integers:	Odd integer: x			Sum of the three consecutive odd integers, simplified:
21. Four consecutive integers:	Integer: x			Sum of the four consecutive integers, simplified:
22. Four consecutive integers:	Integer: x			Sum of the first and fourth consecutive integers, simplified:
23. Three consecutive odd integers:	Odd integer: x			Sum of the second and third consecutive odd integers, simplified:
24. Three consecutive even integers:	Even integer: x			Sum of the three consecutive even integers, simplified:

25. The left and right page numbers of an open book are two consecutive integers whose sum is 469. Find these page numbers.

26. The room numbers of two adjacent classrooms are two consecutive even numbers. If their sum is 654, find the classroom numbers.

27. To make an international telephone call, you need the code for the country you are calling. The codes for Belgium, France, and Spain are three consecutive integers whose sum is 99. Find the code for each country. (*Source: The World Almanac and Book of Facts*, 2007)

28. To make an international telephone call, you need the code for the country you are calling. The codes for Mali Republic, Côte d'Ivoire, and Niger are three consecutive odd integers whose sum is 675. Find the code for each country.

MIXED PRACTICE

Solve. See Examples 1 through 6.

29. The area of the Sahara Desert is 7 times the area of the Gobi Desert. If the sum of their areas is 4,000,000 square miles, find the area of each desert.

30. The largest meteorite in the world is the Hoba West, located in Namibia. Its weight is 3 times the weight of the Armanty meteorite, located in Outer Mongolia. If the sum of their weights is 88 tons, find the weight of each.

31. A 17-foot piece of string is cut into two pieces so that the longer piece is 2 feet longer than twice the length of the shorter piece. Find the lengths of both pieces.

32. A 25-foot wire is to be cut so that the longer piece is one foot longer than 5 times the length of the shorter piece. Find the length of each piece.

33. Five times a number, subtracted from ten, is triple the number. Find the number.

34. Nine is equal to ten subtracted from double a number. Find the number.

35. The greatest producer of diamonds in carats is Botswana. This country produces about four times the amount produced in Angola. If the total produced in both countries is 40,000,000 carats, find the amount produced in each country. (*Source: Diamond Facts.*)

ANGOLA

BOTSWANA

36. Beetles have the greatest number of different species. There are twenty times the number of beetle species as grasshopper species, and the total number of species for both is 420,000. Find the number of species for each type of insect.

37. The measures of the angles of a triangle are 3 consecutive even integers. Find the measure of each angle.

38. A quadrilateral is a polygon with 4 sides. The sum of the measures of the 4 angles in a quadrilateral is 360°. If the measures of the angles of a quadrilateral are consecutive odd integers, find the measures.

39. For the 2010 Winter Olympics, the total number of medals won by athletes from each of the countries of South Korea, Russia, and Austria are three consecutive integers whose sum is 45. Find the number of medals for each country.

40. The code to unlock a student's combination lock happens to be three consecutive odd integers whose sum is 51. Find the integers.

41. If the sum of a number and five is tripled, the result is one less than twice the number. Find the number.

42. Twice the sum of a number and six equals three times the sum of the number and four. Find the number.

43. Two angles are supplementary if their sum is 180°. The larger angle measures eight degrees more than three times the measure of a smaller angle. If x represents the measure of the smaller angle and these two angles are supplementary, find the measure of each angle.

44. Two angles are complementary if their sum is 90°. The larger angle measures three degrees less than twice the measure of a smaller angle. If x represents the measure of the smaller angle and these two angles are complementary, find the measure of each angle.

45. If the quotient of a number and 4 is added to $\frac{1}{2}$, the result is $\frac{3}{4}$. Find the number.

46. The sum of $\frac{1}{5}$ and twice a number is equal to $\frac{4}{5}$ subtracted from three times the number. Find the number.

47. The sum of $\frac{2}{3}$ and four times a number is equal to $\frac{5}{6}$ subtracted from five times the number. Find the number.

48. If $\frac{3}{4}$ is added to three times a number, the result is $\frac{1}{2}$ subtracted from twice the number. Find the number.

49. Currently, the two fastest trains are the Japanese Maglev and the French TGV. The sum of their fastest speeds is 718.2 miles per hour. If the speed of the Maglev is 3.8 mph faster than the speed of the TGV, find the speeds of each.

50. The Pentagon is the world's largest office building in terms of floor space. It has three times the amount of floor space as the Empire State Building. If the total floor space for these two buildings is approximately 8700 thousand square feet, find the floor space of each building.

51. One-third of a number is five-sixths. Find the number.

52. Seven-eighths of a number is one-half. Find the number.

53. The number of counties in California and the number of counties in Montana are consecutive even integers whose sum is 114. If California has more counties than Montana, how many counties does each state have? (*Source: The World Almanac and Book of Facts*)

54. A student is building a bookcase with stepped shelves for her dorm room. She buys a 48-inch board and wants to cut the board into three pieces with lengths equal to three consecutive even integers. Find the three board lengths.

55. A geodesic dome, based on the design by Buckminster Fuller, is composed of two types of triangular panels. One of these is an isosceles triangle. In one geodesic dome, the measure of the third angle is 76.5° more than the measure of either of the two equal angles. Find the measure of the third angle. (*Source:* Buckminster Fuller Institute)

56. The measures of the angles of a particular triangle are such that the second and third angles are each four times larger than the smallest angle. Find the measures of the angles of this triangle.

57. A 30-foot piece of siding is cut into three pieces so that the second piece is four times as long as the first piece and the third piece is five times as long as the first piece. If x represents the length of the first piece, find the lengths of all three pieces.

58. A 48-foot-long piece of cable wire is to be cut into three pieces so that the second piece is five times as long as the first piece and the third piece is six times as long as the first piece. If x represents the length of the first piece, find the lengths of all three pieces.

The graph below shows the best-selling albums of all time. Use this graph for Exercises 59 through 64.

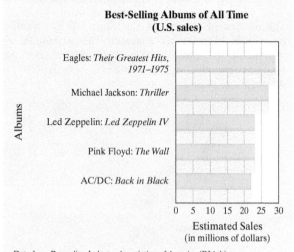

Best-Selling Albums of All Time (U.S. sales)

Eagles: *Their Greatest Hits, 1971–1975*

Michael Jackson: *Thriller*

Led Zeppelin: *Led Zeppelin IV*

Pink Floyd: *The Wall*

AC/DC: *Back in Black*

Albums

0 5 10 15 20 25 30

Estimated Sales (in millions of dollars)

Data from Recording Industry Association of America (RIAA)

(*Note:* These numbers are before the death of Michael Jackson.)

59. Which album is the best-selling album of all time?

60. Which albums had total sales between $20 million and $25 million?

61. *Thriller* and *The Wall* had sales worth a total of $50 million. *Thriller* brought in $4 million more than *The Wall*. Find the amount of sales that each album brought in.

62. Eagles: *Their Greatest Hits, 1971–1975*, and AC/DC: *Back in Black* had sales worth $51 million. Eagles: *Their Greatest Hits, 1971–1975*, sold $7 million more than AC/DC: *Back in Black*. Find the amount of sales for each album.

Compare the lengths of the bars in the graph with your results for the exercises below. Are your answers reasonable?

63. Exercise 61   **64.** Exercise 62

REVIEW AND PREVIEW

Evaluate each expression for the given values. See Section 1.4.

65. $2W + 2L$; $W = 7$ and $L = 10$

66. $\frac{1}{2}Bh$; $B = 14$ and $h = 22$

67. πr^2; $r = 15$ **68.** $r \cdot t$; $r = 15$ and $t = 2$

CONCEPT EXTENSIONS

69. A golden rectangle is a rectangle whose length is approximately 1.6 times its width. The early Greeks thought that a rectangle with these dimensions was the most pleasing to the eye, and examples of the golden rectangle are found in many early works of art. For example, the Parthenon in Athens contains many examples of golden rectangles.

Mike Hallahan would like to plant a rectangular garden in the shape of a golden rectangle. If he has 78 feet of fencing available, find the dimensions of the garden.

70. Dr. Dorothy Smith gave the students in her geometry class at the University of New Orleans the following question. Is it possible to construct a triangle such that the second angle of the triangle has a measure that is twice the measure of the first angle and the measure of the third angle is 5 times the measure of the first? If so, find the measure of each angle. (*Hint:* Recall that the sum of the measures of the angles of a triangle is 180°.)

71. Only male crickets chirp. They chirp at different rates depending on their species and the temperature of their environment. Suppose a certain species is currently chirping at a rate of 90 chirps per minute. At this rate, how many chirps occur in one hour? In one 24-hour day? In one year?

72. The human eye blinks once every 5 seconds on average. How many times does the average eye blink in one hour? In one 16-hour day while awake? In one year while awake?

73. In your own words, explain why a solution of a word problem should be checked using the original wording of the problem and not the equation written from the wording.

74. Give an example of how you recently solved a problem using mathematics.

Recall from Exercise 69 that a golden rectangle is a rectangle whose length is approximately 1.6 times its width.

75. It is thought that for about 75% of adults, a rectangle in the shape of the golden rectangle is the most pleasing to the eye. Draw three rectangles, one in the shape of the golden rectangle, and poll your class. Do the results agree with the percentage given above?

76. Examples of golden rectangles can be found today in architecture and manufacturing packaging. Find an example of a golden rectangle in your home. A few suggestions: the front face of a book, the floor of a room, the front of a box of food.

For Exercises 77 and 78, measure the dimensions of each rectangle and decide which one best approximates the shape of a golden rectangle.

77.

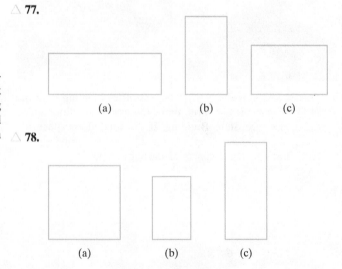

(a)   (b)   (c)

78.

(a)   (b)   (c)

2.5 Formulas and Problem Solving

OBJECTIVES

1 Use Formulas to Solve Problems.

2 Solve a Formula or Equation for One of Its Variables.

OBJECTIVE

1 Using Formulas to Solve Problems

An equation that describes a known relationship among quantities, such as distance, time, volume, weight, and money, is called a **formula.** These quantities are represented by letters and are thus variables of the formula. Here are some common formulas and their meanings.

Formulas	Their Meanings
$A = lw$	Area of a rectangle = length · width
$I = PRT$	Simple interest = principal · rate · time
$P = a + b + c$	Perimeter of a triangle = side a + side b + side c
$d = rt$	distance = rate · time
$V = lwh$	Volume of a rectangular solid = length · width · height
$F = \left(\dfrac{9}{5}\right)C + 32$ or $F = 1.8C + 32$	degrees Fahrenheit = $\left(\dfrac{9}{5}\right)$ · degrees Celsius + 32

Formulas are valuable tools because they allow us to calculate measurements as long as we know certain other measurements. For example, if we know we traveled a distance of 100 miles at a rate of 40 miles per hour, we can replace the variables d and r in the formula $d = rt$ and find our time, t.

$$d = rt \qquad \text{Formula.}$$
$$100 = 40t \qquad \text{Replace } d \text{ with 100 and } r \text{ with 40.}$$

This is a linear equation in one variable, t. To solve for t, divide both sides of the equation by 40.

$$\frac{100}{40} = \frac{40t}{40} \qquad \text{Divide both sides by 40.}$$
$$\frac{5}{2} = t \qquad \text{Simplify.}$$

The time traveled is $\dfrac{5}{2}$ hours, or $2\dfrac{1}{2}$ hours, or 2.5 hours.

In this section, we solve problems that can be modeled by known formulas. We use the same problem-solving steps that were introduced in the previous section. These steps have been slightly revised to include formulas.

EXAMPLE 1 **Finding Time Given Rate and Distance**

A glacier is a giant mass of rocks and ice that flows downhill like a river. Portage Glacier in Alaska is about 6 miles, or 31,680 *feet,* long and moves 400 *feet* per year. Icebergs are created when the front end of the glacier flows into Portage Lake. How long does it take for ice at the head (beginning) of the glacier to reach the lake?

Solution

1. **UNDERSTAND.** Read and reread the problem. The appropriate formula needed to solve this problem is the distance formula, $d = rt$. To become familiar with this formula, let's find the distance that ice traveling at a rate of 400 feet per year travels in 100 years. To do so, we let time t be 100 years and rate r be the given 400 feet per year and substitute these values into the formula $d = rt$. We then have that distance $d = 400(100) = 40,000$ feet. Since we are interested in finding how long it takes ice to travel 31,680 feet, we now know that it is less than 100 years.

   Since we are using the formula $d = rt$, we let

   t = the time in years for ice to reach the lake

   r = rate or speed of ice

   d = distance from beginning of glacier to lake

2. **TRANSLATE.** To translate to an equation, we use the formula $d = rt$ and let distance $d = 31,680$ feet and rate $r = 400$ feet per year.

$$d = r \cdot t$$
$$31,680 = 400 \cdot t \quad \text{Let } d = 31,680 \text{ and } r = 400.$$

3. **SOLVE.** Solve the equation for t. To solve for t, divide both sides by 400.

$$\frac{31,680}{400} = \frac{400 \cdot t}{400} \quad \text{Divide both sides by 400.}$$

$$79.2 = t \quad \text{Simplify.}$$

4. **INTERPRET.**

Check: To check, substitute 79.2 for t and 400 for r in the distance formula and check to see that the distance is 31,680 feet.

State: It takes 79.2 years for the ice at the head of Portage Glacier to reach the lake. ☐

> **Helpful Hint**
> Don't forget to include units if appropriate.

PRACTICE

1 The Stromboli Volcano, in Italy, began erupting in 2002 after a dormant period of over 17 years. In 2007, a volcanologist measured the lava flow to be moving at 5 meters/second. If the path the lava follows to the sea is 580 meters long, how long does it take the lava to reach the sea? (*Source:* Thorsten Boeckel and CNN)

⚠ **EXAMPLE 2**   Calculating the Length of a Garden

Charles Pecot can afford enough fencing to enclose a rectangular garden with a perimeter of 140 feet. If the width of his garden must be 30 feet, find the length.

$w = 30$ feet

l

Solution

1. **UNDERSTAND.** Read and reread the problem. The formula needed to solve this problem is the formula for the perimeter of a rectangle, $P = 2l + 2w$. Before continuing, let's become familiar with this formula.

l = the length of the rectangular garden
w = the width of the rectangular garden
P = perimeter of the garden

2. **TRANSLATE.** To translate to an equation, we use the formula $P = 2l + 2w$ and let perimeter $P = 140$ feet and width $w = 30$ feet.

$$P = 2l + 2w$$
$$\downarrow \qquad \qquad \downarrow$$
$$140 = 2l + 2(30) \quad \text{Let } P = 140 \text{ and } w = 30.$$

3. **SOLVE.**

$$140 = 2l + 2(30)$$
$$140 = 2l + 60 \qquad \text{Multiply } 2(30).$$
$$140 - 60 = 2l + 60 - 60 \quad \text{Subtract 60 from both sides.}$$
$$80 = 2l \qquad \text{Combine like terms.}$$
$$40 = l \qquad \text{Divide both sides by 2.}$$

4. **INTERPRET.**

Check: Substitute 40 for l and 30 for w in the perimeter formula and check to see that the perimeter is 140 feet.

State: The length of the rectangular garden is 40 feet.   □

PRACTICE
2   Evelyn Gryk fenced in part of her backyard for a dog run. The dog run was 40 feet in length and used 98 feet of fencing. Find the width of the dog run.

EXAMPLE 3   Finding an Equivalent Temperature

The average minimum temperature for July in Shanghai, China, is 77° Fahrenheit. Find the equivalent temperature in degrees Celsius.

Solution

1. **UNDERSTAND.** Read and reread the problem. A formula that can be used to solve this problem is the formula for converting degrees Celsius to degrees Fahrenheit, $F = \frac{9}{5}C + 32$. Before continuing, become familiar with this formula. Using this formula, we let

C = temperature in degrees Celsius, and
F = temperature in degrees Fahrenheit.

2. TRANSLATE. To translate to an equation, we use the formula $F = \frac{9}{5}C + 32$ and let degrees Fahrenheit $F = 77$.

$$\text{Formula:} \qquad F = \frac{9}{5}C + 32$$

$$\text{Substitute:} \qquad 77 = \frac{9}{5}C + 32 \qquad \text{Let } F = 77.$$

3. SOLVE.

$$77 = \frac{9}{5}C + 32$$

$$77 - 32 = \frac{9}{5}C + 32 - 32 \qquad \text{Subtract 32 from both sides.}$$

$$45 = \frac{9}{5}C \qquad\qquad\qquad \text{Combine like terms.}$$

$$\frac{5}{9} \cdot 45 = \frac{5}{9} \cdot \frac{9}{5}C \qquad\qquad \text{Multiply both sides by } \frac{5}{9}.$$

$$25 = C \qquad\qquad\qquad \text{Simplify.}$$

4. INTERPRET.

Check: To check, replace C with 25 and F with 77 in the formula and see that a true statement results.

State: Thus, 77° Fahrenheit is equivalent to 25° Celsius.

Note: There is a formula for directly converting degrees Fahrenheit to degrees Celsius. It is $C = \frac{5}{9}(F - 32)$, as we shall see in Example 8.   □

PRACTICE

3   The average minimum temperature for July in Sydney, Australia, is 8° Celsius. Find the equivalent temperature in degrees Fahrenheit.

In the next example, we again use the formula for perimeter of a rectangle as in Example 2. In Example 2, we knew the width of the rectangle. In this example, both the length and width are unknown.

 EXAMPLE 4   **Finding Road Sign Dimensions**

The length of a rectangular road sign is 2 feet less than three times its width. Find the dimensions if the perimeter is 28 feet.

Solution

1. UNDERSTAND. Read and reread the problem. Recall that the formula for the perimeter of a rectangle is $P = 2l + 2w$. Draw a rectangle and guess the solution. If the width of the rectangular sign is 5 feet, its length is 2 feet less than 3 times the width or $3(5 \text{ feet}) - 2 \text{ feet} = 13 \text{ feet}$. The perimeter P of the rectangle is then $2(13 \text{ feet}) + 2(5 \text{ feet}) = 36 \text{ feet}$, too much. We now know that the width is less than 5 feet.

Proposed
rectangle:

5 feet

13 feet

Let

$w =$ the width of the rectangular sign; then
$3w - 2 =$ the length of the sign.

w

$3w - 2$

Draw a rectangle and label it with the assigned variables.

2. TRANSLATE.

Formula: $P = 2l + 2w$ or
Substitute: $28 = 2(3w - 2) + 2w$.

3. SOLVE.

$$28 = 2(3w - 2) + 2w$$
$$28 = 6w - 4 + 2w \qquad \text{Apply the distributive property.}$$
$$28 = 8w - 4$$
$$28 + 4 = 8w - 4 + 4 \qquad \text{Add 4 to both sides.}$$
$$32 = 8w$$
$$\frac{32}{8} = \frac{8w}{8} \qquad \text{Divide both sides by 8.}$$
$$4 = w$$

4. INTERPRET.

Check: If the width of the sign is 4 feet, the length of the sign is $3(4 \text{ feet}) - 2 \text{ feet} =$ 10 feet. This gives a perimeter of $P = 2(4 \text{ feet}) + 2(10 \text{ feet}) = 28 \text{ feet}$, the correct perimeter.

State: The width of the sign is 4 feet, and the length of the sign is 10 feet. □

PRACTICE

4   The new street signs along Route 114 have a length that is 3 inches more than 5 times the width. Find the dimensions of the signs if the perimeter of the signs is 66 inches.

OBJECTIVE

2   **Solving a Formula for One of Its Variables**

We say that the formula

$$F = \frac{9}{5}C + 32$$

is solved for F because F is alone on one side of the equation, and the other side of the equation contains no F's. Suppose that we need to convert many Fahrenheit temperatures to equivalent degrees Celsius. In this case, it is easier to perform this task by solving the formula $F = \frac{9}{5}C + 32$ for C. (See Example 8.) For this reason, it is important to be able to solve an equation for any one of its specified variables. For example, the formula $d = rt$ is solved for d in terms of r and t. We can also solve $d = rt$ for t in terms of d and r. To solve for t, divide both sides of the equation by r.

$$d = rt$$
$$\frac{d}{r} = \frac{rt}{r} \qquad \text{Divide both sides by } r.$$
$$\frac{d}{r} = t \qquad \text{Simplify.}$$

To solve a formula or an equation for a specified variable, we use the same steps as for solving a linear equation. These steps are listed next.

Solving Equations for a Specified Variable

Step 1. Multiply on both sides to clear the equation of fractions if they occur.

Step 2. Use the distributive property to remove parentheses if they occur.

Step 3. Simplify each side of the equation by combining like terms.

Step 4. Get all terms containing the specified variable on one side and all other terms on the other side by using the addition property of equality.

Step 5. Get the specified variable alone by using the multiplication property of equality.

 EXAMPLE 5   Solve $V = lwh$ for l.

Solution   This formula is used to find the volume of a box. To solve for l, divide both sides by wh.

$$V = lwh$$
$$\frac{V}{wh} = \frac{lwh}{wh} \quad \text{Divide both sides by } wh.$$
$$\frac{V}{wh} = l \quad \text{Simplify.}$$

Since we have l alone on one side of the equation, we have solved for l in terms of V, w, and h. Remember that it does not matter on which side of the equation we isolate the variable.

PRACTICE
5   Solve $I = Prt$ for r.

EXAMPLE 6   Solve $y = mx + b$ for x.

Solution   The term containing the variable we are solving for, mx, is on the right side of the equation. Get mx alone by subtracting b from both sides.

$$y = mx + b$$
$$y - b = mx + b - b \quad \text{Subtract } b \text{ from both sides.}$$
$$y - b = mx \quad \text{Combine like terms.}$$

Next, solve for x by dividing both sides by m.

$$\frac{y - b}{m} = \frac{mx}{m}$$
$$\frac{y - b}{m} = x \quad \text{Simplify.}$$

PRACTICE
6   Solve $H = 5as + 10a$ for s.

✓**CONCEPT CHECK**
Solve:

a. $\boxed{} = \boxed{} - \boxed{}$ for $\boxed{}$

b. $\boxed{} = \boxed{} \cdot \triangle - \boxed{}$ for $\boxed{}$

 EXAMPLE 7   Solve $P = 2l + 2w$ for w.

Solution   This formula relates the perimeter of a rectangle to its length and width. Find the term containing the variable w. To get this term, $2w$, alone subtract $2l$ from both sides.

l
w

▶ **Helpful Hint**

The 2's may *not* be divided out here. Although 2 is a factor of the denominator, 2 is *not* a factor of the numerator since it is not a factor of both terms in the numerator.

$$P = 2l + 2w$$

$$P - 2l = 2l + 2w - 2l \quad \text{Subtract } 2l \text{ from both sides.}$$

$$P - 2l = 2w \quad\quad\quad \text{Combine like terms.}$$

$$\frac{P - 2l}{2} = \frac{2w}{2} \quad\quad \text{Divide both sides by 2.}$$

$$\frac{P - 2l}{2} = w \quad\quad\quad \text{Simplify.} \qquad \square$$

PRACTICE
7   Solve $N = F + d(n - 1)$ for d.

The next example has an equation containing a fraction. We will first clear the equation of fractions and then solve for the specified variable.

EXAMPLE 8   Solve $F = \dfrac{9}{5}C + 32$ for C.

Solution

$$F = \frac{9}{5}C + 32$$

$$5(F) = 5\left(\frac{9}{5}C + 32\right) \quad \text{Clear the fraction by multiplying both sides by the LCD.}$$

$$5F = 9C + 160 \quad\quad\quad\quad \text{Distribute the 5.}$$

$$5F - 160 = 9C + 160 - 160 \quad \text{To get the term containing the variable } C \text{ alone, subtract 160 from both sides.}$$

$$5F - 160 = 9C \quad\quad\quad\quad \text{Combine like terms.}$$

$$\frac{5F - 160}{9} = \frac{9C}{9} \quad\quad\quad \text{Divide both sides by 9.}$$

$$\frac{5F - 160}{9} = C \quad\quad\quad\quad \text{Simplify.}$$

Note: An equivalent way to write this formula is $C = \dfrac{5}{9}(F - 32)$. $\qquad \square$

PRACTICE
8   Solve $A = \dfrac{1}{2}a(b + B)$ for B.

Vocabulary, Readiness & Video Check

Martin-Gay Interactive Videos

See Video 2.5

Watch the section lecture video and answer the following questions.

OBJECTIVE
1
1. Complete this statement based on the lecture given before ▣ Example 1. A formula is an equation that describes known _____ among quantities.

OBJECTIVE
1
2. In ▣ Example 2, how are the units for the solution determined?

OBJECTIVE
2
3. During ▣ Example 4, why is the equation $5x = 30$?

2.5   Exercise Set   MyMathLab®

Substitute the given values into each given formula and solve for the unknown variable. If necessary, round to one decimal place. See Examples 1 through 4.

1. $A = bh$; $A = 45, b = 15$ (Area of a parallelogram)

2. $d = rt$; $d = 195, t = 3$ (Distance formula)

3. $S = 4lw + 2wh$; $S = 102, l = 7, w = 3$ (Surface area of a special rectangular box)

4. $V = lwh$; $l = 14, w = 8, h = 3$ (Volume of a rectangular box)

5. $A = \frac{1}{2}h(B + b)$; $A = 180, B = 11, b = 7$ (Area of a trapezoid)

6. $A = \frac{1}{2}h(B + b)$; $A = 60, B = 7, b = 3$ (Area of a trapezoid)

7. $P = a + b + c$; $P = 30, a = 8, b = 10$ (Perimeter of a triangle)

8. $V = \frac{1}{3}Ah$; $V = 45, h = 5$ (Volume of a pyramid)

9. $C = 2\pi r$; $C = 15.7$ (use the approximation 3.14 or a calculator approximation for π) (Circumference of a circle)

10. $A = \pi r^2$; $r = 4.5$ (use the approximation 3.14 or a calculator approximation for π) (Area of a circle)

11. $I = PRT$; $I = 3750, P = 25,000, R = 0.05$ (Simple interest formula)

12. $I = PRT$; $I = 1,056,000, R = 0.055, T = 6$ (Simple interest formula)

13. $V = \frac{1}{3}\pi r^2 h$; $V = 565.2, r = 6$ (use a calculator approximation for π) (Volume of a cone)

14. $V = \frac{4}{3}\pi r^3$; $r = 3$ (use a calculator approximation for π) (Volume of a sphere)

Solve each formula for the specified variable. See Examples 5 through 8.

15. $f = 5gh$ for h

16. $A = \pi ab$ for b

17. $V = lwh$ for w

18. $T = mnr$ for n

19. $3x + y = 7$ for y

20. $-x + y = 13$ for y

21. $A = P + PRT$ for R

22. $A = P + PRT$ for T

23. $V = \frac{1}{3}Ah$ for A

24. $D = \frac{1}{4}fk$ for k

25. $P = a + b + c$ for a

26. $PR = x + y + z + w$ for z

27. $S = 2\pi rh + 2\pi r^2$ for h

28. $S = 4lw + 2wh$ for h

Solve. For Exercises 29 and 30, the solutions have been started for you. See Examples 1 through 4.

29. The iconic NASDAQ sign in New York's Times Square has a width of 84 feet and an area of 10,080 square feet. Find the height (or length) of the sign. (*Source:* livedesignonline.com)

Start the solution:

1. UNDERSTAND the problem. Reread it as many times as needed.

2. TRANSLATE into an equation. (Fill in the blanks below.)

Area	=	length	times	width
↓	↓	↓	↓	↓
___	=	x	·	___

Finish with:

3. SOLVE and 4. INTERPRET

30. The world's largest sign for Coca-Cola is located in Arica, Chile. The rectangular sign has a length of 400 feet and an area of 52,400 square feet. Find the width of the sign. (*Source:* Fabulous Facts about Coca-Cola, Atlanta, GA)

Start the solution:

1. UNDERSTAND the problem. Reread it as many times as needed.

2. TRANSLATE into an equation. (Fill in the blanks below.)

Area	=	length	times	width
↓	↓	↓	↓	↓
___	=	___	·	x

Finish with:

3. SOLVE and 4. INTERPRET

31. For the purpose of purchasing new baseboard and carpet,
   a. Find the area and perimeter of the room below (neglecting doors).
   b. Identify whether baseboard has to do with area or perimeter and the same with carpet.

11.5 ft   9 ft

32. For the purpose of purchasing lumber for a new fence and seed to plant grass,

  a. Find the area and perimeter of the yard below.

  b. Identify whether a fence has to do with area or perimeter and the same with grass seed.

27 ft   45 ft

36 ft

33. A frame shop charges according to both the amount of framing needed to surround the picture and the amount of glass needed to cover the picture.

  a. Find the area and perimeter of the trapezoid-shaped framed picture below.

  b. Identify whether the amount of framing has to do with perimeter or area and the same with the amount of glass.

24 in.

20 in.   20 in.

12 in.

56 in.

34. A decorator is painting and placing a border completely around the parallelogram-shaped wall.

  a. Find the area and perimeter of the wall below.

  b. Identify whether the border has to do with perimeter or area and the same with paint.

11.7 ft

7 ft

9.3 ft

35. Convert Nome, Alaska's 14°F high temperature to Celsius.

36. Convert Paris, France's low temperature of −5°C to Fahrenheit.

37. An architect designs a rectangular flower garden such that the width is exactly two-thirds of the length. If 260 feet of antique picket fencing are to be used to enclose the garden, find the dimensions of the garden.

x feet

38. If the length of a rectangular parking lot is 10 meters less than twice its width, and the perimeter is 400 meters, find the length of the parking lot.

x meters

39. A flower bed is in the shape of a triangle with one side twice the length of the shortest side, and the third side is 30 feet more than the length of the shortest side. Find the dimensions if the perimeter is 102 feet.

x

40. The perimeter of a yield sign in the shape of an isosceles triangle is 22 feet. If the shortest side is 2 feet less than the other two sides, find the length of the shortest side. (*Hint:* An isosceles triangle has two sides the same length.)

x feet   x feet

41. The Cat is a high-speed catamaran auto ferry that operates between Bar Harbor, Maine, and Yarmouth, Nova Scotia. The Cat can make the 138-mile trip in about $2\frac{1}{2}$ hours. Find the catamaran speed for this trip. (*Source:* Bay Ferries)

42. A family is planning their vacation to Disney World. They will drive from a small town outside New Orleans, Louisiana, to Orlando, Florida, a distance of 700 miles. They plan to average a rate of 55 mph. How long will this trip take?

△ **43.** Piranha fish require 1.5 cubic feet of water per fish to maintain a healthy environment. Find the maximum number of piranhas you could put in a tank measuring 8 feet by 3 feet by 6 feet.

6 feet

3 feet 8 feet

△ **44.** Find the maximum number of goldfish you can put in a cylindrical tank whose diameter is 8 meters and whose height is 3 meters if each goldfish needs 2 cubic meters of water.

← 8 meters →

3 meters

Dolbear's Law states the relationship between the rate at which Snowy Tree crickets chirp and the air temperature of their environment. The formula is

$$T = 50 + \frac{N - 40}{4}, where \quad \begin{array}{l} T = \text{temperature in degrees Fahrenheit and} \\ N = \text{number of chirps per minute} \end{array}$$

45. If $N = 86$, find the temperature in degrees Fahrenheit, T.

46. If $N = 94$, find the temperature in degrees Fahrenheit, T.

47. If $T = 55°F$, find the number of chirps per minute.

48. If $T = 65°F$, find the number of chirps per minute.

Use the results of Exercises 45–48 to complete each sentence with "increases" or "decreases."

49. As the number of cricket chirps per minute increases, the air temperature of their environment _____.

50. As the air temperature of their environment decreases, the number of cricket chirps per minute _____.

△ **51.** A lawn is in the shape of a trapezoid with a height of 60 feet and bases of 70 feet and 130 feet. How many whole bags of fertilizer must be purchased to cover the lawn if each bag covers 4000 square feet?

70 feet

60 feet

130 feet

△ **52.** If the area of a right-triangularly shaped sail is 20 square feet and its base is 5 feet, find the height of the sail.

?

5 feet

△ **53.** Maria's Pizza sells one 16-inch cheese pizza or two 10-inch cheese pizzas for $9.99. Determine which size gives more pizza.

16 inches 10 inches 10 inches

△ **54.** Find how much rope is needed to wrap around the earth at the equator if the radius of the earth is 4000 miles. (*Hint:* Use 3.14 for π and the formula for circumference.)

△ **55.** The perimeter of a geometric figure is the sum of the lengths of its sides. If the perimeter of the following pentagon (five-sided figure) is 48 meters, find the length of each side.

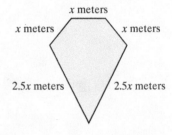

x meters

x meters x meters

$2.5x$ meters $2.5x$ meters

56. The perimeter of the following triangle is 82 feet. Find the length of each side.

$(2x - 8)$ feet

x feet

$(3x - 12)$ feet

57. The Hawaiian volcano Kilauea is one of the world's most active volcanoes and has had continuous eruptive activity since 1983. Erupting lava flows through a tube system about 11 kilometers to the sea. Assume a lava flow speed of 0.5 kilometer per hour and calculate how long it takes to reach the sea.

58. The world's largest pink ribbon, the sign of the fight against breast cancer, was erected out of pink Post-it® notes on a billboard in New York City in October 2004. If the area of the rectangular billboard covered by the ribbon was approximately 3990 square feet, and the width of the billboard was approximately 57 feet, what was the height of this billboard?

59. The perimeter of an equilateral triangle is 7 inches more than the perimeter of a square, and the side of the triangle is 5 inches longer than the side of the square. Find the side of the triangle. (*Hint:* An equilateral triangle has three sides the same length.)

60. A square animal pen and a pen shaped like an equilateral triangle have equal perimeters. Find the length of the sides of each pen if the sides of the triangular pen are fifteen less than twice a side of the square pen.

61. Find how long it takes a person to drive 135 miles on I-10 if she merges onto I-10 at 10 a.m. and drives nonstop with her cruise control set on 60 mph.

62. Beaumont, Texas, is about 150 miles from Toledo Bend. If Leo Miller leaves Beaumont at 4 a.m. and averages 45 mph, when should he arrive at Toledo Bend?

63. The longest runway at Los Angeles International Airport has the shape of a rectangle and an area of 1,813,500 square feet. This runway is 150 feet wide. How long is the runway? (*Source:* Los Angeles World Airports)

64. Normal room temperature is about 78°F. Convert this temperature to Celsius.

65. The highest temperature ever recorded in Europe was 122°F in Seville, Spain, in August 1881. Convert this record high temperature to Celsius. (*Source:* National Climatic Data Center)

66. The lowest temperature ever recorded in Oceania was −10°C at the Haleakala Summit in Maui, Hawaii, in January 1961. Convert this record low temperature to Fahrenheit. (*Source:* National Climatic Data Center)

67. The average temperature on the planet Mercury is 167°C. Convert this temperature to degrees Fahrenheit. (*Source:* National Space Science Data Center)

68. The average temperature on the planet Jupiter is −227°F. Convert this temperature to degrees Celsius. Round to the nearest degree. (*Source:* National Space Science Data Center)

69. The Hoberman Sphere is a toy ball that expands and contracts. When it is completely closed, it has a diameter of 9.5 inches. Find the volume of the Hoberman Sphere when it is

completely closed. Use 3.14 for π. Round to the nearest whole cubic inch. (*Hint:* Volume of a sphere $= \frac{4}{3}\pi r^3$. *Source:* Hoberman Designs, Inc.)

70. When the Hoberman Sphere (see Exercise 69) is completely expanded, its diameter is 30 inches. Find the volume of the Hoberman Sphere when it is completely expanded. Use 3.14 for π. (*Source:* Hoberman Designs, Inc.)

REVIEW AND PREVIEW

Write each percent as a decimal. See Appendix B.2.

71. 32%

72. 8%

73. 200%

74. 0.5%

Write each decimal as a percent. See Appendix B.2.

75. 0.17

76. 0.03

77. 7.2

78. 5

CONCEPT EXTENSIONS

79. The formula $V = lwh$ is used to find the volume of a box. If the length of a box is doubled, the width is doubled, and the height is doubled, how does this affect the volume? Explain your answer.

80. The formula $A = bh$ is used to find the area of a parallelogram. If the base of a parallelogram is doubled and its height is doubled, how does this affect the area? Explain your answer.

81. Use the Dolbear's Law formula for Exercises 45–48 and calculate when the number of cricket chirps per minute is the same as the temperature in degrees Fahrenheit. (*Hint:* Replace T with N and solve for N or replace N with T and solve for T.)

82. Find the temperature at which the Celsius measurement and the Fahrenheit measurement are the same number.

Solve.

83. $N = R + \dfrac{V}{G}$ for V (Urban forestry: tree plantings per year)

84. $B = \dfrac{F}{P - V}$ for V (Business: break-even point)

Solve. See the Concept Check in this section.

85. ▢ − ● · ▮ = △   for ●

86. ⬠ · ▮ + △ = ●   for ▮

87. The distance from the sun to the earth is approximately 93,000,000 miles. If light travels at a rate of 186,000 miles per second, how long does it take light from the sun to reach us?

88. Light travels at a rate of 186,000 miles per second. If our moon is 238,860 miles from the earth, how long does it take light from the moon to reach us? (Round to the nearest tenth of a second.)

89. A glacier is a giant mass of rocks and ice that flows downhill like a river. Exit Glacier, near Seward, Alaska, moves at a rate of 20 inches a day. Find the distance in feet the glacier moves in a year. (Assume 365 days a year. Round to 2 decimal places.)

90. Flying fish do not *actually* fly, but glide. They have been known to travel a distance of 1300 feet at a rate of 20 miles per hour. How many seconds does it take to travel this distance? (*Hint:* First convert miles per hour to feet per second. Recall that 1 mile = 5280 feet. Round to the nearest tenth of a second.)

91. A Japanese "bullet" train set a new world record for train speed at 581 kilometers per hour during a manned test run on the Yamanashi Maglev Test Line in 2003. The Yamanashi Maglev Test Line is 42.8 kilometers long. How many *minutes* would a test run on the Yamanashi Line last at this record-setting speed? Round to the nearest hundredth of a minute. (*Source:* Japan Railways Central Co.)

92. The Boeing X-51 is an unmanned demonstration aircraft for hypersonic flight testing. In May 2010, it successfully completed a free flight at about 3800 mph. Neglecting altitude, if the circumference of Earth is approximately 25,000 miles, how long would it take for the X-51 to travel around Earth? Give your answer in hours and minutes rounded to the nearest whole minute.

93. In the United States, a notable hang glider flight was a 303-mile, $8\frac{1}{2}$-hour flight from New Mexico to Kansas. What was the average rate during this flight?

94. Stalactites join stalagmites to form columns. A column found at Natural Bridge Caverns near San Antonio, Texas, rises 15 feet and has a *diameter* of only 2 inches. Find the volume of this column in cubic inches. (*Hint:* Use the formula for volume of a cylinder and use a calculator approximation for π. Round to the nearest tenth of an inch.)

Graphing

In the previous chapter, we learned to solve and graph the solutions of linear equations and inequalities in one variable. Now we define and present techniques for solving and graphing linear equations and inequalities in two variables.

Tourism 2020 Vision is the World Tourism Organization's long-term forecast of world tourism through 2020. The broken-line graph below shows the forecasts. In Section 3.1, Exercises 1 through 6, we read a bar graph showing the top tourist destinations by country.

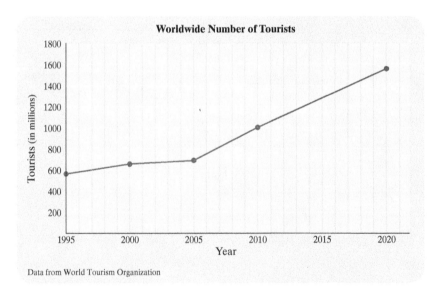

Data from World Tourism Organization

3.2 | Graphing Linear Equations

OBJECTIVES

1 Identify Linear Equations.

2 Graph a Linear Equation by Finding and Plotting Ordered Pair Solutions.

OBJECTIVE

1 Identifying Linear Equations

In the previous section, we found that equations in two variables may have more than one solution. For example, both $(6, 0)$ and $(2, -2)$ are solutions of the equation $x - 2y = 6$. In fact, this equation has an infinite number of solutions. Other solutions include $(0, -3)$, $(4, -1)$, and $(-2, -4)$. If we graph these solutions, notice that a pattern appears.

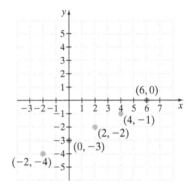

These solutions all appear to lie on the same line, which has been filled in below. It can be shown that every ordered pair solution of the equation corresponds to a point on this line, and every point on this line corresponds to an ordered pair solution. Thus, we say that this line is the **graph of the equation** $x - 2y = 6$.

> ▶ Helpful Hint
>
> Notice that we can only show a part of a line on a graph. The arrowheads on each end of the line remind us that the line actually extends indefinitely in both directions.

The equation $x - 2y = 6$ is called a **linear equation in two variables** and **the graph of every linear equation in two variables is a line.**

Linear Equation in Two Variables

A linear equation in two variables is an equation that can be written in the form

$$Ax + By = C$$

where A, B, and C are real numbers and A and B are not both 0. **The graph of a linear equation in two variables is a straight line.**

The form $Ax + By = C$ is called **standard form.**

> ▶ Helpful Hint
>
> Notice in the form $Ax + By = C$, the understood exponent on both x and y is 1.

Examples of Linear Equations in Two Variables

$$2x + y = 8 \qquad -2x = 7y \qquad y = \frac{1}{3}x + 2 \qquad y = 7$$

(Standard Form)

Before we graph linear equations in two variables, let's practice identifying these equations.

EXAMPLE 1   Determine whether each equation is a linear equation in two variables.

a. $x - 1.5y = -1.6$ **b.** $y = -2x$ **c.** $x + y^2 = 9$ **d.** $x = 5$

Solution

a. This is a linear equation in two variables because it is written in the form $Ax + By = C$ with $A = 1, B = -1.5$, and $C = -1.6$.

b. This is a linear equation in two variables because it can be written in the form $Ax + By = C$.

$$y = -2x$$
$$2x + y = 0 \qquad \text{Add } 2x \text{ to both sides.}$$

c. This is *not* a linear equation in two variables because y is squared.

d. This is a linear equation in two variables because it can be written in the form $Ax + By = C$.

$$x = 5$$
$$x + 0y = 5 \qquad \text{Add } 0 \cdot y.$$

PRACTICE

1   Determine whether each equation is a linear equation in two variables.

a. $3x + 2.7y = -5.3$ **b.** $x^2 + y = 8$ **c.** $y = 12$ **d.** $5x = -3y$

OBJECTIVE

2   Graphing Linear Equations by Plotting Ordered Pair Solutions

From geometry, we know that a straight line is determined by just two points. Graphing a linear equation in two variables, then, requires that we find just two of its infinitely many solutions. Once we do so, we plot the solution points and draw the line connecting the points. Usually, we find a third solution as well, as a check.

EXAMPLE 2   Graph the linear equation $2x + y = 5$.

Solution   Find three ordered pair solutions of $2x + y = 5$. To do this, choose a value for one variable, x or y, and solve for the other variable. For example, let $x = 1$. Then $2x + y = 5$ becomes

$$2x + y = 5$$
$$2(1) + y = 5 \qquad \text{Replace } x \text{ with 1.}$$
$$2 + y = 5 \qquad \text{Multiply.}$$
$$y = 3 \qquad \text{Subtract 2 from both sides.}$$

Since $y = 3$ when $x = 1$, the ordered pair $(1, 3)$ is a solution of $2x + y = 5$. Next, let $x = 0$.

$$2x + y = 5$$
$$2(0) + y = 5 \qquad \text{Replace } x \text{ with 0.}$$
$$0 + y = 5$$
$$y = 5$$

The ordered pair $(0, 5)$ is a second solution.

The two solutions found so far allow us to draw the straight line that is the graph of all solutions of $2x + y = 5$. However, we find a third ordered pair as a check. Let $y = -1$.

$$2x + y = 5$$
$$2x + (-1) = 5 \quad \text{Replace } y \text{ with } -1.$$
$$2x - 1 = 5$$
$$2x = 6 \quad \text{Add 1 to both sides.}$$
$$x = 3 \quad \text{Divide both sides by 2.}$$

The third solution is $(3, -1)$. These three ordered pair solutions are listed in table form as shown. The graph of $2x + y = 5$ is the line through the three points.

x	y
1	3
0	5
3	−1

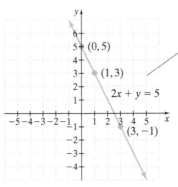

> ▶ Helpful Hint
>
> All three points should fall on the same straight line. If not, check your ordered pair solutions for a mistake.

PRACTICE

2 Graph the linear equation $x + 3y = 9$.

EXAMPLE 3 Graph the linear equation $-5x + 3y = 15$.

Solution Find three ordered pair solutions of $-5x + 3y = 15$.

Let $x = 0$.	**Let $y = 0$.**	**Let $x = -2$.**
$-5x + 3y = 15$	$-5x + 3y = 15$	$-5x + 3y = 15$
$-5 \cdot 0 + 3y = 15$	$-5x + 3 \cdot 0 = 15$	$-5(-2) + 3y = 15$
$0 + 3y = 15$	$-5x + 0 = 15$	$10 + 3y = 15$
$3y = 15$	$-5x = 15$	$3y = 5$
$y = 5$	$x = -3$	$y = \dfrac{5}{3}$

The ordered pairs are $(0, 5)$, $(-3, 0)$, and $\left(-2, \dfrac{5}{3}\right)$. The graph of $-5x + 3y = 15$ is the line through the three points.

x	y
0	5
−3	0
−2	$\dfrac{5}{3} = 1\dfrac{2}{3}$

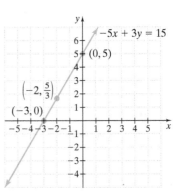

PRACTICE

3 Graph the linear equation $3x - 4y = 12$.

EXAMPLE 4   Graph the linear equation $y = 3x$.

Solution   To graph this linear equation, we find three ordered pair solutions. Since this equation is solved for y, choose three x values.

If $x = 2$, $y = 3 \cdot 2 = 6$.
If $x = 0$, $y = 3 \cdot 0 = 0$.
If $x = -1$, $y = 3 \cdot -1 = -3$.

x	y
2	6
0	0
−1	−3

Next, graph the ordered pair solutions listed in the table above and draw a line through the plotted points as shown below. The line is the graph of $y = 3x$. Every point on the graph represents an ordered pair solution of the equation and every ordered pair solution is a point on this line.

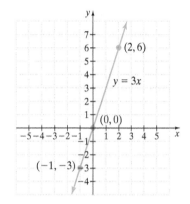

PRACTICE
4   Graph the linear equation $y = -2x$.

> **Helpful Hint**
> When graphing a linear equation in two variables, if it is
> • solved for y, it may be easier to find ordered pair solutions by choosing x-values. If it is
> • solved for x, it may be easier to find ordered pair solutions by choosing y-values.

EXAMPLE 5   Graph the linear equation $y = -\dfrac{1}{3}x + 2$.

Solution   Find three ordered pair solutions, graph the solutions, and draw a line through the plotted solutions. To avoid fractions, choose x values that are multiples of 3 to substitute in the equation. When a multiple of 3 is multiplied by $-\dfrac{1}{3}$, the result is an integer. See the calculations shown above the table.

If $x = 6$, then $y = -\dfrac{1}{3} \cdot 6 + 2 = -2 + 2 = 0$

If $x = 0$, then $y = -\dfrac{1}{3} \cdot 0 + 2 = 0 + 2 = 2$

If $x = -3$, then $y = -\dfrac{1}{3} \cdot -3 + 2 = 1 + 2 = 3$

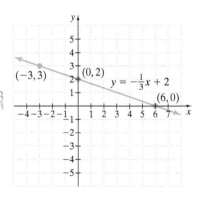

x	y
6	0
0	2
−3	3

PRACTICE
5   Graph the linear equation $y = \dfrac{1}{2}x + 3$.

Let's compare the graphs in Examples 4 and 5. The graph of $y = 3x$ tilts upward (as we follow the line from left to right) and the graph of $y = -\dfrac{1}{3}x + 2$ tilts downward (as we follow the line from left to right). We will learn more about the tilt, or slope, of a line in Section 3.4.

EXAMPLE 6 Graph the linear equation $y = -2$.

Solution: The equation $y = -2$ can be written in standard form as $0x + y = -2$. No matter what value we replace x with, y is always -2.

x	y
0	−2
3	−2
−2	−2

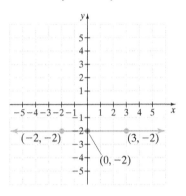

Notice that the graph of $y = -2$ is a horizontal line.

PRACTICE
6 Graph the linear equation $x = -2$.

EXAMPLE 7 Graph the linear equation $y = 3x + 6$ and compare this graph with the graph of $y = 3x$ in Example 4.

Solution Find ordered pair solutions, graph the solutions, and draw a line through the plotted solutions. We choose x values and substitute in the equation $y = 3x + 6$.

If $x = -3$, then $y = 3(-3) + 6 = -3$.
If $x = 0$, then $y = 3(0) + 6 = 6$.
If $x = 1$, then $y = 3(1) + 6 = 9$.

x	y
−3	−3
0	6
1	9

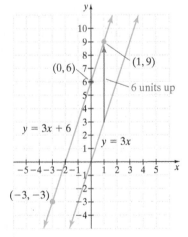

The most startling similarity is that both graphs appear to have the same upward tilt as we move from left to right. Also, the graph of $y = 3x$ crosses the y-axis at the origin, while the graph of $y = 3x + 6$ crosses the y-axis at 6. In fact, the graph of $y = 3x + 6$ is the same as the graph of $y = 3x$ moved vertically upward 6 units.

PRACTICE
7   Graph the linear equation $y = -2x + 3$ and compare this graph with the graph of $y = -2x$ in Practice 4.

Notice that the graph of $y = 3x + 6$ crosses the y-axis at 6. This happens because when $x = 0$, $y = 3x + 6$ becomes $y = 3 \cdot 0 + 6 = 6$. The graph contains the point $(0, 6)$, which is on the y-axis.

In general, if a linear equation in two variables is solved for y, we say that it is written in the form $y = mx + b$. The graph of this equation contains the point $(0, b)$ because when $x = 0$, $y = mx + b$ is $y = m \cdot 0 + b = b$.

> The graph of $y = mx + b$ crosses the y-axis at $(0, b)$.

We will review this again in Section 3.5.
    Linear equations are often used to model real data as seen in the next example.

EXAMPLE 8   Estimating the Number of Registered Nurses

The occupation expected to have the most employment growth in the next few years is registered nurse. The number of people y (in thousands) employed as registered nurses in the United States can be estimated by the linear equation $y = 58.1x + 2619$, where x is the number of years after the year 2008. (Data from U.S. Bureau of Labor Statistics)

a. Graph the equation.

b. Use the graph to predict the number of registered nurses in the year 2018.

Solution:

a. To graph $y = 58.1x + 2619$, choose x-values and substitute in the equation.

If $x = 0$, then $y = 58.1(0) + 2619 = 2619$.
If $x = 2$, then $y = 58.1(2) + 2619 = 2735.2$.
If $x = 5$, then $y = 58.1(5) + 2619 = 2909.5$.

x	y
0	2619
2	2735.2
5	2909.5

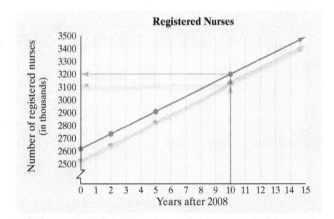

b. To use the graph to *predict* the number of registered nurses in the year 2018, we need to find the y-coordinate that corresponds to $x = 10$. (10 years after 2008 is the year 2018.) To do so, find 10 on the x-axis. Move vertically upward to the graphed line and then horizontally to the left. We approximate the number on the y-axis to be 3200. Thus, in the year 2018, we predict that there will be 3200 thousand registered nurses. (The actual value, using 10 for x, is 3200.)

PRACTICE

8   One of the occupations expected to have a large growth in employment in the next few years is computer software application engineers. The number of people y (in thousands) employed as computer software application engineers in the United States can be estimated by the linear equation $y = 17.5x + 515$, where x is the number of years after 2008. (*Source:* Based on data from the Bureau of Labor Statistics)

a. Graph the equation.

b. Use the graph to predict the number of computer software application engineers in the year 2020.

> **Helpful Hint**
>
> Make sure you understand that models are mathematical approximations of the data for the known years. (For example, see the model in Example 8.) Any number of unknown factors can affect future years, so be cautious when using models to predict.

Graphing Calculator Explorations

In this section, we begin an optional study of graphing calculators and graphing software packages for computers. These graphers use the same point plotting technique that was introduced in this section. The advantage of this graphing technology is, of course, that graphing calculators and computers can find and plot ordered pair solutions much faster than we can. Note, however, that the features described in these boxes may not be available on all graphing calculators.

The rectangular screen where a portion of the rectangular coordinate system is displayed is called a **window**. We call it a **standard window** for graphing when both the x- and y-axes show coordinates between -10 and 10. This information is often displayed in the window menu on a graphing calculator as

$$\text{Xmin} = -10$$
$$\text{Xmax} = 10$$
$$\text{Xscl} = 1 \qquad \text{The scale on the } x\text{-axis is one unit per tick mark.}$$
$$\text{Ymin} = -10$$
$$\text{Ymax} = 10$$
$$\text{Yscl} = 1 \qquad \text{The scale on the } y\text{-axis is one unit per tick mark.}$$

To use a graphing calculator to graph the equation $y = 2x + 3$, press the $\boxed{\text{Y=}}$ key and enter the keystrokes $\boxed{2}\ \boxed{x}\ \boxed{+}\ \boxed{3}$. The top row should now read $Y_1 = 2x + 3$. Next press the $\boxed{\text{GRAPH}}$ key, and the display should look like this:

Use a standard window and graph the following linear equations. (Unless otherwise stated, use a standard window when graphing.)   See graphing answer section.

1. $y = -3x + 7$

2. $y = -x + 5$

3. $y = 2.5x - 7.9$

4. $y = -1.3x + 5.2$

5. $y = -\dfrac{3}{10}x + \dfrac{32}{5}$

6. $y = \dfrac{2}{9}x - \dfrac{22}{3}$

Vocabulary, Readiness & Video Check

Martin-Gay Interactive Videos

See Video 3.2

Watch the section lecture video and answer the following questions.

OBJECTIVE
1

1. Exponents aren't mentioned in the definition of a linear equation in two variables. However, in determining whether ▣ Example 3 is a linear equation in two variables, the exponents or powers on the variables are discussed. Explain.

OBJECTIVE
2

2. In the lecture before ▣ Example 5, it's mentioned that you need only two points to determine a line. Why then are three ordered pair solutions found in ▣ Examples 5–7?

OBJECTIVE
2

3. What does a graphed line represent as discussed at the end of ▣ Examples 5 and 7?

3.2 Exercise Set   MyMathLab®

Determine whether each equation is a linear equation in two variables. See Example 1.

1. $-x = 3y + 10$

2. $y = x - 15$

3. $x = y$

4. $x = y^3$

5. $x^2 + 2y = 0$

6. $0.01x - 0.2y = 8.8$

7. $y = -1$

8. $x = 25$

For each equation, find three ordered pair solutions by completing the table. Then use the ordered pairs to graph the equation. See Examples 2 through 7.

9. $x - y = 6$

x	y
	0
4	
	-1

10. $x - y = 4$

x	y
	0
	2
-1	

11. $y = -4x$

x	y
1	
0	
-1	

12. $y = -5x$

x	y
1	
0	
-1	

13. $y = \frac{1}{3}x$

x	y
0	
6	
-3	

14. $y = \frac{1}{2}x$

x	y
0	
-4	
2	

15. $y = -4x + 3$

x	y
0	
1	
2	

16. $y = -5x + 2$

x	y
0	
1	
2	

MIXED PRACTICE

Graph each linear equation. See Examples 2 through 7.

17. $x + y = 1$

18. $x + y = 7$

19. $x - y = -2$

20. $-x + y = 6$

▶ **21.** $x - 2y = 6$

22. $-x + 5y = 5$

23. $y = 6x + 3$

24. $y = -2x + 7$

25. $x = -4$

26. $y = 5$

27. $y = 3$

28. $x = -1$

29. $y = x$

30. $y = -x$

▶ **31.** $x = -3y$

32. $x = -5y$

33. $x + 3y = 9$

34. $2x + y = 2$

▶ **35.** $y = \frac{1}{2}x + 2$

36. $y = \frac{1}{4}x + 3$

37. $3x - 2y = 12$

38. $2x - 7y = 14$

39. $y = -3.5x + 4$

40. $y = -1.5x - 3$

Graph each pair of linear equations on the same set of axes. Discuss how the graphs are similar and how they are different. See Example 7.

41. $y = 5x; y = 5x + 4$

42. $y = 2x; y = 2x + 5$

43. $y = -2x; y = -2x - 3$

44. $y = x; y = x - 7$

45. $y = \frac{1}{2}x; y = \frac{1}{2}x + 2$

46. $y = -\frac{1}{4}x; y = -\frac{1}{4}x + 3$

The graph of $y = 5x$ is given below as well as Figures a–d. For Exercises 47 through 50, match each equation with its graph. Hint: Recall that if an equation is written in the form $y = mx + b$, its graph crosses the y-axis at $(0, b)$.

47. $y = 5x + 5$ **48.** $y = 5x - 4$

49. $y = 5x - 1$ **50.** $y = 5x + 2$

a.

b.

c.

d.

Solve. See Example 8.

51. Jogging is one of the few sports that has been consistently increasing over the past few years. The number of people jogging (in millions) from the years 2000 to 2009 is given by the equation $y = x + 23$, where x is the number of years after 2000. (*Source:* Based on data from the National Sporting Goods Association)

a. Use this equation or a graph of it to complete the ordered pair (8,   ).

b. Write a sentence explaining the meaning of the answer to part (a).

c. If this trend continues, how many joggers will there be in 2017?

52. The revenue y (in billions of dollars) for Home Depot stores during the years 2006 through 2010 is given by the equation $y = -3x + 79$, where x is the number of years after 2006. (*Source:* Based on data from Home Depot stores)

a. Use this equation or a graph of it to complete the ordered pair (4,   ).

b. Write a sentence explaining the meaning of the answer to part (a).

c. If this trend continues, predict the revenue for Home Depot stores for the year 2015.

53. One American rite of passage is a driver's license. The number of people y (in millions) who have a driver's license can be estimated by the linear equation $y = 2.2x + 190$, where x is the number of years after 2000. (Data from Federal Highway Administration)

a. Use this equation to complete the ordered pair (8,   ).

b. Write a sentence explaining the meaning of the ordered pair in part (a).

c. If this trend continues, predict the number of people with driver's licenses in 2016.

54. The percent of U.S. households y with at least one computer can be approximated by the linear equation $y = 4.3x + 51$, where x is the number of years since 2000. (Data from *Statistical Abstract of the United States*)

a. Use the equation to complete the ordered pair (9,   ).

b. Write a sentence explaining the meaning of the ordered pair found in part (a).

c. If this trend continues, predict the percent of U.S. households that have at least one computer in 2012.

d. Explain any issues with your answer to part (c).

REVIEW AND PREVIEW

△ **55.** The coordinates of three vertices of a rectangle are $(-2, 5)$, $(4, 5)$, and $(-2, -1)$. Find the coordinates of the fourth vertex. See Section 3.1.

△ **56.** The coordinates of two vertices of a square are $(-3, -1)$ and $(2, -1)$. Find the coordinates of two pairs of points possible for the third and fourth vertices. See Section 3.1.

Complete each table. See Section 3.1.

57. $x - y = -3$

x	y
0	
	0

58. $y - x = 5$

x	y
0	
	0

59. $y = 2x$

x	y
0	
	0

60. $x = -3y$

x	y
0	
	0

CONCEPT EXTENSIONS

Write each statement as an equation in two variables. Then graph the equation.

61. The y-value is 5 more than the x-value.

62. The y-value is twice the x-value.

63. Two times the x-value, added to three times the y-value, is 6.

64. Five times the x-value, added to twice the y-value, is -10.

△ **65.** The perimeter of the trapezoid below is 22 centimeters. Write a linear equation in two variables for the perimeter. Find y if x is 3 cm.

△ **66.** The perimeter of the rectangle below is 50 miles. Write a linear equation in two variables for this perimeter. Use this equation to find x when y is 20.

✎ **67.** Explain how to find ordered pair solutions of linear equations in two variables.

✎ **68.** If (a, b) is an ordered pair solution of $x + y = 5$, is (b, a) also a solution? Explain why or why not.

69. Graph the nonlinear equation $y = x^2$ by completing the table shown. Plot the ordered pairs and connect them with a smooth curve.

x	y
0	
1	
-1	
2	
-2	

70. Graph the nonlinear equation $y = |x|$ by completing the table shown. Plot the ordered pairs and connect them. This curve is "V" shaped.

$$y = |x|$$

x	y
0	
1	
-1	
2	
-2	

3.3 Intercepts

OBJECTIVE

1 Identifying Intercepts

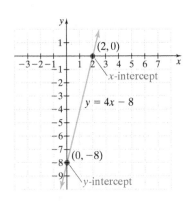

In this section, we graph linear equations in two variables by identifying intercepts. For example, the graph of $y = 4x - 8$ is shown on the right. Notice that this graph crosses the y-axis at the point $(0, -8)$. This point is called the **y-intercept.** Likewise, the graph crosses the x-axis at $(2, 0)$, and this point is called the **x-intercept.**

The intercepts are $(2, 0)$ and $(0, -8)$.

> ▌ Helpful Hint
>
> If a graph crosses the x-axis at $(-3, 0)$ and the y-axis at $(0, 7)$, then
>
> $$\underbrace{(-3, 0)}_{x\text{-intercept}} \qquad \underbrace{(0, 7)}_{y\text{-intercept}}$$
>
> Notice that for the y-intercept, the x-value is 0 and for the x-intercept, the y-value is 0.
> **Note:** Sometimes in mathematics, you may see just the number 7 stated as the y-intercept, and -3 stated as the x-intercept.

EXAMPLES Identify the x- and y-intercepts.

1.

Solution

x-intercept: $(-3, 0)$
y-intercept: $(0, 2)$

2.

Solution

x-intercepts: $(-4, 0), (-1, 0)$
y-intercept: $(0, 1)$

> ▌ Helpful Hint
>
> Notice that any time $(0, 0)$ is a point of a graph, then it is an x-intercept and a y-intercept. Why? It is the only point that lies on both axes.

3.

Solution

x-intercept: $(0, 0)$
y-intercept: $(0, 0)$

4.

Solution

x-intercept: $(2, 0)$
y-intercept: none

5.

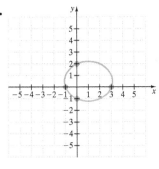

Solution

x-intercepts:
$(-1, 0), (3, 0)$
y-intercepts:
$(0, 2), (0, -1)$

1–5   Identify the *x*- and *y*-intercepts.

1.

2.

3.

4.

5.
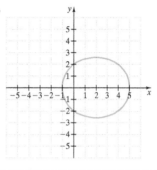

OBJECTIVE

2   Using Intercepts to Graph a Linear Equation

Given the equation of a line, intercepts are usually easy to find since one coordinate is 0.

One way to find the *y*-intercept of a line, given its equation, is to let $x = 0$, since a point on the *y*-axis has an *x*-coordinate of 0. To find the *x*-intercept of a line, let $y = 0$, since a point on the *x*-axis has a *y*-coordinate of 0.

Finding *x*- and *y*-intercepts

To find the *x*-intercept, let $y = 0$ and solve for *x*.
To find the *y*-intercept, let $x = 0$ and solve for *y*.

EXAMPLE 6   Graph $x - 3y = 6$ by finding and plotting intercepts.

Solution   Let $y = 0$ to find the *x*-intercept and let $x = 0$ to find the *y*-intercept.

$$\text{Let } y = 0 \qquad\qquad \text{Let } x = 0$$
$$x - 3y = 6 \qquad\qquad x - 3y = 6$$
$$x - 3(0) = 6 \qquad\qquad 0 - 3y = 6$$
$$x - 0 = 6 \qquad\qquad -3y = 6$$
$$x = 6 \qquad\qquad y = -2$$

The *x*-intercept is $(6, 0)$ and the *y*-intercept is $(0, -2)$. We find a third ordered pair solution to check our work. If we let $y = -1$, then $x = 3$. Plot the points $(6, 0)$, $(0, -2)$, and $(3, -1)$. The graph of $x - 3y = 6$ is the line drawn through these points, as shown on page 196.

x	y
6	0
0	−2
3	−1

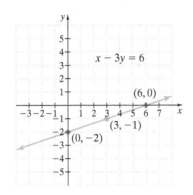

6   Graph $x + 2y = -4$ by finding and plotting intercepts.

EXAMPLE 7   Graph $x = -2y$ by plotting intercepts.

Solution   Let $y = 0$ to find the x-intercept and $x = 0$ to find the y-intercept.

$$\text{Let } y = 0 \qquad\qquad \text{Let } x = 0$$
$$x = -2y \qquad\qquad\quad x = -2y$$
$$x = -2(0) \qquad\qquad 0 = -2y$$
$$x = 0 \qquad\qquad\quad\; 0 = y$$

Both the x-intercept and y-intercept are $(0, 0)$. In other words, when $x = 0$, then $y = 0$, which gives the ordered pair $(0, 0)$. Also, when $y = 0$, then $x = 0$, which gives the same ordered pair $(0, 0)$. This happens when the graph passes through the origin. Since two points are needed to determine a line, we must find at least one more ordered pair that satisfies $x = -2y$. We will let $y = -1$ to find a second ordered pair solution and let $y = 1$ as a checkpoint.

$$\text{Let } y = -1 \qquad\qquad \text{Let } y = 1$$
$$x = -2(-1) \qquad\qquad\; x = -2(1)$$
$$x = 2 \qquad\qquad\qquad\; x = -2$$

The ordered pairs are $(0, 0)$, $(2, -1)$, and $(-2, 1)$. Plot these points to graph $x = -2y$.

x	y
0	0
2	−1
−2	1

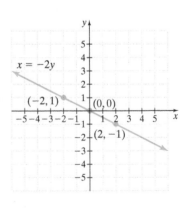

7   Graph $x = 3y$ by plotting intercepts.

EXAMPLE 8   Graph $4x = 3y - 9$.

Solution   Find the x- and y-intercepts, and then choose $x = 2$ to find a checkpoint.

Let $y = 0$	Let $x = 0$	Let $x = 2$
$4x = 3(0) - 9$	$4 \cdot 0 = 3y - 9$	$4(2) = 3y - 9$
$4x = -9$	$9 = 3y$	$8 = 3y - 9$
Solve for x.	Solve for y.	Solve for y.
$x = -\dfrac{9}{4}$ or $-2\dfrac{1}{4}$	$3 = y$	$17 = 3y$
		$\dfrac{17}{3} = y$ or $y = 5\dfrac{2}{3}$

The ordered pairs are $\left(-2\dfrac{1}{4}, 0\right)$, $(0, 3)$, and $\left(2, 5\dfrac{2}{3}\right)$. The equation $4x = 3y - 9$ is graphed as follows.

x	y
$-2\dfrac{1}{4}$	0
0	3
2	$5\dfrac{2}{3}$

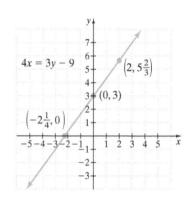

PRACTICE
8   Graph $3x = 2y + 4$.

OBJECTIVE
3   **Graphing Vertical and Horizontal Lines** ▶

The equation $x = c$, where c is a real number constant, is a linear equation in two variables because it can be written in the form $x + 0y = c$. The graph of this equation is a vertical line as shown in the next example.

EXAMPLE 9   Graph $x = 2$.

Solution   The equation $x = 2$ can be written as $x + 0y = 2$. For any y-value chosen, notice that x is 2. No other value for x satisfies $x + 0y = 2$. Any ordered pair whose x-coordinate is 2 is a solution of $x + 0y = 2$. We will use the ordered pair solutions $(2, 3)$, $(2, 0)$, and $(2, -3)$ to graph $x = 2$.

x	y
2	3
2	0
2	-3

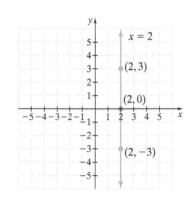

The graph is a vertical line with x-intercept $(2, 0)$. Note that this graph has no y-intercept because x is never 0.

PRACTICE
9   Graph $x = -2$.

Vertical Lines

The graph of $x = c$, where c is a real number, is a vertical line with x-intercept $(c, 0)$.

EXAMPLE 10   Graph $y = -3$.

Solution   The equation $y = -3$ can be written as $0x + y = -3$. For any x-value chosen, y is -3. If we choose 4, 1, and -2 as x-values, the ordered pair solutions are $(4, -3)$, $(1, -3)$, and $(-2, -3)$. Use these ordered pairs to graph $y = -3$. The graph is a horizontal line with y-intercept $(0, -3)$ and no x-intercept.

x	y
4	-3
1	-3
-2	-3

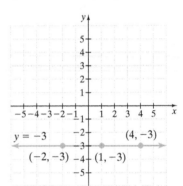

PRACTICE
10   Graph $y = 2$.

Horizontal Lines

The graph of $y = c$, where c is a real number, is a horizontal line with y-intercept $(0, c)$.

Graphing Calculator Explorations

You may have noticed that to use the $\boxed{Y=}$ key on a grapher to graph an equation, the equation must be solved for y. For example, to graph $2x + 3y = 7$, we solve this equation for y.

$$2x + 3y = 7$$
$$3y = -2x + 7 \quad \text{Subtract } 2x \text{ from both sides.}$$
$$\frac{3y}{3} = -\frac{2x}{3} + \frac{7}{3} \quad \text{Divide both sides by 3.}$$
$$y = -\frac{2}{3}x + \frac{7}{3} \quad \text{Simplify.}$$

$2x + 3y = 7$ or $y = -\frac{2}{3}x + \frac{7}{3}$

To graph $2x + 3y = 7$ or $y = -\frac{2}{3}x + \frac{7}{3}$, press the $\boxed{Y=}$ key and enter

$$Y_1 = -\frac{2}{3}x + \frac{7}{3}$$

Graph each linear equation.

1. $x = 3.78y$ **2.** $-2.61y = x$ **3.** $3x + 7y = 21$

4. $-4x + 6y = 21$ **5.** $-2.2x + 6.8y = 15.5$ **6.** $5.9x - 0.8y = -10.4$

Vocabulary, Readiness & Video Check

Use the choices below to fill in each blank. Some choices may be used more than once. Exercises 1 and 2 come from Section 3.2.

x	vertical	x-intercept	linear
y	horizontal	y-intercept	standard

1. An equation that can be written in the form $Ax + By = C$ is called a(n) _____ equation in two variables.

2. The form $Ax + By = C$ is called _____ form.

3. The graph of the equation $y = -1$ is a _____ line.

4. The graph of the equation $x = 5$ is a _____ line.

5. A point where a graph crosses the y-axis is called a(n) _____.

6. A point where a graph crosses the x-axis is called a(n) _____.

7. Given an equation of a line, to find the x-intercept (if there is one), let _____ = 0 and solve for _____.

8. Given an equation of a line, to find the y-intercept (if there is one), let _____ = 0 and solve for _____.

Martin-Gay Interactive Videos

See Video 3.3

Watch the section lecture video and answer the following questions.

OBJECTIVE
1
9. At the end of ▣ Example 2, patterns are discussed. What reason is given for why x-intercepts have y-values of 0? For why y-intercepts have x-values of 0?

OBJECTIVE
2
10. In ▣ Example 3, the goal is to use the x- and y-intercepts to graph a line. Yet once the two intercepts are found, a third point is also found before the line is graphed. Why do think this practice of finding a third point is continued?

OBJECTIVE
3
11. From ▣ Examples 5 and 6, what can you say about the coefficient of x when the equation of a horizontal line is written as $Ax + By = C$? What about the coefficient of y when the equation of a vertical line is written as $Ax + By = C$?

3.3 Exercise Set MyMathLab®

Identify the intercepts. See Examples 1 through 5.

1.

2.

3.

4.

5.

6.

7.

8.

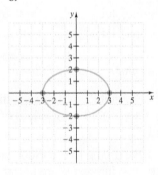

Solve. See Examples 1 through 5.

9. What is the greatest number of intercepts for a line?

10. What is the least number of intercepts for a line?

11. What is the least number of intercepts for a circle?

12. What is the greatest number of intercepts for a circle?

Graph each linear equation by finding and plotting its intercepts. See Examples 6 through 8.

13. $x - y = 3$ **14.** $x - y = -4$ **15.** $x = 5y$

16. $x = 2y$ **17.** $-x + 2y = 6$ **18.** $x - 2y = -8$

19. $2x - 4y = 8$ **20.** $2x + 3y = 6$ **21.** $y = 2x$

22. $y = -2x$ **23.** $y = 3x + 6$ **24.** $y = 2x + 10$

Graph each linear equation. See Examples 9 and 10.

25. $x = -1$ **26.** $y = 5$ **27.** $y = 0$

28. $x = 0$ **29.** $y + 7 = 0$ **30.** $x - 2 = 0$

31. $x + 3 = 0$ **32.** $y - 6 = 0$

MIXED PRACTICE

Graph each linear equation. See Examples 6 through 10.

33. $x = y$ **34.** $x = -y$

35. $x + 8y = 8$ **36.** $x + 3y = 9$

37. $5 = 6x - y$ **38.** $4 = x - 3y$

39. $-x + 10y = 11$ **40.** $-x + 9y = 10$

41. $x = -4\frac{1}{2}$ **42.** $x = -1\frac{3}{4}$

43. $y = 3\frac{1}{4}$ **44.** $y = 2\frac{1}{2}$

45. $y = -\frac{2}{3}x + 1$ **46.** $y = -\frac{3}{5}x + 3$

47. $4x - 6y + 2 = 0$ **48.** $9x - 6y + 3 = 0$

For Exercises 49 through 54, match each equation with its graph. See Graphs A.–F. below and on the next page.

49. $y = 3$ **50.** $y = 2x + 2$

51. $x = -1$ **52.** $x = 3$

53. $y = 2x + 3$ **54.** $y = -2x$

A.

B.

C.

D.

E.   **F.**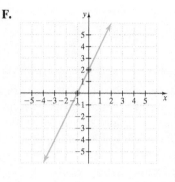

Simplify. See Sections 1.4 through 1.7.

55. $\dfrac{-6-3}{2-8}$

56. $\dfrac{4-5}{-1-0}$

57. $\dfrac{-8-(-2)}{-3-(-2)}$

58. $\dfrac{12-3}{10-9}$

59. $\dfrac{0-6}{5-0}$

60. $\dfrac{2-2}{3-5}$

CONCEPT EXTENSIONS

Answer the following true or false.

61. All lines have an x-intercept *and* a y-intercept.

62. The graph of $y=4x$ contains the point $(0,0)$.

63. The graph of $x+y=5$ has an x-intercept of $(5,0)$ and a y-intercept of $(0,5)$.

64. The graph of $y=5x$ contains the point $(5,1)$.

The production supervisor at Alexandra's Office Products finds that it takes 3 hours to manufacture a particular office chair and 6 hours to manufacture an office desk. A total of 1200 hours is available to produce office chairs and desks of this style. The linear equation that models this situation is $3x+6y=1200$, where x represents the number of chairs produced and y the number of desks manufactured. Use this information for Exercises 65 through 68.

65. Complete the ordered pair solution $(0, \quad)$ of this equation. Describe the manufacturing situation that corresponds to this solution.

66. Complete the ordered pair solution $(\quad, 0)$ of this equation. Describe the manufacturing situation that corresponds to this solution.

67. If 50 desks are manufactured, find the greatest number of chairs that can be made.

68. If 50 chairs are manufactured, find the greatest number of desks that can be made.

69. Since 2002, admissions at movie theaters in the U.S. and Canada have mostly been in a decline. The number of people y (in billions) who go to movie theaters each year can be estimated by the equation $y=-0.025x+1.55$, where x represents the number of years since 2002. (*Source:* Based on data from Motion Picture Association of America)

a. Find the x-intercept of this equation.

b. What does this x-intercept mean?

c. Use part (b) to comment on your opinion of the limitations of using equations to model real data.

70. The price of admission to a movie theater has been steadily increasing. The price of regular admission y (in dollars) to a movie theater may be represented by the equation $y=0.24x+5.28$, where x is the number of years after 2000. (*Source:* Based on data from Motion Picture Association of America)

a. Find the x-intercept of this equation.

b. What does this x-intercept mean?

c. Use part (b) to comment on your opinion of the limitations of using equations to model real data.

Two lines in the same plane that do not intersect are called **parallel lines.**

71. Draw a line parallel to the line $x=5$ that intersects the x-axis at $(1,0)$. What is the equation of this line?

72. Draw a line parallel to the line $y=-1$ that intersects the y-axis at $(0,-4)$. What is the equation of this line?

73. Discuss whether a vertical line ever has a y-intercept.

74. Explain why it is a good idea to use three points to graph a linear equation.

75. Discuss whether a horizontal line ever has an x-intercept.

76. Explain how to find intercepts.

3.4 | Slope and Rate of Change

OBJECTIVES

1 Find the Slope of a Line Given Two Points of the Line.

2 Find the Slope of a Line Given Its Equation.

3 Find the Slopes of Horizontal and Vertical Lines.

4 Compare the Slopes of Parallel and Perpendicular Lines.

5 Interpret Slope as a Rate of Change.

OBJECTIVE

1 Finding the Slope of a Line Given Two Points of the Line

Thus far, much of this chapter has been devoted to graphing lines. You have probably noticed by now that a key feature of a line is its slant or steepness. In mathematics, the slant or steepness of a line is formally known as its **slope.** We measure the slope of a line by the ratio of vertical change to the corresponding horizontal change as we move along the line.

On the line below, for example, suppose that we begin at the point $(1, 2)$ and move to the point $(4, 6)$. The vertical change is the change in y-coordinates: $6 - 2$ or 4 units. The corresponding horizontal change is the change in x-coordinates: $4 - 1 = 3$ units. The ratio of these changes is

$$\text{slope} = \frac{\text{change in } y \text{ (vertical change)}}{\text{change in } x \text{ (horizontal change)}} = \frac{4}{3}$$

The slope of this line, then, is $\frac{4}{3}$. This means that for every 4 units of change in y-coordinates, there is a corresponding change of 3 units in x-coordinates.

▶ **Helpful Hint**

It makes no difference what two points of a line are chosen to find its slope. The slope of a line is the same everywhere on the line.

To find the slope of a line, then, choose two points of the line. Label the two x-coordinates of two points x_1 and x_2 (read "x sub one" and "x sub two"), and label the corresponding y-coordinates y_1 and y_2.

The vertical change or **rise** between these points is the difference in the y-coordinates: $y_2 - y_1$. The horizontal change or **run** between the points is the difference of the x-coordinates: $x_2 - x_1$. The slope of the line is the ratio of $y_2 - y_1$ to $x_2 - x_1$, and we traditionally use the letter m to denote slope: $m = \dfrac{y_2 - y_1}{x_2 - x_1}$.

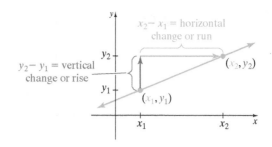

Slope of a Line

The slope m of the line containing the points (x_1, y_1) and (x_2, y_2) is given by

$$m = \frac{\text{rise}}{\text{run}} = \frac{\text{change in } y}{\text{change in } x} = \frac{y_2 - y_1}{x_2 - x_1}, \qquad \text{as long as } x_2 \neq x_1$$

EXAMPLE 1   Find the slope of the line through $(-1, 5)$ and $(2, -3)$. Graph the line.

Solution   If we let (x_1, y_1) be $(-1, 5)$, then $x_1 = -1$ and $y_1 = 5$. Also, let (x_2, y_2) be $(2, -3)$ so that $x_2 = 2$ and $y_2 = -3$. Then, by the definition of slope,

$$m = \frac{y_2 - y_1}{x_2 - x_1}$$

$$= \frac{-3 - 5}{2 - (-1)}$$

$$= \frac{-8}{3} = -\frac{8}{3}$$

The slope of the line is $-\dfrac{8}{3}$.

PRACTICE

1   Find the slope of the line through $(-4, 11)$ and $(2, 5)$.

▶ Helpful Hint

When finding slope, it makes no difference which point is identified as (x_1, y_1) and which is identified as (x_2, y_2). Just remember that whatever y-value is first in the numerator, its corresponding x-value must be first in the denominator. Another way to calculate the slope in Example 1 is:

$$m = \frac{y_2 - y_1}{x_2 - x_1} = \frac{5 - (-3)}{-1 - 2} = \frac{8}{-3} \quad \text{or} \quad -\frac{8}{3} \quad \leftarrow \text{ Same slope as found in Example 1}$$

✓CONCEPT CHECK

The points $(-2, -5)$, $(0, -2)$, $(4, 4)$, and $(10, 13)$ all lie on the same line. Work with a partner and verify that the slope is the same no matter which points are used to find slope.

Answer to Concept Check:
$$m = \frac{3}{2}$$

EXAMPLE 2   Find the slope of the line through $(-1, -2)$ and $(2, 4)$. Graph the line.

Solution   Let (x_1, y_1) be $(2, 4)$ and (x_2, y_2) be $(-1, -2)$.

$$m = \frac{y_2 - y_1}{x_2 - x_1}$$

$$= \frac{-2 - 4}{-1 - 2} \quad \begin{array}{l} y\text{-value} \\ \text{corresponding } x\text{-value} \end{array}$$

$$= \frac{-6}{-3} = 2$$

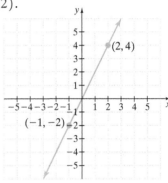

> ▶ **Helpful Hint**
>
> The slope for Example 2 is the same if we let (x_1, y_1) be $(-1, -2)$ and (x_2, y_2) be $(2, 4)$.
>
> $$m = \frac{\overset{y\text{-value}}{4 - (-2)}}{\underset{\text{corresponding } x\text{-value}}{2 - (-1)}} = \frac{6}{3} = 2$$

PRACTICE
2   Find the slope of the line through $(-3, -1)$ and $(3, 1)$.

✓ **CONCEPT CHECK**
What is wrong with the following slope calculation for the points $(3, 5)$ and $(-2, 6)$?

$$m = \frac{5 - 6}{-2 - 3} = \frac{-1}{-5} = \frac{1}{5}$$

Notice that the slope of the line in Example 1 is negative, whereas the slope of the line in Example 2 is positive. Let your eye follow the line with negative slope from left to right and notice that the line "goes down." Following the line with positive slope from left to right, notice that the line "goes up." This is true in general.

Negative slope

Positive slope

> ▶ **Helpful Hint**
>
> To decide whether a line "goes up" or "goes down," always follow the line from left to right.

OBJECTIVE
2   **Finding the Slope of a Line Given Its Equation**

As we have seen, the slope of a line is defined by two points on the line. Thus, if we know the equation of a line, we can find its slope by finding two of its points. For example, let's find the slope of the line

$$y = 3x + 2$$

To find two points, we can choose two values for x and substitute to find corresponding y-values. If $x = 0$, for example, $y = 3 \cdot 0 + 2$ or $y = 2$. If $x = 1$, $y = 3 \cdot 1 + 2$ or $y = 5$. This gives the ordered pairs $(0, 2)$ and $(1, 5)$. Using the definition for slope, we have

$$m = \frac{5 - 2}{1 - 0} = \frac{3}{1} = 3 \qquad \text{The slope is 3.}$$

Notice that the slope, 3, is the same as the coefficient of x in the equation $y = 3x + 2$.
Also, recall from Section 3.2 that the graph of an equation of the form $y = mx + b$ has y-intercept $(0, b)$.

Answer to Concept Check:
The order in which the x- and y-values are used must be the same.

$$m = \frac{5 - 6}{3 - (-2)} = \frac{-1}{5} = -\frac{1}{5}$$

This means that the *y*-intercept of the graph of $y = 3x + 2$ is $(0, 2)$. This is true in general and the form $y = mx + b$ is appropriately called the **slope-intercept form.**

slope   *y*-intercept
$(0, b)$

Slope-Intercept Form

When a linear equation in two variables is written in slope-intercept form,

$$y = mx + b$$

m is the slope of the line and $(0, b)$ is the *y*-intercept of the line.

EXAMPLE 3   Find the slope and *y*-intercept of the line whose equation is $y = \dfrac{3}{4}x + 6$

Solution   The equation is in slope-intercept form, $y = mx + b$.

$$y = \dfrac{3}{4}x + 6$$

The coefficient of *x*, $\dfrac{3}{4}$, is the slope and the constant term, 6, is the *y*-value of the *y*-intercept, $(0, 6)$.

PRACTICE
3   Find the slope and *y*-intercept of the line whose equation is $y = \dfrac{2}{3}x - 2$.

EXAMPLE 4   Find the slope and the *y*-intercept of the line whose equation is $-y = 5x - 2$.

Solution: Remember, the equation must be solved for *y* (not $-y$) in order for it to be written in slope-intercept form.

To solve for *y*, let's divide both sides of the equation by -1.

$$-y = 5x - 2$$
$$\dfrac{-y}{-1} = \dfrac{5x}{-1} - \dfrac{2}{-1} \quad \text{Divide both sides by } -1.$$
$$y = -5x + 2 \quad \text{Simplify.}$$

The coefficient of *x*, -5, is the slope and the constant term, 2, is the *y*-value of the *y*-intercept, $(0, 2)$.

PRACTICE
4   Find the slope and *y*-intercept of the line whose equation is $-y = -6x + 5$.

EXAMPLE 5   Find the slope and the *y*-intercept of the line whose equation is $3x - 4y = 4$.

Solution   Write the equation in slope-intercept form by solving for *y*.

$$3x - 4y = 4$$
$$-4y = -3x + 4 \quad \text{Subtract } 3x \text{ from both sides.}$$
$$\dfrac{-4y}{-4} = \dfrac{-3x}{-4} + \dfrac{4}{-4} \quad \text{Divide both sides by } -4.$$
$$y = \dfrac{3}{4}x - 1 \quad \text{Simplify.}$$

The coefficient of *x*, $\dfrac{3}{4}$, is the slope, and the *y*-intercept is $(0, -1)$.

PRACTICE
5 Find the slope and the *y*-intercept of the line whose equation is $5x + 2y = 8$.

OBJECTIVE
3 Finding Slopes of Horizontal and Vertical Lines

Recall that if a line tilts upward from left to right, its slope is positive. If a line tilts downward from left to right, its slope is negative. Let's now find the slopes of two special lines, horizontal and vertical lines.

EXAMPLE 6 Find the slope of the line $y = -1$.

Solution Recall that $y = -1$ is a horizontal line with *y*-intercept $(0, -1)$. To find the slope, find two ordered pair solutions of $y = -1$. Solutions of $y = -1$ must have a *y*-value of -1. Let's use points $(2, -1)$ and $(-3, -1)$, which are on the line.

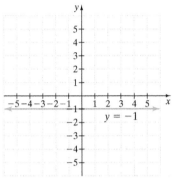

$$m = \frac{y_2 - y_1}{x_2 - x_1} = \frac{-1 - (-1)}{-3 - 2} = \frac{0}{-5} = 0$$

The slope of the line $y = -1$ is 0 and its graph is shown.

PRACTICE
6 Find the slope of the line $y = 3$.

Any two points of a horizontal line will have the same *y*-values. This means that the *y*-values will always have a difference of 0 for all horizontal lines. Thus, **all horizontal lines have a slope 0.**

EXAMPLE 7 Find the slope of the line $x = 5$.

Solution Recall that the graph of $x = 5$ is a vertical line with *x*-intercept $(5, 0)$.

To find the slope, find two ordered pair solutions of $x = 5$. Solutions of $x = 5$ must have an *x*-value of 5. Let's use points $(5, 0)$ and $(5, 4)$, which are on the line.

$$m = \frac{y_2 - y_1}{x_2 - x_1} = \frac{4 - 0}{5 - 5} = \frac{4}{0}$$

Since $\frac{4}{0}$ is undefined, we say the slope of the vertical line $x = 5$ is undefined, and its graph is shown.

PRACTICE
7 Find the slope of the line $x = -4$.

Any two points of a vertical line will have the same *x*-values. This means that the *x*-values will always have a difference of 0 for all vertical lines. Thus **all vertical lines have undefined slope.**

▶ Helpful Hint
Slope of 0 and undefined slope are not the same. Vertical lines have undefined slope or no slope, while horizontal lines have a slope of 0.

Here is a general review of slope.

Summary of Slope

Slope m of the line through (x_1, y_1) and (x_2, y_2) is given by the equation

$$m = \frac{y_2 - y_1}{x_2 - x_1}.$$

Upward
line

Positive slope: $m > 0$

Downward
line

Negative slope: $m < 0$

Horizontal line
$y = c$

Zero slope: $m = 0$

Vertical line
$x = c$

Undefined slope or no slope

OBJECTIVE

4   Slopes of Parallel and Perpendicular Lines

Two lines in the same plane are **parallel** if they do not intersect. Slopes of lines can help us determine whether lines are parallel. Parallel lines have the same steepness, so it follows that they have the same slope.

For example, the graphs of

$$y = -2x + 4$$

and

$$y = -2x - 3$$

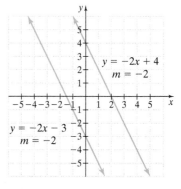

are shown. These lines have the same slope, -2. They also have different y-intercepts, so the lines are distinct and parallel. (If the y-intercepts were the same also, the lines would be the same.)

Parallel Lines

Nonvertical parallel lines have the same slope and different y-intercepts.

Two lines are **perpendicular** if they lie in the same plane and meet at a 90° (right) angle. How do the slopes of perpendicular lines compare? The product of the slopes of two perpendicular lines is -1.

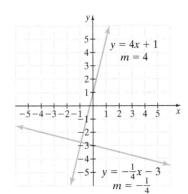

For example, the graphs of

$$y = 4x + 1$$

and

$$y = -\frac{1}{4}x - 3$$

are shown. The slopes of the lines are 4 and $-\frac{1}{4}$. Their product is $4\left(-\frac{1}{4}\right) = -1$, so the lines are perpendicular.

Perpendicular Lines

If the product of the slopes of two lines is -1, then the lines are perpendicular.

(Two nonvertical lines are perpendicular if the slope of one is the negative reciprocal of the slope of the other.)

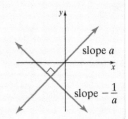

▶ **Helpful Hint**

Here are examples of numbers that are negative (opposite) reciprocals.

Number	Negative Reciprocal	Their Product Is -1.
$\frac{2}{3}$	$-\frac{3}{2}$	$\frac{2}{3} \cdot -\frac{3}{2} = -\frac{6}{6} = -1$
-5 or $-\frac{5}{1}$	$\frac{1}{5}$	$-5 \cdot \frac{1}{5} = -\frac{5}{5} = -1$

▶ **Helpful Hint**

Here are a few important facts about vertical and horizontal lines.

- Two distinct vertical lines are parallel.
- Two distinct horizontal lines are parallel.
- A horizontal line and a vertical line are always perpendicular.

△ **EXAMPLE 8**   Determine whether each pair of lines is parallel, perpendicular, or neither.

a. $y = -\frac{1}{5}x + 1$ **b.** $x + y = 3$ **c.** $3x + y = 5$

$\quad\ 2x + 10y = 3$ $\quad\ -x + y = 4$ $\quad\ 2x + 3y = 6$

Solution

a. The slope of the line $y = -\frac{1}{5}x + 1$ is $-\frac{1}{5}$. We find the slope of the second line by solving its equation for y.

$$2x + 10y = 3$$
$$10y = -2x + 3 \qquad \text{Subtract } 2x \text{ from both sides.}$$
$$y = \frac{-2}{10}x + \frac{3}{10} \qquad \text{Divide both sides by 10.}$$
$$y = -\frac{1}{5}x + \frac{3}{10} \qquad \text{Simplify.}$$

The slope of this line is $-\frac{1}{5}$ also. Since the lines have the same slope and different y-intercepts, they are parallel, as shown in the figure on the next page.

b. To find each slope, we solve each equation for y.

$$x + y = 3 \qquad\qquad -x + y = 4$$
$$y = -x + 3 \qquad\qquad y = x + 4$$

The slope is -1.   The slope is 1.

The slopes are not the same, so the lines are not parallel. Next we check the product of the slopes: $(-1)(1) = -1$. Since the product is -1, the lines are perpendicular, as shown in the figure.

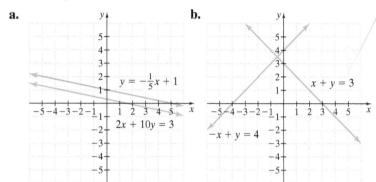

a.

$y = -\frac{1}{5}x + 1$

$2x + 10y = 3$

b.

$x + y = 3$

$-x + y = 4$

c. We solve each equation for y to find each slope. The slopes are -3 and $-\frac{2}{3}$. The slopes are not the same and their product is not -1. Thus, the lines are neither parallel nor perpendicular.   □

PRACTICE

8   Determine whether each pair of lines is parallel, perpendicular, or neither.

a. $y = -5x + 1$ **b.** $x + y = 11$ **c.** $2x + 3y = 21$
    $x - 5y = 10$ $2x + y = 11$ $6y = -4x - 2$

✓CONCEPT CHECK

Consider the line $-6x + 2y = 1$.
a. Write the equations of two lines parallel to this line.
b. Write the equations of two lines perpendicular to this line.

OBJECTIVE

5   **Slope as a Rate of Change**

Slope can also be interpreted as a rate of change. In other words, slope tells us how fast y is changing with respect to x. To see this, let's look at a few of the many real-world applications of slope. For example, the pitch of a roof, used by builders and architects, is its slope. The pitch of the roof on the left is $\frac{7}{10}\left(\frac{\text{rise}}{\text{run}}\right)$. This means that the roof rises vertically 7 feet for every horizontal 10 feet. The rate of change for the roof is 7 vertical feet (y) per 10 horizontal feet (x).

The grade of a road is its slope written as a percent. A 7% grade, as shown below, means that the road rises (or falls) 7 feet for every horizontal 100 feet. $\Big($ Recall that $7\% = \frac{7}{100}.\Big)$ Here, the slope of $\frac{7}{100}$ gives us the rate of change. The road rises (in our diagram) 7 vertical feet (y) for every 100 horizontal feet (x).

$\frac{7}{10}$ pitch

7 feet

10 feet

Answers to Concept Check:
a. any two lines with $m = 3$ and
    y-intercept not $\left(0, \frac{1}{2}\right)$
b. any two lines with $m = -\frac{1}{3}$

$\frac{7}{100} = 7\%$ grade

7 feet

100 feet

EXAMPLE 9 Finding the Grade of a Road

At one part of the road to the summit of Pikes Peak, the road rises at a rate of 15 vertical feet for a horizontal distance of 250 feet. Find the grade of the road.

Solution Recall that the grade of a road is its slope written as a percent.

$$\text{grade} = \frac{\text{rise}}{\text{run}} = \frac{15}{250} = 0.06 = 6\%$$

15 feet

250 feet

The grade is 6%.

PRACTICE

9 One part of the Mt. Washington (New Hampshire) cog railway rises about 1794 feet over a horizontal distance of 7176 feet. Find the grade of this part of the railway.

EXAMPLE 10 Finding the Slope of a Line

The following graph shows annual food and drink sales y (in billions of dollars) for year x. Find the slope of the line and attach the proper units for the rate of change. Then write a sentence explaining the meaning of the slope for this application.

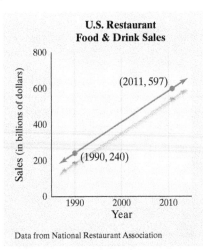

Solution Use (1990, 240) and (2011, 597) to calculate slope.

$$m = \frac{597 - 240}{2011 - 1990} = \frac{357}{21} = \frac{17 \text{ billion dollars}}{1 \text{ year}}$$

This means that the rate of change of restarurant food and drink sales increases by 17 billion dollars every 1 year, or $17 billion per year.

PRACTICE

10 The following graph shows the cost y (in dollars) of having laundry done at the Wash-n-Fold, where x is the number of pounds of laundry. Find the slope of the line, and attach the proper units for the rate of change.

Graphing Calculator Explorations

It is possible to use a grapher to sketch the graph of more than one equation on the same set of axes. This feature can be used to confirm our findings from Section 3.2 when we learned that the graph of an equation written in the form $y = mx + b$ has a y-intercept of b. For example, graph the equations $y = \frac{2}{5}x$, $y = \frac{2}{5}x + 7$, and

$y = \dfrac{2}{5}x - 4$ on the same set of axes. To do so, press the $\boxed{Y=}$ key and enter the equations on the first three lines.

$$Y_1 = \left(\frac{2}{5}\right)x$$

$$Y_2 = \left(\frac{2}{5}\right)x + 7$$

$$Y_3 = \left(\frac{2}{5}\right)x - 4$$

The screen should look like:

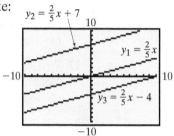

Notice that all three graphs appear to have the same positive slope. The graph of $y = \dfrac{2}{5}x + 7$ is the graph of $y = \dfrac{2}{5}x$ moved 7 units upward with a y-intercept of 7. Also, the graph of $y = \dfrac{2}{5}x - 4$ is the graph of $y = \dfrac{2}{5}x$ moved 4 units downward with a y-intercept of -4.

Graph the equations on the same set of axes. Describe the similarities and differences in their graphs.

1. $y = 3.8x, y = 3.8x - 3, y = 3.8x + 9$

2. $y = -4.9x, y = -4.9x + 1, y = -4.9x + 8$

3. $y = \dfrac{1}{4}x; y = \dfrac{1}{4}x + 5, y = \dfrac{1}{4}x - 8$

4. $y = -\dfrac{3}{4}x, y = -\dfrac{3}{4}x - 5, y = -\dfrac{3}{4}x + 6$

Vocabulary, Readiness & Video Check

Use the choices below to fill in each blank. Not all choices will be used.

m	x	0	positive	undefined
b	y	slope	negative	

1. The measure of the steepness or tilt of a line is called _____.

2. If an equation is written in the form $y = mx + b$, the value of the letter _____ is the value of the slope of the graph.

3. The slope of a horizontal line is _____.

4. The slope of a vertical line is _____.

5. If the graph of a line moves upward from left to right, the line has _____ slope.

6. If the graph of a line moves downward from left to right, the line has _____ slope.

7. Given two points of a line, slope $= \dfrac{\text{change in}\underline{\quad}}{\text{change in}\underline{\quad}}$.

Martin-Gay Interactive Videos

See Video 3.4

Watch the section lecture video and answer the following questions.

OBJECTIVE
1

8. What important point is made during Example 1 having to do with the order of the points in the slope formula?

OBJECTIVE
2

9. From Example 5, how do you write an equation in "slope-intercept form"? Once the equation is in slope-intercept form, how do you identify the slope?

OBJECTIVE
3

10. In the lecture after Example 8, different slopes are summarized. What is the difference between zero slope and undefined slope? What does "no slope" mean?

OBJECTIVE
4

11. From Example 10, what form of the equations is best to determine if two lines are parallel or perpendicular? Why?

OBJECTIVE
5

12. Writing the slope as a rate of change in Example 11 gave real-life meaning to the slope. What step in the general strategy for problem solving does this correspond to?

3.4 Exercise Set

MyMathLab®

Find the slope of the line that passes through the given points. See Examples 1 and 2.

1. $(-1, 5)$ and $(6, -2)$

2. $(3, 1)$ and $(2, 6)$

3. $(-4, 3)$ and $(-4, 5)$

4. $(6, -6)$ and $(6, 2)$

5. $(-2, 8)$ and $(1, 6)$

6. $(4, -3)$ and $(2, 2)$

7. $(5, 1)$ and $(-2, 1)$

8. $(0, 13)$ and $(-4, 13)$

Find the slope of each line if it exists. See Examples 1 and 2.

9.

10.

11.

12.

13.

14.

State whether the slope of the line is positive, negative, 0, or is undefined. See the top box on p. 207.

15.

16.

17.

18.

Decide whether a line with the given slope is upward, downward, horizontal, or vertical. See the top box on p. 207.

19. $m = \dfrac{7}{6}$ _____

20. $m = -3$ _____

21. $m = 0$ _____

22. m is undefined. _____

For each graph, determine which line has the greater slope. See the top box on p. 207.

23.

24.

25.

26.

In Exercises 27 through 32, match each line with its slope. See Examples 1 and 2 and the top box on p. 207.

A. $m = 0$ **B.** undefined slope   **C.** $m = 3$

D. $m = 1$ **E.** $m = -\dfrac{1}{2}$ **F.** $m = -\dfrac{3}{4}$

27.

28.

29.

30.

31.

32.

Find the slope of each line. See Examples 6 and 7.

33. $x = 6$ **34.** $y = 4$

35. $y = -4$ **36.** $x = 2$

37. $x = -3$ **38.** $y = -11$

39. $y = 0$ **40.** $x = 0$

MIXED PRACTICE

Find the slope of each line. See Examples 3 through 7.

41. $y = 5x - 2$ **42.** $y = -2x + 6$

43. $y = -0.3x + 2.5$ **44.** $y = -7.6x - 0.1$

45. $2x + y = 7$ **46.** $-5x + y = 10$

47. $2x - 3y = 10$ **48.** $3x - 5y = 1$

49. $x = 1$ **50.** $y = -2$

51. $x = 2y$ **52.** $x = -4y$

53. $y = -3$ **54.** $x = 5$

55. $-3x - 4y = 6$ **56.** $-4x - 7y = 9$

57. $20x - 5y = 1.2$ **58.** $24x - 3y = 5.7$

Find the slope of the line that is (a) parallel and (b) perpendicular to the line through each pair of points. See Example 8.

59. $(-3, -3)$ and $(0, 0)$

60. $(6, -2)$ and $(1, 4)$

61. $(-8, -4)$ and $(3, 5)$

62. $(6, -1)$ and $(-4, -10)$

Determine whether each pair of lines is parallel, perpendicular, or neither. See Example 8.

63. $y = \dfrac{2}{9}x + 3$ **64.** $y = \dfrac{1}{5}x + 20$

  $y = -\dfrac{2}{9}x$ $y = -\dfrac{1}{5}x$

65. $x - 3y = -6$ **66.** $y = 4x - 2$

  $y = 3x - 9$ $4x + y = 5$

67. $6x = 5y + 1$ **68.** $-x + 2y = -2$

  $-12x + 10y = 1$ $2x = 4y + 3$

69. $6 + 4x = 3y$ **70.** $10 + 3x = 5y$

  $3x + 4y = 8$ $5x + 3y = 1$

The pitch of a roof is its slope. Find the pitch of each roof shown. See Example 9.

71.

72.

The grade of a road is its slope written as a percent. Find the grade of each road shown. See Example 9.

73.

74.

75. One of Japan's superconducting "bullet" trains is researched and tested at the Yamanashi Maglev Test Line near Otsuki City. The steepest section of the track has a rise of 2580 meters for a horizontal distance of 6450 meters. What is the grade of this section of track? (*Source:* Japan Railways Central Co.)

76. Professional plumbers suggest that a sewer pipe should rise 0.25 inch for every horizontal foot. Find the recommended slope for a sewer pipe. Round to the nearest hundredth.

77. There has been controversy over the past few years about the world's steepest street. The *Guinness Book of Records* actually listed Baldwin Street, in Dunedin, New Zealand, as the world's steepest street, but Canton Avenue in the

Pittsburgh neighborhood of Beechview may be steeper. Calculate each grade to the nearest percent.

		Grade (%)
Canton Avenue	for every 30 meters of horizontal distance, the vertical change is 11 meters	
Baldwin Street	for every 2.86 meters of horizontal distance, the vertical change is 1 meter	

78. According to federal regulations, a wheelchair ramp should rise no more than 1 foot for a horizontal distance of 12 feet. Write the slope as a grade. Round to the nearest tenth of a percent.

Find the slope of each line and write the slope as a rate of change. Don't forget to attach the proper units. See Example 10.

79. This graph approximates the number of U.S. households that have televisions y (in millions) for year x.

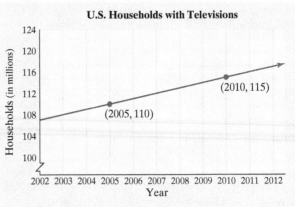

Data from Nielsen Wire, The Nielsen Company

80. The graph approximates the amount of money y (in billions of dollars) spent worldwide on tourism for year x. (Data from World Tourism Organization)

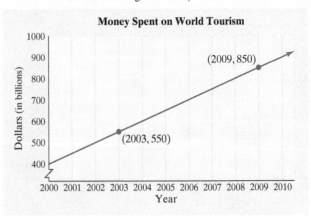

For Exercises 81 and 82, write the slope as a decimal.

81. The graph below shows the total cost y (in dollars) of owning and operating a compact car where x is the number of miles driven.

Owning and Operating a Compact Car

(20,000, 9400)

(5000, 2350)

Data from Federal Highway Administration

82. Americans are keeping their cars longer. The graph below shows the median age y (in years) of automobiles in the United States for the years shown. (Data from Bureau of Transportation Statistics)

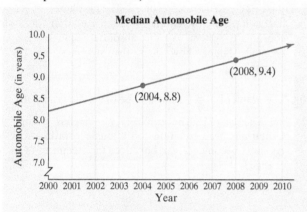

Median Automobile Age

(2008, 9.4)

(2004, 8.8)

REVIEW AND PREVIEW

Solve each equation for y. See Section 2.5.

83. $y - (-6) = 2(x - 4)$

84. $y - 7 = -9(x - 6)$

85. $y - 1 = -6(x - (-2))$

86. $y - (-3) = 4(x - (-5))$

CONCEPT EXTENSIONS

Solve. See a Concept Check in this section.

87. Verify that the points $(2, 1)$, $(0, 0)$, $(-2, -1)$ and $(-4, -2)$ are all on the same line by computing the slope between each pair of points. (See the first Concept Check.)

88. Given the points $(2, 3)$ and $(-5, 1)$, can the slope of the line through these points be calculated by $\dfrac{1 - 3}{2 - (-5)}$? Why or why not? (See the second Concept Check.)

89. Write the equations of three lines parallel to $10x - 5y = -7$. (See the third Concept Check.)

90. Write the equations of two lines perpendicular to $10x - 5y = -7$. (See the third Concept Check.)

The following line graph shows the average fuel economy (in miles per gallon) of passenger automobiles produced during each of the model years shown. Use this graph to answer Exercises 91 through 96.

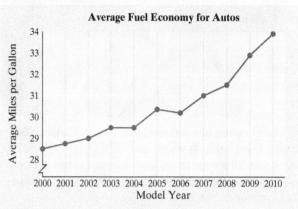

Average Fuel Economy for Autos

Data from U.S. Bureau of Transportation Statistics

91. Between what two years shown was there a decrease in average fuel economy for automobiles?

92. What was the average fuel economy (in miles per gallon) for automobiles produced during 2008?

93. During which of the model years shown was average fuel economy the lowest?
What was the average fuel economy for that year?

94. During which of the model years shown was average fuel economy the highest?
What was the average fuel economy for that year?

95. Of the following line segments, which has the greatest slope: from 2002 to 2003, from 2006 to 2007, or from 2008 to 2009?

96. Which line segment has a slope of 0?

Solve.

97. Find x so that the pitch of the roof is $\dfrac{1}{3}$.

18 feet

x

98. Find x so that the pitch of the roof is $\dfrac{2}{5}$.

4 feet

x

99. Approximately 2207 heart transplants were performed in the United States in 2007. In 2010, the number of heart transplants in the United States rose to 2333. (*Source:* Organ Procurement and Transplantation Network)

   a. Write two ordered pairs of the form (year, number of heart transplants).

   b. Find the slope of the line between the two points.

   c. Write a sentence explaining the meaning of the slope as a rate of change.

100. The average price of an acre of U.S. farmland was $1210 in 2002. In 2008, the price of an acre rose to $2350. (*Source: National Agricultural Statistics Services*)

   a. Write two ordered pairs of the form (year, price of an acre).

   b. Find the slope of the line through the two points.

   c. Write a sentence explaining the meaning of the slope as a rate of change.

101. Show that a triangle with vertices at the points $(1, 1)$, $(-4, 4)$, and $(-3, 0)$ is a right triangle.

102. Show that the quadrilateral with vertices $(1, 3)$, $(2, 1)$, $(-4, 0)$, and $(-3, -2)$ is a parallelogram.

Find the slope of the line through the given points.

103. $(2.1, 6.7)$ and $(-8.3, 9.3)$

104. $(-3.8, 1.2)$ and $(-2.2, 4.5)$

105. $(2.3, 0.2)$ and $(7.9, 5.1)$

106. $(14.3, -10.1)$ and $(9.8, -2.9)$

107. The graph of $y = -\frac{1}{3}x + 2$ has a slope of $-\frac{1}{3}$. The graph of $y = -2x + 2$ has a slope of -2. The graph of $y = -4x + 2$ has a slope of -4. Graph all three equations on a single coordinate system. As the absolute value of the slope becomes larger, how does the steepness of the line change?

108. The graph of $y = \frac{1}{2}x$ has a slope of $\frac{1}{2}$. The graph of $y = 3x$ has a slope of 3. The graph of $y = 5x$ has a slope of 5. Graph all three equations on a single coordinate system. As slope becomes larger, how does the steepness of the line change?

Integrated Review SUMMARY ON SLOPE & GRAPHING LINEAR EQUATIONS

Sections 3.1–3.4

Find the slope of each line.

1.

2.

3.

4.

Graph each linear equation.

5. $y = -2x$

6. $x + y = 3$

7. $x = -1$

8. $y = 4$

9. $x - 2y = 6$

10. $y = 3x + 2$

11. $5x + 3y = 15$

12. $2x - 4y = 8$

Determine whether the lines through the points are parallel, perpendicular, or neither.

13. $y = -\dfrac{1}{5}x + \dfrac{1}{3}$

$3x = -15y$

14. $x - y = \dfrac{1}{2}$

$3x - y = \dfrac{1}{2}$

15. In the years 2000 through 2009 the number of bridges on public roads (in thousands) in the United States can be modeled by the linear equation $y = 1.7x + 587$ where x is years after 2000 and y is number of bridges (in thousands). (*Source:* U.S. Dept. of Transportation)

   a. Find the y-intercept of this line.

   b. Write a sentence explaining the meaning of this intercept.

   c. Find the slope of this line.

   d. Write a sentence explaining the meaning of the slope as a rate of change.

16. Online advertising is a means of promoting products and services using the Internet. The revenue (in billions of dollars) for online advertising for the years 2003 through 2010 is given by $y = 3.3x - 3.1$, where x is the number of years after 2000.

   a. Use this equation to complete the ordered pair $(9, \quad)$.

   b. Write a sentence explaining the meaning of the answer to part (a).

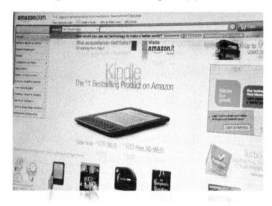

3.5 | Equations of Lines

OBJECTIVES

1 Use the Slope-Intercept Form to Graph a Linear Equation.

2 Use the Slope-Intercept Form to Write an Equation of a Line.

3 Use the Point-Slope Form to Find an Equation of a Line Given Its Slope and a Point of the Line.

4 Use the Point-Slope Form to Find an Equation of a Line Given Two Points of the Line.

5 Find Equations of Vertical and Horizontal Lines.

6 Use the Point-Slope Form to Solve Problems.

Recall that the form $y = mx + b$ is appropriately called the *slope-intercept form* of a linear equation.

slope

y-intercept is $(0, b)$

> **Slope-Intercept Form**
>
> When a linear equation in two variables is written in **slope-intercept form,**
> $$y = mx + b$$
> slope $(0, b)$, y-intercept
>
> then m is the slope of the line and $(0, b)$ is the y-intercept of the line.

OBJECTIVE

1   **Using the Slope-Intercept Form to Graph an Equation**

We can use the slope-intercept form of the equation of a line to graph a linear equation.

EXAMPLE 1 Use the slope-intercept form to graph the equation

$$y = \frac{3}{5}x - 2$$

Solution Since the equation $y = \frac{3}{5}x - 2$ is written

in slope-intercept form $y = mx + b$, the slope of its

graph is $\frac{3}{5}$ and the y-intercept is $(0, -2)$. To graph

this equation, we begin by plotting the point $(0, -2)$.

From this point, we can find another point of the graph

by using the slope $\frac{3}{5}$ and recalling that slope is $\frac{\text{rise}}{\text{run}}$. We start at the y-intercept

and move 3 units up since the numerator of the slope is 3; then we move 5 units to

the right since the denominator of the slope is 5. We stop at the point $(5, 1)$. The line

through $(0, -2)$ and $(5, 1)$ is the graph of $y = \frac{3}{5}x - 2$. □

PRACTICE

1 Graph $y = \frac{2}{3}x - 5$.

EXAMPLE 2 Use the slope-intercept form to graph the equation $4x + y = 1$.

Solution First we write the given equation in slope-intercept form.

$$4x + y = 1$$
$$y = -4x + 1$$

The graph of this equation will have slope -4

and y-intercept $(0, 1)$. To graph this line, we first

plot the point $(0, 1)$. To find another point of the

graph, we use the slope -4, which can be written as

$\frac{-4}{1}$ $\left(\frac{4}{-1} \text{ could also be used} \right)$. We start at the point

$(0, 1)$ and move 4 units down (since the numerator of

the slope is -4) and then 1 unit to the right (since the

denominator of the slope is 1).

   We arrive at the point $(1, -3)$. The line through $(0, 1)$ and $(1, -3)$ is the graph of

$4x + y = 1$. □

> ▶ **Helpful Hint**
>
> In Example 2, if we interpret the
>
> slope of -4 as $\frac{4}{-1}$, we arrive
>
> at $(-1, 5)$ for a second point.
> Notice that this point is also on
> the line.

PRACTICE

2 Use the slope-intercept form to graph the equation $3x - y = 2$.

OBJECTIVE

2 **Using the Slope-Intercept Form to Write an Equation** ▶

The slope-intercept form can also be used to write the equation of a line when we

know its slope and y-intercept.

EXAMPLE 3 Find an equation of the line with y-intercept $(0, -3)$ and slope of $\frac{1}{4}$.

Solution We are given the slope and the y-intercept. We let $m = \frac{1}{4}$ and $b = -3$ and

write the equation in slope-intercept form, $y = mx + b$.

$$y = mx + b$$
$$y = \frac{1}{4}x + (-3) \quad \text{Let } m = \frac{1}{4} \text{ and } b = -3.$$
$$y = \frac{1}{4}x - 3 \quad \text{Simplify.}$$
  □

PRACTICE
3 Find an equation of the line with y-intercept $(0, 7)$ and slope of $\frac{1}{2}$.

OBJECTIVE
3 Writing an Equation Given Slope and a Point

Thus far, we have seen that we can write an equation of a line if we know its slope and y-intercept. We can also write an equation of a line if we know its slope and any point on the line. To see how we do this, let m represent slope and (x_1, y_1) represent the point on the line. Then if (x, y) is any other point of the line, we have that

$$\frac{y - y_1}{x - x_1} = m$$

$$y - y_1 = m(x - x_1) \quad \text{Multiply both sides by } (x - x_1).$$

slope

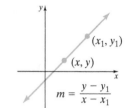

This is the *point-slope form* of the equation of a line.

Point-Slope Form of the Equation of a Line

The **point-slope form** of the equation of a line is

$$y - y_1 = m(x - x_1)$$

slope

(x_1, y_1) point on the line

where m is the slope of the line and (x_1, y_1) is a point on the line.

EXAMPLE 4 Find an equation of the line with slope -2 that passes through $(-1, 5)$. Write the equation in slope-intercept form, $y = mx + b$, and in standard form, $Ax + By = C$.

Solution Since the slope and a point on the line are given, we use point-slope form $y - y_1 = m(x - x_1)$ to write the equation. Let $m = -2$ and $(-1, 5) = (x_1, y_1)$.

$$y - y_1 = m(x - x_1)$$
$$y - 5 = -2[x - (-1)] \quad \text{Let } m = -2 \text{ and } (x_1, y_1) = (-1, 5).$$
$$y - 5 = -2(x + 1) \quad \text{Simplify.}$$
$$y - 5 = -2x - 2 \quad \text{Use the distributive property.}$$

To write the equation in slope-intercept form, $y = mx + b$, we simply solve the equation for y. To do this, we add 5 to both sides.

$$y - 5 = -2x - 2$$
$$y = -2x + 3 \quad \text{Slope-intercept form.}$$
$$2x + y = 3 \quad \text{Add } 2x \text{ to both sides and we have standard form.}$$

PRACTICE
4 Find an equation of the line passing through $(2, 3)$ with slope 4. Write the equation in standard form: $Ax + By = C$.

OBJECTIVE
4 Writing an Equation Given Two Points

We can also find an equation of a line when we are given any two points of the line.

EXAMPLE 5 Find an equation of the line through $(2, 5)$ and $(-3, 4)$. Write the equation in standard form.

Solution First, use the two given points to find the slope of the line.

$$m = \frac{4 - 5}{-3 - 2} = \frac{-1}{-5} = \frac{1}{5}$$

Next we use the slope $\frac{1}{5}$ and either one of the given points to write the equation in point-slope form. We use $(2, 5)$. Let $x_1 = 2$, $y_1 = 5$, and $m = \frac{1}{5}$.

$$y - y_1 = m(x - x_1) \qquad \text{Use point-slope form.}$$

$$y - 5 = \frac{1}{5}(x - 2) \qquad \text{Let } x_1 = 2, y_1 = 5, \text{ and } m = \frac{1}{5}.$$

$$5(y - 5) = 5 \cdot \frac{1}{5}(x - 2) \qquad \text{Multiply both sides by 5 to clear fractions.}$$

$$5y - 25 = x - 2 \qquad \text{Use the distributive property and simplify.}$$

$$-x + 5y - 25 = -2 \qquad \text{Subtract } x \text{ from both sides.}$$

$$-x + 5y = 23 \qquad \text{Add 25 to both sides.} \qquad \square$$

PRACTICE
5 Find an equation of the line through $(-1, 6)$ and $(3, 1)$. Write the equation in standard form.

> **Helpful Hint**
> Multiply both sides of the equation $-x + 5y = 23$ by -1, and it becomes $x - 5y = -23$. Both $-x + 5y = 23$ and $x - 5y = -23$ are in standard form, and they are equations of the same line.

OBJECTIVE
5 **Finding Equations of Vertical and Horizontal Lines**

Recall from Section 3.3 that:

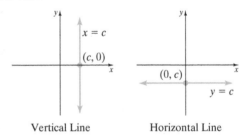

Vertical Line   Horizontal Line

EXAMPLE 6 Find an equation of the vertical line through $(-1, 5)$.

Solution The equation of a vertical line can be written in the form $x = c$, so an equation for a vertical line passing through $(-1, 5)$ is $x = -1$.

PRACTICE
6 Find an equation of the vertical line through $(3, -2)$.

⚠ **EXAMPLE 7**   Find an equation of the line parallel to the line $y = 5$ and passing through $(-2, -3)$.

Solution   Since the graph of $y = 5$ is a horizontal line, any line parallel to it is also horizontal. The equation of a horizontal line can be written in the form $y = c$. An equation for the horizontal line passing through

$$(-2, -3) \text{ is } y = -3.$$

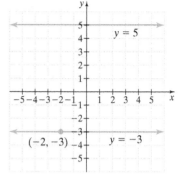

PRACTICE
7   Find an equation of the line parallel to the line $y = -2$ and passing through $(4, 3)$.

OBJECTIVE
6   **Using the Point-Slope Form to Solve Problems**

Problems occurring in many fields can be modeled by linear equations in two variables. The next example is from the field of marketing and shows how consumer demand of a product depends on the price of the product.

EXAMPLE 8   **Predicting the Sales of T-Shirts**

A web-based T-shirt company has learned that by pricing a clearance-sale T-shirt at $6, sales will reach 2000 T-shirts per day. Raising the price to $8 will cause the sales to fall to 1500 T-shirts per day.

a. Assume that the relationship between sales price and number of T-shirts sold is linear and write an equation describing this relationship. Write the equation in slope-intercept form.

b. Predict the daily sales of T-shirts if the price is $7.50.

Solution

a. First, use the given information and write two ordered pairs. Ordered pairs will be in the form (sales price, number sold) so that our ordered pairs are (6, 2000) and (8, 1500). Use the point-slope form to write an equation. To do so, we find the slope of the line that contains these points.

$$m = \frac{2000 - 1500}{6 - 8} = \frac{500}{-2} = -250$$

Next, use the slope and either one of the points to write the equation in point-slope form. We use $(6, 2000)$.

$$y - y_1 = m(x - x_1) \qquad \text{Use point-slope form.}$$
$$y - 2000 = -250(x - 6) \qquad \text{Let } x_1 = 6, y_1 = 2000, \text{ and } m = -250.$$
$$y - 2000 = -250x + 1500 \qquad \text{Use the distributive property.}$$
$$y = -250x + 3500 \qquad \text{Write in slope-intercept form.}$$

b. To predict the sales if the price is $7.50, we find y when $x = 7.50$.

$$y = -250x + 3500$$
$$y = -250(7.50) + 3500 \qquad \text{Let } x = 7.50.$$
$$y = -1875 + 3500$$
$$y = 1625$$

If the price is $7.50, sales will reach 1625 T-shirts per day.

PRACTICE

8   The new *Camelot* condos were selling at a rate of 30 per month when they were priced at $150,000 each. Lowering the price to $120,000 caused the sales to rise to 50 condos per month.

a. Assume that the relationship between number of condos sold and price is linear, and write an equation describing this relationship. Write the equation in slope-intercept form.

b. How should the condos be priced if the developer wishes to sell 60 condos per month?

The preceding example may also be solved by using ordered pairs of the form (number sold, sales price).

Forms of Linear Equations

$Ax + By = C$	**Standard form** of a linear equation.
	A and B are not both 0.
$y = mx + b$	**Slope-intercept form** of a linear equation.
	The slope is m and the y-intercept is $(0, b)$.
$y - y_1 = m(x - x_1)$	**Point-slope form** of a linear equation.
	The slope is m and (x_1, y_1) is a point on the line.
$y = c$	**Horizontal line**
	The slope is 0 and the y-intercept is $(0, c)$.
$x = c$	**Vertical line**
	The slope is undefined and the x-intercept is $(c, 0)$.

Parallel and Perpendicular Lines

Nonvertical parallel lines have the same slope.

The product of the slopes of two nonvertical perpendicular lines is -1.

Graphing Calculator Explorations

A grapher is a very useful tool for discovering patterns. To discover the change in the graph of a linear equation caused by a change in slope, try the following. Use a standard window and graph a linear equation in the form $y = mx + b$. Recall that the graph of such an equation will have slope m and y-intercept b.

First, graph $y = x + 3$. To do so, press the $\boxed{Y =}$ key and enter $Y_1 = x + 3$. Notice that this graph has slope 1 and that the y-intercept is 3. Next, on the same set of axes, graph $y = 2x + 3$ and $y = 3x + 3$ by pressing $\boxed{Y =}$ and entering $Y_2 = 2x + 3$ and $Y_3 = 3x + 3$.

Notice the difference in the graph of each equation as the slope changes from 1 to 2 to 3. How would the graph of $y = 5x + 3$ appear? To see the change in the graph caused by a change in negative slope, try graphing $y = -x + 3$, $y = -2x + 3$, and $y = -3x + 3$ on the same set of axes.

Use a grapher to graph the following equations. For each exercise, graph the first equation and use its graph to predict the appearance of the other equations. Then graph the other equations on the same set of axes and check your prediction.

1. $y = x; y = 6x, y = -6x$

2. $y = -x; y = -5x, y = -10x$

3. $y = \frac{1}{2}x + 2; y = \frac{3}{4}x + 2, y = x + 2$

4. $y = x + 1; y = \frac{5}{4}x + 1, y = \frac{5}{2}x + 1$

5. $y = -7x + 5; y = 7x + 5$

6. $y = 3x - 1; y = -3x - 1$

Vocabulary, Readiness & Video Check

Use the choices below to fill in each blank. Some choices may be used more than once and some not at all.

b (y_1, x_1) point-slope   vertical   standard

m (x_1, y_1) slope-intercept   horizontal

1. The form $y = mx + b$ is called _____ form. When a linear equation in two variables is written in this form, _____ is the slope of its graph and $(0,$ _____ $)$ is its y-intercept.

2. The form $y - y_1 = m(x - x_1)$ is called _____ form. When a linear equation in two variables is written in this form, _____ is the slope of its graph and _____ is a point on the graph.

Martin-Gay Interactive Videos

See Video 3.5

Watch the section lecture video and answer the following questions.

OBJECTIVE 1

3. We can use the slope-intercept form to graph a line. Complete these statements based on ▭ Example 1. Start by graphing the _____.

Find another point by applying the slope to this point—rewrite the slope as a _____ if necessary.

OBJECTIVE 2

4. In ▭ Example 3, what is the y-intercept?

OBJECTIVE 3

5. In ▭ Example 4 we use the point-slope form to find the equation of a line given the slope and a point. How do we then write this equation in standard form?

OBJECTIVE 4

6. The lecture before ▭ Example 5 discusses how to find the equation of a line given two points. Is there any circumstance when you might want to use the slope-intercept form to find the equation of a line given two points? If so, when?

OBJECTIVE 5

7. Solve ▭ Examples 6 and 7 again, this time using the point $(-2, -3)$ in each exercise.

OBJECTIVE 6

8. From ▭ Example 8, we are told to use ordered pairs of the form (time, speed). Explain why it is important to keep track of how you define your ordered pairs and/or define your variables.

3.5 Exercise Set

MyMathLab®

Use the slope-intercept form to graph each equation. See Examples 1 and 2.

1. $y = 2x + 1$
2. $y = -4x - 1$

3. $y = \dfrac{2}{3}x + 5$
4. $y = \dfrac{1}{4}x - 3$

5. $y = -5x$
6. $y = -6x$

7. $4x + y = 6$
8. $-3x + y = 2$

9. $4x - 7y = -14$
10. $3x - 4y = 4$

11. $x = \dfrac{5}{4}y$
12. $x = \dfrac{3}{2}y$

Write an equation of the line with each given slope, m, and y-intercept, (0, b). See Example 3.

13. $m = 5, b = 3$

14. $m = -3, b = -3$

15. $m = -4, b = -\dfrac{1}{6}$

16. $m = 2, b = \dfrac{3}{4}$

17. $m = \dfrac{2}{3}, b = 0$

18. $m = -\dfrac{4}{5}, b = 0$

19. $m = 0, b = -8$

20. $m = 0, b = -2$

21. $m = -\dfrac{1}{5}, b = \dfrac{1}{9}$

22. $m = \dfrac{1}{2}, b = -\dfrac{1}{3}$

Find an equation of each line with the given slope that passes through the given point. Write the equation in the form $Ax + By = C$. See Example 4.

23. $m = 6$; $(2, 2)$

24. $m = 4$; $(1, 3)$

25. $m = -8$; $(-1, -5)$

26. $m = -2$; $(-11, -12)$

27. $m = \dfrac{3}{2}$; $(5, -6)$

28. $m = \dfrac{2}{3}$; $(-8, 9)$

29. $m = -\dfrac{1}{2}$; $(-3, 0)$

30. $m = -\dfrac{1}{5}$; $(4, 0)$

Find an equation of the line passing through each pair of points. Write the equation in the form $Ax + By = C$. See Example 5.

31. $(3, 2)$ and $(5, 6)$

32. $(6, 2)$ and $(8, 8)$

33. $(-1, 3)$ and $(-2, -5)$

34. $(-4, 0)$ and $(6, -1)$

35. $(2, 3)$ and $(-1, -1)$

36. $(7, 10)$ and $(-1, -1)$

37. $(0, 0)$ and $\left(-\dfrac{1}{8}, \dfrac{1}{13}\right)$

38. $(0, 0)$ and $\left(-\dfrac{1}{2}, \dfrac{1}{3}\right)$

Find an equation of each line. See Example 6.

39. Vertical line through $(0, 2)$

40. Horizontal line through $(1, 4)$

41. Horizontal line through $(-1, 3)$

42. Vertical line through $(-1, 3)$

43. Vertical line through $\left(-\dfrac{7}{3}, -\dfrac{2}{5}\right)$

44. Horizontal line through $\left(\dfrac{2}{7}, 0\right)$

Find an equation of each line. See Example 7.

45. Parallel to $y = 5$, through $(1, 2)$

46. Perpendicular to $y = 5$, through $(1, 2)$

47. Perpendicular to $x = -3$, through $(-2, 5)$

48. Parallel to $y = -4$, through $(0, -3)$

49. Parallel to $x = 0$, through $(6, -8)$

50. Perpendicular to $x = 7$, through $(-5, 0)$

MIXED PRACTICE

See Examples 1 through 7. Find an equation of each line described. Write each equation in slope-intercept form (solved for y), when possible.

51. With slope $-\dfrac{1}{2}$, through $\left(0, \dfrac{5}{3}\right)$

52. With slope $\dfrac{5}{7}$, through $(0, -3)$

53. Through $(10, 7)$ and $(7, 10)$

54. Through $(5, -6)$ and $(-6, 5)$

55. With undefined slope, through $\left(-\dfrac{3}{4}, 1\right)$

56. With slope 0, through $(6.7, 12.1)$

57. Slope 1, through $(-7, 9)$

58. Slope 5, through $(6, -8)$

59. Slope -5, y-intercept $(0, 7)$

60. Slope -2; y-intercept $(0, -4)$

61. Through $(6, 7)$, parallel to the x-axis

62. Through $(1, -5)$, parallel to the y-axis

63. Through $(2, 3)$ and $(0, 0)$

64. Through $(4, 7)$ and $(0, 0)$

65. Through $(-2, -3)$, perpendicular to the y-axis

66. Through $(0, 12)$, perpendicular to the x-axis

67. Slope $-\dfrac{4}{7}$, through $(-1, -2)$

68. Slope $-\dfrac{3}{5}$, through $(4, 4)$

Solve. Assume each exercise describes a linear relationship. Write the equations in slope-intercept form. See Example 8.

69. A rock is dropped from the top of a 400-foot cliff. After 1 second, the rock is traveling 32 feet per second. After 3 seconds, the rock is traveling 96 feet per second.

400 feet

a. Assume that the relationship between time and speed is linear and write an equation describing this relationship. Use ordered pairs of the form (time, speed).

b. Use this equation to determine the speed of the rock 4 seconds after it was dropped.

70. A Hawaiian fruit company is studying the sales of a pineapple sauce to see if this product is to be continued. At the end of its first year, profits on this product amounted to $30,000. At the end of the fourth year, profits were $66,000.

a. Assume that the relationship between years on the market and profit is linear and write an equation describing this relationship. Use ordered pairs of the form (years on the market, profit).

b. Use this equation to predict the profit at the end of 7 years.

71. Sales of hybrid (gas-electric) vehicles have been decreasing for the past few years. In 2007, 356 thousand new gasoline-electric hybrid vehicles were sold in the United States. In 2009, only were 290 thousand were sold. (*Source:* U.S. Energy Information Administration)

a. Write an equation describing the relationship between time and number of registered gasoline-electric hybrid vehicles sold. Use ordered pairs of the form (years past 2007, number of hybrids sold).

b. Use this equation to predict the number of gasoline-electric hybrids sold in the year 2015.

72. In 2011, there were 960 thousand eating establishments in the United States. In 2006, there were 935 thousand eating establishments. (*Source:* National Restaurant Association)

a. Write an equation describing the relationship between time and number of eating establishments. Use ordered pairs of the form (years past 2006, number of eating establishments in thousands).

b. Use this equation to predict the number of eating establishments in 2018.

73. In 2006, the U.S. population per square mile of land area was 85. In 2011, the person per square mile population was 88.

a. Write an equation describing the relationship between year and persons per square mile. Use ordered pairs of the form (years past 2006, persons per square mile).

b. Use this equation to predict the person per square mile population in 2020.

74. In 2005, there were a total of 150 thousand apparel and accessory stores. In 2009, there were a total of 157 thousand apparel and accessory stores. (*Source:* U.S. Bureau of the Census. *County Business Patterns*)

a. Write an equation describing this relationship. Use ordered pairs of the form (years past 2005, numbers of stores in thousands).

b. Use this equation to predict the number of apparel and accessory stores in 2015.

75. It has been said that newspapers are disappearing, replaced by various electronic media. In 2001, newspaper circulation (number of copies it distributed in a day) was about 60 million. In 2009, this circulation dropped to 46 million. (*Source:* Newspaper Asso. of America)

a. Write an equation describing the relationship between time and circulation. Use ordered pairs of the form (years past 2001, number of newspapers circulated).

b. Use this equation to predict the newspaper circulation in 2017.

76. A certain chain of book stores is slowly closing down stores. Suppose that in 2006 there were 3991 stores and in 2010 there were 3200 stores.

a. Write an equation describing the relationship between time and number of store locations. Use ordered pairs of the form (years past 2006, number of stores).

b. Use this equation to predict the number of stores in 2018.

77. The Pool Fun Company has learned that, by pricing a newly released Fun Noodle at $3, sales will reach 10,000 Fun Noodles per day during the summer. Raising the price to $5 will cause sales to fall to 8000 Fun Noodles per day.

a. Assume that the relationship between price and number of Fun Noodles sold is linear and write an equation describing this relationship. Use ordered pairs of the form (price, number sold).

b. Predict the daily sales of Fun Noodles if the price is $3.50.

78. The value of a building bought in 2000 may be depreciated (or decreased) as time passes for income tax purposes. Seven years after the building was bought, this value was $225,000 and 12 years after it was bought, this value was $195,000.

   a. If the relationship between number of years past 2000 and the depreciated value of the building is linear, write an equation describing this relationship. Use ordered pairs of the form (years past 2000, value of building).

   b. Use this equation to estimate the depreciated value of the building in 2018.

REVIEW AND PREVIEW

Find the value of $x^2 - 3x + 1$ for each given value of x. See Section 1.7.

79. 2   **80.** 5   **81.** −1   **82.** −3

For each graph, determine whether any x-values correspond to two or more y-values. See Section 3.1.

83.   **84.**

85.   **86.**

CONCEPT EXTENSIONS

For Exercises 87 through 90, identify the form that the linear equation in two variables is written in. For Exercises 91 and 92, identify the appearance of the graph of the equation.

87. $y - 7 = 4(x + 3)$; _____ form

88. $5x - 9y = 11$; _____ form

89. $y = \dfrac{3}{4}x - \dfrac{1}{3}$; _____ form

90. $y + 2 = \dfrac{-1}{3}(x - 2)$; _____ form

91. $y = \dfrac{1}{2}$; _____ line   **92.** $x = -17$; _____ line

93. Given the equation of a nonvertical line, explain how to find the slope without finding two points on the line.

94. Given two points on a nonvertical line, explain how to use the point-slope form to find the equation of the line.

95. Write an equation in standard form of the line that contains the point $(-1, 2)$ and is
   a. parallel to the line $y = 3x - 1$.
   b. perpendicular to the line $y = 3x - 1$.

96. Write an equation in standard form of the line that contains the point $(4, 0)$ and is
   a. parallel to the line $y = -2x + 3$.
   b. perpendicular to the line $y = -2x + 3$.

97. Write an equation in standard form of the line that contains the point $(3, -5)$ and is
   a. parallel to the line $3x + 2y = 7$.
   b. perpendicular to the line $3x + 2y = 7$.

98. Write an equation in standard form of the line that contains the point $(-2, 4)$ and is
   a. parallel to the line $x + 3y = 6$.
   b. perpendicular to the line $x + 3y = 6$.

Solving Systems of Linear Equations

According to the Bureau of Labor Statistics, workers age 55 years and over are projected to have the greatest increase in the labor force during the years 2008 to 2018. These workers are anticipated to increase from 18.1% to 23.9% of the labor force during this period. Workers age 25 to 34 years are projected to increase also, but not at the same rate. In Section 4.3, Exercise 73, we will predict when these two age groups will have the same percent of the labor force.

In Chapter 3, we graphed equations containing two variables. Equations like these are often needed to represent relationships between two different values. There are also many real-life opportunities to compare and contrast two such equations, called a system of equations. This chapter presents linear systems and ways we solve these systems and apply them to real-life situations.

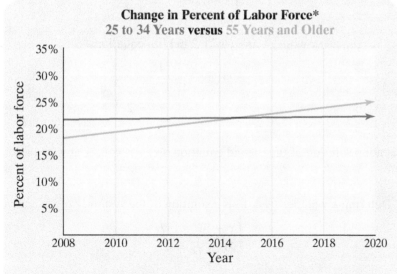

Change in Percent of Labor Force*
25 to 34 Years **versus** 55 Years and Older

Data from U.S. Bureau of Labor Statistics   *Here, we assumed linear growth.

Solving Systems of Linear Equations by Graphing

OBJECTIVES

1 Determine if an Ordered Pair Is a Solution of a System of Equations in Two Variables.

2 Solve a System of Linear Equations by Graphing.

3 Without Graphing, Determine the Number of Solutions of a System.

A **system of linear equations** consists of two or more linear equations. In this section, we focus on solving systems of linear equations containing two equations in two variables. Examples of such linear systems are

$$\begin{cases} 3x - 3y = 0 \\ x = 2y \end{cases} \quad \begin{cases} x - y = 0 \\ 2x + y = 10 \end{cases} \quad \begin{cases} y = 7x - 1 \\ y = 4 \end{cases}$$

OBJECTIVE
1 Deciding Whether an Ordered Pair Is a Solution

A **solution** of a system of two equations in two variables is an ordered pair of numbers that is a solution of both equations in the system.

EXAMPLE 1 Determine whether $(12, 6)$ is a solution of the system

$$\begin{cases} 2x - 3y = 6 \\ x = 2y \end{cases}$$

Solution To determine whether $(12, 6)$ is a solution of the system, we replace x with 12 and y with 6 in both equations.

$2x - 3y = 6$ First equation	$x = 2y$ Second equation
$2(12) - 3(6) \stackrel{?}{=} 6$ Let $x = 12$ and $y = 6$.	$12 \stackrel{?}{=} 2(6)$ Let $x = 12$ and $y = 6$.
$24 - 18 \stackrel{?}{=} 6$ Simplify.	$12 = 12$ True
$6 = 6$ True	

Since $(12, 6)$ is a solution of both equations, it is a solution of the system.   □

PRACTICE
1 Determine whether $(4, 12)$ is a solution of the system.

$$\begin{cases} 4x - y = 2 \\ y = 3x \end{cases}$$

EXAMPLE 2 Determine whether $(-1, 2)$ is a solution of the system

$$\begin{cases} x + 2y = 3 \\ 4x - y = 6 \end{cases}$$

Solution We replace x with -1 and y with 2 in both equations.

$x + 2y = 3$ First equation	$4x - y = 6$ Second equation
$-1 + 2(2) \stackrel{?}{=} 3$ Let $x = -1$ and $y = 2$.	$4(-1) - 2 \stackrel{?}{=} 6$ Let $x = -1$ and $y = 2$.
$-1 + 4 \stackrel{?}{=} 3$ Simplify.	$-4 - 2 \stackrel{?}{=} 6$ Simplify.
$3 = 3$ True	$-6 = 6$ False

$(-1, 2)$ is not a solution of the second equation, $4x - y = 6$, so it is not a solution of the system.   □

PRACTICE
2 Determine whether $(-4, 1)$ is a solution of the system.

$$\begin{cases} x - 3y = -7 \\ 2x + 9y = 1 \end{cases}$$

OBJECTIVE

2   Solving Systems of Equations by Graphing

Since a solution of a system of two equations in two variables is a solution common to both equations, it is also a point common to the graphs of both equations. Let's practice finding solutions of both equations in a system—that is, solutions of a system—by graphing and identifying points of intersection.

EXAMPLE 3   Solve the system of equations by graphing.

$$\begin{cases} -x + 3y = 10 \\ x + y = 2 \end{cases}$$

Solution   On a single set of axes, graph each linear equation.

$-x + 3y = 10$

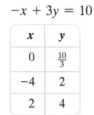

x	y
0	$\frac{10}{3}$
-4	2
2	4

$x + y = 2$

x	y
0	2
2	0
1	1

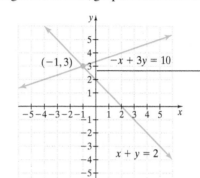

> ▶ Helpful Hint
> The point of intersection gives the solution of the system.

The two lines appear to intersect at the point $(-1, 3)$. To check, we replace x with -1 and y with 3 in both equations.

$$-x + 3y = 10 \quad \text{First equation} \qquad\qquad x + y = 2 \quad \text{Second equation}$$
$$-(-1) + 3(3) \stackrel{?}{=} 10 \quad \text{Let } x = -1 \text{ and } y = 3. \qquad -1 + 3 \stackrel{?}{=} 2 \quad \text{Let } x = -1 \text{ and } y = 3.$$
$$1 + 9 \stackrel{?}{=} 10 \quad \text{Simplify.} \qquad\qquad\qquad 2 = 2 \quad \text{True}$$
$$10 = 10 \quad \text{True}$$

$(-1, 3)$ checks, so it is the solution of the system and the solution set is $\{(-1, 3)\}$. (Note: For single ordered-pair solutions, we shall list the ordered pair only.)   □

PRACTICE

3   Solve the system of equations by graphing:

$$\begin{cases} x - y = 3 \\ x + 2y = 18 \end{cases}$$

> ▶ Helpful Hint
> Neatly drawn graphs can help when you are estimating the solution of a system of linear equations by graphing.
>   In the example above, notice that the two lines intersected in a point. This means that the system has 1 solution.

EXAMPLE 4 Solve the system of equations by graphing.

$$\begin{cases} 2x + 3y = -2 \\ x = 2 \end{cases}$$

Solution We graph each linear equation on a single set of axes.

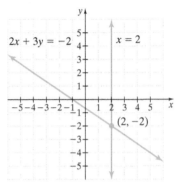

The two lines appear to intersect at the point $(2, -2)$. To determine whether $(2, -2)$ is the solution, we replace x with 2 and y with -2 in both equations.

$2x + 3y = -2$ First equation $x = 2$ Second equation

$2(2) + 3(-2) \stackrel{?}{=} -2$ Let $x = 2$ and $y = -2$. $2 \stackrel{?}{=} 2$ Let $x = 2$.

$4 + (-6) \stackrel{?}{=} -2$ Simplify. $2 = 2$ True

$-2 = -2$ True

Since a true statement results in both equations, $(2, -2)$ is the solution of the system. □

PRACTICE

4   Solve the system of equations by graphing.

$$\begin{cases} -4x + 3y = -3 \\ y = -5 \end{cases}$$

A system of equations that has at least one solution as in Examples 3 and 4 is said to be a **consistent system.** A system that has no solution is said to be an **inconsistent system.**

EXAMPLE 5 Solve the following system of equations by graphing.

$$\begin{cases} 2x + y = 7 \\ 2y = -4x \end{cases}$$

Solution Graph the two lines in the system.

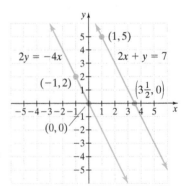

The lines **appear** to be parallel. To confirm this, write both equations in slope-intercept form by solving each equation for y.

$2x + y = 7$ First equation $2y = -4x$ Second equation

$y = -2x + 7$ Subtract $2x$ from both sides. $\dfrac{2y}{2} = \dfrac{-4x}{2}$ Divide both sides by 2.

$y = -2x$

Recall that when an equation is written in slope-intercept form, the coefficient of x is the slope. Since both equations have the same slope, -2, but different y-intercepts, the lines are parallel and have no points in common. Thus, there is no solution of the system and the system is inconsistent. To indicate this, we can say the system has no solution or the solution set is $\{\ \}$ or $\varnothing$.

PRACTICE

5   Solve the system of equations by graphing.

$$\begin{cases} 3y = 9x \\ 6x - 2y = 12 \end{cases}$$

In Examples 3, 4, and 5, the graphs of the two linear equations of each system are different. When this happens, we call these equations **independent equations.** If the graphs of the two equations in a system are identical, we call the equations **dependent equations.**

EXAMPLE 6   Solve the system of equations by graphing.

$$\begin{cases} x - y = 3 \\ -x + y = -3 \end{cases}$$

Solution   Graph each line.

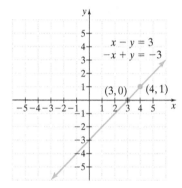

These graphs **appear** to be identical. To confirm this, write each equation in slope-intercept form.

$x - y = 3$ First equation $-x + y = -3$ Second equation

  $-y = -x + 3$ Subtract x from both sides. $y = x - 3$ Add x to both sides.

  $\dfrac{-y}{-1} = \dfrac{-x}{-1} + \dfrac{3}{-1}$ Divide both sides by -1.

  $y = x - 3$

The equations are identical and so must be their graphs. The lines have an infinite number of points in common. Thus, there is an infinite number of solutions of the system and this is a consistent system. The equations are dependent equations. Here, we can say that there are an infinite number of solutions or the solution set is $\{(x, y) \mid x - y = 3\}$ or equivalently $\{(x, y) \mid -x + y = -3\}$ since the equations describe identical ordered pairs. The second set is read "the set of all ordered pairs (x, y) such that $-x + y = -3$.

PRACTICE

6   Solve the system of equations by graphing.

$$\begin{cases} x - y = 4 \\ -2x + 2y = -8 \end{cases}$$

As we have seen, three different situations can occur when graphing the two lines associated with the two equations in a linear system:

One point of intersection: one solution   Parallel lines: no solution   Same line: infinite number of solutions

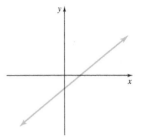

Consistent system
(at least one solution)
Independent equations
(graphs of equations differ)

Inconsistent system
(no solution)
Independent equations
(graphs of equations differ)

Consistent system
(at least one solution)
Dependent equations
(graphs of equations identical)

OBJECTIVE

3   Finding the Number of Solutions of a System without Graphing

You may have suspected by now that graphing alone is not an accurate way to solve a system of linear equations. For example, a solution of $\left(\dfrac{1}{2}, \dfrac{2}{9}\right)$ is unlikely to be read correctly from a graph. The next two sections present two accurate methods of solving these systems. In the meantime, we can decide how many solutions a system has by writing each equation in the slope-intercept form.

EXAMPLE 7   Without graphing, determine the number of solutions of the system.

$$\begin{cases} \dfrac{1}{2}x - y = 2 \\ x = 2y + 5 \end{cases}$$

Solution   First write each equation in slope-intercept form.

$\dfrac{1}{2}x - y = 2$ First equation

$\dfrac{1}{2}x = y + 2$ Add y to both sides.

$\dfrac{1}{2}x - 2 = y$ Subtract 2 from both sides.

$x = 2y + 5$ Second equation

$x - 5 = 2y$ Subtract 5 from both sides.

$\dfrac{x}{2} - \dfrac{5}{2} = \dfrac{2y}{2}$ Divide both sides by 2.

$\dfrac{1}{2}x - \dfrac{5}{2} = y$ Simplify.

The slope of each line is $\dfrac{1}{2}$, but they have different y-intercepts. This tells us that the lines representing these equations are parallel. Since the lines are parallel, the system has no solution and is inconsistent.

PRACTICE

7   Without graphing, determine the number of solutions of the system.

$$\begin{cases} 5x + 4y = 6 \\ x - y = 3 \end{cases}$$

EXAMPLE 8   Without graphing, determine the number of solutions of the system.

$$\begin{cases} 3x - y = 4 \\ x + 2y = 8 \end{cases}$$

Solution   Once again, the slope-intercept form helps determine how many solutions this system has.

$3x - y = 4$ First equation $x + 2y = 8$ Second equation

$\quad\quad 3x = y + 4$ Add y to both sides. $\quad\quad x = -2y + 8$ Subtract $2y$ from both sides.

$3x - 4 = y$ Subtract 4 from both sides. $\quad x - 8 = -2y$ Subtract 8 from both sides.

$$\frac{x}{-2} - \frac{8}{-2} = \frac{-2y}{-2}$$ Divide both sides by -2.

$$-\frac{1}{2}x + 4 = y$$ Simplify.

The slope of the second line is $-\dfrac{1}{2}$, whereas the slope of the first line is 3. Since the slopes are not equal, the two lines are neither parallel nor identical and must intersect. Therefore, this system has one solution and is consistent.   □

PRACTICE
8   Without graphing, determine the number of solutions of the system.

$$\begin{cases} -\dfrac{2}{3}x + y = 6 \\ 3y = 2x + 5 \end{cases}$$

Graphing Calculator Explorations

A graphing calculator may be used to approximate solutions of systems of equations. For example, to approximate the solution of the system

$$\begin{cases} y = -3.14x - 1.35 \\ y = 4.88x + 5.25, \end{cases}$$

first graph each equation on the same set of axes. Then use the intersect feature of your calculator to approximate the point of intersection.

The approximate point of intersection is $(-0.82, 1.23)$.

Solve each system of equations. Approximate the solutions to two decimal places.

1. $\begin{cases} y = -2.68x + 1.21 \\ y = 5.22x - 1.68 \end{cases}$ **2.** $\begin{cases} y = 4.25x + 3.89 \\ y = -1.88x + 3.21 \end{cases}$

3. $\begin{cases} 4.3x - 2.9y = 5.6 \\ 8.1x + 7.6y = -14.1 \end{cases}$ **4.** $\begin{cases} -3.6x - 8.6y = 10 \\ -4.5x + 9.6y = -7.7 \end{cases}$

Vocabulary, Readiness & Video Check

Fill in each blank with one of the words or phrases listed below.

system of linear equations   solution   consistent
dependent   inconsistent   independent

1. In a system of linear equations in two variables, if the graphs of the equations are the same, the equations are _____ equations.

2. Two or more linear equations are called a(n) _____.

3. A system of equations that has at least one solution is called a(n) _____ system.

4. A(n) _____ of a system of two equations in two variables is an ordered pair of numbers that is a solution of both equations in the system.

5. A system of equations that has no solution is called a(n) _____ system.

6. In a system of linear equations in two variables, if the graphs of the equations are different, the equations are _____ equations.

Martin-Gay Interactive Videos

See Video 4.1

Watch the section lecture video and answer the following questions.

OBJECTIVE 1

7. In Example 1, the first ordered pair is a solution of the first equation of the system. Why is this not enough to determine whether the first ordered pair is a solution of the system?

OBJECTIVE 2

8. From Examples 2 and 3, why is finding the solution of a system of equations from a graph considered "guessing" and this proposed solution checked algebraically?

OBJECTIVE 3

9. From Examples 5–7, explain how the slope-intercept form tells us how many solutions a system of equations has.

4.1 Exercise Set   MyMathLab®

Each rectangular coordinate system shows the graph of the equations in a system of equations. Use each graph to determine the number of solutions for each associated system. If the system has only one solution, give its coordinates.

1.

2.

3.

4.

Determine whether each ordered pair is a solution of the system of linear equations. See Examples 1 and 2.

5. $\begin{cases} x + y = 8 \\ 3x + 2y = 21 \end{cases}$
   a. $(2, 4)$
   b. $(5, 3)$

6. $\begin{cases} 2x + y = 5 \\ x + 3y = 5 \end{cases}$
   a. $(5, 0)$
   b. $(2, 1)$

7. $\begin{cases} 3x - y = 5 \\ x + 2y = 11 \end{cases}$
   a. $(3, 4)$
   b. $(0, -5)$

8. $\begin{cases} 2x - 3y = 8 \\ x - 2y = 6 \end{cases}$
   a. $(-2, -4)$
   b. $(7, 2)$

9. $\begin{cases} 2y = 4x + 6 \\ 2x - y = -3 \end{cases}$
   a. $(-3, -3)$
   b. $(0, 3)$

10. $\begin{cases} x + 5y = -4 \\ -2x = 10y + 8 \end{cases}$
   a. $(-4, 0)$
   b. $(6, -2)$

11. $\begin{cases} -2 = x - 7y \\ 6x - y = 13 \end{cases}$
   a. $(-2, 0)$
   b. $\left(\dfrac{1}{2}, \dfrac{5}{14} \right)$

12. $\begin{cases} 4x = 1 - y \\ x - 3y = -8 \end{cases}$
   a. $(0, 1)$
   b. $\left(\dfrac{1}{6}, \dfrac{1}{3} \right)$

MIXED PRACTICE

Solve each system of linear equations by graphing. See Examples 3 through 6.

13. $\begin{cases} x + y = 4 \\ x - y = 2 \end{cases}$

14. $\begin{cases} x + y = 3 \\ x - y = 5 \end{cases}$

15. $\begin{cases} x + y = 6 \\ -x + y = -6 \end{cases}$

16. $\begin{cases} x + y = 1 \\ -x + y = -3 \end{cases}$

17. $\begin{cases} y = 2x \\ 3x - y = -2 \end{cases}$

18. $\begin{cases} y = -3x \\ 2x - y = -5 \end{cases}$

19. $\begin{cases} y = x + 1 \\ y = 2x - 1 \end{cases}$

20. $\begin{cases} y = 3x - 4 \\ y = x + 2 \end{cases}$

21. $\begin{cases} 2x + y = 0 \\ 3x + y = 1 \end{cases}$

22. $\begin{cases} 2x + y = 1 \\ 3x + y = 0 \end{cases}$

23. $\begin{cases} y = -x - 1 \\ y = 2x + 5 \end{cases}$

24. $\begin{cases} y = x - 1 \\ y = -3x - 5 \end{cases}$

25. $\begin{cases} x + y = 5 \\ x + y = 6 \end{cases}$

26. $\begin{cases} x - y = 4 \\ x - y = 1 \end{cases}$

27. $\begin{cases} 2x - y = 6 \\ y = 2 \end{cases}$

28. $\begin{cases} x + y = 5 \\ x = 4 \end{cases}$

29. $\begin{cases} x - 2y = 2 \\ 3x + 2y = -2 \end{cases}$

30. $\begin{cases} x + 3y = 7 \\ 2x - 3y = -4 \end{cases}$

31. $\begin{cases} 2x + y = 4 \\ 6x = -3y + 6 \end{cases}$

32. $\begin{cases} y + 2x = 3 \\ 4x = 2 - 2y \end{cases}$

33. $\begin{cases} y - 3x = -2 \\ 6x - 2y = 4 \end{cases}$

34. $\begin{cases} x - 2y = -6 \\ -2x + 4y = 12 \end{cases}$

35. $\begin{cases} x = 3 \\ y = -1 \end{cases}$

36. $\begin{cases} x = -5 \\ y = 3 \end{cases}$

37. $\begin{cases} y = x - 2 \\ y = 2x + 3 \end{cases}$

38. $\begin{cases} y = x + 5 \\ y = -2x - 4 \end{cases}$

39. $\begin{cases} 2x - 3y = -2 \\ -3x + 5y = 5 \end{cases}$

40. $\begin{cases} 4x - y = 7 \\ 2x - 3y = -9 \end{cases}$

41. $\begin{cases} 6x - y = 4 \\ \frac{1}{2}y = -2 + 3x \end{cases}$ **42.** $\begin{cases} 3x - y = 6 \\ \frac{1}{3}y = -2 + x \end{cases}$

Without graphing, decide.

   a. Are the graphs of the equations identical lines, parallel lines, or lines intersecting at a single point?

   b. How many solutions does the system have? See Examples 7 and 8.

43. $\begin{cases} 4x + y = 24 \\ x + 2y = 2 \end{cases}$ **44.** $\begin{cases} 3x + y = 1 \\ 3x + 2y = 6 \end{cases}$

45. $\begin{cases} 2x + y = 0 \\ 2y = 6 - 4x \end{cases}$ **46.** $\begin{cases} 3x + y = 0 \\ 2y = -6x \end{cases}$

47. $\begin{cases} 6x - y = 4 \\ \frac{1}{2}y = -2 + 3x \end{cases}$ **48.** $\begin{cases} 3x - y = 2 \\ \frac{1}{3}y = -2 + 3x \end{cases}$

49. $\begin{cases} x = 5 \\ y = -2 \end{cases}$ **50.** $\begin{cases} y = 3 \\ x = -4 \end{cases}$

51. $\begin{cases} 3y - 2x = 3 \\ x + 2y = 9 \end{cases}$ **52.** $\begin{cases} 2y = x + 2 \\ y + 2x = 3 \end{cases}$

53. $\begin{cases} 6y + 4x = 6 \\ 3y - 3 = -2x \end{cases}$ **54.** $\begin{cases} 8y + 6x = 4 \\ 4y - 2 = 3x \end{cases}$

55. $\begin{cases} x + y = 4 \\ x + y = 3 \end{cases}$ **56.** $\begin{cases} 2x + y = 0 \\ y = -2x + 1 \end{cases}$

REVIEW AND PREVIEW

Solve each equation. See Section 2.3.

57. $5(x - 3) + 3x = 1$

58. $-2x + 3(x + 6) = 17$

59. $4\left(\dfrac{y + 1}{2}\right) + 3y = 0$

60. $-y + 12\left(\dfrac{y - 1}{4}\right) = 3$

61. $8a - 2(3a - 1) = 6$

62. $3z - (4z - 2) = 9$

CONCEPT EXTENSIONS

63. Draw a graph of two linear equations whose associated system has the solution $(-1, 4)$.

64. Draw a graph of two linear equations whose associated system has the solution $(3, -2)$.

65. Draw a graph of two linear equations whose associated system has no solution.

66. Draw a graph of two linear equations whose associated system has an infinite number of solutions.

67. The ordered pair $(-2, 3)$ is a solution of all three independent equations:
$$x + y = 1$$
$$2x - y = -7$$
$$x + 3y = 7$$
Describe the graph of all three equations on the same axes.

68. Explain how to use a graph to determine the number of solutions of a system.

The double-line graph below shows the number of pounds of fishery products from U.S. domestic catch and from imports. Use this graph to answer Exercises 69 and 70.

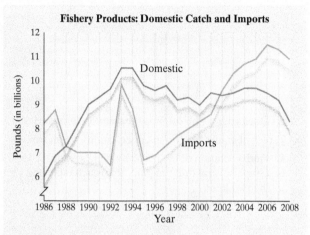

Data from *Statistical Abstract of the United States,* 2011

69. Between what pairs of years did the number of pounds of imported fishery products equal the number of pounds of domestic catch?

70. For what year(s) was the number of pounds of imported fishery products less than the number of pounds of domestic catch?

The double-line graph below shows the average attendance per game for the years shown for the Minnesota Twins and the Texas Rangers baseball teams. Use this for Exercises 71 and 72.

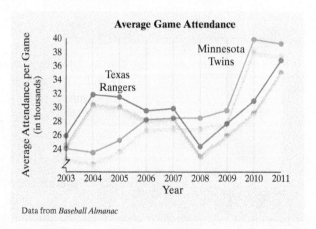

Data from *Baseball Almanac*

71. In what year(s) was the average attendance per game for the Texas Rangers greater than the average attendance per game for the Minnesota Twins?

72. In what year was the average attendance per game for the Texas Rangers closest to the average attendance per game for the Minnesota Twins, 2006 or 2009?

73. Construct a system of two linear equations that has $(1, 3)$ as a solution.

74. Construct a system of two linear equations that has $(0, 7)$ as a solution.

75. Below are tables of values for two linear equations.
   a. Find a solution of the corresponding system.
   b. Graph several ordered pairs from each table and sketch the two lines.

x	y
1	3
2	5
3	7
4	9
5	11

x	y
1	6
2	7
3	8
4	9
5	10

   c. Does your graph confirm the solution from part (a)?

76. Tables of values for two linear equations are shown.

   a. Find a solution of the corresponding system.
   b. Graph several ordered pairs from each table and sketch the two lines.

x	y
-3	5
-1	1
0	-1
1	-3
2	-5

x	y
-3	7
-1	1
0	-2
1	-5
2	-8

   c. Does your graph confirm the solution from part (a)?

77. Explain how writing each equation in a linear system in slope-intercept form helps determine the number of solutions of a system.

78. Is it possible for a system of two linear equations in two variables to be inconsistent but with dependent equations? Why or why not?

4.2 Solving Systems of Linear Equations by Substitution

OBJECTIVE

1 Use the Substitution Method to Solve a System of Linear Equations.

OBJECTIVE

1 Using the Substitution Method

As we stated in the preceding section, graphing alone is not an accurate way to solve a system of linear equations. In this section, we discuss a second, more accurate method for solving systems of equations. This method is called the **substitution method** and is introduced in the next example.

EXAMPLE 1 Solve the system:

$$\begin{cases} 2x + y = 10 & \text{First equation} \\ x = y + 2 & \text{Second equation} \end{cases}$$

Solution The second equation in this system is $x = y + 2$. This tells us that x and $y + 2$ have the same value. This means that we may substitute $y + 2$ for x in the first equation.

$$2x + y = 10 \quad \text{First equation}$$

$$2(y + 2) + y = 10 \quad \text{Substitute } y + 2 \text{ for } x \text{ since } x = y + 2.$$

Notice that this equation now has one variable, y. Let's now solve this equation for y.

▶ **Helpful Hint**
Don't forget the distributive property.

$$2(y + 2) + y = 10$$
$$2y + 4 + y = 10 \quad \text{Use the distributive property.}$$
$$3y + 4 = 10 \quad \text{Combine like terms.}$$
$$3y = 6 \quad \text{Subtract 4 from both sides.}$$
$$y = 2 \quad \text{Divide both sides by 3.}$$

Now we know that the y-value of the ordered pair solution of the system is 2. To find the corresponding x-value, we replace y with 2 in the equation $x = y + 2$ and solve for x.

$$x = y + 2$$
$$x = 2 + 2 \quad \text{Let } y = 2.$$
$$x = 4$$

The solution of the system is the ordered pair $(4, 2)$. Since an ordered pair solution must satisfy both linear equations in the system, we could have chosen the equation $2x + y = 10$ to find the corresponding x-value. The resulting x-value is the same.

Check: We check to see that $(4, 2)$ satisfies both equations of the original system.

<table>
<tr><td align="center">***First Equation***</td><td align="center">***Second Equation***</td></tr>
<tr><td align="center">$2x + y = 10$</td><td align="center">$x = y + 2$</td></tr>
<tr><td align="center">$2(4) + 2 \overset{?}{=} 10$</td><td align="center">$4 \overset{?}{=} 2 + 2$ Let $x = 4$ and $y = 2$.</td></tr>
<tr><td align="center">$10 = 10$ True</td><td align="center">$4 = 4$ True</td></tr>
</table>

The solution of the system is $(4, 2)$.

A graph of the two equations shows the two lines intersecting at the point $(4, 2)$.

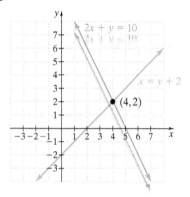

PRACTICE
1   Solve the system:

$$\begin{cases} 2x - y = 9 \\ x = y + 1 \end{cases}$$

EXAMPLE 2   Solve the system:

$$\begin{cases} 5x - y = -2 \\ y = 3x \end{cases}$$

Solution   The second equation is solved for y in terms of x. We substitute $3x$ for y in the first equation.

$$5x - y = -2 \quad \text{First equation}$$

$$5x - (3x) = -2 \quad \text{Substitute } 3x \text{ for } y.$$

Now we solve for x.

$$5x - 3x = -2$$

$$2x = -2 \quad \text{Combine like terms.}$$

$$x = -1 \quad \text{Divide both sides by 2.}$$

The x-value of the ordered pair solution is -1. To find the corresponding y-value, we replace x with -1 in the second equation, $y = 3x$.

$$y = 3x \quad \text{Second equation}$$

$$y = 3(-1) \quad \text{Let } x = -1.$$

$$y = -3$$

Check to see that the solution of the system is $(-1, -3)$.

(Continued on next page)

PRACTICE
2   Solve the system:

$$\begin{cases} 7x - y = -15 \\ y = 2x \end{cases}$$

To solve a system of equations by substitution, we first need an equation solved for one of its variables, as in Examples 1 and 2. If neither equation in a system is solved for x or y, this will be our first step.

EXAMPLE 3   Solve the system:

$$\begin{cases} x + 2y = 7 \\ 2x + 2y = 13 \end{cases}$$

Solution   We choose one of the equations and solve for x or y. We will solve the first equation for x by subtracting $2y$ from both sides.

$$x + 2y = 7 \qquad \text{First equation}$$
$$x = 7 - 2y \qquad \text{Subtract } 2y \text{ from both sides.}$$

Since $x = 7 - 2y$, we now substitute $7 - 2y$ for x in the second equation and solve for y.

$$2x + 2y = 13 \qquad \text{Second equation}$$
$$2(7 - 2y) + 2y = 13 \qquad \text{Let } x = 7 - 2y.$$
$$14 - 4y + 2y = 13 \qquad \text{Use the distributive property.}$$
$$14 - 2y = 13 \qquad \text{Simplify.}$$
$$-2y = -1 \qquad \text{Subtract 14 from both sides.}$$
$$y = \frac{1}{2} \qquad \text{Divide both sides by } -2.$$

> **Helpful Hint**
> Don't forget to insert parentheses when substituting $7 - 2y$ for x.

To find x, we let $y = \frac{1}{2}$ in the equation $x = 7 - 2y$.

$$x = 7 - 2y$$
$$x = 7 - 2\left(\frac{1}{2}\right) \qquad \text{Let } y = \frac{1}{2}.$$
$$x = 7 - 1$$
$$x = 6$$

> **Helpful Hint**
> To find x, any equation in two variables equivalent to the original equations of the system may be used. We used this equation since it is solved for x.

The solution is $\left(6, \frac{1}{2}\right)$. Check the solution in both equations of the original system. □

PRACTICE
3   Solve the system: $\begin{cases} x + 3y = 6 \\ 2x + 3y = 10 \end{cases}$

The following steps may be used to solve a system of equations by the substitution method.

Solving a System of Two Linear Equations by the Substitution Method

Step 1.   Solve one of the equations for one of its variables.

Step 2.   Substitute the expression for the variable found in Step 1 into the other equation.

Step 3.   Solve the equation from Step 2 to find the value of one variable.

Step 4.   Substitute the value found in Step 3 in any equation containing both variables to find the value of the other variable.

Step 5.   Check the proposed solution in the original system.

✓CONCEPT CHECK

As you solve the system $\begin{cases} 2x + y = -5 \\ x - y = 5 \end{cases}$ you find that $y = -5$. Is this the solution of the system?

EXAMPLE 4   Solve the system:

$$\begin{cases} 7x - 3y = -14 \\ -3x + y = 6 \end{cases}$$

Solution   To avoid introducing fractions, we will solve the second equation for y.

$$-3x + y = 6 \qquad \text{Second equation}$$
$$y = 3x + 6$$

Next, substitute $3x + 6$ for y in the first equation.

$$7x - 3y = -14 \qquad \text{First equation}$$
$$7x - 3(\overline{3x + 6}) = -14 \qquad \text{Let } y = 3x + 6.$$
$$7x - 9x - 18 = -14 \qquad \text{Use the distributive property.}$$
$$-2x - 18 = -14 \qquad \text{Simplify.}$$
$$-2x = 4 \qquad \text{Add 18 to both sides.}$$
$$x = -2 \qquad \text{Divide both sides by } -2.$$

To find the corresponding y-value, substitute -2 for x in the equation $y = 3x + 6$. Then $y = 3(-2) + 6$ or $y = 0$. The solution of the system is $(-2, 0)$. Check this solution in both equations of the system. ☐

PRACTICE
4   Solve the system:

$$\begin{cases} 5x + 3y = -9 \\ -2x + y = 8 \end{cases}$$

▶ Helpful Hint

When solving a system of equations by the substitution method, begin by solving an equation for one of its variables. If possible, solve for a variable that has a coefficient of 1 or -1. This way, we avoid working with time-consuming fractions.

✓CONCEPT CHECK

To avoid fractions, which of the equations below would you use to solve for x?
   a. $3x - 4y = 15$ **b.** $14 - 3y = 8x$ **c.** $7y + x = 12$

Answers to Concept Check:
1. No, the solution will be an ordered pair.
2. c

EXAMPLE 5   Solve the system:

$$\begin{cases} \dfrac{1}{2}x - y = 3 \\ x = 6 + 2y \end{cases}$$

(Continued on next page)

Solution The second equation is already solved for x in terms of y. Thus we substitute $6 + 2y$ for x in the first equation and solve for y.

$$\frac{1}{2}x - y = 3 \quad \text{First equation}$$

$$\frac{1}{2}(\overbrace{6 + 2y}) - y = 3 \quad \text{Let } x = 6 + 2y.$$

$$3 + y - y = 3 \quad \text{Use the distributive property.}$$

$$3 = 3 \quad \text{Simplify.}$$

Arriving at a true statement such as $3 = 3$ indicates that the two linear equations in the original system are equivalent. This means that their graphs are identical and there is an infinite number of solutions of the system. Any solution of one equation is also a solution of the other. For the solution, we can write "infinite number of solutions" or, in set notation, $\left\{ (x, y) \mid \frac{1}{2}x - y = 3 \right\}$ or $\{(x, y) \mid x = 6 + 2y\}$.

PRACTICE
5   Solve the system:

$$\begin{cases} \frac{1}{4}x - y = 2 \\ x = 4y + 8 \end{cases}$$

EXAMPLE 6   Use substitution to solve the system.

$$\begin{cases} 6x + 12y = 5 \\ -4x - 8y = 0 \end{cases}$$

Solution   Choose the second equation and solve for y.

$$-4x - 8y = 0 \quad \text{Second equation}$$

$$-8y = 4x \quad \text{Add } 4x \text{ to both sides.}$$

$$\frac{-8y}{-8} = \frac{4x}{-8} \quad \text{Divide both sides by } -8.$$

$$y = -\frac{1}{2}x \quad \text{Simplify.}$$

Now replace y with $-\frac{1}{2}x$ in the first equation.

$$6x + 12y = 5 \quad \text{First equation}$$

$$6x + 12\left(-\frac{1}{2}x \right) = 5 \quad \text{Let } y = -\frac{1}{2}x.$$

$$6x + (-6x) = 5 \quad \text{Simplify.}$$

$$0 = 5 \quad \text{Combine like terms.}$$

The false statement $0 = 5$ indicates that this system has no solution and is inconsistent. The graph of the linear equations in the system is a pair of parallel lines. For the solution, we can write "no solution" or, in set notation, write { } or $\varnothing$.

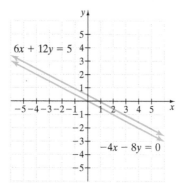

PRACTICE

6   Use substitution to solve the system.

$$\begin{cases} 4x - 3y = 12 \\ -8x + 6y = -30 \end{cases}$$

✓CONCEPT CHECK

Describe how the graphs of the equations in a system appear if the system has
a. no solution
b. one solution
c. an infinite number of solutions

Vocabulary, Readiness & Video Check

Give the solution of each system. If the system has no solution or an infinite number of solutions, say so. If the system has one solution, find it.

1. $\begin{cases} y = 4x \\ -3x + y = 1 \end{cases}$
When solving, you obtain $x = 1$

2. $\begin{cases} 4x - y = 17 \\ -8x + 2y = 0 \end{cases}$
When solving, you obtain $0 = 34$

3. $\begin{cases} 4x - y = 17 \\ -8x + 2y = -34 \end{cases}$
When solving, you obtain $0 = 0$

4. $\begin{cases} 5x + 2y = 25 \\ x = y + 5 \end{cases}$
When solving, you obtain $y = 0$

5. $\begin{cases} x + y = 0 \\ 7x - 7y = 0 \end{cases}$
When solving, you obtain $x = 0$

6. $\begin{cases} y = -2x + 5 \\ 4x + 2y = 10 \end{cases}$
When solving, you obtain $0 = 0$

Martin-Gay Interactive Videos

See Video 4.2

Watch the section lecture video and answer the following question.

OBJECTIVE
1

7. The systems in ▱ Examples 2–4 all need one of their equations solved for a variable as a first step. What important part of the substitution method is emphasized in each example?

4.2 Exercise Set MyMathLab®

Solve each system of equations by the substitution method. See Examples 1 and 2.

1. $\begin{cases} x + y = 3 \\ x = 2y \end{cases}$ **2.** $\begin{cases} x + y = 20 \\ x = 3y \end{cases}$

3. $\begin{cases} x + y = 6 \\ y = -3x \end{cases}$ **4.** $\begin{cases} x + y = 6 \\ y = -4x \end{cases}$

5. $\begin{cases} y = 3x + 1 \\ 4y - 8x = 12 \end{cases}$ **6.** $\begin{cases} y = 2x + 3 \\ 5y - 7x = 18 \end{cases}$

7. $\begin{cases} y = 2x + 9 \\ y = 7x + 10 \end{cases}$ **8.** $\begin{cases} y = 5x - 3 \\ y = 8x + 4 \end{cases}$

MIXED PRACTICE

Solve each system of equations by the substitution method. See Examples 1 through 6.

9. $\begin{cases} 3x - 4y = 10 \\ y = x - 3 \end{cases}$ **10.** $\begin{cases} 4x - 3y = 10 \\ y = x - 5 \end{cases}$

11. $\begin{cases} x + 2y = 6 \\ 2x + 3y = 8 \end{cases}$ **12.** $\begin{cases} x + 3y = -5 \\ 2x + 2y = 6 \end{cases}$

13. $\begin{cases} 3x + 2y = 16 \\ x = 3y - 2 \end{cases}$ **14.** $\begin{cases} 2x + 3y = 18 \\ x = 2y - 5 \end{cases}$

15. $\begin{cases} 2x - 5y = 1 \\ 3x + y = -7 \end{cases}$ **16.** $\begin{cases} 3y - x = 6 \\ 4x + 12y = 0 \end{cases}$

17. $\begin{cases} 4x + 2y = 5 \\ -2x = y + 4 \end{cases}$ **18.** $\begin{cases} 2y = x + 2 \\ 6x - 12y = 0 \end{cases}$

19. $\begin{cases} 4x + y = 11 \\ 2x + 5y = 1 \end{cases}$ **20.** $\begin{cases} 3x + y = -14 \\ 4x + 3y = -22 \end{cases}$

21. $\begin{cases} x + 2y + 5 = -4 + 5y - x \\ \quad\quad 2x + x = y + 4 \end{cases}$
(*Hint:* First simplify each equation.)

22. $\begin{cases} 5x + 4y - 2 = -6 + 7y - 3x \\ \quad\quad 3x + 4x = y + 3 \end{cases}$
(*Hint:* See Exercise 21.)

23. $\begin{cases} 6x - 3y = 5 \\ x + 2y = 0 \end{cases}$ **24.** $\begin{cases} 10x - 5y = -21 \\ x + 3y = 0 \end{cases}$

25. $\begin{cases} 3x - y = 1 \\ 2x - 3y = 10 \end{cases}$ **26.** $\begin{cases} 2x - y = -7 \\ 4x - 3y = -11 \end{cases}$

27. $\begin{cases} -x + 2y = 10 \\ -2x + 3y = 18 \end{cases}$ **28.** $\begin{cases} -x + 3y = 18 \\ -3x + 2y = 19 \end{cases}$

29. $\begin{cases} 5x + 10y = 20 \\ 2x + 6y = 10 \end{cases}$ **30.** $\begin{cases} 6x + 3y = 12 \\ 9x + 6y = 15 \end{cases}$

31. $\begin{cases} 3x + 6y = 9 \\ 4x + 8y = 16 \end{cases}$ **32.** $\begin{cases} 2x + 4y = 6 \\ 5x + 10y = 16 \end{cases}$

33. $\begin{cases} \dfrac{1}{3}x - y = 2 \\ x - 3y = 6 \end{cases}$ **34.** $\begin{cases} \dfrac{1}{4}x - 2y = 1 \\ x - 8y = 4 \end{cases}$

35. $\begin{cases} x = \dfrac{3}{4}y - 1 \\ 8x - 5y = -6 \end{cases}$ **36.** $\begin{cases} x = \dfrac{5}{6}y - 2 \\ 12x - 5y = -9 \end{cases}$

Solve each system by the substitution method. First, simplify each equation by combining like terms.

37. $\begin{cases} -5y + 6y = 3x + 2(x - 5) - 3x + 5 \\ 4(x + y) - x + y = -12 \end{cases}$

38. $\begin{cases} 5x + 2y - 4x - 2y = 2(2y + 6) - 7 \\ 3(2x - y) - 4x = 1 + 9 \end{cases}$

REVIEW AND PREVIEW

Write equivalent equations by multiplying both sides of the given equation by the given nonzero number. See Section 2.2.

39. $3x + 2y = 6$ by -2

40. $-x + y = 10$ by 5

41. $-4x + y = 3$ by 3

42. $5a - 7b = -4$ by -4

Add the expressions by combining any like terms. See Section 2.1.

43. $\begin{array}{r} 3n + 6m \\ \underline{2n - 6m} \end{array}$ **44.** $\begin{array}{r} -2x + 5y \\ \underline{2x + 11y} \end{array}$ **45.** $\begin{array}{r} -5a - 7b \\ \underline{5a - 8b} \end{array}$ **46.** $\begin{array}{r} 9q + p \\ \underline{-9q - p} \end{array}$

CONCEPT EXTENSIONS

47. Explain how to identify a system with no solution when using the substitution method.

48. Occasionally, when using the substitution method, we obtain the equation $0 = 0$. Explain how this result indicates that the graphs of the equations in the system are identical.

Solve. See a Concept Check in this section.

49. As you solve the system $\begin{cases} 3x - y = -6 \\ -3x + 2y = 7 \end{cases}$, you find that $y = 1$. Is this the solution to the system?

50. As you solve the system $\begin{cases} x = 5y \\ y = 2x \end{cases}$, you find that $x = 0$ and $y = 0$. What is the solution to this system?

51. To avoid fractions, which of the equations below would you use if solving for y? Explain why.

a. $\dfrac{1}{2}x - 4y = \dfrac{3}{4}$ **b.** $8x - 5y = 13$

c. $7x - y = 19$

52. Give the number of solutions for a system if the graphs of the equations in the system are

a. lines intersecting in one point

b. parallel lines

c. same line

53. The number of men and women receiving bachelor's degrees each year has been steadily increasing. For the years 1970 through the projection of 2014, the number of men receiving degrees (in thousands) is given by the equation $y = 3.9x + 443$, and for women, the equation is $y = 14.2x + 314$ where x is the number of years after 1970. (*Source:* National Center for Education Statistics)

a. Use the substitution method to solve this system of equations. (Round your final results to the nearest whole numbers.)

b. Explain the meaning of your answer to part (a).

c. Sketch a graph of the system of equations. Write a sentence describing the trends for men and women receiving bachelor's degrees.

54. The number of Adult Contemporary Music radio stations in the United States from 2000 to 2009 is given by the equation $y = -11x + 734$, where x is the number of years after 2000. The number of Spanish radio stations is given by $y = 31x + 542$ for the same time period. (*Source:* M Street Corporation)

a. Use the substitution method to solve this system of equations. (Round your numbers to the nearest tenth.)

b. Explain the meaning of your answer to part (a).

c. Sketch a graph of the system of equations. Write a sentence describing the trends in the popularity of these two types of music formats.

 Solve each system by substitution. When necessary, round answers to the nearest hundredth.

55. $\begin{cases} y = 5.1x + 14.56 \\ y = -2x - 3.9 \end{cases}$

56. $\begin{cases} y = 3.1x - 16.35 \\ y = -9.7x + 28.45 \end{cases}$

57. $\begin{cases} 3x + 2y = 14.05 \\ 5x + y = 18.5 \end{cases}$

58. $\begin{cases} x + y = -15.2 \\ -2x + 5y = -19.3 \end{cases}$

4.3   Solving Systems of Linear Equations by Addition

OBJECTIVE

1 Use the Addition Method to Solve a System of Linear Equations.

OBJECTIVE

1   Using the Addition Method

We have seen that substitution is an accurate way to solve a linear system. Another method for solving a system of equations accurately is the **addition** or **elimination method.** The addition method is based on the addition property of equality: adding equal quantities to both sides of an equation does not change the solution of the equation. In symbols,

$$\text{if } A = B \text{ and } C = D, \text{ then } A + C = B + D.$$

EXAMPLE 1   Solve the system:

$$\begin{cases} x + y = 7 \\ x - y = 5 \end{cases}$$

Solution   Since the left side of each equation is equal to the right side, we add equal quantities by adding the left sides of the equations together and the right sides of the equations together. This adding eliminates the variable y and gives us an equation in one variable, x. We can then solve for x.

> **Helpful Hint**
> Notice in Example 1 that our goal when solving a system of equations by the addition method is to eliminate a variable when adding the equations.

$$
\begin{array}{ll}
x + y = 7 & \text{First equation} \\
\underline{x - y = 5} & \text{Second equation} \\
2x = 12 & \text{Add the equations.} \\
x = 6 & \text{Divide both sides by 2.}
\end{array}
$$

The x-value of the solution is 6. To find the corresponding y-value, let $x = 6$ in either equation of the system. We will use the first equation.

$$
\begin{array}{ll}
x + y = 7 & \text{First equation} \\
6 + y = 7 & \text{Let } x = 6. \\
y = 7 - 6 & \text{Solve for } y. \\
y = 1 & \text{Simplify.}
\end{array}
$$

(Continued on next page)

Check: The solution is $(6, 1)$. Check this in both equations.

<table>
<tr><td align="center">***First Equation***</td><td align="center">***Second Equation***</td></tr>
</table>

$$x + y = 7 \qquad\qquad x - y = 5$$
$$6 + 1 \overset{?}{=} 7 \qquad\qquad 6 - 1 \overset{?}{=} 5 \quad \text{Let } x = 6 \text{ and } y = 1.$$
$$7 = 7 \quad \text{True} \qquad\qquad 5 = 5 \quad \text{True}$$

Thus, the solution of the system is $(6, 1)$ and the graphs of the two equations intersect at the point $(6, 1)$ as shown next.

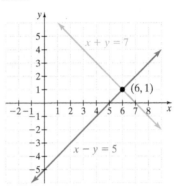

PRACTICE
1 Solve the system: $\begin{cases} x - y = 2 \\ x + y = 8 \end{cases}$

EXAMPLE 2 Solve the system: $\begin{cases} -2x + y = 2 \\ -x + 3y = -4 \end{cases}$

Solution If we simply add the two equations, the result is still an equation in two variables. However, remember from Example 1 that our goal is to eliminate one of the variables. Notice what happens if we multiply *both sides* of the first equation by -3, which we are allowed to do by the multiplication property of equality. The system

$$\begin{cases} -3(-2x + y) = -3(2) \\ -x + 3y = -4 \end{cases} \quad \text{simplifies to} \quad \begin{cases} 6x - 3y = -6 \\ -x + 3y = -4 \end{cases}$$

Now add the resulting equations and the y-variable is eliminated.

$$\begin{aligned} 6x - 3y &= -6 \\ \underline{-x + 3y} &= \underline{-4} \\ 5x \quad\;\; &= -10 \quad \text{Add.} \\ x &= -2 \quad \text{Divide both sides by 5.} \end{aligned}$$

To find the corresponding y-value, let $x = -2$ in any of the preceding equations containing both variables. We use the first equation of the original system.

$$-2x + y = 2 \quad \text{First equation}$$
$$-2(-2) + y = 2 \quad \text{Let } x = -2.$$
$$4 + y = 2$$
$$y = -2 \quad \text{Subtract 4 from both sides.}$$

The solution is $(-2, -2)$. Check this ordered pair in both equations of the original system.

PRACTICE
2 Solve the system: $\begin{cases} x - 2y = 11 \\ 3x - y = 13 \end{cases}$

> ▶ **Helpful Hint**
> When finding the second value of an ordered pair solution, any equation equivalent to one of the original equations in the system may be used.

In Example 2, the decision to multiply the first equation by -3 was no accident. **To eliminate a variable** when adding two equations, **the coefficient of the variable in one equation must be the opposite of its coefficient in the other equation.**

▶ **Helpful Hint**

Be sure to multiply *both sides* of an equation by a chosen number when solving by the addition method. A common mistake is to multiply only the side containing the variables.

EXAMPLE 3   Solve the system: $\begin{cases} 2x - y = 7 \\ 8x - 4y = 1 \end{cases}$

Solution   Multiply both sides of the first equation by -4 and the resulting coefficient of x is -8, the opposite of 8, the coefficient of x in the second equation. The system becomes

▶ **Helpful Hint**

Don't forget to multiply **both** sides by -4.

$$\begin{cases} -4(2x - y) = -4(7) \\ 8x - 4y = 1 \end{cases} \text{ simplifies to } \begin{cases} -8x + 4y = -28 \\ 8x - 4y = 1 \end{cases}$$

Now add the resulting equations.

$$\begin{array}{r} -8x + 4y = -28 \\ \underline{8x - 4y = 1} \quad \text{Add the equations.} \\ 0 = -27 \quad \text{False} \end{array}$$

When we add the equations, both variables are eliminated and we have $0 = -27$, a false statement. This means that the system has no solution. The graphs of these equations are parallel lines. For the solution, we can write "no solution" or, in set notation, $\{\ \}$ or $\varnothing$.   □

PRACTICE
3   Solve the system: $\begin{cases} x - 3y = 5 \\ 2x - 6y = -3 \end{cases}$

EXAMPLE 4   Solve the system: $\begin{cases} 3x - 2y = 2 \\ -9x + 6y = -6 \end{cases}$

Solution   First we multiply both sides of the first equation by 3, then we add the resulting equations.

$$\begin{cases} 3(3x - 2y) = 3(2) \\ -9x + 6y = -6 \end{cases} \text{ simplifies to } \begin{cases} 9x - 6y = 6 \\ \underline{-9x + 6y = -6} \quad \text{Add the equations.} \\ 0 = 0 \quad \text{True} \end{cases}$$

Both variables are eliminated and we have $0 = 0$, a true statement. Whenever you eliminate a variable and get the equation $0 = 0$, the system has an infinite number of solutions. The graphs of these equations are identical. The solution is "infinite number of solutions" or, in set notation, $\{(x, y) \mid 3x - 2y = 2\}$ or $\{(x, y) \mid -9x + 6y = -6\}$ □

PRACTICE
4   Solve the system: $\begin{cases} 4x - 3y = 5 \\ -8x + 6y = -10 \end{cases}$

Answer to Concept Check: **b**

✓**CONCEPT CHECK**

Suppose you are solving the system

$$\begin{cases} 3x + 8y = -5 \\ 2x - 4y = 3 \end{cases}$$

You decide to use the addition method and begin by multiplying both sides of the first equation by -2. In which of the following was the multiplication performed correctly? Explain.

a. $-6x - 16y = -5$ **b.** $-6x - 16y = 10$

EXAMPLE 5   Solve the system: $\begin{cases} 3x + 4y = 13 \\ 5x - 9y = 6 \end{cases}$

Solution   We can eliminate the variable y by multiplying the first equation by 9 and the second equation by 4.

$$\begin{cases} 9(3x + 4y) = 9(13) \\ 4(5x - 9y) = 4(6) \end{cases}$$ simplifies to $\begin{cases} 27x + 36y = 117 \\ 20x - 36y = 24 \end{cases}$

$$\overline{47x = 141}$$ Add the equations.

$$x = 3$$ Divide both sides by 47.

To find the corresponding y-value, we let $x = 3$ in any equation in this example containing two variables. Doing so in any of these equations will give $y = 1$. The solution to this system is $(3, 1)$. Check to see that $(3, 1)$ satisfies each equation in the original system.   □

PRACTICE
5   Solve the system: $\begin{cases} 4x + 3y = 14 \\ 3x - 2y = 2 \end{cases}$

If we had decided to eliminate x instead of y in Example 5, the first equation could have been multiplied by 5 and the second by -3. Try solving the original system this way to check that the solution is $(3, 1)$.

The following steps summarize how to solve a system of linear equations by the addition method.

Solving a System of Two Linear Equations by the Addition Method

Step 1.   Rewrite each equation in standard form $Ax + By = C$.

Step 2.   If necessary, multiply one or both equations by a nonzero number so that the coefficients of a chosen variable in the system are opposites.

Step 3.   Add the equations.

Step 4.   Find the value of one variable by solving the resulting equation from Step 3.

Step 5.   Find the value of the second variable by substituting the value found in Step 4 into either of the original equations.

Step 6.   Check the proposed solution in the original system.

✓CONCEPT CHECK

Suppose you are solving the system

$$\begin{cases} -4x + 7y = 6 \\ x + 2y = 5 \end{cases}$$

by the addition method.
a. What step(s) should you take if you wish to eliminate x when adding the equations?
b. What step(s) should you take if you wish to eliminate y when adding the equations?

EXAMPLE 6   Solve the system: $\begin{cases} -x - \dfrac{y}{2} = \dfrac{5}{2} \\ \dfrac{x}{6} - \dfrac{y}{2} = 0 \end{cases}$

Answers to Concept Check:
a. multiply the second equation by 4
b. possible answer: multiply the first equation by -2 and the second equation by 7

Solution: We begin by clearing each equation of fractions. To do so, we multiply both sides of the first equation by the LCD, 2, and both sides of the second equation by the LCD, 6. Then the system

$$\begin{cases} 2\left(-x - \dfrac{y}{2}\right) = 2\left(\dfrac{5}{2}\right) \\ 6\left(\dfrac{x}{6} - \dfrac{y}{2}\right) = 6(0) \end{cases} \quad \text{simplifies to} \quad \begin{cases} -2x - y = 5 \\ x - 3y = 0 \end{cases}$$

We can now eliminate the variable x by multiplying the second equation by 2.

$$\begin{cases} -2x - y = 5 \\ 2(x - 3y) = 2(0) \end{cases} \quad \text{simplifies to} \quad \begin{cases} -2x - y = 5 \\ \underline{2x - 6y = 0} \end{cases}$$

$$-7y = 5 \quad \text{Add the equations.}$$

$$y = -\frac{5}{7} \quad \text{Solve for } y.$$

To find x, we could replace y with $-\dfrac{5}{7}$ in one of the equations with two variables.

Instead, let's go back to the simplified system and multiply by appropriate factors to eliminate the variable y and solve for x. To do this, we multiply the first equation by -3. Then the system

$$\begin{cases} -3(-2x - y) = -3(5) \\ x - 3y = 0 \end{cases} \quad \text{simplifies to} \quad \begin{cases} 6x + 3y = -15 \\ \underline{x - 3y = 0} \end{cases}$$

$$7x = -15 \quad \text{Add the equations.}$$

$$x = -\frac{15}{7} \quad \text{Solve for } x.$$

Check the ordered pair $\left(-\dfrac{15}{7}, -\dfrac{5}{7}\right)$ in both equations of the original system. The solution is $\left(-\dfrac{15}{7}, -\dfrac{5}{7}\right)$.

PRACTICE
6   Solve the system: $\begin{cases} -2x + \dfrac{3y}{2} = 5 \\ -\dfrac{x}{2} - \dfrac{y}{4} = \dfrac{1}{2} \end{cases}$

Vocabulary, Readiness & Video Check

Given the system $\begin{cases} 3x - 2y = -9 \\ x + 5y = 14 \end{cases}$ *read each row (Step 1, Step 2, and Result). Then answer whether the result is true or false.*

	Step 1	*Step 2*	*Result*	*True or False?*
1.	Multiply 2nd equation through by −3.	Add the resulting equation to the 1st equation.	The y's are eliminated.	
2.	Multiply 2nd equation through by −3.	Add the resulting equation to the 1st equation.	The x's are eliminated.	
3.	Multiply 1st equation by 5 and 2nd equation by 2.	Add the two new equations.	The y's are eliminated.	
4.	Multiply 1st equation by 5 and 2nd equation by −2.	Add the two new equations.	The y's are eliminated.	

Martin-Gay Interactive Videos

Watch the section lecture video and answer the following question.

OBJECTIVE
1

5. For the addition/elimination methods, sometimes you need to multiply an equation through by a nonzero number so that the coefficients of a variable are opposites, as is shown in ▣ Example 2. What property allows us to do this? What important reminder is made at this step?

See Video 4.3 🍎

4.3 Exercise Set   MyMathLab®

Solve each system of equations by the addition method. See Example 1.

1. $\begin{cases} 3x + y = 5 \\ 6x - y = 4 \end{cases}$ **2.** $\begin{cases} 4x + y = 13 \\ 2x - y = 5 \end{cases}$

3. $\begin{cases} x - 2y = 8 \\ -x + 5y = -17 \end{cases}$ **4.** $\begin{cases} x - 2y = -11 \\ -x + 5y = 23 \end{cases}$

Solve each system of equations by the addition method. If a system contains fractions or decimals, you may want to clear each equation of fractions or decimals first. See Examples 2 through 6.

5. $\begin{cases} 3x + y = -11 \\ 6x - 2y = -2 \end{cases}$ **6.** $\begin{cases} 4x + y = -13 \\ 6x - 3y = -15 \end{cases}$

7. $\begin{cases} 3x + 2y = 11 \\ 5x - 2y = 29 \end{cases}$ **8.** $\begin{cases} 4x + 2y = 2 \\ 3x - 2y = 12 \end{cases}$

9. $\begin{cases} x + 5y = 18 \\ 3x + 2y = -11 \end{cases}$ **10.** $\begin{cases} x + 4y = 14 \\ 5x + 3y = 2 \end{cases}$

11. $\begin{cases} x + y = 6 \\ x - y = 6 \end{cases}$ **12.** $\begin{cases} x - y = 1 \\ -x + 2y = 0 \end{cases}$

13. $\begin{cases} 2x + 3y = 0 \\ 4x + 6y = 3 \end{cases}$ **14.** $\begin{cases} 3x + y = 4 \\ 9x + 3y = 6 \end{cases}$

15. $\begin{cases} -x + 5y = -1 \\ 3x - 15y = 3 \end{cases}$ **16.** $\begin{cases} 2x + y = 6 \\ 4x + 2y = 12 \end{cases}$

17. $\begin{cases} 3x - 2y = 7 \\ 5x + 4y = 8 \end{cases}$ **18.** $\begin{cases} 6x - 5y = 25 \\ 4x + 15y = 13 \end{cases}$

19. $\begin{cases} 8x = -11y - 16 \\ 2x + 3y = -4 \end{cases}$ **20.** $\begin{cases} 10x + 3y = -12 \\ 5x = -4y - 16 \end{cases}$

21. $\begin{cases} 4x - 3y = 7 \\ 7x + 5y = 2 \end{cases}$ **22.** $\begin{cases} -2x + 3y = 10 \\ 3x + 4y = 2 \end{cases}$

23. $\begin{cases} 4x - 6y = 8 \\ 6x - 9y = 16 \end{cases}$ **24.** $\begin{cases} 9x - 3y = 12 \\ 12x - 4y = 18 \end{cases}$

25. $\begin{cases} 2x - 5y = 4 \\ 3x - 2y = 4 \end{cases}$ **26.** $\begin{cases} 6x - 5y = 7 \\ 4x - 6y = 7 \end{cases}$

27. $\begin{cases} \dfrac{x}{3} + \dfrac{y}{6} = 1 \\ \dfrac{x}{2} - \dfrac{y}{4} = 0 \end{cases}$ **28.** $\begin{cases} \dfrac{x}{2} + \dfrac{y}{8} = 3 \\ x - \dfrac{y}{4} = 0 \end{cases}$

29. $\begin{cases} \dfrac{10}{3}x + 4y = -4 \\ 5x + 6y = -6 \end{cases}$ **30.** $\begin{cases} \dfrac{3}{2}x + 4y = 1 \\ 9x + 24y = 6 \end{cases}$

31. $\begin{cases} x - \dfrac{y}{3} = -1 \\ -\dfrac{x}{2} + \dfrac{y}{8} = \dfrac{1}{4} \end{cases}$ **32.** $\begin{cases} 2x - \dfrac{3y}{4} = -3 \\ x + \dfrac{y}{9} = \dfrac{13}{3} \end{cases}$

33. $\begin{cases} -4(x + 2) = 3y \\ 2x - 2y = 3 \end{cases}$ **34.** $\begin{cases} -9(x + 3) = 8y \\ 3x - 3y = 8 \end{cases}$

35. $\begin{cases} \dfrac{x}{3} - y = 2 \\ -\dfrac{x}{2} + \dfrac{3y}{2} = -3 \end{cases}$ **36.** $\begin{cases} \dfrac{x}{2} + \dfrac{y}{4} = 1 \\ -\dfrac{x}{4} - \dfrac{y}{8} = 1 \end{cases}$

37. $\begin{cases} \dfrac{3}{5}x - y = -\dfrac{4}{5} \\ 3x + \dfrac{y}{2} = -\dfrac{9}{5} \end{cases}$ **38.** $\begin{cases} 3x + \dfrac{7}{2}y = \dfrac{3}{4} \\ -\dfrac{x}{2} + \dfrac{5}{3}y = -\dfrac{5}{4} \end{cases}$

39. $\begin{cases} 3.5x + 2.5y = 17 \\ -1.5x - 7.5y = -33 \end{cases}$ **40.** $\begin{cases} -2.5x - 6.5y = 47 \\ 0.5x - 4.5y = 37 \end{cases}$

41. $\begin{cases} 0.02x + 0.04y = 0.09 \\ -0.1x + 0.3y = 0.8 \end{cases}$ **42.** $\begin{cases} 0.04x - 0.05y = 0.105 \\ 0.2x - 0.6y = 1.05 \end{cases}$

MIXED PRACTICE

Solve each system by either the addition method or the substitution method.

43. $\begin{cases} 2x - 3y = -11 \\ y = 4x - 3 \end{cases}$ **44.** $\begin{cases} 4x - 5y = 6 \\ y = 3x - 10 \end{cases}$

45. $\begin{cases} x + 2y = 1 \\ 3x + 4y = -1 \end{cases}$ **46.** $\begin{cases} x + 3y = 5 \\ 5x + 6y = -2 \end{cases}$

47. $\begin{cases} 2y = x + 6 \\ 3x - 2y = -6 \end{cases}$ **48.** $\begin{cases} 3y = x + 14 \\ 2x - 3y = -16 \end{cases}$

49. $\begin{cases} y = 2x - 3 \\ y = 5x - 18 \end{cases}$ **50.** $\begin{cases} y = 6x - 5 \\ y = 4x - 11 \end{cases}$

51. $\begin{cases} x + \dfrac{1}{6}y = \dfrac{1}{2} \\ 3x + 2y = 3 \end{cases}$

52. $\begin{cases} x + \dfrac{1}{3}y = \dfrac{5}{12} \\ 8x + 3y = 4 \end{cases}$

53. $\begin{cases} \dfrac{x+2}{2} = \dfrac{y+11}{3} \\ \dfrac{x}{2} = \dfrac{2y+16}{6} \end{cases}$

54. $\begin{cases} \dfrac{2x+5}{2} = \dfrac{4y+14}{4} \\ \dfrac{x}{3} = \dfrac{2y+2}{6} \end{cases}$

55. $\begin{cases} 2x + 3y = 14 \\ 3x - 4y = -69.1 \end{cases}$

56. $\begin{cases} 5x - 2y = -19.8 \\ -3x + 5y = -3.7 \end{cases}$

REVIEW AND PREVIEW

Translating *Rewrite the following sentences using mathematical symbols. Do not solve the equations. See Sections 2.3 and 2.4.*

57. Twice a number, added to 6, is 3 less than the number.

58. The sum of three consecutive integers is 66.

59. Three times a number, subtracted from 20, is 2.

60. Twice the sum of 8 and a number is the difference of the number and 20.

61. The product of 4 and the sum of a number and 6 is twice the number.

62. If the quotient of twice a number and 7 is subtracted from the reciprocal of the number, the result is 2.

CONCEPT EXTENSIONS

Solve. See a Concept Check in this section.

63. To solve this system by the addition method and eliminate the variable y,

$$\begin{cases} 4x + 2y = -7 \\ 3x - y = -12 \end{cases}$$

by what value would you multiply the second equation? What do you get when you complete the multiplication?

64. Given the system of linear equations $\begin{cases} 3x - y = -8 \\ 5x + 3y = 2 \end{cases}$, use the addition method and

a. Solve the system by eliminating x.

b. Solve the system by eliminating y.

65. Suppose you are solving the system $\begin{cases} 3x + 8y = -5 \\ 2x - 4y = 3. \end{cases}$

You decide to use the addition method by multiplying both sides of the second equation by 2. In which of the following was the multiplication performed correctly? Explain.

a. $4x - 8y = 3$

b. $4x - 8y = 6$

66. Suppose you are solving the system $\begin{cases} -2x - y = 0 \\ -2x + 3y = 6. \end{cases}$

You decide to use the addition method by multiplying both sides of the first equation by 3, then adding the resulting equation to the second equation. Which of the following is the correct sum? Explain.

a. $-8x = 6$

b. $-8x = 9$

67. When solving a system of equations by the addition method, how do we know when the system has no solution?

68. Explain why the addition method might be preferred over the substitution method for solving the system $\begin{cases} 2x - 3y = 5 \\ 5x + 2y = 6. \end{cases}$

69. Use the system of linear equations below to answer the questions.

$$\begin{cases} x + y = 5 \\ 3x + 3y = b \end{cases}$$

a. Find the value of b so that the system has an infinite number of solutions.

b. Find a value of b so that there are no solutions to the system.

70. Use the system of linear equations below to answer the questions.

$$\begin{cases} x + y = 4 \\ 2x + by = 8 \end{cases}$$

a. Find the value of b so that the system has an infinite number of solutions.

b. Find a value of b so that the system has a single solution.

Solve each system by the addition method.

71. $\begin{cases} 1.2x + 3.4y = 27.6 \\ 7.2x - 1.7y = -46.56 \end{cases}$

72. $\begin{cases} 5.1x - 2.4y = 3.15 \\ -15.3x + 1.2y = 27.75 \end{cases}$

73. Two age groups predicted to increase in percent of the workforce are those age 25–34 and those age 55 and older. The percent of workers age 25–34 predicted for 2008 through 2018 can be approximated by $0.05x - y = -21.6$. The percent of workers age 55 and older for the same years can be approximated by $0.58x - y = -18.1$. For both equations, x is the number of years since 2008 and y is the percent of the workforce. (*Source:* Bureau of Labor Statistics)

a. Use the addition method to solve the system:

$$\begin{cases} 0.05x - y = -21.6 \\ 0.58x - y = -18.1 \end{cases}$$

(Round answer to the nearest whole.)

b. Use your result from part (a) and estimate the year in which both percents will be the same.

c. Use your results from part (a) and part (b) to estimate the percent of workers age 25–34 and those age 55 and older.

74. Two occupations predicted to greatly increase in the number of jobs are pharmacy technicians and network system analysts. The number of pharmacy technician jobs predicted for 2006 through 2016 can be approximated by $9.1x - y = -295$. The number of network system analyst jobs predicted for 2006 through 2016 can be approximated by $14x - y = -262$. For both equations, x is the number of years since 2006, and y is the number of jobs in the thousands. (*Source:* Bureau of Labor Statistics)

a. Use the addition method to solve this system of equations.

$$\begin{cases} 9.1x - y = -295 \\ 14x - y = -262 \end{cases}$$

(Eliminate y first and solve for x. Round this result to the nearest whole.)

b. Interpret your solution from part (a).

c. Using the year in your answer to part (b), estimate the number of pharmacy technician jobs and network system analyst jobs in that year.

(**Integrated Review**) SOLVING SYSTEMS OF EQUATIONS

Sections 4.1–4.3

Solve each system by either the addition method or the substitution method.

1. $\begin{cases} 2x - 3y = -11 \\ y = 4x - 3 \end{cases}$

2. $\begin{cases} 4x - 5y = 6 \\ y = 3x - 10 \end{cases}$

3. $\begin{cases} x + y = 3 \\ x - y = 7 \end{cases}$

4. $\begin{cases} x - y = 20 \\ x + y = -8 \end{cases}$

5. $\begin{cases} x + 2y = 1 \\ 3x + 4y = -1 \end{cases}$

6. $\begin{cases} x + 3y = 5 \\ 5x + 6y = -2 \end{cases}$

7. $\begin{cases} y = x + 3 \\ 3x - 2y = -6 \end{cases}$

8. $\begin{cases} y = -2x \\ 2x - 3y = -16 \end{cases}$

9. $\begin{cases} y = 2x - 3 \\ y = 5x - 18 \end{cases}$

10. $\begin{cases} y = 6x - 5 \\ y = 4x - 11 \end{cases}$

11. $\begin{cases} x + \dfrac{1}{6}y = \dfrac{1}{2} \\ 3x + 2y = 3 \end{cases}$

12. $\begin{cases} x + \dfrac{1}{3}y = \dfrac{5}{12} \\ 8x + 3y = 4 \end{cases}$

13. $\begin{cases} x - 5y = 1 \\ -2x + 10y = 3 \end{cases}$

14. $\begin{cases} -x + 2y = 3 \\ 3x - 6y = -9 \end{cases}$

15. $\begin{cases} 0.2x - 0.3y = -0.95 \\ 0.4x + 0.1y = 0.55 \end{cases}$

16. $\begin{cases} 0.08x - 0.04y = -0.11 \\ 0.02x - 0.06y = -0.09 \end{cases}$

17. $\begin{cases} x = 3y - 7 \\ 2x - 6y = -14 \end{cases}$

18. $\begin{cases} y = \dfrac{x}{2} - 3 \\ 2x - 4y = 0 \end{cases}$

19. $\begin{cases} 2x + 5y = -1 \\ 3x - 4y = 33 \end{cases}$

20. $\begin{cases} 7x - 3y = 2 \\ 6x + 5y = -21 \end{cases}$

21. Which method, substitution or addition, would you prefer to use to solve the system below? Explain your reasoning.

$$\begin{cases} 3x + 2y = -2 \\ y = -2x \end{cases}$$

22. Which method, substitution or addition, would you prefer to use to solve the system below? Explain your reasoning.

$$\begin{cases} 3x - 2y = -3 \\ 6x + 2y = 12 \end{cases}$$

Factoring Polynomials

As shown on the circle graph below, games and music are the leading moneymakers in the digital market. Record companies' revenue from digital music channels grew 6% in a recent year to total $4.6 billion in the United States alone. From 2004 to 2010, the digital music market increased 1000%.

In Section 6.1, Exercise 109, we explore digital music downloads further.

In Chapter 5, you learned how to multiply polynomials. This chapter deals with an operation that is the reverse process of multiplying, called *factoring*. Factoring is an important algebraic skill because this process allows us to write a sum as a product.

At the end of this chapter, we use factoring to help us solve equations other than linear equations, and in Chapter 7, we use factoring to simplify and perform arithmetic operations on rational expressions.

Global Digital Revenues

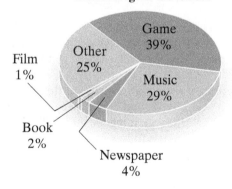

Game 39%
Other 25%
Music 29%
Film 1%
Book 2%
Newspaper 4%

Data from NPD Group; Pollstar; Recording Industry Association of America (RIAA); U.S. Department of Labor; and Tera Consultants

6.1 The Greatest Common Factor and Factoring by Grouping

In the product $2 \cdot 3 = 6$, the numbers 2 and 3 are called **factors** of 6 and $2 \cdot 3$ is a **factored form** of 6. This is true of polynomials also. Since $(x + 2)(x + 3) = x^2 + 5x + 6$, $(x + 2)$ and $(x + 3)$ are factors of $x^2 + 5x + 6$, and $(x + 2)(x + 3)$ is a factored form of the polynomial.

a factored form of 6

$$\underset{\text{factor}}{2} \cdot \underset{\text{factor}}{3} = \underset{\text{product}}{6}$$

a factored form of x^5

$$\underset{\text{factor}}{x^2} \cdot \underset{\text{factor}}{x^3} = \underset{\text{product}}{x^5}$$

a factored form of $x^2 + 5x + 6$

$$\underset{\text{factor}}{(x + 2)} \underset{\text{factor}}{(x + 3)} = \underset{\text{product}}{x^2 + 5x + 6}$$

The process of writing a polynomial as a product is called **factoring** the polynomial.

Do you see that factoring is the reverse process of multiplying?

$$x^2 + 5x + 6 = (x + 2)(x + 3)$$

factoring →
← multiplying

✓ CONCEPT CHECK

Multiply: $2(x - 4)$

What do you think the result of factoring $2x - 8$ would be? Why?

OBJECTIVE

1 Finding the Greatest Common Factor of a List of Integers

The first step in factoring a polynomial is to see whether the terms of the polynomial have a common factor. If there is one, we can write the polynomial as a product by **factoring out** the common factor. We will usually factor out the **greatest common factor (GCF).**

The GCF of a list of integers is the largest integer that is a factor of all the integers in the list. For example, the GCF of 12 and 20 is 4 because 4 is the largest integer that is a factor of both 12 and 20. With large integers, the GCF may not be found easily by inspection. When this happens, use the following steps.

Finding the GCF of a List of Integers

Step 1. Write each number as a product of prime numbers.

Step 2. Identify the common prime factors.

Step 3. The product of all common prime factors found in Step 2 is the greatest common factor. If there are no common prime factors, the greatest common factor is 1.

Recall from Section 1.3 that a prime number is a whole number other than 1 whose only factors are 1 and itself.

EXAMPLE 1   Find the GCF of each list of numbers.

a. 28 and 40   **b.** 55 and 21   **c.** 15, 18, and 66

Solution

a. Write each number as a product of primes.

$$28 = 2 \cdot 2 \cdot 7 = 2^2 \cdot 7$$
$$40 = 2 \cdot 2 \cdot 2 \cdot 5 = 2^3 \cdot 5$$

There are two common factors, each of which is 2, so the GCF is

$$\text{GCF} = 2 \cdot 2 = 4$$

b. $55 = 5 \cdot 11$

$21 = 3 \cdot 7$

There are no common prime factors; thus, the GCF is 1.

c. $15 = 3 \cdot 5$

$18 = 2 \cdot 3 \cdot 3 = 2 \cdot 3^2$

$66 = 2 \cdot 3 \cdot 11$

The only prime factor common to all three numbers is 3, so the GCF is

$$\text{GCF} = 3$$

PRACTICE

1   Find the GCF of each list of numbers.

a. 36 and 42   **b.** 35 and 44   **c.** 12, 16, and 40

OBJECTIVE

2   **Finding the Greatest Common Factor of a List of Terms**

The greatest common factor of a list of variables raised to powers is found in a similar way. For example, the GCF of x^2, x^3, and x^5 is x^2 because each term contains a factor of x^2 and no higher power of x is a factor of each term.

$$x^2 = x \cdot x$$
$$x^3 = x \cdot x \cdot x$$
$$x^5 = x \cdot x \cdot x \cdot x \cdot x$$

There are two common factors, each of which is x, so the GCF $= x \cdot x$ or x^2.

From this example, we see that **the GCF of a list of common variables raised to powers is the variable raised to the smallest exponent in the list.**

EXAMPLE 2   Find the GCF of each list of terms.

a. x^3, x^7, and x^5 **b.** y, y^4, and y^7

Solution

a. The GCF is x^3, since 3 is the smallest exponent to which x is raised.

b. The GCF is y^1 or y, since 1 is the smallest exponent on y.

PRACTICE

2   Find the GCF of each list of terms.

a. y^7, y^4, and y^6 **b.** x, x^4, and x^2

In general, the **greatest common factor (GCF) of a list of terms** is the product of the GCF of the numerical coefficients and the GCF of the variable factors.

$$20x^2y^2 = 2 \cdot 2 \cdot 5 \cdot x \cdot x \cdot y \cdot y$$
$$6xy^3 = 2 \cdot 3 \cdot x \cdot y \cdot y \cdot y$$
$$\text{GCF} = 2 \cdot x \cdot y \cdot y = 2xy^2$$

> ▌ Helpful Hint
>
> Remember that the GCF of a list of terms contains the smallest exponent on each common variable.
>
> The GCF of x^5y^6, x^2y^7, and x^3y^4 is x^2y^4. ⎯⎯⎯ Smallest exponent on x
> ⎯⎯⎯ Smallest exponent on y

EXAMPLE 3 Find the GCF of each list of terms.

a. $6x^2$, $10x^3$, and $-8x$ **b.** $-18y^2$, $-63y^3$, and $27y^4$ **c.** a^3b^2, a^5b, and a^6b^2

Solution

a.
$$\left. \begin{array}{l} 6x^2 = 2 \cdot 3 \cdot x^2 \\ 10x^3 = 2 \cdot 5 \cdot x^3 \\ -8x = -1 \cdot 2 \cdot 2 \cdot 2 \cdot x^1 \end{array} \right\} \rightarrow \text{The GCF of } x^2, x^3, \text{ and } x^1 \text{ is } x^1 \text{ or } x.$$
$$\text{GCF} = 2 \cdot x^1 \quad \text{or} \quad 2x$$

b.
$$\left. \begin{array}{l} -18y^2 = -1 \cdot 2 \cdot 3 \cdot 3 \cdot y^2 \\ -63y^3 = -1 \cdot 3 \cdot 3 \cdot 7 \cdot y^3 \\ 27y^4 = 3 \cdot 3 \cdot 3 \cdot y^4 \end{array} \right\} \rightarrow \text{The GCF of } y^2, y^3, \text{ and } y^4 \text{ is } y^2.$$
$$\text{GCF} = 3 \cdot 3 \cdot y^2 \quad \text{or} \quad 9y^2$$

c. The GCF of a^3, a^5, and a^6 is a^3.

The GCF of b^2, b, and b^2 is b.

Thus, the GCF of a^3b^2, a^5b, and a^6b^2 is a^3b.

□

PRACTICE

3 Find the GCF of each list of terms.

a. $5y^4$, $15y^2$, and $-20y^3$ **b.** $4x^2$, x^3, and $3x^8$ **c.** a^4b^2, a^3b^5, and a^2b^3

OBJECTIVE

3 Factoring Out the Greatest Common Factor

The first step in factoring a polynomial is to find the GCF of its terms. Once we do so, we can write the polynomial as a product by **factoring out** the GCF.

The polynomial $8x + 14$, for example, contains two terms: $8x$ and 14. The GCF of these terms is 2. We factor out 2 from each term by writing each term as a product of 2 and the term's remaining factors.

$$8x + 14 = 2 \cdot 4x + 2 \cdot 7$$

Using the distributive property, we can write

$$8x + 14 = 2 \cdot 4x + 2 \cdot 7$$
$$= 2(4x + 7)$$

Thus, a factored form of $8x + 14$ is $2(4x + 7)$. We can check by multiplying:

$$2(4x + 7) = 2 \cdot 4x + 2 \cdot 7 = 8x + 14.$$

> ▌ Helpful Hint
>
> A factored form of $8x + 14$ is *not*
>
> $$2 \cdot 4x + 2 \cdot 7$$
>
> Although the *terms* have been factored (written as a product), the *polynomial* $8x + 14$ has not been factored (written as a product).
>
> A factored form of $8x + 14$ is the *product* $2(4x + 7)$.

Which of the following is/are factored form(s) of $7t + 21$?

   a. 7   **b.** $7 \cdot t + 7 \cdot 3$ **c.** $7(t + 3)$ **d.** $7(t + 21)$

EXAMPLE 4   Factor each polynomial by factoring out the GCF.

a. $6t + 18$ **b.** $y^5 - y^7$

Solution

a. The GCF of terms $6t$ and 18 is 6.

$$6t + 18 = 6 \cdot t + 6 \cdot 3$$
$$= 6(t + 3)\quad\text{Apply the distributive property.}$$

Our work can be checked by multiplying 6 and $(t + 3)$.

$$6(t + 3) = 6 \cdot t + 6 \cdot 3 = 6t + 18, \text{ the original polynomial.}$$

b. The GCF of y^5 and y^7 is y^5. Thus,

$$y^5 - y^7 = y^5(1) - y^5(y^2)$$
$$= y^5(1 - y^2)$$

> **Helpful Hint**
> Don't forget the 1.

PRACTICE

4   Factor each polynomial by factoring out the GCF.

a. $4t + 12$ **b.** $y^8 + y^4$

EXAMPLE 5   Factor: $-9a^5 + 18a^2 - 3a$

Solution

$$-9a^5 + 18a^2 - 3a = (3a)(-3a^4) + (3a)(6a) + (3a)(-1)$$
$$= 3a(-3a^4 + 6a - 1)$$

> **Helpful Hint**
> Don't forget the -1.

PRACTICE

5   Factor $-8b^6 + 16b^4 - 8b^2$.

In Example 5, we could have chosen to factor out a $-3a$ instead of $3a$. If we factor out a $-3a$, we have

$$-9a^5 + 18a^2 - 3a = (-3a)(3a^4) + (-3a)(-6a) + (-3a)(1)$$
$$= -3a(3a^4 - 6a + 1)$$

> **Helpful Hint**
> Notice the changes in signs when factoring out $-3a$.

EXAMPLES   Factor.

6. $6a^4 - 12a = 6a(a^3 - 2)$

7. $\dfrac{3}{7}x^4 + \dfrac{1}{7}x^3 - \dfrac{5}{7}x^2 = \dfrac{1}{7}x^2(3x^2 + x - 5)$

8. $15p^2q^4 + 20p^3q^5 + 5p^3q^3 = 5p^2q^3(3q + 4pq^2 + p)$

PRACTICES

6–8   Factor.

6. $5x^4 - 20x$ **7.** $\dfrac{5}{9}z^5 + \dfrac{1}{9}z^4 - \dfrac{2}{9}z^3$ **8.** $8a^2b^4 - 20a^3b^3 + 12ab^3$

EXAMPLE 9   Factor: $5(x + 3) + y(x + 3)$

Solution   The binomial $(x + 3)$ is the greatest common factor. Use the distributive property to factor out $(x + 3)$.

$$5(x + 3) + y(x + 3) = (x + 3)(5 + y)$$

□

PRACTICE
9   Factor $8(y - 2) + x(y - 2)$.

EXAMPLE 10   Factor: $3m^2n(a + b) - (a + b)$

Solution   The greatest common factor is $(a + b)$.

$$3m^2n(a + b) - 1(a + b) = (a + b)(3m^2n - 1)$$

□

PRACTICE
10   Factor $7xy^3(p + q) - (p + q)$

OBJECTIVE
4   Factoring by Grouping ▶

Once the GCF is factored out, we can often continue to factor the polynomial, using a variety of techniques. We discuss here a technique for factoring polynomials called **factoring by grouping.**

EXAMPLE 11   Factor $xy + 2x + 3y + 6$ by grouping. Check by multiplying.

Solution   The GCF of the first two terms is x, and the GCF of the last two terms is 3.

$$xy + 2x + 3y + 6 = (xy + 2x) + (3y + 6) \quad \text{Group terms.}$$
$$= x(y + 2) + 3(y + 2) \quad \text{Factor out GCF from each grouping.}$$

> ▶ **Helpful Hint**
> Notice that this form, $x(y + 2) + 3(y + 2)$, is *not* a factored form of the original polynomial. It is a sum, not a product.

Next we factor out the common binomial factor, $(y + 2)$.

$$x(y + 2) + 3(y + 2) = (y + 2)(x + 3)$$

Now the result is a factored form because it is a product. We were able to write the polynomial as a product because of the common binomial factor, $(y + 2)$, that appeared. If this does not happen, try rearranging the terms of the original polynomial.

Check: Multiply $(y + 2)$ by $(x + 3)$.

$$(y + 2)(x + 3) = xy + 2x + 3y + 6,$$

the original polynomial.
Thus, the factored form of $xy + 2x + 3y + 6$ is the product $(y + 2)(x + 3)$.

□

PRACTICE
11   Factor $xy + 3y + 4x + 12$ by grouping. Check by multiplying.

You may want to try these steps when factoring by grouping.

To Factor a Four-Term Polynomial by Grouping

Step 1.   Group the terms in two groups of two terms so that each group has a common factor.

Step 2.   Factor out the GCF from each group.

Step 3.   If there is now a common binomial factor in the groups, factor it out.

Step 4.   If not, rearrange the terms and try these steps again.

EXAMPLES   Factor by grouping.

12. $15x^3 - 10x^2 + 6x - 4$

$\quad = (15x^3 - 10x^2) + (6x - 4)$ Group the terms.

$\quad = 5x^2(3x - 2) + 2(3x - 2)$ Factor each group.

$\quad = (3x - 2)(5x^2 + 2)$ Factor out the common factor, $(3x - 2)$.

13. $3x^2 + 4xy - 3x - 4y$

$\quad = (3x^2 + 4xy) + (-3x - 4y)$

$\quad = x(3x + 4y) - 1(3x + 4y)$ Factor each group. A -1 is factored from the second pair of terms so that there is a common factor, $(3x + 4y)$.

$\quad = (3x + 4y)(x - 1)$ Factor out the common factor, $(3x + 4y)$.

14. $2a^2 + 5ab + 2a + 5b$

$\quad = (2a^2 + 5ab) + (2a + 5b)$ Factor each group. An understood 1 is written before $(2a + 5b)$ to help remember that $(2a + 5b)$ is $1(2a + 5b)$.

$\quad = a(2a + 5b) + 1(2a + 5b)$

$\quad = (2a + 5b)(a + 1)$ Factor out the common factor, $(2a + 5b)$.   □

> ▶ **Helpful Hint**
> Notice the factor of 1 is written when $(2a + 5b)$ is factored out.

PRACTICES
12–14

12. Factor $40x^3 - 24x^2 + 15x - 9$ by grouping.

13. Factor $2xy + 3y^2 - 2x - 3y$ by grouping.

14. Factor $7a^3 + 5a^2 + 7a + 5$ by grouping.

EXAMPLES   Factor by grouping.

15. $3xy + 2 - 3x - 2y$

Notice that the first two terms have no common factor other than 1. However, if we rearrange these terms, a grouping emerges that does lead to a common factor.

$\quad 3xy + 2 - 3x - 2y$

$\quad = (3xy - 3x) + (-2y + 2)$

$\quad = 3x(y - 1) - 2(y - 1)$ Factor -2 from the second group so that there is a common factor, $(y - 1)$.

$\quad = (y - 1)(3x - 2)$ Factor out the common factor, $(y - 1)$.

16. $5x - 10 + x^3 - x^2 = 5(x - 2) + x^2(x - 1)$

There is no common binomial factor that can now be factored out. No matter how we rearrange the terms, no grouping will lead to a common factor. Thus, this polynomial is not factorable by grouping.   □

PRACTICES
15–16

15. Factor $4xy + 15 - 12x - 5y$ by grouping.

16. Factor $9y - 18 + y^3 - 4y^2$ by grouping.

> ▶ **Helpful Hint**
> One more reminder: When **factoring** a polynomial, make sure the polynomial is written as a **product.** For example, it is true that
> $$3x^2 + 4xy - 3x - 4y = \underline{x(3x + 4y) - 1(3x + 4y)},$$
> but is not a factored form
>
> since it is a **sum (difference),** not a **product.** A factored form of $3x^2 + 4xy - 3x - 4y$ is the product $(3x + 4y)(x - 1)$.

Factoring out a greatest common factor first makes factoring by any method easier, as we see in the next example.

EXAMPLE 17 Factor: $4ax - 4ab - 2bx + 2b^2$

Solution First, factor out the common factor 2 from all four terms.

$$4ax - 4ab - 2bx + 2b^2$$
$$= 2(2ax - 2ab - bx + b^2) \qquad \text{Factor out 2 from all four terms.}$$
$$= 2[2a(x - b) - b(x - b)] \qquad \text{Factor each pair of terms. A "}-b\text{" is factored from the}$$
$$\qquad\qquad\qquad\qquad\qquad\qquad \text{second pair so that there is a common factor, } x - b.$$
$$= 2(x - b)(2a - b) \qquad \text{Factor out the common binomial.} \qquad \square$$

> ▶ **Helpful Hint**
> Throughout this chapter, we will be factoring polynomials. Even when the instructions do not so state, it is always a good idea to check your answers by multiplying.

PRACTICE
17 Factor $3xy - 3ay - 6ax + 6a^2$.

Vocabulary, Readiness & Video Check

Use the choices below to fill in each blank. Some choices may be used more than once and some may not be used at all.

greatest common factor   factors   factoring   true   false   least   greatest

1. Since $5 \cdot 4 = 20$, the numbers 5 and 4 are called _____ of 20.
2. The _____ of a list of integers is the largest integer that is a factor of all the integers in the list.
3. The greatest common factor of a list of common variables raised to powers is the variable raised to the _____ exponent in the list.
4. The process of writing a polynomial as a product is called _____.
5. True or false: A factored form of $7x + 21 + xy + 3y$ is $7(x + 3) + y(x + 3)$. _____
6. True or false: A factored form of $3x^3 + 6x + x^2 + 2$ is $3x(x^2 + 2)$. _____

Martin-Gay Interactive Videos

See Video 6.1

Watch the section lecture video and answer the following questions.

OBJECTIVE
1   7. Based on ▣ Example 1, give a general definition for the greatest common factor (GCF) of a list of numbers.

OBJECTIVE
2   8. In ▣ Example 3, why are the numbers factored out, but not the variables?

OBJECTIVE
3   9. From ▣ Example 5, how can the number of terms in the other factor, once you factor out the GCF, help you determine if your factorization is correct?

OBJECTIVE
4   10. In ▣ Examples 7 and 8, what are you reminded to always do first when factoring a polynomial? Also, explain how a polynomial looks if it suggests it might be factored by grouping.

6.1 Exercise Set

Find the GCF for each list. See Examples 1 through 3.

1. $32, 36$
2. $36, 90$
3. $18, 42, 84$
4. $30, 75, 135$
5. $24, 14, 21$
6. $15, 25, 27$
7. y^2, y^4, y^7
8. x^3, x^2, x^5
9. z^7, z^9, z^{11}
10. y^8, y^{10}, y^{12}
11. $x^{10}y^2, xy^2, x^3y^3$
12. p^7q, p^8q^2, p^9q^3
13. $14x, 21$
14. $20y, 15$
15. $12y^4, 20y^3$
16. $32x^5, 18x^2$
17. $-10x^2, 15x^3$
18. $-21x^3, 14x$
19. $12x^3, -6x^4, 3x^5$
20. $15y^2, 5y^7, -20y^3$

21. $-18x^2y, 9x^3y^3, 36x^3y$

22. $7x^3y^3, -21x^2y^2, 14xy^4$

23. $20a^6b^2c^8, 50a^7b$

24. $40x^7y^2z, 64x^9y$

Factor out the GCF from each polynomial. See Examples 4 through 10.

25. $3a + 6$

26. $18a + 12$

27. $30x - 15$

28. $42x - 7$

29. $x^3 + 5x^2$

30. $y^5 + 6y^4$

31. $6y^4 + 2y^3$

32. $5x^2 + 10x^6$

33. $4x - 8y + 4$

34. $7x + 21y - 7$

35. $6x^3 - 9x^2 + 12x$

36. $12x^3 + 16x^2 - 8x$

37. $a^7b^6 - a^3b^2 + a^2b^5 - a^2b^2$

38. $x^9y^6 + x^3y^5 - x^4y^3 + x^3y^3$

39. $8x^5 + 16x^4 - 20x^3 + 12$

40. $9y^6 - 27y^4 + 18y^2 + 6$

41. $\frac{1}{3}x^4 + \frac{2}{3}x^3 - \frac{4}{3}x^5 + \frac{1}{3}x$

42. $\frac{2}{5}y^7 - \frac{4}{5}y^5 + \frac{3}{5}y^2 - \frac{2}{5}y$

43. $y(x^2 + 2) + 3(x^2 + 2)$

44. $x(y^2 + 1) - 3(y^2 + 1)$

45. $z(y + 4) - 3(y + 4)$

46. $8(x + 2) - y(x + 2)$

47. $r(z^2 - 6) + (z^2 - 6)$

48. $q(b^3 - 5) + (b^3 - 5)$

Factor a negative number or a GCF with a negative coefficient from each polynomial. See Example 5.

49. $-2x - 14$

50. $-7y - 21$

51. $-2x^5 + x^7$

52. $-5y^3 + y^6$

53. $-6a^4 + 9a^3 - 3a^2$

54. $-5m^6 + 10m^5 - 5m^3$

Factor each four-term polynomial by grouping. If this is not possible, write "not factorable by grouping." See Examples 11 through 17.

55. $x^3 + 2x^2 + 5x + 10$

56. $x^3 + 4x^2 + 3x + 12$

57. $5x + 15 + xy + 3y$

58. $xy + y + 2x + 2$

59. $6x^3 - 4x^2 + 15x - 10$

60. $16x^3 - 28x^2 + 12x - 21$

61. $5m^3 + 6mn + 5m^2 + 6n$

62. $8w^2 + 7wv + 8w + 7v$

63. $2y - 8 + xy - 4x$

64. $6x - 42 + xy - 7y$

65. $2x^3 - x^2 + 8x - 4$

66. $2x^3 - x^2 - 10x + 5$

67. $3x - 3 + x^3 - 4x^2$

68. $7x - 21 + x^3 - 2x^2$

69. $4x^2 - 8xy - 3x + 6y$

70. $5xy - 15x - 6y + 18$

71. $5q^2 - 4pq - 5q + 4p$

72. $6m^2 - 5mn - 6m + 5n$

73. $2x^4 + 5x^3 + 2x^2 + 5x$

74. $4y^4 + y^2 + 20y^3 + 5y$

75. $12x^2y - 42x^2 - 4y + 14$

76. $90 + 15y^2 - 18x - 3xy^2$

MIXED PRACTICE

Factor. See Examples 4 through 17.

77. $32xy - 18x^2$

78. $10xy - 15x^2$

79. $y(x + 2) - 3(x + 2)$

80. $z(y - 4) + 3(y - 4)$

81. $14x^3y + 7x^2y - 7xy$

82. $5x^3y - 15x^2y + 10xy$

83. $28x^3 - 7x^2 + 12x - 3$

84. $15x^3 + 5x^2 - 6x - 2$

85. $-40x^8y^6 - 16x^9y^5$

86. $-21x^3y - 49x^2y^2$

87. $6a^2 + 9ab^2 + 6ab + 9b^3$

88. $16x^2 + 4xy^2 + 8xy + 2y^3$

REVIEW AND PREVIEW

Multiply. See Section 5.3.

89. $(x + 2)(x + 5)$

90. $(y + 3)(y + 6)$

91. $(b + 1)(b - 4)$

92. $(x - 5)(x + 10)$

Fill in the chart by finding two numbers that have the given product and sum. The first column is filled in for you.

	93.	94.	95.	96.	97.	98.
Two Numbers	4, 7					
Their Product	28	12	20	8	16	−10	−24
Their Sum	11	8	9	−9	−10	3	−5

CONCEPT EXTENSIONS

See the Concept Checks in this section.

99. Which of the following is/are factored form(s) of $8a - 24$?

    a. $8 \cdot a - 24$ **b.** $8(a - 3)$

    c. $4(2a - 12)$ **d.** $8 \cdot a - 2 \cdot 12$

100. Which of the following is/are factored form(s) of $-2x + 14$?

    a. $-2(x + 7)$ **b.** $-2 \cdot x + 14$

    c. $-2(x - 14)$ **d.** $-2(x - 7)$

Determine whether the following expressions are factored.

101. $(a + 6)(a + 2)$

102. $(x + 5)(x + y)$

103. $5(2y + z) - b(2y + z)$

104. $3x(a + 2b) + 2(a + 2b)$

105. Construct a binomial whose greatest common factor is $5a^3$. (*Hint:* Multiply $5a^3$ by a binomial whose terms contain no common factor other than 1. $5a^3(\square + \square)$.)

106. Construct a trinomial whose greatest common factor is $2x^2$. See the hint for Exercise 105.

107. Explain how you can tell whether a polynomial is written in factored form.

108. Construct a four-term polynomial that can be factored by grouping.

109. The number (in millions) of single digital downloads annually in the United States each year during 2004–2010 can be modeled by the polynomial $-20x^2 + 300x + 120$, where x is the number of years since 2004. (*Source:* Recording Industry Association of America)

   a. Find the number of single digital downloads in 2010. To do so, let $x = 6$ and evaluate $-20x^2 + 300x + 120$.

   b. Use this expression to predict the number of single digital downloads in 2014.

   c. Factor the polynomial $-20x^2 + 300x + 120$ by factoring -20 from each term.

110. The number (in thousands) of students who graduated from U.S. public high schools each year during 2000–2009 can be modeled by $0.8x^2 + 44x + 2552$, where x is the number of years since 2000. (*Source:* Digest of Education Statistics)

   a. Find the number of students who graduated from U.S. high schools in 2005. To do so, let $x = 5$ and evaluate $0.8x^2 + 44x + 2552$.

   b. Use this expression to predict the number of students who will graduate from U.S. high schools in 2015.

   c. Factor the polynomial $0.8x^2 + 44x + 2552$ by factoring out 0.8 from each term.

Write an expression for the area of each shaded region. Then write the expression as a factored polynomial.

△ **111.**

△ **112.**

*Write an expression for the length of each rectangle. (**Hint:** Factor the area binomial and recall that Area = width · length.)*

△ **113.**   △ **114.**

Factor each polynomial by grouping.

115. $x^{2n} + 2x^n + 3x^n + 6$
   (**Hint:** Don't forget that $x^{2n} = x^n \cdot x^n$.)

116. $x^{2n} + 6x^n + 10x^n + 60$

117. $3x^{2n} + 21x^n - 5x^n - 35$

118. $12x^{2n} - 10x^n - 30x^n + 25$

6.2 | Factoring Trinomials of the Form $x^2 + bx + c$

OBJECTIVES

1 Factor Trinomials of the Form $x^2 + bx + c$.

2 Factor Out the Greatest Common Factor and Then Factor a Trinomial of the Form $x^2 + bx + c$.

OBJECTIVE

1 Factoring Trinomials of the Form $x^2 + bx + c$

In this section, we factor trinomials of the form $x^2 + bx + c$, such as

$$x^2 + 4x + 3, \quad x^2 - 8x + 15, \quad x^2 + 4x - 12, \quad r^2 - r - 42$$

Notice that for these trinomials, the coefficient of the squared variable is 1.

   Recall that factoring means to write as a product and that factoring and multiplying are reverse processes. Using the FOIL method of multiplying binomials, we have that

$$\overset{\text{F\quad O\quad I\quad L}}{(x + 3)(x + 1)} = x^2 + 1x + 3x + 3$$
$$= x^2 + 4x + 3$$

Thus, a factored form of $x^2 + 4x + 3$ is $(x + 3)(x + 1)$.

Notice that the product of the first terms of the binomials is $x \cdot x = x^2$, the first term of the trinomial. Also, the product of the last two terms of the binomials is $3 \cdot 1 = 3$, the third term of the trinomial. The sum of these same terms is $3 + 1 = 4$, the coefficient of the middle term, x, of the trinomial.

The product of these numbers is 3.

$$x^2 + 4x + 3 = (x + 3)(x + 1)$$

The sum of these numbers is 4.

Many trinomials, such as the one above, factor into two binomials. To factor $x^2 + 7x + 10$, let's assume that it factors into two binomials and begin by writing two pairs of parentheses. The first term of the trinomial is x^2, so we use x and x as the first terms of the binomial factors.

$$x^2 + 7x + 10 = (x + \square)(x + \square)$$

To determine the last term of each binomial factor, we look for two integers whose product is 10 and whose sum is 7. Since our numbers must have a positive product and a positive sum, we list pairs of positive integer factors of 10 only.

Positive Factors of 10	Sum of Factors
1, 10	$1 + 10 = 11$
2, 5	$2 + 5 = 7$

The correct pair of numbers is 2 and 5 because their product is 10 and their sum is 7. Now we can fill in the last terms of the binomial factors.

$$x^2 + 7x + 10 = (x + 2)(x + 5)$$

Check: To see if we have factored correctly, multiply.

$$(x + 2)(x + 5) = x^2 + 5x + 2x + 10$$
$$= x^2 + 7x + 10 \qquad \text{Combine like terms.}$$

> ▶ Helpful Hint
>
> Since multiplication is commutative, the factored form of $x^2 + 7x + 10$ can be written as either $(x + 2)(x + 5)$ or $(x + 5)(x + 2)$.

Factoring a Trinomial of the Form $x^2 + bx + c$

The factored form of $x^2 + bx + c$ is

The product of these numbers is c.

$$x^2 + bx + c = (x + \square)(x + \square)$$

The sum of these numbers is b.

EXAMPLE 1   Factor: $x^2 + 7x + 12$

Solution   We begin by writing the first terms of the binomial factors.

$$(x + \square)(x + \square)$$

Next we look for two numbers whose product is 12 and whose sum is 7. Since our numbers must have a positive product and a positive sum, we look at pairs of positive factors of 12 only.

(Continued on next page)

Positive Factors of 12	*Sum of Factors*
1, 12	13
2, 6	8
3, 4	7

Correct sum, so the numbers are 3 and 4.

Thus, $x^2 + 7x + 12 = (x + 3)(x + 4)$

Check: $(x + 3)(x + 4) = x^2 + 4x + 3x + 12 = x^2 + 7x + 12.$

PRACTICE

1   Factor $x^2 + 5x + 6$.

EXAMPLE 2   Factor: $x^2 - 12x + 35$

Solution   Again, we begin by writing the first terms of the binomials.

$$(x + \square)(x + \square)$$

Now we look for two numbers whose product is 35 and whose sum is −12. Since our numbers must have a positive product and a negative sum, we look at pairs of negative factors of 35 only.

Negative Factors of 35	*Sum of Factors*
−1, −35	−36
−5, −7	−12

Correct sum, so the numbers are −5 and −7.

Thus, $x^2 - 12x + 35 = (x - 5)(x - 7)$

Check: To check, multiply $(x - 5)(x - 7)$.

PRACTICE

2   Factor $x^2 - 17x + 70$.

EXAMPLE 3   Factor: $x^2 + 4x - 12$

Solution $x^2 + 4x - 12 = (x + \square)(x + \square)$

We look for two numbers whose product is −12 and whose sum is 4. Since our numbers must have a negative product, we look at pairs of factors with opposite signs.

Factors of −12	*Sum of Factors*
−1, 12	11
1, −12	−11
−2, 6	4
2, −6	−4
−3, 4	1
3, −4	−1

Correct sum, so the numbers are −2 and 6.

Thus, $x^2 + 4x - 12 = (x - 2)(x + 6)$

PRACTICE

3   Factor $x^2 + 5x - 14$.

EXAMPLE 4   Factor: $r^2 - r - 42$

Solution   Because the variable in this trinomial is r, the first term of each binomial factor is r.

$$r^2 - r - 42 = (r + \square)(r + \square)$$

Now we look for two numbers whose product is -42 and whose sum is -1, the numerical coefficient of r. The numbers are 6 and -7. Therefore,

$$r^2 - r - 42 = (r + 6)(r - 7)$$

PRACTICE
4   Factor $p^2 - 2p - 63$.

EXAMPLE 5   Factor: $a^2 + 2a + 10$

Solution   Look for two numbers whose product is 10 and whose sum is 2. Neither 1 and 10 nor 2 and 5 give the required sum, 2. We conclude that $a^2 + 2a + 10$ is not factorable with integers. A polynomial such as $a^2 + 2a + 10$ is called a **prime polynomial.**

PRACTICE
5   Factor $b^2 + 5b + 1$.

EXAMPLE 6   Factor: $x^2 + 7xy + 6y^2$

Solution

$$x^2 + 7xy + 6y^2 = (x + \square)(x + \square)$$

Recall that the middle term $7xy$ is the same as $7yx$. Thus, we can see that $7y$ is the "coefficient" of x. We then look for two terms whose product is $6y^2$ and whose sum is $7y$. The terms are $6y$ and $1y$ or $6y$ and y because $6y \cdot y = 6y^2$ and $6y + y = 7y$. Therefore,

$$x^2 + 7xy + 6y^2 = (x + 6y)(x + y)$$

PRACTICE
6   Factor $x^2 + 7xy + 12y^2$.

EXAMPLE 7   Factor: $x^4 + 5x^2 + 6$

Solution   As usual, we begin by writing the first terms of the binomials. Since the greatest power of x in this polynomial is x^4, we write

$$(x^2 + \square)(x^2 + \square) \quad \text{since } x^2 \cdot x^2 = x^4$$

Now we look for two factors of 6 whose sum is 5. The numbers are 2 and 3. Thus,

$$x^4 + 5x^2 + 6 = (x^2 + 2)(x^2 + 3)$$

PRACTICE
7   Factor $x^4 + 13x^2 + 12$.

If the terms of a polynomial are not written in descending powers of the variable, you may want to do so before factoring.

EXAMPLE 8   Factor: $40 - 13t + t^2$

Solution   First, we rearrange terms so that the trinomial is written in descending powers of t.

$$40 - 13t + t^2 = t^2 - 13t + 40$$

(Continued on next page)

Next, try to factor.

$$t^2 - 13t + 40 = (t + \square)(t + \square)$$

Now we look for two factors of 40 whose sum is -13. The numbers are -8 and -5. Thus,

$$t^2 - 13t + 40 = (t - 8)(t - 5) \qquad \square$$

PRACTICE
8   Factor $48 - 14x + x^2$.

The following sign patterns may be useful when factoring trinomials.

> ▶ Helpful Hint
>
> A positive constant in a trinomial tells us to look for two numbers with the same sign. The sign of the coefficient of the middle term tells us whether the signs are both positive or both negative.
>
> $$\begin{array}{cc} \text{both} & \text{same} \\ \text{positive} & \text{sign} \\ \downarrow & \swarrow \end{array} \qquad \begin{array}{cc} \text{both} & \text{same} \\ \text{negative} & \text{sign} \\ \downarrow & \swarrow \end{array}$$
>
> $$x^2 + 10x + 16 = (x + 2)(x + 8) \qquad x^2 - 10x + 16 = (x - 2)(x - 8)$$
>
> A negative constant in a trinomial tells us to look for two numbers with opposite signs.
>
> $$\begin{array}{c} \text{opposite} \\ \text{signs} \\ \downarrow \end{array} \qquad \begin{array}{c} \text{opposite} \\ \text{signs} \\ \downarrow \end{array}$$
>
> $$x^2 + 6x - 16 = (x + 8)(x - 2) \qquad x^2 - 6x - 16 = (x - 8)(x + 2)$$

OBJECTIVE
2   Factoring Out the Greatest Common Factor

Remember that the first step in factoring any polynomial is to factor out the greatest common factor (if there is one other than 1 or -1).

EXAMPLE 9   Factor: $3m^2 - 24m - 60$

Solution   First we factor out the greatest common factor, 3, from each term.

$$3m^2 - 24m - 60 = 3(m^2 - 8m - 20)$$

Now we factor $m^2 - 8m - 20$ by looking for two factors of -20 whose sum is -8. The factors are -10 and 2. Therefore, the complete factored form is

$$3m^2 - 24m - 60 = 3(m + 2)(m - 10) \qquad \square$$

> ▶ Helpful Hint
>
> Remember to write the common factor 3 as part of the factored form.

PRACTICE
9   Factor $4x^2 - 24x + 36$.

EXAMPLE 10   Factor: $2x^4 - 26x^3 + 84x^2$

Solution

$$\begin{aligned} 2x^4 - 26x^3 + 84x^2 &= 2x^2(x^2 - 13x + 42) &&\text{Factor out common factor, } 2x^2. \\ &= 2x^2(x - 6)(x - 7) &&\text{Factor } x^2 - 13x + 42. \qquad \square \end{aligned}$$

PRACTICE
10   Factor $3y^4 - 18y^3 - 21y^2$.

Vocabulary, Readiness & Video Check

Fill in each blank with "true" or "false."

1. To factor $x^2 + 7x + 6$, we look for two numbers whose product is 6 and whose sum is 7. _____

2. We can write the factorization $(y + 2)(y + 4)$ also as $(y + 4)(y + 2)$. _____

3. The factorization $(4x - 12)(x - 5)$ is completely factored. _____

4. The factorization $(x + 2y)(x + y)$ may also be written as $(x + 2y)^2$. _____

Complete each factored form.

5. $x^2 + 9x + 20 = (x + 4)(x \quad)$

6. $x^2 + 12x + 35 = (x + 5)(x \quad)$

7. $x^2 - 7x + 12 = (x - 4)(x \quad)$

8. $x^2 - 13x + 22 = (x - 2)(x \quad)$

9. $x^2 + 4x + 4 = (x + 2)(x \quad)$

10. $x^2 + 10x + 24 = (x + 6)(x \quad)$

Martin-Gay Interactive Videos

See Video 6.2

Watch the section lecture video and answer the following questions.

OBJECTIVE
1

11. In Example 2, why are only negative factors of 15 considered?

OBJECTIVE
2

12. In Example 5, we know we need a positive and a negative factor of -10. How do we determine which factor is negative?

6.2 Exercise Set   MyMathLab®

Factor each trinomial completely. If a polynomial can't be factored, write "prime." See Examples 1 through 8.

1. $x^2 + 7x + 6$

2. $x^2 + 6x + 8$

3. $y^2 - 10y + 9$

4. $y^2 - 12y + 11$

5. $x^2 - 6x + 9$

6. $x^2 - 10x + 25$

7. $x^2 - 3x - 18$

8. $x^2 - x - 30$

9. $x^2 + 3x - 70$

10. $x^2 + 4x - 32$

11. $x^2 + 5x + 2$

12. $x^2 - 7x + 5$

13. $x^2 + 8xy + 15y^2$

14. $x^2 + 6xy + 8y^2$

15. $a^4 - 2a^2 - 15$

16. $y^4 - 3y^2 - 70$

17. $13 + 14m + m^2$

18. $17 + 18n + n^2$

19. $10t - 24 + t^2$

20. $6q - 27 + q^2$

21. $a^2 - 10ab + 16b^2$

22. $a^2 - 9ab + 18b^2$

MIXED PRACTICE

Factor each trinomial completely. Some of these trinomials contain a greatest common factor (other than 1). Don't forget to factor out the GCF first. See Examples 1 through 10.

23. $2z^2 + 20z + 32$

24. $3x^2 + 30x + 63$

25. $2x^3 - 18x^2 + 40x$

26. $3x^3 - 12x^2 - 36x$

27. $x^2 - 3xy - 4y^2$

28. $x^2 - 4xy - 77y^2$

29. $x^2 + 15x + 36$

30. $x^2 + 19x + 60$

31. $x^2 - x - 2$

32. $x^2 - 5x - 14$

33. $r^2 - 16r + 48$

34. $r^2 - 10r + 21$

35. $x^2 + xy - 2y^2$

36. $x^2 - xy - 6y^2$
37. $3x^2 + 9x - 30$
38. $4x^2 - 4x - 48$
39. $3x^2 - 60x + 108$
40. $2x^2 - 24x + 70$
41. $x^2 - 18x - 144$
42. $x^2 + x - 42$
43. $r^2 - 3r + 6$
44. $x^2 + 4x - 10$
45. $x^2 - 8x + 15$
46. $x^2 - 9x + 14$
47. $6x^3 + 54x^2 + 120x$
48. $3x^3 + 3x^2 - 126x$
49. $4x^2y + 4xy - 12y$
50. $3x^2y - 9xy + 45y$
51. $x^2 - 4x - 21$
52. $x^2 - 4x - 32$
53. $x^2 + 7xy + 10y^2$
54. $x^2 - 2xy - 15y^2$
55. $64 + 24t + 2t^2$
56. $50 + 20t + 2t^2$
57. $x^3 - 2x^2 - 24x$
58. $x^3 - 3x^2 - 28x$
59. $2t^5 - 14t^4 + 24t^3$
60. $3x^6 + 30x^5 + 72x^4$
61. $5x^3y - 25x^2y^2 - 120xy^3$
62. $7a^3b - 35a^2b^2 + 42ab^3$
63. $162 - 45m + 3m^2$
64. $48 - 20n + 2n^2$
65. $-x^2 + 12x - 11$ (Factor out -1 first.)
66. $-x^2 + 8x - 7$ (Factor out -1 first.)
67. $\frac{1}{2}y^2 - \frac{9}{2}y - 11$ (Factor out $\frac{1}{2}$ first.)
68. $\frac{1}{3}y^2 - \frac{5}{3}y - 8$ (Factor out $\frac{1}{3}$ first.)
69. $x^3y^2 + x^2y - 20x$
70. $a^2b^3 + ab^2 - 30b$

REVIEW AND PREVIEW

Multiply. See Section 5.3.

71. $(2x + 1)(x + 5)$
72. $(3x + 2)(x + 4)$
73. $(5y - 4)(3y - 1)$
74. $(4z - 7)(7z - 1)$
75. $(a + 3b)(9a - 4b)$
76. $(y - 5x)(6y + 5x)$

CONCEPT EXTENSIONS

77. Write a polynomial that factors as $(x - 3)(x + 8)$.
78. To factor $x^2 + 13x + 42$, think of two numbers whose _____ is 42 and whose _____ is 13.

Complete each sentence in your own words.

79. If $x^2 + bx + c$ is factorable and c is negative, then the signs of the last-term factors of the binomials are opposite because…

80. If $x^2 + bx + c$ is factorable and c is positive, then the signs of the last-term factors of the binomials are the same because…

Remember that perimeter means distance around. Write the perimeter of each rectangle as a simplified polynomial. Then factor the polynomial.

81.
$4x + 33$
$x^2 + 10x$

82.
$12x^2$
$2x^3 + 16x$

83. An object is thrown upward from the top of an 80-foot building with an initial velocity of 64 feet per second. Neglecting air resistance, the height of the object after t seconds is given by $-16t^2 + 64t + 80$. Factor this polynomial.

$-16t^2 + 64t + 80$

84. An object is thrown upward from the top of a 112-foot building with an initial velocity of 96 feet per second. Neglecting air resistance, the height of the object after t seconds is given by $-16t^2 + 96t + 112$. Factor this polynomial.

$-16t^2 + 96t + 112$

Factor each trinomial completely.

85. $x^2 + \dfrac{1}{2}x + \dfrac{1}{16}$

86. $x^2 + x + \dfrac{1}{4}$

87. $z^2(x + 1) - 3z(x + 1) - 70(x + 1)$

88. $y^2(x + 1) - 2y(x + 1) - 15(x + 1)$

Factor each trinomial. (**Hint:** *Notice that $x^{2n} + 4x^n + 3$ factors as* $(x^n + 1)(x^n + 3)$. **Remember:** $x^n \cdot x^n = x^{n+n}$ or x^{2n}.)

89. $x^{2n} + 8x^n - 20$

90. $x^{2n} + 5x^n + 6$

Find a positive value of c so that each trinomial is factorable.

91. $x^2 + 6x + c$

92. $t^2 + 8t + c$

93. $y^2 - 4y + c$

94. $n^2 - 16n + c$

Find a positive value of b so that each trinomial is factorable.

95. $x^2 + bx + 15$

96. $y^2 + by + 20$

97. $m^2 + bm - 27$

98. $x^2 + bx - 14$

6.3 | # Factoring Trinomials of the Form $ax^2 + bx + c$ and Perfect Square Trinomials

OBJECTIVES

1 Factor Trinomials of the Form $ax^2 + bx + c$, Where $a \neq 1$.

2 Factor Out a GCF Before Factoring a Trinomial of the Form $ax^2 + bx + c$.

3 Factor Perfect Square Trinomials.

OBJECTIVE

1   Factoring Trinomials of the Form $ax^2 + bx + c$

In this section, we factor trinomials of the form $ax^2 + bx + c$, such as

$$3x^2 + 11x + 6, \qquad 8x^2 - 22x + 5, \qquad \text{and} \qquad 2x^2 + 13x - 7$$

Notice that the coefficient of the squared variable in these trinomials is a number other than 1. We will factor these trinomials using a trial-and-check method based on our work in the last section.

To begin, let's review the relationship between the numerical coefficients of the trinomial and the numerical coefficients of its factored form. For example, since $(2x + 1)(x + 6) = 2x^2 + 13x + 6$,

$$\text{a factored form of } 2x^2 + 13x + 6 \text{ is } (2x + 1)(x + 6)$$

Notice that $2x$ and x are factors of $2x^2$, the first term of the trinomial. Also, 6 and 1 are factors of 6, the last term of the trinomial, as shown:

$$2x^2 + 13x + 6 = (2x + 1)(x + 6)$$

Also notice that $13x$, the middle term, is the sum of the following products:

$$2x^2 + 13x + 6 = (2x + 1)(x + 6)$$

$$\begin{array}{c} 1x \\ +12x \\ \hline 13x \end{array} \quad \text{Middle term}$$

Let's use this pattern to factor $5x^2 + 7x + 2$. First, we find factors of $5x^2$. Since all numerical coefficients in this trinomial are positive, we will use factors with positive numerical coefficients only. Thus, the factors of $5x^2$ are $5x$ and x. Let's try these factors as first terms of the binomials. Thus far, we have

$$5x^2 + 7x + 2 = (5x + \square)(x + \square)$$

Next, we need to find positive factors of 2. Positive factors of 2 are 1 and 2. Now we try possible combinations of these factors as second terms of the binomials until we obtain a middle term of $7x$.

$$(5x + 1)(x + 2) = 5x^2 + 11x + 2$$

$$\frac{+10x}{11x} \longrightarrow \text{Incorrect middle term}$$

Let's try switching factors 2 and 1.

$$(5x + 2)(x + 1) = 5x^2 + 7x + 2$$

$$\frac{+5x}{7x} \longrightarrow \text{Correct middle term}$$

Thus the factored form of $5x^2 + 7x + 2$ is $(5x + 2)(x + 1)$. To check, we multiply $(5x + 2)$ and $(x + 1)$. The product is $5x^2 + 7x + 2$.

EXAMPLE 1 Factor: $3x^2 + 11x + 6$

Solution Since all numerical coefficients are positive, we use factors with positive numerical coefficients. We first find factors of $3x^2$.

$$\text{Factors of } 3x^2: \quad 3x^2 = 3x \cdot x$$

If factorable, the trinomial will be of the form

$$3x^2 + 11x + 6 = (3x + \square)(x + \square)$$

Next we factor 6.

$$\text{Factors of 6:} \quad 6 = 1 \cdot 6, \quad 6 = 2 \cdot 3$$

Now we try combinations of factors of 6 until a middle term of $11x$ is obtained. Let's try 1 and 6 first.

$$(3x + 1)(x + 6) = 3x^2 + 19x + 6$$

$$\frac{+18x}{19x} \longrightarrow \text{Incorrect middle term}$$

Now let's next try 6 and 1.

$$(3x + 6)(x + 1)$$

Before multiplying, notice that the terms of the factor $3x + 6$ have a common factor of 3. The terms of the original trinomial $3x^2 + 11x + 6$ have no common factor other than 1, so the terms of its factors will also contain no common factor other than 1. This means that $(3x + 6)(x + 1)$ is not a factored form.

Next let's try 2 and 3 as last terms.

$$(3x + 2)(x + 3) = 3x^2 + 11x + 6$$

$$\frac{+9x}{11x} \longrightarrow \text{Correct middle term}$$

Thus a factored form of $3x^2 + 11x + 6$ is $(3x + 2)(x + 3)$. ☐

PRACTICE

1 Factor: $2x^2 + 11x + 15$.

▶ Helpful Hint

If the terms of a trinomial have no common factor (other than 1), then the terms of neither of its binomial factors will contain a common factor (other than 1).

✓CONCEPT CHECK

Do the terms of $3x^2 + 29x + 18$ have a common factor? Without multiplying, decide which of the following factored forms could not be a factored form of $3x^2 + 29x + 18$.

a. $(3x + 18)(x + 1)$ **b.** $(3x + 2)(x + 9)$ **c.** $(3x + 6)(x + 3)$ **d.** $(3x + 9)(x + 2)$

EXAMPLE 2   Factor: $8x^2 - 22x + 5$

Solution   Factors of $8x^2$: $8x^2 = 8x \cdot x$, $8x^2 = 4x \cdot 2x$

We'll try $8x$ and x.

$$8x^2 - 22x + 5 = (8x + \square)(x + \square)$$

Since the middle term, $-22x$, has a negative numerical coefficient, we factor 5 into negative factors.

$$\text{Factors of 5:}\quad 5 = -1 \cdot -5$$

Let's try -1 and -5.

$$(8x - 1)(x - 5) = 8x^2 - 41x + 5$$

$$\begin{array}{c} -1x \\ +(-40x) \\ \hline -41x \end{array} \longrightarrow \text{Incorrect middle term}$$

Now let's try -5 and -1.

$$(8x - 5)(x - 1) = 8x^2 - 13x + 5$$

$$\begin{array}{c} -5x \\ +(-8x) \\ \hline -13x \end{array} \longrightarrow \text{Incorrect middle term}$$

Don't give up yet! We can still try other factors of $8x^2$. Let's try $4x$ and $2x$ with -1 and -5.

$$(4x - 1)(2x - 5) = 8x^2 - 22x + 5$$

$$\begin{array}{c} -2x \\ +(-20x) \\ \hline -22x \end{array} \longrightarrow \text{Correct middle term}$$

A factored form of $8x^2 - 22x + 5$ is $(4x - 1)(2x - 5)$.   □

PRACTICE

2   Factor: $15x^2 - 22x + 8$.

EXAMPLE 3   Factor: $2x^2 + 13x - 7$

Solution   Factors of $2x^2$: $2x^2 = 2x \cdot x$

Factors of -7: $-7 = -1 \cdot 7$, $-7 = 1 \cdot -7$

Answers to Concept Check:
no; a, c, d

(Continued on next page)

We try possible combinations of these factors:

$$(2x + 1)(x - 7) = 2x^2 - 13x - 7 \quad \text{Incorrect middle term}$$
$$(2x - 1)(x + 7) = 2x^2 + 13x - 7 \quad \text{Correct middle term}$$

A factored form of $2x^2 + 13x - 7$ is $(2x - 1)(x + 7)$.

PRACTICE
3 Factor: $4x^2 + 11x - 3$.

EXAMPLE 4   Factor: $10x^2 - 13xy - 3y^2$

Solution Factors of $10x^2$: $10x^2 = 10x \cdot x, \quad 10x^2 = 2x \cdot 5x$

Factors of $-3y^2$: $-3y^2 = -3y \cdot y, \quad -3y^2 = 3y \cdot -y$

We try some combinations of these factors:

Correct   Correct

$$(10x - 3y)(x + y) = 10x^2 + 7xy - 3y^2$$
$$(x + 3y)(10x - y) = 10x^2 + 29xy - 3y^2$$
$$(5x + 3y)(2x - y) = 10x^2 + xy - 3y^2$$
$$(2x - 3y)(5x + y) = 10x^2 - 13xy - 3y^2 \quad \text{Correct middle term}$$

A factored form of $10x^2 - 13xy - 3y^2$ is $(2x - 3y)(5x + y)$.

PRACTICE
4 Factor: $21x^2 + 11xy - 2y^2$.

EXAMPLE 5   Factor: $3x^4 - 5x^2 - 8$

Solution Factors of $3x^4$: $3x^4 = 3x^2 \cdot x^2$

Factors of -8: $-8 = -2 \cdot 4, 2 \cdot -4, -1 \cdot 8, 1 \cdot -8$

Try combinations of these factors:

Correct   Correct

$$(3x^2 - 2)(x^2 + 4) = 3x^4 + 10x^2 - 8$$
$$(3x^2 + 4)(x^2 - 2) = 3x^4 - 2x^2 - 8$$
$$(3x^2 + 8)(x^2 - 1) = 3x^4 + 5x^2 - 8 \quad \text{Incorrect sign on middle term, so switch signs in binomial factors.}$$
$$(3x^2 - 8)(x^2 + 1) = 3x^4 - 5x^2 - 8 \quad \text{Correct middle term.}$$

A factored form of $3x^4 - 5x^2 - 8$ is $(3x^2 - 8)(x^2 + 1)$.

PRACTICE
5 Factor: $2x^4 - 5x^2 - 7$.

▶ **Helpful Hint**

Study the last two lines of Example 5. If a factoring attempt gives you a middle term whose numerical coefficient is the opposite of the desired numerical coefficient, try switching the signs of the last terms in the binomials.

Switched signs $(3x^2 + 8)(x^2 - 1) = 3x^4 + 5x^2 - 8$ Middle term: $+5x^2$
$(3x^2 - 8)(x^2 + 1) = 3x^4 - 5x^2 - 8$ Middle term: $-5x^2$

OBJECTIVE

2   Factoring Out the Greatest Common Factor

Don't forget that the first step in factoring any polynomial is to look for a common factor to factor out.

EXAMPLE 6   Factor: $24x^4 + 40x^3 + 6x^2$

Solution   Notice that all three terms have a common factor of $2x^2$. Thus we factor out $2x^2$ first.

$$24x^4 + 40x^3 + 6x^2 = 2x^2(12x^2 + 20x + 3)$$

Next we factor $12x^2 + 20x + 3$.

Factors of $12x^2$: $12x^2 = 4x \cdot 3x$, $12x^2 = 12x \cdot x$, $12x^2 = 6x \cdot 2x$

Since all terms in the trinomial have positive numerical coefficients, we factor 3 using positive factors only.

Factors of 3: $3 = 1 \cdot 3$

We try some combinations of the factors.

$$2x^2(4x + 3)(3x + 1) = 2x^2(12x^2 + 13x + 3)$$
$$2x^2(12x + 1)(x + 3) = 2x^2(12x^2 + 37x + 3)$$
$$2x^2(2x + 3)(6x + 1) = 2x^2(12x^2 + 20x + 3) \quad \text{Correct middle term}$$

> **Helpful Hint**
> Don't forget to include the common factor in the factored form.

A factored form of $24x^4 + 40x^3 + 6x^2$ is $2x^2(2x + 3)(6x + 1)$.   □

PRACTICE

6   Factor: $3x^3 + 17x^2 + 10x$

When the term containing the squared variable has a negative coefficient, you may want to first factor out a common factor of -1.

EXAMPLE 7   Factor: $-6x^2 - 13x + 5$

Solution   We begin by factoring out a common factor of -1.

$$-6x^2 - 13x + 5 = -1(6x^2 + 13x - 5) \quad \text{Factor out } -1.$$
$$= -1(3x - 1)(2x + 5) \quad \text{Factor } 6x^2 + 13x - 5.$$ □

PRACTICE

7   Factor: $-8x^2 + 2x + 3$

OBJECTIVE

3   Factoring Perfect Square Trinomials

A trinomial that is the square of a binomial is called a **perfect square trinomial.** For example,

$$(x + 3)^2 = (x + 3)(x + 3)$$
$$= x^2 + 6x + 9$$

Thus $x^2 + 6x + 9$ is a perfect square trinomial.

In Chapter 5, we discovered special product formulas for squaring binomials.

$$(a + b)^2 = a^2 + 2ab + b^2 \quad \text{and} \quad (a - b)^2 = a^2 - 2ab + b^2$$

Because multiplication and factoring are reverse processes, we can now use these special products to help us factor perfect square trinomials. If we reverse these equations, we have the following.

Factoring Perfect Square Trinomials

$$a^2 + 2ab + b^2 = (a + b)^2$$
$$a^2 - 2ab + b^2 = (a - b)^2$$

> **Helpful Hint**
> Notice that for both given forms of a perfect square trinomial, the last term is positive. This is because the last term is a square.

To use these equations to help us factor, we must first be able to recognize a perfect square trinomial. A trinomial is a perfect square when

1. two terms, a^2 and b^2, are squares and
2. the remaining term is $2 \cdot a \cdot b$ or $-2 \cdot a \cdot b$. That is, this term is twice the product of a and b, or its opposite.

When a trinomial fits this description, its factored form is $(a + b)^2$ or $(a - b)^2$.

EXAMPLE 8 Factor: $x^2 + 12x + 36$

Solution First, is this a perfect square trinomial?

$$x^2 + 12x + 36$$

1. $x^2 = (x)^2$ and $36 = 6^2$.
2. Is the middle term $2 \cdot x \cdot 6$? Yes, $2 \cdot x \cdot 6 = 12x$, the middle term.

Thus, $x^2 + 12x + 36$ factors as $(x + 6)^2$.

PRACTICE
8 Factor $x^2 + 14x + 49$.

EXAMPLE 9 Factor: $25x^2 + 25xy + 4y^2$

Solution Is this a perfect square trinomial?

$$25x^2 + 25xy + 4y^2$$

1. $25x^2 = (5x)^2$ and $4y^2 = (2y)^2$.
2. Is the middle term $2 \cdot 5x \cdot 2y$? **No**, $2 \cdot 5x \cdot 2y = 20xy$, **not** the middle term $25xy$.

Therefore, $25x^2 + 25xy + 4y^2$ is not a perfect square trinomial. It is factorable, though. Using earlier techniques, we find that $25x^2 + 25xy + 4y^2$ factors as $(5x + 4y)(5x + y)$.

> **Helpful Hint**
> A perfect square trinomial can also be factored by other methods.

PRACTICE
9 Factor $4x^2 + 20xy + 9y^2$.

EXAMPLE 10 Factor: $4m^4 - 4m^2 + 1$

Solution Is this a perfect square trinomial?

$$4m^4 - 4m^2 + 1$$

1. $4m^4 = (2m^2)^2$ and $1 = 1^2$.
2. Is the middle term $2 \cdot 2m^2 \cdot 1$ or $-2 \cdot 2m^2 \cdot 1$? Yes, $-2 \cdot 2m^2 \cdot 1 = -4m^2$, the middle term.

Thus, $4m^4 - 4m^2 + 1$ factors as $(2m^2 - 1)^2$.

PRACTICE
10 Factor $36n^4 - 12n^2 + 1$.

EXAMPLE 11   Factor: $162x^3 - 144x^2 + 32x$

Solution   Don't forget to look first for a common factor. There is a greatest common factor of $2x$ in this trinomial.

$$162x^3 - 144x^2 + 32x = 2x(81x^2 - 72x + 16)$$
$$= 2x[(9x)^2 - 2 \cdot 9x \cdot 4 + 4^2]$$
$$= 2x(9x - 4)^2$$

PRACTICE
11   Factor $12x^3 - 84x^2 + 147x$.

Vocabulary, Readiness & Video Check

Use the choices below to fill in each blank. Some choices will be used more than once and some not used at all.

$5y^2$	$(x + 5y)^2$	perfect square trinomial
$(5y)^2$	$(x - 5y)^2$	perfect square binomial

1. A _____ is a trinomial that is the square of a binomial.

2. The term $25y^2$ written as a square is _____ .

3. The expression $x^2 + 10xy + 25y^2$ is called a _____ .

4. The factorization $(x + 5y)(x + 5y)$ may also be written as _____ .

Complete each factorization.

5. $2x^2 + 5x + 3$ factors as $(2x + 3)(\ ?\ )$.
   a. $(x + 3)$ **b.** $(2x + 1)$ **c.** $(3x + 4)$ **d.** $(x + 1)$

6. $7x^2 + 9x + 2$ factors as $(7x + 2)(\ ?\ )$.
   a. $(3x + 1)$ **b.** $(x + 1)$ **c.** $(x + 2)$ **d.** $(7x + 1)$

Martin-Gay Interactive Videos

See Video 6.3

Watch the section lecture video and answer the following questions.

OBJECTIVE
1   7. From Example 1, explain in general terms how you would go about factoring a trinomial with a first-term coefficient $\neq 1$.

OBJECTIVE
2   8. From Examples 3 and 5, how can factoring the GCF from a trinomial help you save time when trying to factor the remaining trinomial?

OBJECTIVE
3   9. Describe in words the special patterns that the trinomials in Examples 7 and 8 have that identify them as perfect square trinomials.

6.3 **Exercise Set**   MyMathLab®

Complete each factored form. See Examples 1 through 5, and 8 through 10.

1. $5x^2 + 22x + 8 = (5x + 2)(\quad)$

2. $2y^2 + 27y + 25 = (2y + 25)(\quad)$

3. $50x^2 + 15x - 2 = (5x + 2)(\quad)$

4. $6y^2 + 11y - 10 = (2y + 5)(\quad)$

5. $25x^2 - 20x + 4 = (5x - 2)(\quad)$

6. $4y^2 - 20y + 25 = (2y - 5)(\quad)$

Factor completely. See Examples 1 through 5.

7. $2x^2 + 13x + 15$

8. $3x^2 + 8x + 4$

9. $8y^2 - 17y + 9$

10. $21x^2 - 31x + 10$

11. $2x^2 - 9x - 5$

12. $36r^2 - 5r - 24$

13. $20r^2 + 27r - 8$

14. $3x^2 + 20x - 63$

▶ **15.** $10x^2 + 31x + 3$

16. $12x^2 + 17x + 5$

17. $2m^2 + 17m + 10$

18. $3n^2 + 20n + 5$

19. $6x^2 - 13xy + 5y^2$

20. $8x^2 - 14xy + 3y^2$

21. $15m^2 - 16m - 15$

22. $25n^2 - 5n - 6$

Factor completely. See Examples 1 through 7.

23. $12x^3 + 11x^2 + 2x$

24. $8a^3 + 14a^2 + 3a$

25. $21b^2 - 48b - 45$

26. $12x^2 - 14x - 10$

27. $7z + 12z^2 - 12$

28. $16t + 15t^2 - 15$

29. $6x^2y^2 - 2xy^2 - 60y^2$

30. $8x^2y + 34xy - 84y$

▶ **31.** $4x^2 - 8x - 21$

32. $6x^2 - 11x - 10$

33. $-x^2 + 2x + 24$

34. $-x^2 + 4x + 21$

▶ **35.** $4x^3 - 9x^2 - 9x$

36. $6x^3 - 31x^2 + 5x$

37. $24x^2 - 58x + 9$

38. $36x^2 + 55x - 14$

Factor each perfect square trinomial completely. See Examples 8 through 11.

▶ **39.** $x^2 + 22x + 121$

40. $x^2 + 18x + 81$

41. $x^2 - 16x + 64$

42. $x^2 - 12x + 36$

43. $16a^2 - 24a + 9$

44. $25x^2 - 20x + 4$

45. $x^4 + 4x^2 + 4$

46. $m^4 + 10m^2 + 25$

47. $2n^2 - 28n + 98$

48. $3y^2 - 6y + 3$

49. $16y^2 + 40y + 25$

50. $9y^2 + 48y + 64$

MIXED PRACTICE

Factor each trinomial completely. See Examples 1 through 11 and Section 6.2.

51. $2x^2 - 7x - 99$

52. $2x^2 + 7x - 72$

53. $24x^2 + 41x + 12$

54. $24x^2 - 49x + 15$

55. $3a^2 + 10ab + 3b^2$

56. $2a^2 + 11ab + 5b^2$

57. $-9x + 20 + x^2$

58. $-7x + 12 + x^2$

59. $p^2 + 12pq + 36q^2$

60. $m^2 + 20mn + 100n^2$

61. $x^2y^2 - 10xy + 25$

62. $x^2y^2 - 14xy + 49$

63. $40a^2b + 9ab - 9b$

64. $24y^2x + 7yx - 5x$

▶ **65.** $30x^3 + 38x^2 + 12x$

66. $6x^3 - 28x^2 + 16x$

67. $6y^3 - 8y^2 - 30y$

68. $12x^3 - 34x^2 + 24x$

69. $10x^4 + 25x^3y - 15x^2y^2$

70. $42x^4 - 99x^3y - 15x^2y^2$

▶ **71.** $-14x^2 + 39x - 10$

72. $-15x^2 + 26x - 8$

73. $16p^4 - 40p^3 + 25p^2$

74. $9q^4 - 42q^3 + 49q^2$

75. $x + 3x^2 - 2$

76. $y + 8y^2 - 9$

77. $8x^2 + 6xy - 27y^2$

78. $54a^2 + 39ab - 8b^2$

79. $1 + 6x^2 + x^4$

80. $1 + 16x^2 + x^4$

▶ **81.** $9x^2 - 24xy + 16y^2$

82. $25x^2 - 60xy + 36y^2$

83. $18x^2 - 9x - 14$

84. $42a^2 - 43a + 6$

85. $-27t + 7t^2 - 4$

86. $-3t + 4t^2 - 7$

87. $49p^2 - 7p - 2$

88. $3r^2 + 10r - 8$

89. $m^3 + 18m^2 + 81m$

90. $y^3 + 12y^2 + 36y$

91. $5x^2y^2 + 20xy + 1$

92. $3a^2b^2 + 12ab + 1$

93. $6a^5 + 37a^3b^2 + 6ab^4$

94. $5m^5 + 26m^3h^2 + 5mh^4$

REVIEW AND PREVIEW

Multiply the following. See Section 5.4.

95. $(x - 2)(x + 2)$

96. $(y^2 + 3)(y^2 - 3)$

97. $(a + 3)(a^2 - 3a + 9)$

98. $(z - 2)(z^2 + 2z + 4)$

The following graph shows the percent of text message users in each age group. See Section 3.1.

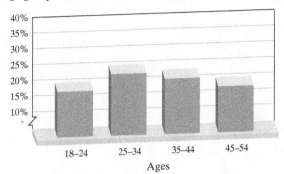

Data from CellSigns, Inc.

99. What range of ages shown has the highest percent of text message users?

100. What range of ages shown has the lowest percent of text message users?

101. Describe any trend you see.

102. Why don't the percents shown in the graph add to 100%?

CONCEPT EXTENSIONS

See the Concept Check in this section.

103. Do the terms of $4x^2 + 19x + 12$ have a common factor (other than 1)?

104. Without multiplying, decide which of the following factored forms is not a factored form of $4x^2 + 19x + 12$.

a. $(2x + 4)(2x + 3)$ **b.** $(4x + 4)(x + 3)$
c. $(4x + 3)(x + 4)$ **d.** $(2x + 2)(2x + 6)$

105. Describe a perfect square trinomial.

106. Write the perfect square trinomial that factors as $(x + 3y)^2$.

Write the perimeter of each figure as a simplified polynomial. Then factor the polynomial.

107.

108.

Factor each trinomial completely.

109. $4x^2 + 2x + \dfrac{1}{4}$

110. $27x^2 + 2x - \dfrac{1}{9}$

111. $4x^2(y - 1)^2 + 10x(y - 1)^2 + 25(y - 1)^2$

112. $3x^2(a + 3)^3 - 10x(a + 3)^3 + 25(a + 3)^3$

113. Fill in the blank so that $x^2 + \underline{\hspace{1cm}} x + 16$ is a perfect square trinomial.

114. Fill in the blank so that $9x^2 + \underline{\hspace{1cm}} x + 25$ is a perfect square trinomial.

The area of the largest square in the figure is $(a + b)^2$. Use this figure to answer Exercises 115 and 116.

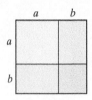

△ **115.** Write the area of the largest square as the sum of the areas of the smaller squares and rectangles.

△ **116.** What factoring formula from this section is visually represented by this square?

Find a positive value of b so that each trinomial is factorable.

117. $3x^2 + bx - 5$ **118.** $2y^2 + by + 3$

Find a positive value of c so that each trinomial is factorable.

119. $5x^2 + 7x + c$ **120.** $11y^2 - 40y + c$

Factor completely. Don't forget to first factor out the greatest common factor.

121. $-12x^3y^2 + 3x^2y^2 + 15xy^2$

122. $-12r^3x^2 + 38r^2x^2 + 14rx^2$

123. $4x^2(y - 1)^2 + 20x(y - 1)^2 + 25(y - 1)^2$

124. $3x^2(a + 3)^3 - 28x(a + 3)^3 + 25(a + 3)^3$

Factor.

125. $3x^{2n} + 17x^n + 10$

126. $2x^{2n} + 5x^n - 12$

127. In your own words, describe the steps you will use to factor a trinomial.

6.4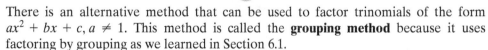

Factoring Trinomials of the Form $ax^2 + bx + c$ by Grouping

OBJECTIVE

1 Use the Grouping Method to Factor Trinomials of the Form $ax^2 + bx + c$.

OBJECTIVE

1 Using the Grouping Method

There is an alternative method that can be used to factor trinomials of the form $ax^2 + bx + c, a \neq 1$. This method is called the **grouping method** because it uses factoring by grouping as we learned in Section 6.1.

To see how this method works, recall from Section 6.2 that to factor a trinomial such as $x^2 + 11x + 30$, we find two numbers such that

Product is 30
↓
$$x^2 + 11x + 30$$
↓
Sum is 11.

To factor a trinomial such as $2x^2 + 11x + 12$ by grouping, we use an extension of the method in Section 6.2. Here we look for two numbers such that

Product is $2 \cdot 12 = 24$
$$2x^2 + 11x + 12$$
Sum is 11.

This time, we use the two numbers to write

$$2x^2 + 11x + 12 \text{ as}$$
$$= 2x^2 + \square x + \square x + 12$$

Then we factor by grouping. Since we want a positive product, 24, and a positive sum, 11, we consider pairs of positive factors of 24 only.

Factors of 24	Sum of Factors	
1, 24	25	
2, 12	14	
3, 8	11	Correct sum

The factors are 3 and 8. Now we use these factors to write the middle term $11x$ as $3x + 8x$ (or $8x + 3x$). We replace $11x$ with $3x + 8x$ in the original trinomial and then we can factor by grouping.

$$
\begin{aligned}
2x^2 + 11x + 12 &= 2x^2 + 3x + 8x + 12 \\
&= (2x^2 + 3x) + (8x + 12) \quad \text{Group the terms.} \\
&= x(2x + 3) + 4(2x + 3) \quad \text{Factor each group.} \\
&= (2x + 3)(x + 4) \quad \text{Factor out } (2x + 3).
\end{aligned}
$$

In general, we have the following procedure.

To Factor Trinomials by Grouping

Step 1. Factor out a greatest common factor if there is one other than 1.

Step 2. For the resulting trinomial $ax^2 + bx + c$, find two numbers whose product is $a \cdot c$ and whose sum is b.

Step 3. Write the middle term, bx, using the factors found in Step 2.

Step 4. Factor by grouping.

EXAMPLE 1 Factor $3x^2 + 31x + 10$ by grouping.

Solution

Step 1. The terms of this trinomial contain no greatest common factor other than 1 (or -1).

Step 2. In $3x^2 + 31x + 10$, $a = 3$, $b = 31$, and $c = 10$.

Let's find two numbers whose product is $a \cdot c$ or $3(10) = 30$ and whose sum is b or 31. The numbers are 1 and 30.

Factors of 30	Sum of Factors
5, 6	11
3, 10	13
2, 15	17
1, 30	31	Correct sum

Step 3. Write $31x$ as $1x + 30x$ so that $3x^2 + 31x + 10 = 3x^2 + 1x + 30x + 10$.

Step 4. Factor by grouping.

$$3x^2 + 1x + 30x + 10 = x(3x + 1) + 10(3x + 1)$$
$$= (3x + 1)(x + 10) \qquad \square$$

PRACTICE
1 Factor $5x^2 + 61x + 12$ by grouping.

EXAMPLE 2 Factor $8x^2 - 14x + 5$ by grouping.

Solution

Step 1. The terms of this trinomial contain no greatest common factor other than 1.

Step 2. This trinomial is of the form $ax^2 + bx + c$ with $a = 8$, $b = -14$, and $c = 5$. Find two numbers whose product is $a \cdot c$ or $8 \cdot 5 = 40$, and whose sum is b or -14.

The numbers are -4 and -10.

Factors of 40	Sum of Factors
$-40, -1$	-41
$-20, -2$	-22
$-10, -4$	-14	Correct sum

Step 3. Write $-14x$ as $-4x - 10x$ so that

$$8x^2 - 14x + 5 = 8x^2 - 4x - 10x + 5$$

Step 4. Factor by grouping.

$$8x^2 - 4x - 10x + 5 = 4x(2x - 1) - 5(2x - 1)$$
$$= (2x - 1)(4x - 5) \qquad \square$$

PRACTICE
2 Factor $12x^2 - 19x + 5$ by grouping.

EXAMPLE 3 Factor $6x^2 - 2x - 20$ by grouping.

Solution

Step 1. First factor out the greatest common factor, 2.

$$6x^2 - 2x - 20 = 2(3x^2 - x - 10)$$

Step 2. Next, notice that $a = 3$, $b = -1$, and $c = -10$ in the resulting trinomial. Find two numbers whose product is $a \cdot c$ or $3(-10) = -30$ and whose sum is b, -1. The numbers are -6 and 5.

Step 3. $3x^2 - x - 10 = 3x^2 - 6x + 5x - 10$

(Continued on next page)

Step 4. $3x^2 - 6x + 5x - 10 = 3x(x - 2) + 5(x - 2)$
$$= (x - 2)(3x + 5)$$

The factored form of $6x^2 - 2x - 20 = 2(x - 2)(3x + 5)$.

$\llcorner$ Don't forget to include the common factor of 2. □

PRACTICE
3   Factor $30x^2 - 14x - 4$ by grouping.

EXAMPLE 4   Factor $18y^4 + 21y^3 - 60y^2$ by grouping.

Solution

Step 1. First factor out the greatest common factor, $3y^2$.
$$18y^4 + 21y^3 - 60y^2 = 3y^2(6y^2 + 7y - 20)$$

Step 2. Notice that $a = 6, b = 7$, and $c = -20$ in the resulting trinomial. Find two numbers whose product is $a \cdot c$ or $6(-20) = -120$ and whose sum is 7. It may help to factor -120 as a product of primes and -1.
$$-120 = 2 \cdot 2 \cdot 2 \cdot 3 \cdot 5 \cdot (-1)$$

Then choose pairings of factors until you have a pairing whose sum is 7.

The numbers are -8 and 15.

Step 3. $6y^2 + 7y - 20 = 6y^2 - 8y + 15y - 20$
Step 4. $6y^2 - 8y + 15y - 20 = 2y(3y - 4) + 5(3y - 4)$
$$= (3y - 4)(2y + 5)$$

The factored form of $18y^4 + 21y^3 - 60y^2$ is $3y^2(3y - 4)(2y + 5)$.

$\llcorner$ Don't forget to include the common factor of $3y^2$. □

PRACTICE
4   Factor $40m^4 + 5m^3 - 35m^2$ by grouping.

EXAMPLE 5   Factor $4x^2 + 20x + 25$ by grouping.

Solution

Step 1. The terms of this trinomial contain no greatest common factor other than 1 (or -1).

Step 2. In $4x^2 + 20x + 25, a = 4, b = 20$, and $c = 25$. Find two numbers whose product is $a \cdot c$ or $4 \cdot 25 = 100$ and whose sum is 20. The numbers are 10 and 10.

Step 3. Write $20x$ as $10x + 10x$ so that
$$4x^2 + 20x + 25 = 4x^2 + 10x + 10x + 25$$

Step 4. Factor by grouping.
$$4x^2 + 10x + 10x + 25 = 2x(2x + 5) + 5(2x + 5)$$
$$= (2x + 5)(2x + 5)$$

The factored form of $4x^2 + 20x + 25$ is $(2x + 5)(2x + 5)$ or $(2x + 5)^2$. □

PRACTICE
5   Factor $16x^2 + 24x + 9$ by grouping.

A trinomial that is the square of a binomial, such as the trinomial in Example 5, is called a **perfect square trinomial.** From Chapter 5, there are special product formulas we can use to help us recognize and factor these trinomials. To study these formulas further, see Section 6.3, Objective 3. **Remember:** A perfect square trinomial, such as the one in Example 5, may be factored by special product formulas or by other methods of factoring trinomials, such as by grouping.

Vocabulary, Readiness & Video Check

For each trinomial $ax^2 + bx + c$, choose two numbers whose product is $a \cdot c$ and whose sum is b.

1. $x^2 + 6x + 8$
  a. 4, 2   **b.** 7, 1   **c.** 6, 2   **d.** 6, 8

2. $x^2 + 11x + 24$
  a. 6, 4   **b.** 24, 1   **c.** 8, 3   **d.** 2, 12

3. $2x^2 + 13x + 6$
  a. 2, 6   **b.** 12, 1   **c.** 13, 1   **d.** 3, 4

4. $4x^2 + 8x + 3$
  a. 4, 3   **b.** 4, 4   **c.** 12, 1   **d.** 2, 6

Martin-Gay Interactive Videos

See Video 6.4

Watch the section lecture video and answer the following question.

OBJECTIVE
1   **5.** In the lecture following Example 1, why does writing a term as the sum or difference of two terms suggest we'd then try to factor by grouping?

6.4 Exercise Set   MyMathLab®

Factor each polynomial by grouping. Notice that Step 3 has already been done in these exercises. See Examples 1 through 5.

1. $x^2 + 3x + 2x + 6$

2. $x^2 + 5x + 3x + 15$

3. $y^2 + 8y - 2y - 16$

4. $z^2 + 10z - 7z - 70$

5. $8x^2 - 5x - 24x + 15$

6. $4x^2 - 9x - 32x + 72$

7. $5x^4 - 3x^2 + 25x^2 - 15$

8. $2y^4 - 10y^2 + 7y^2 - 35$

MIXED PRACTICE

Factor each trinomial by grouping. Exercises 9–12 are broken into parts to help you get started. See Examples 1 through 5.

9. $6x^2 + 11x + 3$
  a. Find two numbers whose product is $6 \cdot 3 = 18$ and whose sum is 11.

b. Write $11x$ using the factors from part (a).
c. Factor by grouping.

10. $8x^2 + 14x + 3$
  a. Find two numbers whose product is $8 \cdot 3 = 24$ and whose sum is 14.
  b. Write $14x$ using the factors from part (a).
  c. Factor by grouping.

11. $15x^2 - 23x + 4$
  a. Find two numbers whose product is $15 \cdot 4 = 60$ and whose sum is -23.
  b. Write $-23x$ using the factors from part (a).
  c. Factor by grouping.

12. $6x^2 - 13x + 5$
  a. Find two numbers whose product is $6 \cdot 5 = 30$ and whose sum is -13.
  b. Write $-13x$ using the factors from part (a).
  c. Factor by grouping.

13. $21y^2 + 17y + 2$

14. $15x^2 + 11x + 2$

15. $7x^2 - 4x - 11$

16. $8x^2 - x - 9$

17. $10x^2 - 9x + 2$

18. $30x^2 - 23x + 3$

19. $2x^2 - 7x + 5$

20. $2x^2 - 7x + 3$

21. $12x + 4x^2 + 9$

22. $20x + 25x^2 + 4$

23. $4x^2 - 8x - 21$

24. $6x^2 - 11x - 10$

25. $10x^2 - 23x + 12$

26. $21x^2 - 13x + 2$

27. $2x^3 + 13x^2 + 15x$

28. $3x^3 + 8x^2 + 4x$

29. $16y^2 - 34y + 18$

30. $4y^2 - 2y - 12$

31. $-13x + 6 + 6x^2$

32. $-25x + 12 + 12x^2$

33. $54a^2 - 9a - 30$

34. $30a^2 + 38a - 20$

35. $20a^3 + 37a^2 + 8a$

36. $10a^3 + 17a^2 + 3a$

37. $12x^3 - 27x^2 - 27x$

38. $30x^3 - 155x^2 + 25x$

39. $3x^2y + 4xy^2 + y^3$

40. $6r^2t + 7rt^2 + t^3$

41. $20z^2 + 7z + 1$

42. $36z^2 + 6z + 1$

43. $5x^2 + 50xy + 125y^2$

44. $3x^2 + 42xy + 147y^2$

45. $24a^2 - 6ab - 30b^2$

46. $30a^2 + 5ab - 25b^2$

47. $15p^4 + 31p^3q + 2p^2q^2$

48. $20s^4 + 61s^3t + 3s^2t^2$

49. $162a^4 - 72a^2 + 8$

50. $32n^4 - 112n^2 + 98$

51. $35 + 12x + x^2$

52. $33 + 14x + x^2$

53. $6 - 11x + 5x^2$

54. $5 - 12x + 7x^2$

REVIEW AND PREVIEW

Multiply. See Sections 5.3 and 5.4.

55. $(x - 2)(x + 2)$

56. $(y - 5)(y + 5)$

57. $(y + 4)(y + 4)$

58. $(x + 7)(x + 7)$

59. $(9z + 5)(9z - 5)$

60. $(8y + 9)(8y - 9)$

61. $(x - 3)(x^2 + 3x + 9)$

62. $(2z - 1)(4z^2 + 2z + 1)$

CONCEPT EXTENSIONS

Write the perimeter of each figure as a simplified polynomial. Then factor the polynomial.

63.

Regular Pentagon $2x^2 + 9x + 9$

64.

Equilateral Triangle $7x^2 + 11xy + 4y^2$

Factor each polynomial by grouping.

65. $x^{2n} + 2x^n + 3x^n + 6$

(***Hint:*** Don't forget that $x^{2n} = x^n \cdot x^n$.)

66. $x^{2n} + 6x^n + 10x^n + 60$

67. $3x^{2n} + 16x^n - 35$

68. $12x^{2n} - 40x^n + 25$

69. In your own words, explain how to factor a trinomial by grouping.

6.5 | Factoring Binomials

OBJECTIVES

1 Factor the Difference of Two Squares.

2 Factor the Sum or Difference of Two Cubes.

OBJECTIVE

1 Factoring the Difference of Two Squares

When learning to multiply binomials in Chapter 5, we studied a special product, the product of the sum and difference of two terms, a and b:

$$(a + b)(a - b) = a^2 - b^2$$

For example, the product of $x + 3$ and $x - 3$ is

$$(x + 3)(x - 3) = x^2 - 9$$

The binomial $x^2 - 9$ is called a **difference of squares**. In this section, we reverse the pattern for the product of a sum and difference to factor the binomial difference of squares.

> **Factoring the Difference of Two Squares**
> $$a^2 - b^2 = (a + b)(a - b)$$

> ▌ Helpful Hint
> Since multiplication is commutative, remember that the order of factors does not matter. In other words,
> $$a^2 - b^2 = (a + b)(a - b) \text{ or } (a - b)(a + b)$$

EXAMPLE 1   Factor: $x^2 - 25$

Solution $x^2 - 25$ is the difference of two squares since $x^2 - 25 = x^2 - 5^2$. Therefore,
$$x^2 - 25 = x^2 - 5^2 = (x + 5)(x - 5)$$
Multiply to check.

PRACTICE
1   Factor $x^2 - 81$.

EXAMPLE 2   Factor each difference of squares.

a. $4x^2 - 1$ **b.** $25a^2 - 9b^2$ **c.** $y^2 - \dfrac{4}{9}$

Solution

a. $4x^2 - 1 = (2x)^2 - 1^2 = (2x + 1)(2x - 1)$
b. $25a^2 - 9b^2 = (5a)^2 - (3b)^2 = (5a + 3b)(5a - 3b)$
c. $y^2 - \dfrac{4}{9} = y^2 - \left(\dfrac{2}{3}\right)^2 = \left(y + \dfrac{2}{3}\right)\left(y - \dfrac{2}{3}\right)$

PRACTICE
2   Factor each difference of squares.

a. $9x^2 - 1$ **b.** $36a^2 - 49b^2$ **c.** $p^2 - \dfrac{25}{36}$

EXAMPLE 3   Factor: $x^4 - y^6$

Solution   This is a difference of squares since $x^4 = (x^2)^2$ and $y^6 = (y^3)^2$. Thus,
$$x^4 - y^6 = (x^2)^2 - (y^3)^2 = (x^2 + y^3)(x^2 - y^3)$$

PRACTICE
3   Factor $p^4 - q^{10}$.

EXAMPLE 4   Factor each binomial.
a. $y^4 - 16$ **b.** $x^2 + 4$

Solution

a. $y^4 - 16 = (y^2)^2 - 4^2$
         $= (y^2 + 4)\underbrace{(y^2 - 4)}$ Factor the difference of two squares. This binomial can be factored further since it is the difference of two squares.
         $= (y^2 + 4)(y + 2)(y - 2)$ Factor the difference of two squares.

(Continued on next page)

b. $x^2 + 4$

Note that the binomial $x^2 + 4$ is the *sum* of two squares since we can write $x^2 + 4$ as $x^2 + 2^2$. We might try to factor using $(x + 2)(x + 2)$ or $(x - 2)(x - 2)$. But when we multiply to check, we find that neither factoring is correct.

$$(x + 2)(x + 2) = x^2 + 4x + 4$$
$$(x - 2)(x - 2) = x^2 - 4x + 4$$

In both cases, the product is a trinomial, not the required binomial. In fact, $x^2 + 4$ is a prime polynomial.

PRACTICE

4 Factor each binomial.

a. $z^4 - 81$　　　　　　　　**b.** $m^2 + 49$

▶ Helpful Hint

When factoring, don't forget:
- See whether the terms have a greatest common factor (GCF) (other than 1) that can be factored out.
- Other than a GCF, the **sum** of two squares cannot be factored using real numbers.
- Factor completely. Always check to see whether any factors can be factored further.

EXAMPLES　Factor each binomial.

5. $4x^3 - 49x = x(4x^2 - 49)$　　　　　Factor out the common factor, x.

$\qquad = x[(2x)^2 - 7^2]$

$\qquad = x(2x + 7)(2x - 7)$　　　　Factor the difference of two squares.

6. $162x^4 - 2 = 2(81x^4 - 1)$　　　　　Factor out the common factor, 2.

$\qquad = 2(9x^2 + 1)(9x^2 - 1)$　　　Factor the difference of two squares.

$\qquad = 2(9x^2 + 1)(3x + 1)(3x - 1)$　Factor the difference of two squares.

PRACTICES

5–6 Factor each binomial.

5. $36y^3 - 25y$　　　　　　　　**6.** $80y^4 - 5$

EXAMPLE 7　Factor: $-49x^2 + 16$

Solution　Factor as is, or, if you like, rearrange terms.

Factor as is: $-49x^2 + 16 = -1(49x^2 - 16)$　　　Factor out -1.

$\qquad\qquad\qquad = -1(7x + 4)(7x - 4)$　　Factor the difference of two squares.

▶ Helpful Hint

When rearranging terms, keep in mind that the sign of a term is in front of the term.

Rewrite binomial: $-49x^2 + 16 = 16 - 49x^2 = 4^2 - (7x)^2$

$\qquad\qquad\qquad = (4 + 7x)(4 - 7x)$

Both factorizations are correct and are equal. To see this, factor -1 from $(4 - 7x)$ in the second factorization.

PRACTICE

7 Factor $-9x^2 + 100$.

OBJECTIVE

2   Factoring the Sum or Difference of Two Cubes

Although the sum of two squares usually does not factor, the sum or difference of two cubes can be factored and reveals factoring patterns. The pattern for the sum of cubes is illustrated by multiplying the binomial $x + y$ and the trinomial $x^2 - xy + y^2$.

$$
\begin{array}{r}
x^2 - xy + y^2 \\
x + y \\
\hline
x^2y - xy^2 + y^3 \\
x^3 - x^2y + xy^2 \\
\hline
x^3 \qquad\qquad + y^3
\end{array}
$$

Thus, $(x + y)(x^2 - xy + y^2) = x^3 + y^3$ Sum of cubes

The pattern for the difference of two cubes is illustrated by multiplying the binomial $x - y$ by the trinomial $x^2 + xy + y^2$. The result is

$$(x - y)(x^2 + xy + y^2) = x^3 - y^3 \qquad \text{Difference of cubes}$$

Factoring the Sum or Difference of Two Cubes

$$a^3 + b^3 = (a + b)(a^2 - ab + b^2)$$
$$a^3 - b^3 = (a - b)(a^2 + ab + b^2)$$

Recall that "factor" means "to write as a product." Above are patterns for writing sums and differences as products.

EXAMPLE 8   Factor: $x^3 + 8$

Solution   First, write the binomial in the form $a^3 + b^3$.

$$x^3 + 8 = x^3 + 2^3 \qquad \text{Write in the form } a^3 + b^3.$$

If we replace a with x and b with 2 in the formula above, we have

$$x^3 + 2^3 = (x + 2)[x^2 - (x)(2) + 2^2]$$
$$= (x + 2)(x^2 - 2x + 4)$$

PRACTICE

8   Factor $x^3 + 64$.

▶ Helpful Hint

When factoring sums or differences of cubes, notice the sign patterns.

$$\overset{\text{same sign}}{x^3 + y^3} = (x + y)(x^2 - xy + y^2)$$

opposite signs   always positive

$$\overset{\text{same sign}}{x^3 - y^3} = (x - y)(x^2 + xy + y^2)$$

opposite signs   always positive

EXAMPLE 9   Factor: $y^3 - 27$

Solution $y^3 - 27 = y^3 - 3^3$ \qquad\qquad Write in the form $a^3 - b^3$.

$$= (y - 3)[y^2 + (y)(3) + 3^2]$$
$$= (y - 3)(y^2 + 3y + 9)$$

PRACTICE

9   Factor $x^3 - 125$.

EXAMPLE 10 Factor: $64x^3 + 1$

Solution
$$64x^3 + 1 = (4x)^3 + 1^3$$
$$= (4x + 1)[(4x)^2 - (4x)(1) + 1^2]$$
$$= (4x + 1)(16x^2 - 4x + 1)$$

PRACTICE
10 Factor $27y^3 + 1$.

EXAMPLE 11 Factor: $54a^3 - 16b^3$

Solution Remember to factor out common factors first before using other factoring methods.

$$54a^3 - 16b^3 = 2(27a^3 - 8b^3) \quad \text{Factor out the GCF 2.}$$
$$= 2[(3a)^3 - (2b)^3] \quad \text{Difference of two cubes}$$
$$= 2(3a - 2b)[(3a)^2 + (3a)(2b) + (2b)^2]$$
$$= 2(3a - 2b)(9a^2 + 6ab + 4b^2)$$

PRACTICE
11 Factor $32x^3 - 500y^3$.

Graphing Calculator Explorations

Graphing

A graphing calculator is a convenient tool for evaluating an expression at a given replacement value. For example, let's evaluate $x^2 - 6x$ when $x = 2$. To do so, store the value 2 in the variable x and then enter and evaluate the algebraic expression.

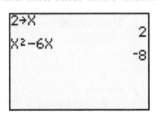

The value of $x^2 - 6x$ when $x = 2$ is -8. You may want to use this method for evaluating expressions as you explore the following.

We can use a graphing calculator to explore factoring patterns numerically. Use your calculator to evaluate $x^2 - 2x + 1$, $x^2 - 2x - 1$, and $(x - 1)^2$ for each value of x given in the table. What do you observe?

	$x^2 - 2x + 1$	$x^2 - 2x - 1$	$(x - 1)^2$
$x = 5$			
$x = -3$			
$x = 2.7$			
$x = -12.1$			
$x = 0$			

Notice in each case that $x^2 - 2x - 1 \neq (x - 1)^2$. Because for each x in the table the value of $x^2 - 2x + 1$ and the value of $(x - 1)^2$ are the same, we might guess that $x^2 - 2x + 1 = (x - 1)^2$. We can verify our guess algebraically with multiplication:

$$(x - 1)(x - 1) = x^2 - x - x + 1 = x^2 - 2x + 1$$

Vocabulary, Readiness & Video Check

Use the choices below to fill in each blank. Some choices may be used more than once and some choices may not be used at all.

true	difference of two squares	sum of two cubes
false	difference of two cubes	

1. The expression $x^3 - 27$ is called a _____.

2. The expression $x^2 - 49$ is called a _____.

3. The expression $z^3 + 1$ is called a _____.

4. True or false: The binomial $y^2 + 9$ factors as $(y + 3)^2$. _____

Write each term as a square.

5. $49x^2$ **6.** $25y^4$

Write each term as a cube.

7. $8y^3$ **8.** x^6

Martin-Gay Interactive Videos

See Video 6.5

Watch the section lecture video and answer the following questions.

OBJECTIVE 1

9. In Examples 1 and 2, what are two reasons the original binomial is rewritten so that each term is a square?

OBJECTIVE 1

10. From Example 3, what is a prime polynomial?

OBJECTIVE 2

11. In ▭ Examples 6–8, what tips are given to remember how to factor the sum or difference of two cubes rather than memorizing the formulas?

6.5 Exercise Set   MyMathLab®

Factor each binomial completely. See Examples 1 through 7.

1. $x^2 - 4$

2. $x^2 - 36$

3. $81p^2 - 1$

4. $49m^2 - 1$

5. $25y^2 - 9$

6. $49a^2 - 16$

7. $121m^2 - 100n^2$

8. $169a^2 - 49b^2$

9. $x^2y^2 - 1$

10. $a^2b^2 - 16$

11. $x^2 - \dfrac{1}{4}$

12. $y^2 - \dfrac{1}{16}$

13. $-4r^2 + 1$

14. $-9t^2 + 1$

15. $16r^2 + 1$

16. $49y^2 + 1$

17. $-36 + x^2$

18. $-1 + y^2$

19. $m^4 - 1$

20. $n^4 - 16$

21. $m^4 - n^{18}$

22. $n^4 - r^6$

Factor the sum or difference of two cubes. See Examples 8 through 11.

23. $x^3 + 125$

24. $p^3 + 1$

25. $8a^3 - 1$

26. $27y^3 - 1$

27. $m^3 + 27n^3$

28. $y^3 + 64z^3$

29. $5k^3 + 40$

30. $6r^3 + 162$

31. $x^3y^3 - 64$

32. $a^3b^3 - 8$

33. $250r^3 - 128t^3$

34. $24x^3 - 81y^3$

MIXED PRACTICE

Factor each binomial completely. See Examples 1 through 11.

35. $r^2 - 64$

36. $q^2 - 121$

37. $x^2 - 169y^2$

38. $x^2 - 225y^2$

39. $27 - t^3$

40. $125 - r^3$

41. $18r^2 - 8$

42. $32t^2 - 50$

43. $9xy^2 - 4x$

44. $36x^2y - 25y$

45. $8m^3 + 64$

46. $2x^3 + 54$

47. $xy^3 - 9xyz^2$

48. $x^3y - 4xy^3$

49. $36x^2 - 64y^2$

50. $225a^2 - 81b^2$

51. $144 - 81x^2$

52. $12x^2 - 27$

53. $x^3y^3 - z^6$

54. $a^3b^3 - c^9$

55. $49 - \dfrac{9}{25}m^2$

56. $100 - \dfrac{4}{81}n^2$

57. $t^3 + 343$

58. $s^3 + 216$

59. $n^3 + 49n$

60. $y^3 + 64y$

61. $x^6 - 81x^2$

62. $n^9 - n^5$

63. $64p^3q - 81pq^3$

64. $100x^3y - 49xy^3$

65. $27x^2y^3 + xy^2$

66. $8x^3y^3 + x^3y$

67. $125a^4 - 64ab^3$

68. $64m^4 - 27mn^3$

69. $16x^4 - 64x^2$

70. $25y^4 - 100y^2$

REVIEW AND PREVIEW

Solve each equation. See Section 2.2.

71. $x - 6 = 0$

72. $y + 5 = 0$

73. $2m + 4 = 0$

74. $3x - 9 = 0$

75. $5z - 1 = 0$

76. $4a + 2 = 0$

CONCEPT EXTENSIONS

Factor each expression completely.

77. $(x + 2)^2 - y^2$

78. $(y - 6)^2 - z^2$

79. $a^2(b - 4) - 16(b - 4)$

80. $m^2(n + 8) - 9(n + 8)$

81. $(x^2 + 6x + 9) - 4y^2$ (*Hint:* Factor the trinomial in parentheses first.)

82. $(x^2 + 2x + 1) - 36y^2$

83. $x^{2n} - 100$

84. $x^{2n} - 81$

85. What binomial multiplied by $(x - 6)$ gives the difference of two squares?

86. What binomial multiplied by $(5 + y)$ gives the difference of two squares?

87. In your own words, explain how to tell whether a binomial is a difference of squares. Then explain how to factor a difference of squares.

88. In your own words, explain how to tell whether a binomial is a sum of cubes. Then explain how to factor a sum of cubes.

89. The Toroweap Overlook, on the North Rim of the Grand Canyon, lies 3000 vertical feet above the Colorado River. The view is spectacular, and the sheer drop is dramatic. A film crew creating a documentary about the Grand Canyon has suspended a camera platform 296 feet below the Overlook. A camera filter comes loose and falls to the river below. The height of the filter above the river after t seconds is given by the expression $2704 - 16t^2$.

   a. Find the height of the filter above the river after 3 seconds.

   b. Find the height of the filter above the river after 7 seconds.

   c. To the nearest whole second, estimate when the filter lands in the river.

   d. Factor $2704 - 16t^2$.

90. An object is dropped from the top of Pittsburgh's USX Tower, which is 841 feet tall. (*Source: World Almanac* research) The height of the object after t seconds is given by the expression $841 - 16t^2$.

   a. Find the height of the object after 2 seconds.

   b. Find the height of the object after 5 seconds.

   c. To the nearest whole second, estimate when the object hits the ground.

   d. Factor $841 - 16t^2$.

841 feet

91. At this writing, the world's second tallest building is the Taipei 101 in Taipei, Taiwan, at a height of 1671 feet. (*Source:* Council on Tall Buildings and Urban Habitat) Suppose a worker is suspended 71 feet below the top of the pinnacle atop the building, at a height of 1600 feet above the ground. If the worker accidentally drops a bolt, the height of the bolt after t seconds is given by the expression $1600 - 16t^2$.

  a. Find the height of the bolt after 3 seconds.

  b. Find the height of the bolt after 7 seconds.

  c. To the nearest whole second, estimate when the bolt hits the ground.

  d. Factor $1600 - 16t^2$.

92. A performer with the Moscow Circus is planning a stunt involving a free fall from the top of the Moscow State University building, which is 784 feet tall. (*Source:* Council on Tall Buildings and Urban Habitat) Neglecting air resistance, the performer's height above gigantic cushions positioned at ground level after t seconds is given by the expression $784 - 16t^2$.

  a. Find the performer's height after 2 seconds.

  b. Find the performer's height after 5 seconds.

  c. To the nearest whole second, estimate when the performer reaches the cushions positioned at ground level.

  d. Factor $784 - 16t^2$.

Integrated Review   CHOOSING A FACTORING STRATEGY

Sections 6.1–6.5

The following steps may be helpful when factoring polynomials.

Factoring a Polynomial

Step 1.   Are there any common factors? If so, factor out the GCF.

Step 2.   How many terms are in the polynomial?

  a. If there are **two** terms, decide if one of the following can be applied.

   i. Difference of two squares: $a^2 - b^2 = (a + b)(a - b)$.

   ii. Difference of two cubes: $a^3 - b^3 = (a - b)(a^2 + ab + b^2)$.

   iii. Sum of two cubes: $a^3 + b^3 = (a + b)(a^2 - ab + b^2)$.

  b. If there are **three** terms, try one of the following.

   i. Perfect square trinomial: $a^2 + 2ab + b^2 = (a + b)^2$
   $$a^2 - 2ab + b^2 = (a - b)^2.$$

   ii. If not a perfect square trinomial, factor using the methods presented in Sections 6.2 through 6.4.

  c. If there are **four** or more terms, try factoring by grouping.

Step 3.   See if any factors in the factored polynomial can be factored further.

Step 4.   Check by multiplying.

Study the next five examples to help you use the steps above.

EXAMPLE 1   Factor $10t^2 - 17t + 3$.

Solution

Step 1.   The terms of this polynomial have no common factor (other than 1).

Step 2.   There are three terms, so this polynomial is a trinomial. This trinomial is not a perfect square trinomial, so factor using methods from earlier sections.

Factors of $10t^2$: $10t^2 = 2t \cdot 5t$, $10t^2 = t \cdot 10t$

(Continued on next page)

Since the middle term, $-17t$, has a negative numerical coefficient, find negative factors of 3.

$$\text{Factors of 3: } 3 = -1 \cdot -3$$

Try different combinations of these factors. The correct combination is

$$(2t - 3)(5t - 1) = 10t^2 - 17t + 3$$

$$-15t$$
$$-2t$$
$$-17t \quad \text{Correct middle term}$$

Step 3. No factor can be factored further, so we have factored completely.

Step 4. To check, multiply $2t - 3$ and $5t - 1$.

$$(2t - 3)(5t - 1) = 10t^2 - 2t - 15t + 3 = 10t^2 - 17t + 3$$

The factored form of $10t^2 - 17t + 3$ is $(2t - 3)(5t - 1)$.

PRACTICE
1 Factor $6x^2 - 11x + 3$.

EXAMPLE 2 Factor $2x^3 + 3x^2 - 2x - 3$.

Solution

Step 1. There are no factors common to all terms.

Step 2. Try factoring by grouping since this polynomial has four terms.

$$2x^3 + 3x^2 - 2x - 3 = x^2(2x + 3) - 1(2x + 3) \quad \text{Factor out the greatest common factor for each pair of terms.}$$

$$= (2x + 3)(x^2 - 1) \quad \text{Factor out } 2x + 3.$$

Step 3. The binomial $x^2 - 1$ can be factored further. It is the difference of two squares.

$$= (2x + 3)(x + 1)(x - 1) \quad \text{Factor } x^2 - 1 \text{ as a difference of squares.}$$

Step 4. Check by finding the product of the three binomials. The polynomial factored completely is $(2x + 3)(x + 1)(x - 1)$.

PRACTICE
2 Factor $3x^3 + x^2 - 12x - 4$.

EXAMPLE 3 Factor $12m^2 - 3n^2$.

Solution

Step 1. The terms of this binomial contain a greatest common factor of 3.

$$12m^2 - 3n^2 = 3(4m^2 - n^2) \quad \text{Factor out the greatest common factor.}$$

Step 2. The binomial $4m^2 - n^2$ is a difference of squares.

$$= 3(2m + n)(2m - n) \quad \text{Factor the difference of squares.}$$

Step 3. No factor can be factored further.

Step 4. We check by multiplying.

$$3(2m + n)(2m - n) = 3(4m^2 - n^2) = 12m^2 - 3n^2$$

The factored form of $12m^2 - 3n^2$ is $3(2m + n)(2m - n)$.

PRACTICE
3 Factor $27x^2 - 3y^2$.

EXAMPLE 4 Factor $x^3 + 27y^3$.

Solution

Step 1. The terms of this binomial contain no common factor (other than 1).

Step 2. This binomial is the sum of two cubes.

$$\begin{aligned}
x^3 + 27y^3 &= (x)^3 + (3y)^3 \\
&= (x + 3y)[x^2 - x(3y) + (3y)^2] \\
&= (x + 3y)(x^2 - 3xy + 9y^2)
\end{aligned}$$

Step 3. No factor can be factored further.

Step 4. We check by multiplying.

$$\begin{aligned}
(x + 3y)(x^2 - 3xy + 9y^2) &= x(x^2 - 3xy + 9y^2) + 3y(x^2 - 3xy + 9y^2) \\
&= x^3 - 3x^2y + 9xy^2 + 3x^2y - 9xy^2 + 27y^3 \\
&= x^3 + 27y^3
\end{aligned}$$

Thus, $x^3 + 27y^3$ factored completely is $(x + 3y)(x^2 - 3xy + 9y^2)$. ☐

PRACTICE
4 Factor $8a^3 + b^3$.

EXAMPLE 5 Factor $30a^2b^3 + 55a^2b^2 - 35a^2b$.

Solution

Step 1. $30a^2b^3 + 55a^2b^2 - 35a^2b = 5a^2b(6b^2 + 11b - 7)$ Factor out the GCF.

Step 2. $= 5a^2b(2b - 1)(3b + 7)$ Factor the resulting trinomial.

Step 3. No factor can be factored further.

Step 4. Check by multiplying.

The trinomial factored completely is $5a^2b(2b - 1)(3b + 7)$. ☐

PRACTICE
5 Factor $60x^3y^2 - 66x^2y^2 - 36xy^2$.

Factor the following completely.

1. $x^2 + 2xy + y^2$

2. $x^2 - 2xy + y^2$

3. $a^2 + 11a - 12$

4. $a^2 - 11a + 10$

5. $a^2 - a - 6$

6. $a^2 - 2a + 1$

7. $x^2 + 2x + 1$

8. $x^2 + x - 2$

9. $x^2 + 4x + 3$

10. $x^2 + x - 6$

11. $x^2 + 7x + 12$

12. $x^2 + x - 12$

13. $x^2 + 3x - 4$

14. $x^2 - 7x + 10$

15. $x^2 + 2x - 15$

16. $x^2 + 11x + 30$

17. $x^2 - x - 30$

18. $x^2 + 11x + 24$

19. $2x^2 - 98$

20. $3x^2 - 75$

21. $x^2 + 3x + xy + 3y$

22. $3y - 21 + xy - 7x$

23. $x^2 + 6x - 16$

24. $x^2 - 3x - 28$

25. $4x^3 + 20x^2 - 56x$

26. $6x^3 - 6x^2 - 120x$

27. $12x^2 + 34x + 24$

28. $8a^2 + 6ab - 5b^2$

29. $4a^2 - b^2$

30. $28 - 13x - 6x^2$

31. $20 - 3x - 2x^2$

32. $x^2 - 2x + 4$

33. $a^2 + a - 3$

34. $6y^2 + y - 15$

35. $4x^2 - x - 5$

36. $x^2y - y^3$

37. $4t^2 + 36$

38. $x^2 + x + xy + y$

39. $ax + 2x + a + 2$

40. $18x^3 - 63x^2 + 9x$

41. $12a^3 - 24a^2 + 4a$

42. $x^2 + 14x - 32$

43. $x^2 - 14x - 48$

44. $16a^2 - 56ab + 49b^2$

45. $25p^2 - 70pq + 49q^2$

46. $7x^2 + 24xy + 9y^2$

47. $125 - 8y^3$

48. $64x^3 + 27$

49. $-x^2 - x + 30$
50. $-x^2 + 6x - 8$
51. $14 + 5x - x^2$
52. $3 - 2x - x^2$
53. $3x^4y + 6x^3y - 72x^2y$
54. $2x^3y + 8x^2y^2 - 10xy^3$
55. $5x^3y^2 - 40x^2y^3 + 35xy^4$
56. $4x^4y - 8x^3y - 60x^2y$
57. $12x^3y + 243xy$
58. $6x^3y^2 + 8xy^2$
59. $4 - x^2$
60. $9 - y^2$
61. $3rs - s + 12r - 4$
62. $x^3 - 2x^2 + 3x - 6$
63. $4x^2 - 8xy - 3x + 6y$
64. $4x^2 - 2xy - 7yz + 14xz$
65. $6x^2 + 18xy + 12y^2$
66. $12x^2 + 46xy - 8y^2$
67. $xy^2 - 4x + 3y^2 - 12$
68. $x^2y^2 - 9x^2 + 3y^2 - 27$
69. $5(x + y) + x(x + y)$
70. $7(x - y) + y(x - y)$
71. $14t^2 - 9t + 1$
72. $3t^2 - 5t + 1$
73. $3x^2 + 2x - 5$
74. $7x^2 + 19x - 6$
75. $x^2 + 9xy - 36y^2$
76. $3x^2 + 10xy - 8y^2$
77. $1 - 8ab - 20a^2b^2$
78. $1 - 7ab - 60a^2b^2$
79. $9 - 10x^2 + x^4$
80. $36 - 13x^2 + x^4$
81. $x^4 - 14x^2 - 32$
82. $x^4 - 22x^2 - 75$
83. $x^2 - 23x + 120$
84. $y^2 + 22y + 96$

85. $6x^3 - 28x^2 + 16x$
86. $6y^3 - 8y^2 - 30y$
87. $27x^3 - 125y^3$
88. $216y^3 - z^3$
89. $x^3y^3 + 8z^3$
90. $27a^3b^3 + 8$
91. $2xy - 72x^3y$
92. $2x^3 - 18x$
93. $x^3 + 6x^2 - 4x - 24$
94. $x^3 - 2x^2 - 36x + 72$
95. $6a^3 + 10a^2$
96. $4n^2 - 6n$
97. $a^2(a + 2) + 2(a + 2)$
98. $a - b + x(a - b)$
99. $x^3 - 28 + 7x^2 - 4x$
100. $a^3 - 45 - 9a + 5a^2$

CONCEPT EXTENSIONS

Factor.

101. $(x - y)^2 - z^2$
102. $(x + 2y)^2 - 9$
103. $81 - (5x + 1)^2$
104. $b^2 - (4a + c)^2$
105. Explain why it makes good sense to factor out the GCF first, before using other methods of factoring.
106. The sum of two squares usually does not factor. Is the sum of two squares $9x^2 + 81y^2$ factorable?
107. Which of the following are equivalent to $(x + 10)(x - 7)$?
  a. $(x - 7)(x + 10)$ **b.** $-1(x + 10)(x - 7)$
  c. $-1(x + 10)(7 - x)$ **d.** $-1(-x - 10)(7 - x)$
108. Which of the following are equivalent to $(x - 2)(x - 5)$?
  a. $-1(x + 2)(x + 5)$ **b.** $(x - 5)(x - 2)$
  c. $(5 - x)(2 - x)$ **d.** $-1(x + 2)(x - 5)$

6.6 Solving Quadratic Equations by Factoring

OBJECTIVES

1 Solve Quadratic Equations by Factoring.

2 Solve Equations with Degree Greater than 2 by Factoring.

3 Find the *x*-Intercepts of the Graph of a Quadratic Equation in Two Variables.

In this section, we introduce a new type of equation—the **quadratic equation.**

Quadratic Equation

A quadratic equation is one that can be written in the form
$$ax^2 + bx + c = 0$$
where $a, b,$ and c are real numbers and $a \neq 0$.

Some examples of quadratic equations are shown below.

$$x^2 - 9x - 22 = 0 \qquad 4x^2 - 28 = -49 \qquad x(2x - 7) = 4$$

The form $ax^2 + bx + c = 0$ is called the **standard form** of a quadratic equation. The quadratic equation $x^2 - 9x - 22 = 0$ is the only equation above that is in standard form.

144 feet

Quadratic equations model many real-life situations. For example, let's suppose we want to know how long before a person diving from a 144-foot cliff reaches the ocean. The answer to this question is found by solving the quadratic equation $-16t^2 + 144 = 0$. (See Example 1 in Section 6.7.)

OBJECTIVE

1 Solving Quadratic Equations by Factoring

Some quadratic equations can be solved by making use of factoring and the **zero factor property.**

Zero Factor Theorem

If a and b are real numbers and if $ab = 0$, then $a = 0$ or $b = 0$.

This theorem states that if the product of two numbers is 0, then at least one of the numbers must be 0.

EXAMPLE 1 Solve: $(x - 3)(x + 1) = 0$

Solution If this equation is to be a true statement, then either the factor $x - 3$ must be 0 or the factor $x + 1$ must be 0. In other words, either

$$x - 3 = 0 \quad \text{or} \quad x + 1 = 0$$

If we solve these two linear equations, we have

$$x = 3 \quad \text{or} \quad x = -1$$

Thus, 3 and -1 are both solutions of the equation $(x - 3)(x + 1) = 0$. To check, we replace x with 3 in the original equation. Then we replace x with -1 in the original equation.

Check: Let $x = 3$. | Let $x = -1$.
$(x - 3)(x + 1) = 0$ | $(x - 3)(x + 1) = 0$
$(3 - 3)(3 + 1) \overset{?}{=} 0$ Replace x with 3. | $(-1 - 3)(-1 + 1) \overset{?}{=} 0$ Replace x with -1.
$0(4) = 0$ True | $(-4)(0) = 0$ True

The solutions are 3 and -1, or we say that the solution set is $\{-1, 3\}$. □

PRACTICE

1 Solve: $(x + 4)(x - 5) = 0$.

▶ Helpful Hint

The zero factor property says that *if a product is 0, then a factor is 0.*

If $a \cdot b = 0$, then $a = 0$ or $b = 0$.
If $x(x + 5) = 0$, then $x = 0$ or $x + 5 = 0$.
If $(x + 7)(2x - 3) = 0$, then $x + 7 = 0$ or $2x - 3 = 0$.

Use this property only when the product is 0.
For example, if $a \cdot b = 8$, we do not know the value of a or b. The values may be $a = 2, b = 4$ or $a = 8, b = 1$, or any other two numbers whose product is 8.

EXAMPLE 2 Solve: $(x - 5)(2x + 7) = 0$

Solution: The product is 0. By the zero factor property, this is true only when a factor is 0. To solve, we set each factor equal to 0 and solve the resulting linear equations.

$$(x - 5)(2x + 7) = 0$$
$$x - 5 = 0 \quad \text{or} \quad 2x + 7 = 0$$
$$x = 5 \qquad\qquad 2x = -7$$
$$x = -\frac{7}{2}$$

(Continued on next page)

Check: Let $x = 5$.

$$(x - 5)(2x + 7) = 0$$
$$(5 - 5)(2 \cdot 5 + 7) \stackrel{?}{=} 0 \quad \text{Replace } x \text{ with 5.}$$
$$0 \cdot 17 \stackrel{?}{=} 0$$
$$0 = 0 \quad \text{True}$$

Let $x = -\dfrac{7}{2}$.

$$(x - 5)(2x + 7) = 0$$
$$\left(-\frac{7}{2} - 5\right)\left(2\left(-\frac{7}{2}\right) + 7\right) \stackrel{?}{=} 0 \quad \text{Replace } x \text{ with } -\frac{7}{2}.$$
$$\left(-\frac{17}{2}\right)(-7 + 7) \stackrel{?}{=} 0$$
$$\left(-\frac{17}{2}\right) \cdot 0 \stackrel{?}{=} 0$$
$$0 = 0 \quad \text{True}$$

The solutions are 5 and $-\dfrac{7}{2}$.

PRACTICE
2 Solve: $(x - 12)(4x + 3) = 0$

EXAMPLE 3 Solve: $x(5x - 2) = 0$

Solution
$$x(5x - 2) = 0$$
$$x = 0 \quad \text{or} \quad 5x - 2 = 0 \quad \text{Use the zero factor property.}$$
$$5x = 2$$
$$x = \frac{2}{5}$$

Check: Let $x = 0$.

$$x(5x - 2) = 0$$
$$0(5 \cdot 0 - 2) \stackrel{?}{=} 0 \quad \text{Replace } x \text{ with 0.}$$
$$0(-2) \stackrel{?}{=} 0$$
$$0 = 0 \quad \text{True}$$

Let $x = \dfrac{2}{5}$.

$$x(5x - 2) = 0$$
$$\frac{2}{5}\left(5 \cdot \frac{2}{5} - 2\right) \stackrel{?}{=} 0 \quad \text{Replace } x \text{ with } \frac{2}{5}.$$
$$\frac{2}{5}(2 - 2) \stackrel{?}{=} 0$$
$$\frac{2}{5}(0) \stackrel{?}{=} 0$$
$$0 = 0 \quad \text{True}$$

The solutions are 0 and $\dfrac{2}{5}$.

PRACTICE
3 Solve: $x(7x - 6) = 0$.

EXAMPLE 4 Solve: $x^2 - 9x - 22 = 0$

Solution One side of the equation is 0. However, to use the zero factor property, one side of the equation must be 0 *and* the other side must be written as a product (must be factored). Thus, we must first factor this polynomial.

$$x^2 - 9x - 22 = 0$$
$$(x - 11)(x + 2) = 0 \quad \text{Factor.}$$

Now we can apply the zero factor property.

$$x - 11 = 0 \quad \text{or} \quad x + 2 = 0$$
$$x = 11 \qquad\qquad x = -2$$

Check: Let $x = 11$.

$$x^2 - 9x - 22 = 0$$
$$11^2 - 9 \cdot 11 - 22 \stackrel{?}{=} 0$$
$$121 - 99 - 22 \stackrel{?}{=} 0$$
$$22 - 22 \stackrel{?}{=} 0$$
$$0 = 0 \quad \text{True}$$

Let $x = -2$.

$$x^2 - 9x - 22 = 0$$
$$(-2)^2 - 9(-2) - 22 \stackrel{?}{=} 0$$
$$4 + 18 - 22 \stackrel{?}{=} 0$$
$$22 - 22 \stackrel{?}{=} 0$$
$$0 = 0 \quad \text{True}$$

The solutions are 11 and -2.

PRACTICE
4   Solve: $x^2 - 8x - 48 = 0$.

EXAMPLE 5   Solve: $4x^2 - 28x = -49$

Solution   First we rewrite the equation in standard form so that one side is 0. Then we factor the polynomial.

$$4x^2 - 28x = -49$$
$$4x^2 - 28x + 49 = 0 \qquad \text{Write in standard form by adding 49 to both sides.}$$
$$(2x - 7)(2x - 7) = 0 \qquad \text{Factor.}$$

Next we use the zero factor property and set each factor equal to 0. Since the factors are the same, the related equations will give the same solution.

$$2x - 7 = 0 \quad \text{or} \quad 2x - 7 = 0 \qquad \text{Set each factor equal to 0.}$$
$$2x = 7 \qquad\qquad 2x = 7 \qquad \text{Solve.}$$
$$x = \frac{7}{2} \qquad\qquad x = \frac{7}{2}$$

Check: Although $\frac{7}{2}$ occurs twice, there is a single solution. Check this solution in the original equation. The solution is $\frac{7}{2}$.

PRACTICE
5   Solve: $9x^2 - 24x = -16$.

The following steps may be used to solve a quadratic equation by factoring.

> **To Solve Quadratic Equations by Factoring**
>
> **Step 1.**   Write the equation in standard form so that one side of the equation is 0.
> **Step 2.**   Factor the quadratic expression completely.
> **Step 3.**   Set each factor containing a variable equal to 0.
> **Step 4.**   Solve the resulting equations.
> **Step 5.**   Check each solution in the original equation.

Since it is not always possible to factor a quadratic polynomial, not all quadratic equations can be solved by factoring. Other methods of solving quadratic equations are presented in Chapter 11.

EXAMPLE 6 Solve: $x(2x - 7) = 4$

Solution First we write the equation in standard form; then we factor.

$$x(2x - 7) = 4$$
$$2x^2 - 7x = 4 \qquad \text{Multiply.}$$
$$2x^2 - 7x - 4 = 0 \qquad \text{Write in standard form.}$$
$$(2x + 1)(x - 4) = 0 \qquad \text{Factor.}$$
$$2x + 1 = 0 \quad \text{or} \quad x - 4 = 0 \qquad \text{Set each factor equal to zero.}$$
$$2x = -1 \qquad\qquad x = 4 \qquad \text{Solve.}$$
$$x = -\frac{1}{2}$$

Check the solutions in the original equation. The solutions are $-\frac{1}{2}$ and 4.

> **Helpful Hint**
>
> To solve the equation $x(2x - 7) = 4$, do **not** set each factor equal to 4. Remember that to apply the zero factor property, one side of the equation must be 0 and the other side of the equation must be in factored form.

PRACTICE
6 Solve: $x(3x + 7) = 6$.

✓**CONCEPT CHECK**
Explain the error and solve the equation correctly.

$$(x - 3)(x + 1) = 5$$
$$x - 3 = 5 \quad \text{or} \quad x + 1 = 5$$
$$x = 8 \quad \text{or} \quad x = 4$$

EXAMPLE 7 Solve: $-2x^2 - 4x + 30 = 0$.

Solution The equation is in standard form, so we begin by factoring out a common factor of -2.

$$-2x^2 - 4x + 30 = 0$$
$$-2(x^2 + 2x - 15) = 0 \qquad \text{Factor out } -2.$$
$$-2(x + 5)(x - 3) = 0 \qquad \text{Factor the quadratic.}$$

Next, set each factor **containing a variable** equal to 0.

$$x + 5 = 0 \qquad \text{or} \qquad x - 3 = 0 \qquad \text{Set each factor containing a variable equal to 0.}$$
$$x = -5 \qquad \text{or} \qquad x = 3 \qquad \text{Solve.}$$

Note: The factor -2 is a constant term containing no variables and can never equal 0. The solutions are -5 and 3.

PRACTICE
7 Solve: $-3x^2 - 6x + 72 = 0$.

Answer to Concept Check:
To use the zero factor property, one side of the equation must be 0, not 5. Correctly, $(x - 3)(x + 1) = 5$, $x^2 - 2x - 3 = 5$, $x^2 - 2x - 8 = 0$, $(x - 4)(x + 2) = 0$, $x - 4 = 0$ or $x + 2 = 0$, $x = 4$ or $x = -2$.

OBJECTIVE
2 Solving Equations with Degree Greater than Two by Factoring

Some equations involving polynomials of degree higher than 2 may also be solved by factoring and then applying the zero factor theorem.

EXAMPLE 8   Solve: $3x^3 - 12x = 0$.

Solution   Factor the left side of the equation. Begin by factoring out the common factor of $3x$.

$$3x^3 - 12x = 0$$
$$3x(x^2 - 4) = 0 \quad \text{Factor out the GCF } 3x.$$
$$3x(x + 2)(x - 2) = 0 \quad \text{Factor } x^2 - 4, \text{ a difference of squares.}$$
$$3x = 0 \quad \text{or} \quad x + 2 = 0 \quad \text{or} \quad x - 2 = 0 \quad \text{Set each factor equal to 0.}$$
$$x = 0 \quad \text{or} \quad x = -2 \quad \text{or} \quad x = 2 \quad \text{Solve.}$$

Thus, the equation $3x^3 - 12x = 0$ has three solutions: 0, -2, and 2. To check, replace x with each solution in the original equation.

Let x = 0.	**Let x = -2.**	**Let x = 2.**
$3(0)^3 - 12(0) \stackrel{?}{=} 0$	$3(-2)^3 - 12(-2) \stackrel{?}{=} 0$	$3(2)^3 - 12(2) \stackrel{?}{=} 0$
$0 = 0$	$3(-8) + 24 \stackrel{?}{=} 0$	$3(8) - 24 \stackrel{?}{=} 0$
	$0 = 0$	$0 = 0$

Substituting 0, -2, or 2 into the original equation results each time in a true equation. The solutions are 0, -2, and 2.   □

PRACTICE
8   Solve: $7x^3 - 63x = 0$.

EXAMPLE 9   Solve: $(5x - 1)(2x^2 + 15x + 18) = 0$.

Solution

$$(5x - 1)(2x^2 + 15x + 18) = 0$$
$$(5x - 1)(2x + 3)(x + 6) = 0 \quad \text{Factor the trinomial.}$$
$$5x - 1 = 0 \quad \text{or} \quad 2x + 3 = 0 \quad \text{or} \quad x + 6 = 0 \quad \text{Set each factor equal to 0.}$$
$$5x = 1 \quad \text{or} \quad 2x = -3 \quad \text{or} \quad x = -6 \quad \text{Solve.}$$
$$x = \frac{1}{5} \quad \text{or} \quad x = -\frac{3}{2}$$

The solutions are $\frac{1}{5}$, $-\frac{3}{2}$, and -6. Check by replacing x with each solution in the original equation. The solutions are -6, $-\frac{3}{2}$, and $\frac{1}{5}$.   □

PRACTICE
9   Solve: $(3x - 2)(2x^2 - 13x + 15) = 0$.

EXAMPLE 10   Solve: $2x^3 - 4x^2 - 30x = 0$.

Solution   Begin by factoring out the GCF $2x$.

$$2x^3 - 4x^2 - 30x = 0$$
$$2x(x^2 - 2x - 15) = 0 \quad \text{Factor out the GCF } 2x.$$
$$2x(x - 5)(x + 3) = 0 \quad \text{Factor the quadratic.}$$
$$2x = 0 \quad \text{or} \quad x - 5 = 0 \quad \text{or} \quad x + 3 = 0 \quad \text{Set each factor containing a variable equal to 0.}$$
$$x = 0 \quad \text{or} \quad x = 5 \quad \text{or} \quad x = -3 \quad \text{Solve.}$$

Check by replacing x with each solution in the cubic equation. The solutions are -3, 0, and 5.   □

PRACTICE
10   Solve: $5x^3 + 5x^2 - 30x = 0$.

OBJECTIVE

3 Finding *x*-Intercepts of the Graph of a Quadratic Equation

In Chapter 3, we graphed linear equations in two variables, such as $y = 5x - 6$. Recall that to find the *x*-intercept of the graph of a linear equation, let $y = 0$ and solve for *x*. This is also how to find the *x*-intercepts of the graph of a **quadratic equation in two variables,** such as $y = x^2 - 5x + 4$.

EXAMPLE 11 Find the *x*-intercepts of the graph of $y = x^2 - 5x + 4$.

Solution Let $y = 0$ and solve for *x*.

$$y = x^2 - 5x + 4$$
$$0 = x^2 - 5x + 4 \qquad \text{Let } y = 0.$$
$$0 = (x - 1)(x - 4) \qquad \text{Factor.}$$
$$x - 1 = 0 \quad \text{or} \quad x - 4 = 0 \qquad \text{Set each factor equal to 0.}$$
$$x = 1 \quad \text{or} \quad x = 4 \qquad \text{Solve.}$$

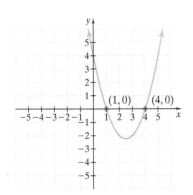

The *x*-intercepts of the graph of $y = x^2 - 5x + 4$ are $(1, 0)$ and $(4, 0)$.

The graph of $y = x^2 - 5x + 4$ is shown in the margin.

PRACTICE

11 Find the *x*-intercepts of the graph of $y = x^2 - 6x + 8$.

In general, a quadratic equation in two variables is one that can be written in the form $y = ax^2 + bx + c$ where $a \neq 0$. The graph of such an equation is called a **parabola** and will open up or down depending on the sign of *a*.

Notice that the *x*-intercepts of the graph of $y = ax^2 + bx + c$ are the real number solutions of $0 = ax^2 + bx + c$. Also, the real number solutions of $0 = ax^2 + bx + c$ are the *x*-intercepts of the graph of $y = ax^2 + bx + c$. We study more about graphs of quadratic equations in two variables in Chapter 11.

Graph of $y = ax^2 + bx + c$
x-intercepts are solutions of $0 = ax^2 + bx + c$

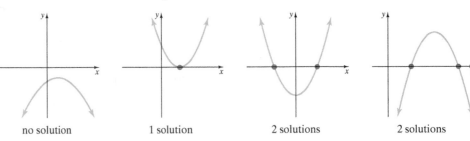

| no solution | 1 solution | 2 solutions | 2 solutions |

Graphing Calculator Explorations

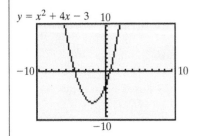

$y = x^2 + 4x - 3$

A grapher may be used to find solutions of a quadratic equation whether the related quadratic polynomial is factorable or not. For example, let's use a grapher to approximate the solutions of $0 = x^2 + 4x - 3$. To do so, graph $y_1 = x^2 + 4x - 3$. Recall that the *x*-intercepts of this graph are the solutions of $0 = x^2 + 4x - 3$.

Notice that the graph appears to have an *x*-intercept between -5 and -4 and one between 0 and 1. Many graphers contain a TRACE feature. This feature activates a graph cursor that can be used to *trace* along a graph while the corresponding *x*- and *y*-coordinates are shown on the screen. Use the TRACE feature to confirm that *x*-intercepts lie between -5 and -4 and between 0 and 1. To approximate the *x*-intercepts to the nearest tenth, use a ROOT or a ZOOM feature on your grapher or redefine the viewing window. (A ROOT feature calculates the *x*-intercept. A ZOOM feature magnifies the viewing window around a specific location such as the graph cursor.) If we redefine the window to $[0, 1]$ on the x-axis and $[-1, 1]$ on the y-axis, the graph to the left is generated.

By using the TRACE feature, we can conclude that one x-intercept is approximately 0.6 to the nearest tenth. By repeating these steps for the other x-intercept, we find that it is approximately -4.6.

Use a grapher to approximate the real number solutions to the nearest tenth. If an equation has no real number solution, state so.

1. $3x^2 - 4x - 6 = 0$ **2.** $x^2 - x - 9 = 0$

3. $2x^2 + x + 2 = 0$ **4.** $-4x^2 - 5x - 4 = 0$

5. $-x^2 + x + 5 = 0$ **6.** $10x^2 + 6x - 3 = 0$

Vocabulary, Readiness & Video Check

Use the choices below to fill in each blank. Not all choices will be used.

$-3, 5$	$a = 0$ or $b = 0$	0	linear
$3, -5$	quadratic	1	

1. An equation that can be written in the form $ax^2 + bx + c = 0$, with $a \neq 0$, is called a _____ equation.

2. If the product of two numbers is 0, then at least one of the numbers must be _____.

3. The solutions to $(x - 3)(x + 5) = 0$ are _____.

4. If $a \cdot b = 0$, then _____.

Martin-Gay Interactive Videos

See Video 6.6

Watch the section lecture video and answer the following questions.

OBJECTIVE 1

5. As shown in Examples 1–3, what two things have to be true in order to use the zero factor theorem?

OBJECTIVE 2

6. Example 4 implies that the zero factor theorem can be used with any number of factors on one side of the equation so long as the other side of the equation is zero. Why do you think this is true?

OBJECTIVE 3

7. From Example 5, how does finding the x-intercepts of the graph of a quadratic equation in two variables lead to solving a quadratic equation?

6.6 Exercise Set   MyMathLab®

Solve each equation. See Examples 1 through 3.

1. $(x - 6)(x - 7) = 0$

2. $(x - 10)(x - 5) = 0$

3. $(x - 2)(x + 1) = 0$

4. $(x + 4)(x - 10) = 0$

5. $(x + 9)(x + 17) = 0$

6. $(x + 11)(x + 1) = 0$

7. $x(x + 6) = 0$

8. $x(x - 7) = 0$

9. $3x(x - 8) = 0$

10. $2x(x + 12) = 0$

11. $(2x + 3)(4x - 5) = 0$

12. $(3x - 2)(5x + 1) = 0$

13. $(2x - 7)(7x + 2) = 0$

14. $(9x + 1)(4x - 3) = 0$

15. $\left(x - \dfrac{1}{2}\right)\left(x + \dfrac{1}{3}\right) = 0$

16. $\left(x + \dfrac{2}{9}\right)\left(x - \dfrac{1}{4}\right) = 0$

17. $(x + 0.2)(x + 1.5) = 0$

18. $(x + 1.7)(x + 2.3) = 0$

Solve. See Examples 4 through 7.

19. $x^2 - 13x + 36 = 0$

20. $x^2 + 2x - 63 = 0$

21. $x^2 + 2x - 8 = 0$

22. $x^2 - 5x + 6 = 0$

23. $x^2 - 7x = 0$

24. $x^2 - 3x = 0$

25. $x^2 - 4x = 32$

26. $x^2 - 5x = 24$

27. $x^2 = 16$

28. $x^2 = 9$

29. $(x + 4)(x - 9) = 4x$

30. $(x + 3)(x + 8) = x$

31. $x(3x - 1) = 14$

32. $x(4x - 11) = 3$

33. $-3x^2 + 75 = 0$

34. $-2y^2 + 72 = 0$

35. $24x^2 + 44x = 8$

36. $6x^2 + 57x = 30$

Solve each equation. See Examples 8 through 10.

37. $x^3 - 12x^2 + 32x = 0$

38. $x^3 - 14x^2 + 49x = 0$

39. $(4x - 3)(16x^2 - 24x + 9) = 0$

40. $(2x + 5)(4x^2 + 20x + 25) = 0$

41. $4x^3 - x = 0$ **42.** $4y^3 - 36y = 0$

43. $32x^3 - 4x^2 - 6x = 0$ **44.** $15x^3 + 24x^2 - 63x = 0$

MIXED PRACTICE

Solve each equation. See Examples 1 through 10. (A few exercises are linear equations.)

45. $(x + 3)(x - 2) = 0$ **46.** $(x - 6)(x + 7) = 0$

47. $x^2 + 20x = 0$ **48.** $x^2 + 15x = 0$

49. $4(x - 7) = 6$ **50.** $5(3 - 4x) = 9$

51. $4y^2 - 1 = 0$ **52.** $4y^2 - 81 = 0$

53. $(2x + 3)(2x^2 - 5x - 3) = 0$

54. $(2x - 9)(x^2 + 5x - 36) = 0$

55. $x^2 - 15 = -2x$ **56.** $x^2 - 26 = -11x$

57. $30x^2 - 11x - 30 = 0$ **58.** $12x^2 + 7x - 12 = 0$

59. $5x^2 - 6x - 8 = 0$ **60.** $9x^2 + 7x = 2$

61. $6y^2 - 22y - 40 = 0$ **62.** $3x^2 - 6x - 9 = 0$

63. $(y - 2)(y + 3) = 6$ **64.** $(y - 5)(y - 2) = 28$

65. $3x^3 + 19x^2 - 72x = 0$

66. $36x^3 + x^2 - 21x = 0$

67. $x^2 + 14x + 49 = 0$

68. $x^2 + 22x + 121 = 0$

69. $12y = 8y^2$

70. $9y = 6y^2$

71. $7x^3 - 7x = 0$

72. $3x^3 - 27x = 0$

73. $3x^2 + 8x - 11 = 13 - 6x$

74. $2x^2 + 12x - 1 = 4 + 3x$

75. $3x^2 - 20x = -4x^2 - 7x - 6$

76. $4x^2 - 20x = -5x^2 - 6x - 5$

Find the x-intercepts of the graph of each equation. See Example 11.

77. $y = (3x + 4)(x - 1)$

78. $y = (5x - 3)(x - 4)$

79. $y = x^2 - 3x - 10$

80. $y = x^2 + 7x + 6$

81. $y = 2x^2 + 11x - 6$

82. $y = 4x^2 + 11x + 6$

For Exercises 83 through 88, match each equation with its graph. See Example 11.

83. $y = (x + 2)(x - 1)$ **84.** $y = (x - 5)(x + 2)$

85. $y = x(x + 3)$ **86.** $y = x(x - 4)$

87. $y = 2x^2 - 8$ **88.** $y = 2x^2 - 2$

a.

b.

c.

d.

e.

f.

REVIEW AND PREVIEW

Perform the following operations. Write all results in lowest terms. See Section 1.3.

89. $\dfrac{3}{5} + \dfrac{4}{9}$ **90.** $\dfrac{2}{3} + \dfrac{3}{7}$

91. $\dfrac{7}{10} - \dfrac{5}{12}$ **92.** $\dfrac{5}{9} - \dfrac{5}{12}$

93. $\dfrac{7}{8} \div \dfrac{7}{15}$ **94.** $\dfrac{5}{12} - \dfrac{3}{10}$

95. $\dfrac{4}{5} \cdot \dfrac{7}{8}$ **96.** $\dfrac{3}{7} \cdot \dfrac{12}{17}$

CONCEPT EXTENSIONS

For Exercises 97 and 98, see the Concept Check in this section.

97. Explain the error and solve correctly:

$$x(x - 2) = 8$$
$$x = 8 \quad \text{or} \quad x - 2 = 8$$
$$x = 10$$

98. Explain the error and solve correctly:

$$(x - 4)(x + 2) = 0$$
$$x = -4 \quad \text{or} \quad x = 2$$

99. Write a quadratic equation that has two solutions, 6 and −1. Leave the polynomial in the equation in factored form.

100. Write a quadratic equation that has two solutions, 0 and −2. Leave the polynomial in the equation in factored form.

101. Write a quadratic equation in standard form that has two solutions, 5 and 7.

102. Write an equation that has three solutions, 0, 1, and 2.

103. A compass is accidentally thrown upward and out of an air balloon at a height of 300 feet. The height, y, of the compass at time x in seconds is given by the equation

$$y = -16x^2 + 20x + 300$$

300 ft

a. Find the height of the compass at the given times by filling in the table below.

time, x	0	1	2	3	4	5	6
height, y							

b. Use the table to determine when the compass strikes the ground.

c. Use the table to approximate the maximum height of the compass.

d. Plot the points (x, y) on a rectangular coordinate system and connect them with a smooth curve. Explain your results.

104. A rocket is fired upward from the ground with an initial velocity of 100 feet per second. The height, y, of the rocket at any time x is given by the equation

$$y = -16x^2 + 100x$$

y

a. Find the height of the rocket at the given times by filling in the table below.

time, x	0	1	2	3	4	5	6	7
height, y								

b. Use the table to approximate when the rocket strikes the ground to the nearest second.

c. Use the table to approximate the maximum height of the rocket.

d. Plot the points (x, y) on a rectangular coordinate system and connect them with a smooth curve. Explain your results.

Solve each equation. First, multiply the binomial.

To solve $(x - 6)(2x - 3) = (x + 2)(x + 9)$, see below.

$$(x - 6)(2x - 3) = (x + 2)(x + 9)$$
$$2x^2 - 15x + 18 = x^2 + 11x + 18$$
$$x^2 - 26x = 0$$
$$x(x - 26) = 0$$
$$x = 0 \quad \text{or} \quad x - 26 = 0$$
$$x = 26$$

105. $(x - 3)(3x + 4) = (x + 2)(x - 6)$

106. $(2x - 3)(x + 6) = (x - 9)(x + 2)$

107. $(2x - 3)(x + 8) = (x - 6)(x + 4)$

108. $(x + 6)(x - 6) = (2x - 9)(x + 4)$

  6.7   **Quadratic Equations and Problem Solving**

OBJECTIVE

1 Solve Problems That Can Be Modeled by Quadratic Equations.

OBJECTIVE

1   Solving Problems Modeled by Quadratic Equations

Some problems may be modeled by quadratic equations. To solve these problems, we use the same problem-solving steps that were introduced in Section 2.4. When solving these problems, keep in mind that a solution of an equation that models a problem may not be a solution to the problem. For example, a person's age or the length of a rectangle is always a positive number. Discard solutions that do not make sense as solutions of the problem.

EXAMPLE 1 Finding Free-Fall Time

Since the 1940s, one of the top tourist attractions in Aca-pulco, Mexico, is watching the cliff divers off the La Quebrada. The divers' platform is about 144 feet above the sea. These divers must time their descent just right, since they land in the crashing Pacific, in an inlet that is at most $9\frac{1}{2}$ feet deep. Neglecting air resistance, the height h in feet of a cliff diver above the ocean after t seconds is given by the quadratic equation $h = -16t^2 + 144$.

Find out how long it takes the diver to reach the ocean.

Solution

1. UNDERSTAND. Read and reread the problem. Then draw a picture of the problem.

   The equation $h = -16t^2 + 144$ models the height of the fall-ing diver at time t. Familiarize yourself with this equation by finding the height of the diver at time $t = 1$ second and $t = 2$ seconds.
   When $t = 1$ second, the height of the diver is $h = -16(1)^2 + 144 = 128$ feet.
   When $t = 2$ seconds, the height of the diver is $h = -16(2)^2 + 144 = 80$ feet.

2. TRANSLATE. To find out how long it takes the diver to reach the ocean, we want to know the value of t for which $h = 0$.

3. SOLVE.
$$0 = -16t^2 + 144$$
$$0 = -16(t^2 - 9) \qquad \text{Factor out } -16.$$
$$0 = -16(t - 3)(t + 3) \qquad \text{Factor completely.}$$
$$t - 3 = 0 \quad \text{or} \quad t + 3 = 0 \qquad \text{Set each factor containing a variable equal to 0.}$$
$$t = 3 \quad \text{or} \qquad t = -3 \qquad \text{Solve.}$$

4. INTERPRET. Since the time t cannot be negative, the proposed solution is 3 seconds.

Check: Verify that the height of the diver when t is 3 seconds is 0.

   When $t = 3$ seconds, $h = -16(3)^2 + 144 = -144 + 144 = 0$.

State: It takes the diver 3 seconds to reach the ocean. □

PRACTICE

1   Cliff divers also frequent the falls at Waimea Falls Park in Oahu, Hawaii. One of the popular diving spots is 64 feet high. Neglecting air resistance, the height of a diver above the pool after t seconds is $h = -16t^2 + 64$. Find how long it takes a diver to reach the pool.

EXAMPLE 2 Finding an Unknown Number

The square of a number plus three times the number is 70. Find the number.

Solution

1. UNDERSTAND. Read and reread the problem. Suppose that the number is 5. The square of 5 is 5^2 or 25. Three times 5 is 15. Then $25 + 15 = 40$, not 70, so the number is not 5. Remember, the purpose of proposing a number, such as 5, is to un-derstand the problem better. Now that we do, we will let $x =$ the number.

2. TRANSLATE.

the square of a number	plus	three times the number	is	70
↓	↓	↓	↓	↓
x^2	$+$	$3x$	$=$	70

3. SOLVE.

$$x^2 + 3x = 70$$
$$x^2 + 3x - 70 = 0 \qquad \text{Subtract 70 from both sides.}$$
$$(x + 10)(x - 7) = 0 \qquad \text{Factor.}$$
$$x + 10 = 0 \quad \text{or} \quad x - 7 = 0 \quad \text{Set each factor equal to 0.}$$
$$x = -10 \qquad\qquad x = 7 \quad \text{Solve.}$$

4. INTERPRET.

Check: The square of -10 is $(-10)^2$, or 100. Three times -10 is $3(-10)$ or -30. Then $100 + (-30) = 70$, the correct sum, so -10 checks.

The square of 7 is 7^2 or 49. Three times 7 is $3(7)$, or 21. Then $49 + 21 = 70$, the correct sum, so 7 checks.

State: There are two numbers. They are -10 and 7.   □

PRACTICE

2   The square of a number minus eight times the number is equal to forty-eight. Find the number.

△   **EXAMPLE 3**   **Finding the Dimensions of a Sail**

The height of a triangular sail is 2 meters less than twice the length of the base. If the sail has an area of 30 square meters, find the length of its base and the height.

Solution

1. UNDERSTAND. Read and reread the problem. Since we are finding the length of the base and the height, we let

$$x = \text{the length of the base}$$

and since the height is 2 meters less than twice the base,

$$2x - 2 = \text{the height}$$

An illustration is shown to the right.

Height = 2x − 2

Base = x

2. TRANSLATE. We are given that the area of the triangle is 30 square meters, so we use the formula for area of a triangle.

area of triangle	=	$\dfrac{1}{2}$	·	base	·	height
↓		↓		↓		↓
30	$=$	$\dfrac{1}{2}$	·	x	·	$(2x - 2)$

(Continued on next page)

3. SOLVE. Now we solve the quadratic equation.

$$30 = \frac{1}{2}x(2x - 2)$$

$$30 = x^2 - x \qquad \text{Multiply.}$$

$$x^2 - x - 30 = 0 \qquad \text{Write in standard form.}$$

$$(x - 6)(x + 5) = 0 \qquad \text{Factor.}$$

$$x - 6 = 0 \quad \text{or} \quad x + 5 = 0 \qquad \text{Set each factor equal to 0.}$$

$$x = 6 \qquad\qquad x = -5$$

4. INTERPRET. Since x represents the length of the base, we discard the solution -5. The base of a triangle cannot be negative. The base is then 6 meters and the height is $2(6) - 2 = 10$ meters.

Check: To check this problem, we recall that $\frac{1}{2}$base $\cdot$ height $=$ area, or

$$\frac{1}{2}(6)(10) = 30 \qquad \text{The required area}$$

State: The base of the triangular sail is 6 meters and the height is 10 meters. □

PRACTICE

3 An engineering team from Georgia Tech earned second place in a flight competition, with their triangular shaped paper hang glider. The base of their prize-winning entry was 1 foot less than three times the height. If the area of the triangular glider wing was 210 square feet, find the dimensions of the wing. (*Source: The Technique* [Georgia Tech's newspaper], April 18, 2003)

Study the following diagrams for a review of consecutive integers.

Examples

If x is the first integer, then consecutive integers are
$x, x + 1, x + 2, \ldots$

If x is the first even integer, then consecutive even integers are
$x, x + 2, x + 4, \ldots$

If x is the first odd integer, then consecutive odd integers are
$x, x + 2, x + 4, \ldots$

EXAMPLE 4 **Finding Consecutive Even Integers**

Find two consecutive even integers whose product is 34 more than their sum.

Solution

1. UNDERSTAND. Read and reread the problem. Let's just choose two consecutive even integers to help us better understand the problem. Let's choose 10 and 12. Their product is $10(12) = 120$ and their sum is $10 + 12 = 22$. The product is $120 - 22$, or 98 greater than the sum. Thus our guess is incorrect, but we have a better understanding of this example.

Let's let x and $x + 2$ be the consecutive even integers.

2. TRANSLATE.

Product of integers	is	34	more than	sum of integers
↓	↓	↓	↓	↓
$x(x + 2)$	$=$	34	$+$	$x + (x + 2)$

3. SOLVE. Now we solve the equation.

$$x(x + 2) = 34 + x + (x + 2)$$
$$x^2 + 2x = 34 + x + x + 2 \qquad \text{Multiply.}$$
$$x^2 + 2x = 2x + 36 \qquad \text{Combine like terms.}$$
$$x^2 - 36 = 0 \qquad \text{Write in standard form.}$$
$$(x + 6)(x - 6) = 0 \qquad \text{Factor.}$$
$$x + 6 = 0 \quad \text{or} \quad x - 6 = 0 \qquad \text{Set each factor equal to 0.}$$
$$x = -6 \qquad\qquad x = 6 \qquad \text{Solve.}$$

4. INTERPRET. If $x = -6$, then $x + 2 = -6 + 2$, or -4.
If $x = 6$, then $x + 2 = 6 + 2$, or 8.

Check: $-6, -4$ $6, 8$

$$-6(-4) \stackrel{?}{=} 34 + (-6) + (-4) \qquad\qquad 6(8) \stackrel{?}{=} 34 + 6 + 8$$
$$24 \stackrel{?}{=} 34 + (-10) \qquad\qquad\qquad\qquad 48 \stackrel{?}{=} 34 + 14$$
$$24 = 24 \qquad \text{True} \qquad\qquad\qquad 48 = 48 \qquad \text{True}$$

State: The two consecutive even integers are -6 and -4 or 6 and 8.   □

PRACTICE
4   Find two consecutive integers whose product is 41 more than their sum.

The next example uses the **Pythagorean theorem** and consecutive integers. Before we review this theorem, recall that a **right triangle** is a triangle that contains a 90° or right angle. The **hypotenuse** of a right triangle is the side opposite the right angle and is the longest side of the triangle. The **legs** of a right triangle are the other sides of the triangle.

> **Helpful Hint**
> If you use this formula, don't forget that c represents the length of the hypotenuse.

Pythagorean Theorem

In a right triangle, the sum of the squares of the lengths of the two legs is equal to the square of the length of the hypotenuse.

$$(\text{leg})^2 + (\text{leg})^2 = (\text{hypotenuse})^2 \qquad \text{or} \qquad a^2 + b^2 = c^2$$

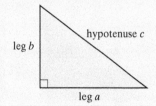

△ **EXAMPLE 5**   **Finding the Dimensions of a Triangle**

Find the lengths of the sides of a right triangle if the lengths can be expressed as three consecutive even integers.

(Continued on next page)

Solution

1. UNDERSTAND. Read and reread the problem. Let's suppose that the length of one leg of the right triangle is 4 units. Then the other leg is the next even integer, or 6 units, and the hypotenuse of the triangle is the next even integer, or 8 units. Remember that the hypotenuse is the longest side. Let's see if a triangle with sides of these lengths forms a right triangle. To do this, we check to see whether the Pythagorean theorem holds true.

$$4^2 + 6^2 \stackrel{?}{=} 8^2$$
$$16 + 36 \stackrel{?}{=} 64$$
$$52 = 64 \quad \text{False}$$

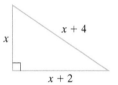

Our proposed numbers do not check, but we now have a better understanding of the problem.

We let $x, x + 2$, and $x + 4$ be three consecutive even integers. Since these integers represent lengths of the sides of a right triangle, we have the following.

$$x = \text{one leg}$$
$$x + 2 = \text{other leg}$$
$$x + 4 = \text{hypotenuse (longest side)}$$

2. TRANSLATE. By the Pythagorean theorem, we have that

$$(\text{leg})^2 + (\text{leg})^2 = (\text{hypotenuse})^2$$
$$(x)^2 + (x + 2)^2 = (x + 4)^2$$

3. SOLVE. Now we solve the equation.

$$x^2 + (x + 2)^2 = (x + 4)^2$$
$$x^2 + x^2 + 4x + 4 = x^2 + 8x + 16 \qquad \text{Multiply.}$$
$$2x^2 + 4x + 4 = x^2 + 8x + 16 \qquad \text{Combine like terms.}$$
$$x^2 - 4x - 12 = 0 \qquad \text{Write in standard form.}$$
$$(x - 6)(x + 2) = 0 \qquad \text{Factor.}$$
$$x - 6 = 0 \quad \text{or} \quad x + 2 = 0 \qquad \text{Set each factor equal to 0.}$$
$$x = 6 \qquad\qquad x = -2$$

4. INTERPRET. We discard $x = -2$ since length cannot be negative. If $x = 6$, then $x + 2 = 8$ and $x + 4 = 10$.

Check: Verify that

$$(\text{leg})^2 + (\text{leg})^2 = (\text{hypotenuse})^2$$
$$6^2 + 8^2 \stackrel{?}{=} 10^2$$
$$36 + 64 \stackrel{?}{=} 100$$
$$100 = 100 \qquad\qquad \text{True}$$

State: The sides of the right triangle have lengths 6 units, 8 units, and 10 units.

PRACTICE
5   Find the dimensions of a right triangle where the second leg is 1 unit less than double the first leg, and the hypotenuse is 1 unit more than double the length of the first leg.

Vocabulary, Readiness & Video Check

Martin-Gay Interactive Videos

See Video 6.7

Watch the section lecture video and answer the following question.

OBJECTIVE
1

1. In each of Examples 1–3, why aren't both solutions of the translated equation accepted as solutions to the application?

6.7 Exercise Set   MyMathLab®

MIXED PRACTICE

See Examples 1 through 5 for all exercises.

TRANSLATING

For Exercises 1 through 6, represent each given condition using a single variable, x.

△ **1.** The length and width of a rectangle whose length is 4 centimeters more than its width

△ **2.** The length and width of a rectangle whose length is twice its width

3. Two consecutive odd integers

4. Two consecutive even integers

△ **5.** The base and height of a triangle whose height is one more than four times its base

△ **6.** The base and height of a trapezoid whose base is three less than five times its height

Use the information given to find the dimensions of each figure.

△ **7.** The *area* of the square is 121 square units. Find the length of its sides.

△ **8.** The *area* of the rectangle is 84 square inches. Find its length and width.

△ **9.** The *perimeter* of the quadrilateral is 120 centimeters. Find the lengths of the sides.

△ **10.** The *perimeter* of the triangle is 85 feet. Find the lengths of its sides.

△ **11.** The *area* of the parallelogram is 96 square miles. Find its base and height.

△ **12.** The *area* of the circle is 25π square kilometers. Find its radius.

Solve.

▷ **13.** An object is thrown upward from the top of an 80-foot building with an initial velocity of 64 feet per second. The height h of the object after t seconds is given by the quadratic equation $h = -16t^2 + 64t + 80$. When will the object hit the ground?

14. A hang glider pilot accidentally drops her compass from the top of a 400-foot cliff. The height h of the compass after t seconds is given by the quadratic equation $h = -16t^2 + 400$. When will the compass hit the ground?

△ **15.** The width of a rectangle is 7 centimeters less than twice its length. Its area is 30 square centimeters. Find the dimensions of the rectangle.

△ **16.** The length of a rectangle is 9 inches more than its width. Its area is 112 square inches. Find the dimensions of the rectangle.

The equation $D = \frac{1}{2}n(n-3)$ gives the number of diagonals D for a polygon with n sides. For example, a polygon with 6 sides has $D = \frac{1}{2} \cdot 6(6-3)$ or $D = 9$ diagonals. (See if you can count all 9 diagonals. Some are shown in the figure.) Use this equation, $D = \frac{1}{2}n(n-3)$, for Exercises 17 through 20.

△ **17.** Find the number of diagonals for a polygon that has 12 sides.

△ **18.** Find the number of diagonals for a polygon that has 15 sides.

△ **19.** Find the number of sides n for a polygon that has 35 diagonals.

△ **20.** Find the number of sides n for a polygon that has 14 diagonals.

Solve.

21. The sum of a number and its square is 132. Find the number(s).

▷ **22.** The sum of a number and its square is 182. Find the number(s).

23. The product of two consecutive room numbers is 210. Find the room numbers.

▷ **24.** The product of two consecutive page numbers is 420. Find the page numbers.

25. A ladder is leaning against a building so that the distance from the ground to the top of the ladder is one foot less than the length of the ladder. Find the length of the ladder if the distance from the bottom of the ladder to the building is 5 feet.

26. Use the given figure to find the length of the guy wire.

△ **27.** If the sides of a square are increased by 3 inches, the area becomes 64 square inches. Find the length of the sides of the original square.

△ **28.** If the sides of a square are increased by 5 meters, the area becomes 100 square meters. Find the length of the sides of the original square.

29. One leg of a right triangle is 4 millimeters longer than the smaller leg and the hypotenuse is 8 millimeters longer than the smaller leg. Find the lengths of the sides of the triangle.

30. One leg of a right triangle is 9 centimeters longer than the other leg and the hypotenuse is 45 centimeters. Find the lengths of the legs of the triangle.

31. The length of the base of a triangle is twice its height. If the area of the triangle is 100 square kilometers, find the height.

32. The height of a triangle is 2 millimeters less than the base. If the area is 60 square millimeters, find the base.

33. Find the length of the shorter leg of a right triangle if the longer leg is 12 feet more than the shorter leg and the hypotenuse is 12 feet less than twice the shorter leg.

34. Find the length of the shorter leg of a right triangle if the longer leg is 10 miles more than the shorter leg and the hypotenuse is 10 miles less than twice the shorter leg.

35. An object is dropped from 39 feet below the tip of the pinnacle atop one of the 1483-foot-tall Petronas Twin Towers in Kuala Lumpur, Malaysia. (*Source:* Council on Tall Buildings and Urban Habitat) The height h of the object after t seconds is given by the equation $h = -16t^2 + 1444$. Find how many seconds pass before the object reaches the ground.

36. An object is dropped from the top of 311 South Wacker Drive, a 961-foot-tall office building in Chicago. (*Source:* Council on Tall Buildings and Urban Habitat) The height h of the object after t seconds is given by the equation $h = -16t^2 + 961$. Find how many seconds pass before the object reaches the ground.

37. At the end of 2 years, P dollars invested at an interest rate r compounded annually increases to an amount, A dollars, given by

$$A = P(1 + r)^2$$

Find the interest rate if $100 increased to $144 in 2 years. Write your answer as a percent.

38. At the end of 2 years, P dollars invested at an interest rate r compounded annually increases to an amount, A dollars, given by

$$A = P(1 + r)^2$$

Find the interest rate if $2000 increased to $2420 in 2 years. Write your answer as a percent.

39. Find the dimensions of a rectangle whose width is 7 miles less than its length and whose area is 120 square miles.

40. Find the dimensions of a rectangle whose width is 2 inches less than half its length and whose area is 160 square inches.

41. If the cost, C, for manufacturing x units of a certain product is given by $C = x^2 - 15x + 50$, find the number of units manufactured at a cost of $9500.

42. If a switchboard handles n telephones, the number C of telephone connections it can make simultaneously is given by the equation $C = \dfrac{n(n-1)}{2}$. Find how many telephones are handled by a switchboard making 120 telephone connections simultaneously.

REVIEW AND PREVIEW

The following double-line graph shows a comparison of the number of annual visitors (in millions) to Glacier National Park and Gettysburg National Military Park for the years shown. Use this graph to answer Exercises 43 through 50. See Section 3.1.

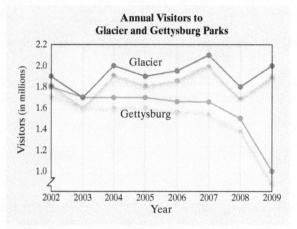

43. Approximate the number of visitors to Glacier National Park in 2009.

44. Approximate the number of visitors to Gettysburg National Military Park in 2009.

45. Approximate the number of visitors to Glacier National Park in 2005.

46. Approximate the number of visitors to Gettysburg National Military Park in 2005.

47. Determine the year that the colored lines in this graph intersect.

48. For what years on the graph is the number of visitors to Glacier Park greater than the number of visitors to Gettysburg Park?

49. In your own words, explain the meaning of the point of intersection in the graph.

50. Describe the trends shown in this graph and speculate as to why these trends have occurred.

Write each fraction in simplest form. See Section 1.3.

51. $\dfrac{20}{35}$ **52.** $\dfrac{24}{32}$ **53.** $\dfrac{27}{18}$

54. $\dfrac{15}{27}$ **55.** $\dfrac{14}{42}$ **56.** $\dfrac{45}{50}$

CONCEPT EXTENSIONS

△ **57.** Two boats travel at right angles to each other after leaving the same dock at the same time. One hour later, the boats are 17 miles apart. If one boat travels 7 miles per hour faster than the other boat, find the rate of each boat.

17 miles

△ **58.** The side of a square equals the width of a rectangle. The length of the rectangle is 6 meters longer than its width. The sum of the areas of the square and the rectangle is 176 square meters. Find the side of the square.

59. The sum of two numbers is 20, and the sum of their squares is 218. Find the numbers.

60. The sum of two numbers is 25, and the sum of their squares is 325. Find the numbers.

△ **61.** A rectangular pool is surrounded by a walk 4 meters wide. The pool is 6 meters longer than its width. If the total area of the pool and walk is 576 square meters more than the area of the pool, find the dimensions of the pool.

△ **62.** A rectangular garden is surrounded by a walk of uniform width. The area of the garden is 180 square yards. If the dimensions of the garden plus the walk are 16 yards by 24 yards, find the width of the walk.

63. Write down two numbers whose sum is 10. Square each number and find the sum of the squares. Use this work to write a word problem like Exercise 59. Then give the word problem to a classmate to solve.

64. Write down two numbers whose sum is 12. Square each number and find the sum of the squares. Use this work to write a word problem like Exercise 60. Then give the word problem to a classmate to solve.

Many sport statistics are calculated using formulas containing rational expressions. Below are a few examples:

Sport	Formula	Explanation
Baseball	$S = \dfrac{h + d + 2t + 3r}{b}$	A baseball player's slugging percentage S, where h = number of hits, d = number of doubles, t = number of triples, r = number of home runs, and b = number of at bats
NCAA Football	$R_{\text{NCAA}} = \dfrac{100C + 330T - 200I + 8.4Y}{A}$	A quarterback's rating in NCAA football R, where C = the number of completed passes, A = the number of attempted passes, T = the number of touchdown passes, Y = the number of yards in the completed passes, and I = the number of interceptions
NFL Football	$R_{\text{NFL}} = \dfrac{a + b + c + d}{6} \times 100$	A quarterback's rating in NFL football R, where $a, b, c,$ and d are each formulas containing rational expressions.

(*Source:* Wikipedia.org.)

In Section 7.1, Exercises 65 and 66, you will have the opportunity to calculate some sport statistics.

In this chapter, we expand our knowledge of algebraic expressions to include algebraic fractions, called *rational expressions*. We explore the operations of addition, subtraction, multiplication, and division using principles similar to the principles for numerical fractions.

7.1 Rational Functions and Simplifying Rational Expressions

OBJECTIVES

1 Find the Domain of a Rational Function.

2 Simplify or Write Rational Expressions in Lowest Terms.

3 Write Equivalent Rational Expressions of the Form $-\dfrac{a}{b} = \dfrac{-a}{b} = \dfrac{a}{-b}$.

4 Use Rational Functions in Applications.

As we reviewed in Chapter 1, a rational number is a number that can be written as a quotient of integers. A **rational expression** is also a quotient; it is a quotient of polynomials.

Rational Expression

A rational expression is an expression that can be written in the form

$$\frac{P}{Q},$$

where P and Q are polynomials and $Q \neq 0$.

Rational Expressions

$$-\frac{2}{7} \qquad \frac{3y^3}{8} \qquad \frac{-4p}{p^3 + 2p + 1} \qquad \frac{5x^2 - 3x + 2}{3x + 7}$$

The first rational expression (or fraction) above is $-\dfrac{2}{7}$. For a negative fraction such as $-\dfrac{2}{7}$, recall from Section 1.7 that

$$-\frac{2}{7} = \frac{2}{-7} = \frac{-2}{7}$$

In general, for any fraction,

$$\frac{-a}{b} = \frac{a}{-b} = -\frac{a}{b}, \qquad b \neq 0$$

This is also true for rational expressions. For example,

$$\underbrace{\frac{-(x + 2)}{x}}_{} = \frac{x + 2}{-x} = -\frac{x + 2}{x}$$

$\uparrow$
Notice the parentheses.

Rational expressions are sometimes used to describe functions. For example, we call the function $f(x) = \dfrac{x^2 + 2}{x - 3}$ a **rational function** since $\dfrac{x^2 + 2}{x - 3}$ is a rational expression.

OBJECTIVE
1 Finding the Domain of a Rational Function

As with fractions, a rational expression is **undefined** if the denominator is 0. If a variable in a rational expression is replaced with a number that makes the denominator 0, we say that the rational expression is **undefined** for this value of the variable. For example, the rational expression $\dfrac{x^2 + 2}{x - 3}$ is undefined when x is 3, because replacing x with 3 results in a denominator of 0. For this reason, we must exclude 3 from the domain of the function $f(x) = \dfrac{x^2 + 2}{x - 3}$.

The domain of f is then

$$\{x \mid x \text{ is a real number and } x \neq 3\}$$

"The set of all x such that x is a real number and x is not equal to 3."

In this section, we will use this set builder notation to write domains.
Unless told otherwise, we assume that the domain of a function described by an equation is the set of all real numbers for which the equation is defined.

EXAMPLE 1 Find the domain of each rational function.

a. $f(x) = \dfrac{8x^3 + 7x^2 + 20}{2}$ **b.** $g(x) = \dfrac{5x^2 - 3}{x - 1}$ **c.** $f(x) = \dfrac{7x - 2}{x^2 - 2x - 15}$

Solution The domain of each function will contain all real numbers except those values that make the denominator 0.

a. No matter what the value of x, the denominator of $f(x) = \dfrac{8x^3 + 7x^2 + 20}{2}$ is never 0, so the domain of f is $\{x \mid x$ is a real number$\}$.

b. To find the values of x that make the denominator of $g(x)$ equal to 0, we solve the equation "denominator $= 0$":

$$x - 1 = 0, \quad \text{or} \quad x = 1$$

The domain must exclude 1 since the rational expression is undefined when x is 1. The domain of g is $\{x \mid x$ is a real number and $x \neq 1\}$.

c. We find the domain by setting the denominator equal to 0.

$$x^2 - 2x - 15 = 0 \quad \text{Set the denominator equal to 0 and solve.}$$
$$(x - 5)(x + 3) = 0$$
$$x - 5 = 0 \quad \text{or} \quad x + 3 = 0$$
$$x = 5 \quad \text{or} \quad x = -3$$

If x is replaced with 5 or with -3, the rational expression is undefined.
The domain of f is $\{x \mid x$ is a real number and $x \neq 5, x \neq -3\}$. □

PRACTICE
1   Find the domain of each rational function.

a. $f(x) = \dfrac{4x^5 - 3x^2 + 2}{-6}$ **b.** $g(x) = \dfrac{6x^2 + 1}{x + 3}$ **c.** $h(x) = \dfrac{8x - 3}{x^2 - 5x + 6}$

✓CONCEPT CHECK

For which of these values (if any) is the rational expression $\dfrac{x - 3}{x^2 + 2}$ undefined?

a. 2   **b.** 3   **c.** -2 **d.** 0   **e.** None of these

OBJECTIVE
2   **Simplifying Rational Expressions**

Recall that a fraction is in lowest terms or simplest form if the numerator and denominator have no common factors other than 1 (or -1). For example, $\dfrac{3}{13}$ is in lowest terms since 3 and 13 have no common factors other than 1 (or -1).

To **simplify** a rational expression, or to write it in lowest terms, we use a method similar to simplifying a fraction.

Recall that to simplify a fraction, we essentially "remove factors of 1." Our ability to do this comes from these facts:

- If $c \neq 0$, then $\dfrac{c}{c} = 1$. For example, $\dfrac{7}{7} = 1$ and $\dfrac{-8.65}{-8.65} = 1$.

- $n \cdot 1 = n$. For example, $-5 \cdot 1 = -5$, $126.8 \cdot 1 = 126.8$, and $\dfrac{a}{b} \cdot 1 = \dfrac{a}{b}, b \neq 0$.

In other words, we have the following:

$$\frac{a \cdot c}{b \cdot c} = \frac{a}{b} \cdot \frac{c}{c} = \frac{a}{b}$$

Since $\frac{a}{b} \cdot 1 = \frac{a}{b}$

Let's practice simplifying a fraction by simplifying $\frac{15}{65}$.

$$\frac{15}{65} = \frac{3 \cdot 5}{13 \cdot 5} = \frac{3}{13} \cdot \frac{5}{5} = \frac{3}{13} \cdot 1 = \frac{3}{13}$$

Let's use the same technique and simplify the rational expression $\frac{x^2 - 9}{x^2 + x - 6}$.

$$\frac{x^2 - 9}{x^2 + x - 6} = \frac{(x - 3)(x + 3)}{(x - 2)(x + 3)} \qquad \text{Factor the numerator and the denominator.}$$

$$= \frac{(x - 3)\,(x + 3)}{(x - 2)\,(x + 3)} \qquad \text{Look for common factors.}$$

$$= \frac{x - 3}{x - 2} \cdot \frac{x + 3}{x + 3}$$

$$= \frac{x - 3}{x - 2} \cdot 1 \qquad \text{Write } \frac{x + 3}{x + 3} \text{ as 1.}$$

$$= \frac{x - 3}{x - 2} \qquad \text{Multiply to remove a factor of 1.}$$

This "removing a factor of 1" is stated in the principle below:

Fundamental Principle of Rational Expressions

For any rational expression $\frac{P}{Q}$ and any polynomial R, where $R \neq 0$,

$$\frac{PR}{QR} = \frac{P}{Q} \cdot \frac{R}{R} = \frac{P}{Q} \cdot 1 = \frac{P}{Q}$$

or, simply,

$$\frac{PR}{QR} = \frac{P}{Q}$$

In general, the following steps may be used to simplify rational expressions or to write a rational expression in lowest terms.

Simplifying or Writing a Rational Expression in Lowest Terms

Step 1. Completely factor the numerator and denominator of the rational expression.

Step 2. Divide out factors common to the numerator and denominator. (This is the same as "removing a factor of 1.")

For now, we assume that variables in a rational expression do not represent values that make the denominator 0.

EXAMPLE 2   Simplify each rational expression.

a. $\dfrac{2x^2}{10x^3 - 2x^2}$ b. $\dfrac{9x^2 + 13x + 4}{8x^2 + x - 7}$

Solution

a. $\dfrac{2x^2}{10x^3 - 2x^2} = \dfrac{2x^2 \cdot 1}{2x^2\,(5x - 1)} = 1 \cdot \dfrac{1}{5x - 1} = \dfrac{1}{5x - 1}$

b. $\dfrac{9x^2 + 13x + 4}{8x^2 + x - 7} = \dfrac{(9x + 4)\,(x + 1)}{(8x - 7)\,(x + 1)}$ Factor the numerator and denominator.

$= \dfrac{9x + 4}{8x - 7} \cdot 1$ Since $\dfrac{x + 1}{x + 1} = 1$

$= \dfrac{9x + 4}{8x - 7}$ Simplest form   □

PRACTICE

2   Simplify each rational expression.

a. $\dfrac{5z^4}{10z^5 - 5z^4}$ b. $\dfrac{5x^2 + 13x + 6}{6x^2 + 7x - 10}$

Just as for numerical fractions, we can use a shortcut notation. Remember that as long as exact factors in both the numerator and denominator are divided out, we are "removing a factor of 1." We will use the following notation to show this:

$$\dfrac{x^2 - 9}{x^2 + x - 6} = \dfrac{(x - 3)\,(x + 3)}{(x - 2)\,(x + 3)}$$ A factor of 1 is identified by the shading.

$$= \dfrac{x - 3}{x - 2}$$ Remove a factor of 1.

Thus, the rational expression $\dfrac{x^2 - 9}{x^2 + x - 6}$ has the same value as the rational expression $\dfrac{x - 3}{x - 2}$ for all values of x except 2 and −3. (Remember that when x is 2, the denominator of both rational expressions is 0 and when x is −3, the original rational expression has a denominator of 0.)

As we simplify rational expressions, we will assume that the simplified rational expression is equal to the original rational expression for all real numbers except those for which the original denominator is 0.

EXAMPLE 3   Simplify each rational expression.

a. $\dfrac{2 + x}{x + 2}$ b. $\dfrac{2 - x}{x - 2}$

Solution

a. $\dfrac{2 + x}{x + 2} = \dfrac{x + 2}{x + 2} = 1$ By the commutative property of addition, $2 + x = x + 2$.

b. $\dfrac{2 - x}{x - 2}$

The terms in the numerator of $\dfrac{2 - x}{x - 2}$ differ by sign from the terms of the denominator, so the polynomials are opposites of each other and the expression simplifies to −1. To see this, we factor out −1 from the numerator or the denominator. If −1 is factored from the numerator, then

$$\dfrac{2 - x}{x - 2} = \dfrac{-1(-2 + x)}{x - 2} = \dfrac{-1\,(x - 2)}{x - 2} = \dfrac{-1}{1} = -1$$

(Continued on next page)

▶ **Helpful Hint**

When the numerator and the denominator of a rational expression are opposites of each other, the expression simplifies to -1.

If -1 is factored from the denominator, the result is the same.

$$\frac{2-x}{x-2} = \frac{2-x}{-1(-x+2)} = \frac{2-x}{-1(2-x)} = \frac{1}{-1} = -1$$

PRACTICE
3 Simplify each rational expression.

a. $\dfrac{x+3}{3+x}$ **b.** $\dfrac{3-x}{x-3}$

EXAMPLE 4 Simplify $\dfrac{18-2x^2}{x^2-2x-3}$.

Solution

$$\frac{18-2x^2}{x^2-2x-3} = \frac{2(9-x^2)}{(x+1)(x-3)} \qquad \text{Factor.}$$

$$= \frac{2(3+x)(3-x)}{(x+1)(x-3)} \qquad \text{Factor completely.}$$

$$= \frac{2(3+x)\cdot-1(x-3)}{(x+1)(x-3)} \qquad \begin{array}{l}\text{Notice the opposites } 3-x \\ \text{and } x-3. \text{ Write } 3-x \text{ as} \\ -1(x-3) \text{ and simplify.}\end{array}$$

$$= -\frac{2(3+x)}{x+1}$$

PRACTICE
4 Simplify $\dfrac{20-5x^2}{x^2+x-6}$.

▶ **Helpful Hint**

When simplifying a rational expression, we look for **common *factors*, not common *terms*.**

$$\frac{x\cdot(x+2)}{x\cdot x} = \frac{x+2}{x} \qquad\qquad \frac{x+2}{x}$$

Common factors. These can be divided out.   Common terms. There is no factor of 1 that can be generated.

✓**CONCEPT CHECK**

Recall that we can only remove *factors* of 1. Which of the following are *not* true? Explain why.

a. $\dfrac{3-1}{3+5}$ simplifies to $-\dfrac{1}{5}$.   **b.** $\dfrac{2x+10}{2}$ simplifies to $x+5$.

c. $\dfrac{37}{72}$ simplifies to $\dfrac{3}{2}$.   **d.** $\dfrac{2x+3}{2}$ simplifies to $x+3$.

EXAMPLE 5 Simplify each rational expression.

a. $\dfrac{x^3+8}{2+x}$ **b.** $\dfrac{2y^2+2}{y^3-5y^2+y-5}$

Solution

a. $\dfrac{x^3+8}{2+x} = \dfrac{(x+2)(x^2-2x+4)}{x+2}$ Factor the sum of the two cubes.

$= x^2-2x+4$ Divide out common factors.

Answers to Concept Check: a, c, d

b. $\dfrac{2y^2 + 2}{y^3 - 5y^2 + y - 5} = \dfrac{2(y^2 + 1)}{(y^3 - 5y^2) + (y - 5)}$ Factor the numerator; group the denominator.

$$= \dfrac{2(y^2 + 1)}{y^2(y - 5) + 1(y - 5)}$$ Factor the denominator by grouping.

$$= \dfrac{2\,(y^2 + 1)}{(y - 5)\,(y^2 + 1)}$$

$$= \dfrac{2}{y - 5}$$ Divide out common factors.   □

PRACTICE
5   Simplify each rational expression.

a. $\dfrac{x^3 + 64}{4 + x}$ **b.** $\dfrac{5z^2 + 10}{z^3 - 3z^2 + 2z - 6}$

✔**CONCEPT CHECK**

Does $\dfrac{n}{n + 2}$ simplify to $\dfrac{1}{2}$? Why or why not?

OBJECTIVE
3   Writing Equivalent Forms of Rational Expressions

From Example 3, we have

$$\dfrac{2 + x}{x + 2} = \dfrac{x + 2}{x + 2} = 1 \quad \text{and} \quad \dfrac{2 - x}{x - 2} = \dfrac{2 - x}{-1\,(2 - x)} = \dfrac{1}{-1} = -1.$$

When performing operations on rational expressions, equivalent forms of answers often result. For this reason, it is very important to be able to recognize equivalent answers.

EXAMPLE 6   List some equivalent forms of $-\dfrac{5x - 1}{x + 9}$.

Solution   To do so, recall that $-\dfrac{a}{b} = \dfrac{-a}{b} = \dfrac{a}{-b}$. Thus

$$-\dfrac{5x - 1}{x + 9} = \dfrac{-(5x - 1)}{x + 9} = \dfrac{-5x + 1}{x + 9} \quad \text{or} \quad \dfrac{1 - 5x}{x + 9}$$

Also,

$$-\dfrac{5x - 1}{x + 9} = \dfrac{5x - 1}{-(x + 9)} = \dfrac{5x - 1}{-x - 9} \quad \text{or} \quad \dfrac{5x - 1}{-9 - x}$$

> **Helpful Hint**
> Remember, a negative sign in front of a fraction or rational expression may be moved to the numerator or the denominator, but *not* both.

Thus $-\dfrac{5x - 1}{x + 9} = \dfrac{-(5x - 1)}{x + 9} = \dfrac{-5x + 1}{x + 9} = \dfrac{5x - 1}{-(x + 9)} = \dfrac{5x - 1}{-x - 9}$ □

PRACTICE
6   List some equivalent forms of $-\dfrac{x + 3}{6x - 11}$.

Keep in mind that many rational expressions may look different, but in fact be equivalent.

OBJECTIVE

4   Using Rational Functions in Applications

Rational functions occur often in real-life situations.

EXAMPLE 7   Cost for Pressing Compact Discs

For the ICL Production Company, the rational function $C(x) = \dfrac{2.6x + 10,000}{x}$ describes the company's cost per disc of pressing x compact discs. Find the cost per disc for pressing:

a. 100 compact discs   **b.** 1000 compact discs

Solution

a. $C(100) = \dfrac{2.6(100) + 10,000}{100} = \dfrac{10,260}{100} = 102.6$

The cost per disc for pressing 100 compact discs is $102.60.

b. $C(1000) = \dfrac{2.6(1000) + 10,000}{1000} = \dfrac{12,600}{1000} = 12.6$

The cost per disc for pressing 1000 compact discs is $12.60. Notice that as more compact discs are produced, the cost per disc decreases.   □

PRACTICE

7   A company's cost per tee shirt for silk screening x tee shirts is given by the rational function $C(x) = \dfrac{3.2x + 400}{x}$. Find the cost per tee shirt for printing:

a. 100 tee shirts   **b.** 1000 tee shirts

Graphing Calculator Explorations

(Note: The information below about *connected* mode and *dot* mode may not apply to your graphing calculator.)

Recall that since the rational expression $\dfrac{7x - 2}{(x - 2)(x + 5)}$ is not defined when $x = 2$ or when $x = -5$, we say that the domain of the rational function $f(x) = \dfrac{7x - 2}{(x - 2)(x + 5)}$ is all real numbers except 2 and −5. This domain can be written as $\{x \mid x$ is a real number and $x \neq 2, x \neq -5\}$. This means that the graph of $f(x)$ should not cross the vertical lines $x = 2$ and $x = -5$. The graph of $f(x)$ in *connected* mode is to the left. In connected mode the graphing calculator tries to connect all dots of the graph so that the result is a smooth curve. This is what has happened in the graph. Notice that the graph appears to contain vertical lines at $x = 2$ and at $x = -5$. We know that this cannot happen because the function is not defined at $x = 2$ and at $x = -5$. We also know that this cannot happen because the graph of this function would not pass the vertical line test.

The graph of $f(x)$ in *dot* mode is to the left. In dot mode the graphing calculator will not connect dots with a smooth curve. Notice that the vertical lines have disappeared, and we have a better picture of the graph. The graph, however, actually appears more like the hand-drawn graph below. By using a Table feature, a Calculate Value feature, or by tracing, we can see that the function is not defined at $x = 2$ and at $x = -5$.

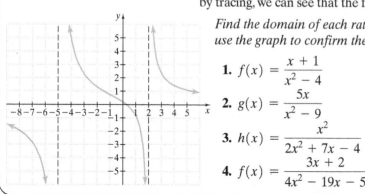

Find the domain of each rational function. Then graph each rational function and use the graph to confirm the domain.

1. $f(x) = \dfrac{x + 1}{x^2 - 4}$

2. $g(x) = \dfrac{5x}{x^2 - 9}$

3. $h(x) = \dfrac{x^2}{2x^2 + 7x - 4}$

4. $f(x) = \dfrac{3x + 2}{4x^2 - 19x - 5}$

Vocabulary, Readiness & Video Check

Use the choices below to fill in each blank. Some choices may not be used.

1	true	rational	simplified	$\dfrac{-a}{-b}$	$\dfrac{-a}{b}$	$\dfrac{a}{-b}$
-1	false	domain	0			

1. A _____ expression is an expression that can be written as the quotient $\dfrac{P}{Q}$ of two polynomials P and Q as long as $Q \neq 0$.

2. A rational expression is undefined if the denominator is _____.

3. The _____ of the rational function $f(x) = \dfrac{2}{x}$ is $\{x \,|\, x \text{ is a real number and } x \neq 0\}$.

4. A rational expression is _____ if the numerator and denominator have no common factors other than 1 or -1.

5. The expression $\dfrac{x^2 + 2}{2 + x^2}$ simplifies to _____.

6. The expression $\dfrac{y - z}{z - y}$ simplifies to _____.

7. For a rational expression, $-\dfrac{a}{b} = \dfrac{}{} = \dfrac{}{}$.

8. True or false: $\dfrac{a - 6}{a + 2} = \dfrac{-(a - 6)}{-(a + 2)} = \dfrac{-a + 6}{-a - 2}$. _____

Martin-Gay Interactive Videos

See Video 7.1

Watch the section lecture video and answer the following questions.

OBJECTIVE 1
9. Why can't the denominators of rational expressions be zero? How can we find the domain of a rational function?

OBJECTIVE 2
10. In ▭ Example 6, why isn't a factor of x divided out of the expression at the end?

OBJECTIVE 3
11. From ▭ Example 8, if we move a negative sign from in front of a rational expression to either the numerator or denominator, when do we insert parentheses and why?

OBJECTIVE 4
12. From ▭ Example 9, why do we subtract parts a. and b. to find the answer to part c.?

7.1 Exercise Set   MyMathLab®

Find the domain of each rational expression. See Example 1.

1. $f(x) = \dfrac{5x - 7}{4}$

2. $g(x) = \dfrac{4 - 3x}{2}$

3. $s(t) = \dfrac{t^2 + 1}{2t}$

4. $v(t) = -\dfrac{5t + t^2}{3t}$

▶ **5.** $f(x) = \dfrac{3x}{7 - x}$

6. $f(x) = \dfrac{-4x}{-2 + x}$

7. $f(x) = \dfrac{x}{3x - 1}$

8. $g(x) = \dfrac{-2}{2x + 5}$

9. $R(x) = \dfrac{3 + 2x}{x^3 + x^2 - 2x}$

10. $h(x) = \dfrac{5 - 3x}{2x^2 - 14x + 20}$

▶ **11.** $C(x) = \dfrac{x + 3}{x^2 - 4}$

12. $R(x) = \dfrac{5}{x^2 - 7x}$

Study Example 6. Then list four equivalent forms for each rational expression.

13. $-\dfrac{x - 10}{x + 8}$

⊙ **14.** $-\dfrac{x + 11}{x - 4}$

15. $-\dfrac{5y - 3}{y - 12}$

16. $-\dfrac{8y - 1}{y - 15}$

MIXED PRACTICE

Simplify each expression. See Examples 2 through 5.

⊙ **17.** $\dfrac{x + 7}{7 + x}$

18. $\dfrac{y + 9}{9 + y}$

⊙ **19.** $\dfrac{x - 7}{7 - x}$

20. $\dfrac{y - 9}{9 - y}$

21. $\dfrac{2}{8x + 16}$

22. $\dfrac{3}{9x + 6}$

⊙ **23.** $\dfrac{-5a - 5b}{a + b}$

24. $\dfrac{-4x - 4y}{x + y}$

25. $\dfrac{7x + 35}{x^2 + 5x}$

26. $\dfrac{9x + 99}{x^2 + 11x}$

27. $\dfrac{x + 5}{x^2 - 4x - 45}$

28. $\dfrac{x - 3}{x^2 - 6x + 9}$

29. $\dfrac{5x^2 + 11x + 2}{x + 2}$

30. $\dfrac{12x^2 + 4x - 1}{2x + 1}$

⊙ **31.** $\dfrac{x^3 + 7x^2}{x^2 + 5x - 14}$

32. $\dfrac{x^4 - 10x^3}{x^2 - 17x + 70}$

33. $\dfrac{2x^2 - 8}{4x - 8}$

34. $\dfrac{5x^2 - 500}{35x + 350}$

⊙ **35.** $\dfrac{4 - x^2}{x - 2}$

36. $\dfrac{49 - y^2}{y - 7}$

37. $\dfrac{11x^2 - 22x^3}{6x - 12x^2}$

38. $\dfrac{24y^2 - 8y^3}{15y - 5y^2}$

39. $\dfrac{x^2 + xy + 2x + 2y}{x + 2}$

40. $\dfrac{ab + ac + b^2 + bc}{b + c}$

41. $\dfrac{x^3 + 8}{x + 2}$

42. $\dfrac{x^3 + 64}{x + 4}$

43. $\dfrac{x^3 - 1}{1 - x}$

44. $\dfrac{3 - x}{x^3 - 27}$

45. $\dfrac{2xy + 5x - 2y - 5}{3xy + 4x - 3y - 4}$

46. $\dfrac{2xy + 2x - 3y - 3}{2xy + 4x - 3y - 6}$

47. $\dfrac{3x^2 - 5x - 2}{6x^3 + 2x^2 + 3x + 1}$

48. $\dfrac{2x^2 - x - 3}{2x^3 - 3x^2 + 2x - 3}$

49. $\dfrac{9x^2 - 15x + 25}{27x^3 + 125}$

50. $\dfrac{8x^3 - 27}{4x^2 + 6x + 9}$

MIXED PRACTICE

Simplify each expression. Then determine whether the given answer is correct. See Examples 3 through 6.

51. $\dfrac{9 - x^2}{x - 3}$; Answer: $-3 - x$

52. $\dfrac{100 - x^2}{x - 10}$; Answer: $-10 - x$

53. $\dfrac{7 - 34x - 5x^2}{25x^2 - 1}$; Answer: $\dfrac{x + 7}{-5x - 1}$

54. $\dfrac{2 - 15x - 8x^2}{64x^2 - 1}$; Answer: $\dfrac{x + 2}{-8x - 1}$

Find each function value. See Example 7.

55. If $f(x) = \dfrac{x + 8}{2x - 1}$, find $f(2)$, $f(0)$, and $f(-1)$.

56. If $f(x) = \dfrac{x - 2}{-5 + x}$, find $f(-5)$, $f(0)$, and $f(10)$.

57. If $g(x) = \dfrac{x^2 + 8}{x^3 - 25x}$, find $g(3)$, $g(-2)$, and $g(1)$.

58. If $s(t) = \dfrac{t^3 + 1}{t^2 + 1}$, find $s(-1)$, $s(1)$, and $s(2)$.

Solve. See Example 7.

⊙ **59.** The total revenue from the sale of a popular book is approximated by the rational function $R(x) = \dfrac{1000x^2}{x^2 + 4}$, where x is the number of years since publication and $R(x)$ is the total revenue in millions of dollars.

   a. Find the total revenue at the end of the first year.

   b. Find the total revenue at the end of the second year.

   c. Find the revenue during the second year only.

   d. Find the domain of function R.

60. The function $f(x) = \dfrac{100,000x}{100 - x}$ models the cost in dollars for removing x percent of the pollutants from a bayou in which a nearby company dumped creosol.

   a. Find the cost of removing 20% of the pollutants from the bayou. [*Hint:* Find $f(20)$.]

   b. Find the cost of removing 60% of the pollutants and then 80% of the pollutants.

   c. Find $f(90)$, then $f(95)$, and then $f(99)$. What happens to the cost as x approaches 100%?

   d. Find the domain of function f.

61. The dose of medicine prescribed for a child depends on the child's age A in years and the adult dose D for the medication. Young's Rule is a formula used by pediatricians that gives a child's dose C as

$$C = \frac{DA}{A + 12}$$

Suppose that an 8-year-old child needs medication, and the normal adult dose is 1000 mg. What size dose should the child receive?

62. Calculating body-mass index is a way to gauge whether a person should lose weight. Doctors recommend that body-mass index values fall between 18.5 and 25. The formula for body-mass index B is

$$B = \frac{703w}{h^2}$$

where w is weight in pounds and h is height in inches. Should a 148-pound person who is 5 feet 6 inches tall lose weight?

63. Anthropologists and forensic scientists use a measure called the cephalic index to help classify skulls. The cephalic index of a skull with width W and length L from front to back is given by the formula

$$C = \frac{100W}{L}$$

A long skull has an index value less than 75, a medium skull has an index value between 75 and 85, and a broad skull has an index value over 85. Find the cephalic index of a skull that is 5 inches wide and 6.4 inches long. Classify the skull.

64. A company's gross profit margin P can be computed with the formula $P = \dfrac{R - C}{R}$, where R = the company's revenue and C = cost of goods sold. During a recent fiscal year, computer company Apple had revenues of $32.5 billion and cost of goods sold $21.3 billion. (*Source:* Apple, Inc.) What was Apple's gross profit margin in this year? Express the answer as a percent, rounded to the nearest tenth of a percent.

65. A baseball player's slugging percentage S can be calculated with the following formula:

$$S = \frac{h + d + 2t + 3r}{b}, \text{ where } h = \text{ number of hits,}$$

d = number of doubles, t = number of triples, r = number of home runs, and b = number of at bats. In 2010, Albert Pujols of the St. Louis Cardinals led Major League Baseball in slugging percent. During the 2010 season, Pujols had 587 at bats, 183 hits, 39 doubles, 1 triple, and 42 home runs. (*Source:* Major League Baseball) Calculate Pujols' 2010 slugging percent. Round to the nearest tenth of a percent.

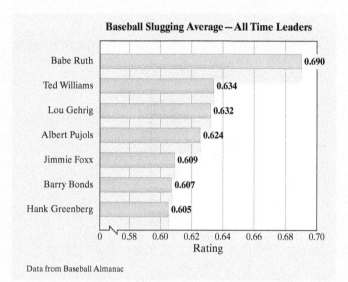

Data from Baseball Almanac

66. To calculate a quarterback's rating in NCAA football, you may use the formula $\dfrac{100C + 330T - 200I + 8.4Y}{A}$, where C = the number of completed passes, A = the number of attempted passes, T = the number of touchdown passes, Y = the number of yards in the completed passes, and I = the number of interceptions. Cam Newton of Auburn University was selected as the 2010 winner of the Heisman Memorial Trophy as the Most Outstanding Football Player. Newton, a junior quarterback, ended the season with 280 attempts, 185 completions, 2854 yards, 30 touchdowns, and only 7 interceptions. Calculate Newton's quarterback rating for the 2010 season. (*Source:* NCAA) Round the answer to the nearest tenth.

REVIEW AND PREVIEW

Perform each indicated operation. See Section 1.3.

67. $\dfrac{1}{3} \cdot \dfrac{9}{11}$

68. $\dfrac{5}{27} \cdot \dfrac{2}{5}$

69. $\dfrac{1}{3} \div \dfrac{1}{4}$

70. $\dfrac{7}{8} \div \dfrac{1}{2}$

71. $\dfrac{13}{20} \div \dfrac{2}{9}$

72. $\dfrac{8}{15} \div \dfrac{5}{8}$

CONCEPT EXTENSIONS

Which of the following are incorrect and why? See the second Concept Check in this section.

73. $\dfrac{5a - 15}{5}$ simplifies to $a - 3$?

74. $\dfrac{7m - 9}{7}$ simplifies to $m - 9$?

75. $\dfrac{1 + 2}{1 + 3}$ simplifies to $\dfrac{2}{3}$?

76. $\dfrac{46}{54}$ simplifies to $\dfrac{6}{5}$?

Determine whether each rational expression can be simplified. If yes, does it simplify to 1, –1, or neither? (Do not actually simplify.)

77. $\dfrac{x}{x + 7}$ **78.** $\dfrac{x + 9}{x - 9}$

79. $\dfrac{3 + x}{x + 3}$ **80.** $\dfrac{8 + x}{x + 8}$

81. $\dfrac{5 - x}{x - 5}$ **82.** $\dfrac{x - 7}{-x + 7}$

83. Does $\dfrac{x}{x + 5}$ simplify to $\dfrac{1}{5}$? Why or why not?

84. Does $\dfrac{x + 7}{x}$ simplify to 7? Why or why not?

85. In your own words explain how to simplify a rational expression.

86. In your own words, explain how to find the domain of a rational function.

87. Graph a portion of the function $f(x) = \dfrac{20x}{100 - x}$. To do so, complete the given table, plot the points, and then connect the plotted points with a smooth curve. (Note: The domain of this function is all real numbers except 100. We are graphing just a portion of this function.)

x	0	10	30	50	70	90	95	99
y or $f(x)$								

88. The domain of the function $f(x) = \dfrac{1}{x}$ is all real numbers except 0. This means that the graph of this function will be in two pieces: one piece corresponding to x values less than 0 and one piece corresponding to x values greater than 0. Graph the function by completing the following tables, separately plotting the points, and connecting each set of plotted points with a smooth curve.

x	$\dfrac{1}{4}$	$\dfrac{1}{2}$	1	2	4
y or $f(x)$					

x	-4	-2	-1	$-\dfrac{1}{2}$	$-\dfrac{1}{4}$
y or $f(x)$					

How does the graph of $y = \dfrac{x^2 - 9}{x - 3}$ compare to the graph of $y = x + 3$? Recall that $\dfrac{x^2 - 9}{x - 3} = \dfrac{(x + 3)(x - 3)}{x - 3} = x + 3$ as long as x is not 3. This means that the graph of $y = \dfrac{x^2 - 9}{x - 3}$ is the same as the graph of $y = x + 3$ with $x \neq 3$. To graph $y = \dfrac{x^2 - 9}{x - 3}$, then, graph the linear equation $y = x + 3$ and place an open dot on the graph at 3. This open dot or interruption of the line at 3 means $x \neq 3$.

89. Graph $y = \dfrac{x^2 - 16}{x - 4}$.   **90.** Graph $y = \dfrac{x^2 - 25}{x + 5}$.

91. Graph $y = \dfrac{x^2 - 6x + 8}{x - 2}$.   **92.** Graph $y = \dfrac{x^2 + x - 12}{x + 4}$.

7.2 Multiplying and Dividing Rational Expressions

OBJECTIVES

1 Multiply Rational Expressions.

2 Divide Rational Expressions.

3 Multiply or Divide Rational Expressions.

4 Convert Between Units of Measure.

OBJECTIVE

1 Multiplying Rational Expressions

Just as simplifying rational expressions is similar to simplifying number fractions, multiplying and dividing rational expressions is similar to multiplying and dividing number fractions.

Fractions	*Rational Expressions*
Multiply: $\dfrac{3}{5} \cdot \dfrac{10}{11}$	Multiply: $\dfrac{x-3}{x+5} \cdot \dfrac{2x+10}{x^2-9}$

Multiply numerators and multiply denominators.

$$\frac{3}{5} \cdot \frac{10}{11} = \frac{3 \cdot 10}{5 \cdot 11} \qquad\qquad \frac{x-3}{x+5} \cdot \frac{2x+10}{x^2-9} = \frac{(x-3) \cdot (2x+10)}{(x+5) \cdot (x^2-9)}$$

Simplify by factoring numerators and denominators.

$$= \frac{3 \cdot 2 \cdot 5}{5 \cdot 11} \qquad\qquad = \frac{(x-3) \cdot 2 (x+5)}{(x+5)(x+3)(x-3)}$$

Apply the fundamental principle.

$$= \frac{3 \cdot 2}{11} \quad \text{or} \quad \frac{6}{11} \qquad\qquad = \frac{2}{x+3}$$

Multiplying Rational Expressions

If $\dfrac{P}{Q}$ and $\dfrac{R}{S}$ are rational expressions, then

$$\frac{P}{Q} \cdot \frac{R}{S} = \frac{PR}{QS}$$

To multiply rational expressions, multiply the numerators and multiply the denominators.

Note: Recall that for Sections 7.1 through 7.4, we assume variables in rational expressions have only those replacement values for which the expressions are defined.

EXAMPLE 1 Multiply.

a. $\dfrac{25x}{2} \cdot \dfrac{1}{y^3}$ **b.** $\dfrac{-7x^2}{5y} \cdot \dfrac{3y^5}{14x^2}$

Solution To multiply rational expressions, multiply the numerators and multiply the denominators of both expressions. Then simplify if possible.

a. $\dfrac{25x}{2} \cdot \dfrac{1}{y^3} = \dfrac{25x \cdot 1}{2 \cdot y^3} = \dfrac{25x}{2y^3}$

The expression $\dfrac{25x}{2y^3}$ is in simplest form.

b. $\dfrac{-7x^2}{5y} \cdot \dfrac{3y^5}{14x^2} = \dfrac{-7x^2 \cdot 3y^5}{5y \cdot 14x^2}$ Multiply.

The expression $\dfrac{-7x^2 \cdot 3y^5}{5y \cdot 14x^2}$ is not in simplest form, so we factor the numerator and the denominator and divide out common factors.

$$= \frac{-1 \cdot 7 \cdot 3 \cdot x^2 \cdot y \cdot y^4}{5 \cdot 2 \cdot 7 \cdot x^2 \cdot y}$$

$$= -\frac{3y^4}{10}$$

(Continued on next page)

PRACTICE
1 Multiply.

a. $\dfrac{4a}{5} \cdot \dfrac{3}{b^2}$

b. $\dfrac{-3p^4}{q^2} \cdot \dfrac{2q^3}{9p^4}$

When multiplying rational expressions, it is usually best to factor each numerator and denominator. This will help us when we divide out common factors to write the product in lowest terms.

EXAMPLE 2 Multiply: $\dfrac{x^2 + x}{3x} \cdot \dfrac{6}{5x + 5}$

Solution $\dfrac{x^2 + x}{3x} \cdot \dfrac{6}{5x + 5} = \dfrac{x(x + 1)}{3x} \cdot \dfrac{2 \cdot 3}{5(x + 1)}$ Factor numerators and denominators.

$= \dfrac{x(x + 1) \cdot 2 \cdot 3}{3x \cdot 5 \,(x + 1)}$ Multiply.

$= \dfrac{2}{5}$ Simplify by dividing out common factors.

PRACTICE
2   Multiply: $\dfrac{x^2 - x}{5x} \cdot \dfrac{15}{x^2 - 1}$

The following steps may be used to multiply rational expressions.

Multiplying Rational Expressions

Step 1. Completely factor numerators and denominators.

Step 2. Multiply numerators and multiply denominators.

Step 3. Simplify or write the product in lowest terms by dividing out common factors.

✓CONCEPT CHECK

Which of the following is a true statement?

a. $\dfrac{1}{3} \cdot \dfrac{1}{2} = \dfrac{1}{5}$ **b.** $\dfrac{2}{x} \cdot \dfrac{5}{x} = \dfrac{10}{x}$ **c.** $\dfrac{3}{x} \cdot \dfrac{1}{2} = \dfrac{3}{2x}$ **d.** $\dfrac{x}{7} \cdot \dfrac{x + 5}{4} = \dfrac{2x + 5}{28}$

EXAMPLE 3 Multiply: $\dfrac{3x + 3}{5x - 5x^2} \cdot \dfrac{2x^2 + x - 3}{4x^2 - 9}$

Solution

$\dfrac{3x + 3}{5x - 5x^2} \cdot \dfrac{2x^2 + x - 3}{4x^2 - 9} = \dfrac{3(x + 1)}{5x(1 - x)} \cdot \dfrac{(2x + 3)(x - 1)}{(2x - 3)(2x + 3)}$ Factor.

$= \dfrac{3(x + 1)(2x + 3)(x - 1)}{5x(1 - x)(2x - 3)(2x + 3)}$ Multiply.

$= \dfrac{3(x + 1)(x - 1)}{5x(1 - x)(2x - 3)}$ Divide out common factors.

Next, recall that $x - 1$ and $1 - x$ are opposites so that $x - 1 = -1(1 - x)$.

$$= \frac{3(x + 1)(-1)(1 - x)}{5x(1 - x)(2x - 3)}$$ Write $x - 1$ as $-1(1 - x)$.

$$= \frac{-3(x + 1)}{5x(2x - 3)} \quad \text{or} \quad -\frac{3(x + 1)}{5x(2x - 3)}$$ Divide out common factors.   □

PRACTICE
3   Multiply: $\dfrac{6 - 3x}{6x + 6x^2} \cdot \dfrac{3x^2 - 2x - 5}{x^2 - 4}$.

OBJECTIVE
2   Dividing Rational Expressions

We can divide by a rational expression in the same way we divide by a fraction. To divide by a fraction, multiply by its reciprocal.

> ▶ Helpful Hint
>
> Don't forget how to find reciprocals. The reciprocal of $\dfrac{a}{b}$ is $\dfrac{b}{a}$, $a \neq 0, b \neq 0$.

For example, to divide $\dfrac{3}{2}$ by $\dfrac{7}{8}$, multiply $\dfrac{3}{2}$ by $\dfrac{8}{7}$.

$$\frac{3}{2} \div \frac{7}{8} = \frac{3}{2} \cdot \frac{8}{7} = \frac{3 \cdot 4 \cdot 2}{2 \cdot 7} = \frac{12}{7}$$

Dividing Rational Expressions

If $\dfrac{P}{Q}$ and $\dfrac{R}{S}$ are rational expressions and $\dfrac{R}{S}$ is not 0, then

$$\frac{P}{Q} \div \frac{R}{S} = \frac{P}{Q} \cdot \frac{S}{R} = \frac{PS}{QR}$$

To divide two rational expressions, multiply the first rational expression by the reciprocal of the second rational expression.

EXAMPLE 4   Divide: $\dfrac{3x^3y^7}{40} \div \dfrac{4x^3}{y^2}$

Solution $\dfrac{3x^3y^7}{40} \div \dfrac{4x^3}{y^2} = \dfrac{3x^3y^7}{40} \cdot \dfrac{y^2}{4x^3}$ Multiply by the reciprocal of $\dfrac{4x^3}{y^2}$.

$$= \frac{3x^3y^9}{160x^3}$$

$$= \frac{3y^9}{160}$$ Simplify.   □

PRACTICE
4   Divide: $\dfrac{5a^3b^2}{24} \div \dfrac{10a^5}{6}$

EXAMPLE 5 Divide: $\dfrac{(x+2)^2}{10} \div \dfrac{2x+4}{5}$

Solution:

$$\dfrac{(x+2)^2}{10} \div \dfrac{2x+4}{5} = \dfrac{(x+2)^2}{10} \cdot \dfrac{5}{2x+4}$$ Multiply by the reciprocal of $\dfrac{2x+4}{5}$.

$$= \dfrac{(x+2)(x+2)\cdot 5}{5\cdot 2\cdot 2\cdot (x+2)}$$ Factor and multiply.

$$= \dfrac{x+2}{4}$$ Simplify. □

> **Helpful Hint**
> Remember, **to Divide by a Rational Expression**, multiply by its reciprocal.

PRACTICE
5 Divide $\dfrac{(x-5)^2}{3}$ by $\dfrac{4x-20}{9}$.

The following may be used to divide by a rational expression.

> **Dividing by a Rational Expression**
> Multiply by its reciprocal.

EXAMPLE 6 Divide: $\dfrac{6x+2}{x^2-1} \div \dfrac{3x^2+x}{x-1}$

Solution

$$\dfrac{6x+2}{x^2-1} \div \dfrac{3x^2+x}{x-1} = \dfrac{6x+2}{x^2-1} \cdot \dfrac{x-1}{3x^2+x}$$ Multiply by the reciprocal.

$$= \dfrac{2(3x+1)(x-1)}{(x+1)(x-1)\cdot x(3x+1)}$$ Factor and multiply.

$$= \dfrac{2}{x(x+1)}$$ Simplify. □

PRACTICE
6 Divide $\dfrac{10x-2}{x^2-9} \div \dfrac{5x^2-x}{x+3}$.

EXAMPLE 7 Divide: $\dfrac{2x^2-11x+5}{5x-25} \div \dfrac{4x-2}{10}$

Solution

$$\dfrac{2x^2-11x+5}{5x-25} \div \dfrac{4x-2}{10} = \dfrac{2x^2-11x+5}{5x-25} \cdot \dfrac{10}{4x-2}$$ Multiply by the reciprocal.

$$= \dfrac{(2x-1)(x-5)\cdot 2\cdot 5}{5(x-5)\cdot 2(2x-1)}$$ Factor and multiply.

$$= \dfrac{1}{1} \quad \text{or} \quad 1$$ Simplify. □

PRACTICE
7 Divide $\dfrac{3x^2-11x-4}{2x-8} \div \dfrac{9x+3}{6}$.

OBJECTIVE

3 **Multiplying or Dividing Rational Expressions**

Let's make sure that we understand the difference between multiplying and dividing rational expressions.

Rational Expressions	
Multiplication	Multiply the numerators and multiply the denominators.
Division	Multiply by the reciprocal of the divisor.

EXAMPLE 8   Multiply or divide as indicated.

a. $\dfrac{x-4}{5} \cdot \dfrac{x}{x-4}$ **b.** $\dfrac{x-4}{5} \div \dfrac{x}{x-4}$ **c.** $\dfrac{x^2-4}{2x+6} \cdot \dfrac{x^2+4x+3}{2-x}$

Solution

a. $\dfrac{x-4}{5} \cdot \dfrac{x}{x-4} = \dfrac{(x-4)\cdot x}{5\cdot(x-4)} = \dfrac{x}{5}$

b. $\dfrac{x-4}{5} \div \dfrac{x}{x-4} = \dfrac{x-4}{5} \cdot \dfrac{x-4}{x} = \dfrac{(x-4)^2}{5x}$

c. $\dfrac{x^2-4}{2x+6} \cdot \dfrac{x^2+4x+3}{2-x} = \dfrac{(x-2)(x+2)\cdot(x+1)(x+3)}{2(x+3)\cdot(2-x)}$ Factor and multiply.

$\qquad = \dfrac{(x-2)(x+2)\cdot(x+1)(x+3)}{2(x+3)\cdot(2-x)}$

$\qquad = \dfrac{-1(x+2)(x+1)}{2}$ Divide out common factors. Recall that

$\qquad = -\dfrac{(x+2)(x+1)}{2}$ $\dfrac{x-2}{2-x} = -1$ ☐

PRACTICE

8   Multiply or divide as indicated.

a. $\dfrac{y+9}{8x} \cdot \dfrac{y+9}{2x}$ **b.** $\dfrac{y+9}{8x} \div \dfrac{y+9}{2}$ **c.** $\dfrac{35x-7x^2}{x^2-25} \cdot \dfrac{x^2+3x-10}{x^2+4x}$

OBJECTIVE

4 **Converting Between Units of Measure**

How many square inches are in 1 square foot?

How many cubic feet are in a cubic yard?

If you have trouble answering these questions, this section will be helpful to you.

Now that we know how to multiply fractions and rational expressions, we can use this knowledge to help us convert between units of measure. To do so, we will use **unit fractions.** A unit fraction is a fraction that equals 1. For example, since 12 in. = 1 ft, we have the unit fractions

$$\dfrac{12 \text{ in.}}{1 \text{ ft}} = 1 \qquad \text{and} \qquad \dfrac{1 \text{ ft}}{12 \text{ in.}} = 1$$

EXAMPLE 9 18 square feet = _____ square yards

Solution: Let's multiply 18 square feet by a unit fraction that has square feet in the denominator and square yards in the numerator. From the diagram, you can see that

1 square yard = 9 square feet

Thus,

1 yd = 3 ft

1 yd = 3 ft

Area: 1 sq yd or 9 sq ft

$$18 \text{ sq ft} = \frac{18 \text{ sq ft}}{1} \cdot 1 = \frac{\overset{2}{\cancel{18}} \text{ } \cancel{\text{sq ft}}}{1} \cdot \frac{1 \text{ sq yd}}{\underset{1}{\cancel{9}} \text{ } \cancel{\text{sq ft}}}$$

$$= \frac{2 \cdot 1}{1 \cdot 1} \text{ sq yd} = 2 \text{ sq yd}$$

Thus, 18 sq ft = 2 sq yd.

Draw a diagram of 18 sq ft to help you see that this is reasonable. ☐

PRACTICE
9 288 square inches = _____ square feet

EXAMPLE 10 5.2 square yards = _____ square feet

Solution:

$$5.2 \text{ sq yd} = \frac{5.2 \text{ sq yd}}{1} \cdot 1 = \frac{5.2 \text{ } \cancel{\text{sq yd}}}{1} \cdot \frac{9 \text{ sq ft}}{1 \text{ } \cancel{\text{sq yd}}} \quad \begin{matrix} \leftarrow \text{Units converting to} \\ \leftarrow \text{Units given} \end{matrix}$$

$$= \frac{5.2 \cdot 9}{1 \cdot 1} \text{ sq ft}$$

$$= 46.8 \text{ sq ft}$$

Thus, 5.2 sq yd = 46.8 sq ft.

Draw a diagram to see that this is reasonable. ☐

PRACTICE
10 3.5 square feet = _____ square inches

EXAMPLE 11 **Converting from Cubic Feet to Cubic Yards**

The largest building in the world by volume is The Boeing Company's Everett, Washington, factory complex, where Boeing's wide-body jetliners, the 747, 767, and 777, are built. The volume of this factory complex is 472,370,319 cubic feet. Find the volume of this Boeing facility in cubic yards. (*Source:* The Boeing Company)

Solution: There are 27 cubic feet in 1 cubic yard. (See the diagram.)

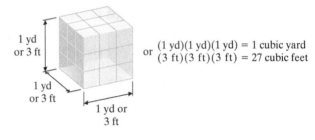

1 yd or 3 ft

1 yd or 3 ft

1 yd or 3 ft

or (1 yd)(1 yd)(1 yd) = 1 cubic yard
(3 ft)(3 ft)(3 ft) = 27 cubic feet

$$472{,}370{,}319 \text{ cu ft} = 472{,}370{,}319 \text{ cu ft} \cdot \frac{1 \text{ cu yd}}{27 \text{ cu ft}}$$

$$= \frac{472{,}370{,}319}{27} \text{ cu yd}$$

$$= 17{,}495{,}197 \text{ cu yd}$$

PRACTICE
11 The largest casino in the world is the Venetian, in Macau, on the southern tip of China. The gaming area for this casino is approximately 61,000 *square yards*. Find the size of the gaming area in *square feet*. (*Source: USA Today*)

> **▶ Helpful Hint**
>
> When converting among units of measurement, if possible write the unit fraction so that **the numerator contains the units you are converting to** and **the denominator contains the original units**.
>
> Unit fraction
>
> $$48 \text{ in.} = \frac{48 \text{ in.}}{1} \cdot \frac{1 \text{ ft}}{12 \text{ in.}} \quad \begin{array}{l}\leftarrow \text{Units converting to} \\ \leftarrow \text{Original units}\end{array}$$
>
> $$= \frac{48}{12} \text{ ft} = 4 \text{ ft}$$

EXAMPLE 12 At the 2008 Summer Olympics, Jamaican athlete Usain Bolt won the gold medal in the men's 100-meter track event. He ran the distance at an average speed of 33.9 feet per second. Convert this speed to miles per hour. (*Source:* Beijing 2008 Olympics Committee)

Solution: Recall that 1 mile = 5280 feet and 1 hour = 3600 seconds (60 · 60).

Unit fractions

$$33.9 \text{ feet/second} = \frac{33.9 \text{ feet}}{1 \text{ second}} \cdot \frac{3600 \text{ seconds}}{1 \text{ hour}} \cdot \frac{1 \text{ mile}}{5280 \text{ feet}}$$

$$= \frac{33.9 \cdot 3600}{5280} \text{ miles/hour}$$

$$\approx 23.1 \text{ miles/hour (rounded to the nearest tenth)}$$

PRACTICE
12 The cheetah is the fastest land animal, being clocked at about 102.7 feet per second. Convert this to miles per hour. Round to the nearest tenth. (*Source: World Almanac and Book of Facts*)

Vocabulary, Readiness & Video Check

Use one of the choices below to fill in the blank.

opposites   reciprocals

1. The expressions $\dfrac{x}{2y}$ and $\dfrac{2y}{x}$ are called _____.

Multiply or divide as indicated.

2. $\dfrac{a}{b} \cdot \dfrac{c}{d} = $ _____

3. $\dfrac{a}{b} \div \dfrac{c}{d} = $ _____

4. $\dfrac{x}{7} \cdot \dfrac{x}{6} = $ _____

5. $\dfrac{x}{7} \div \dfrac{x}{6} = $ _____

Martin-Gay Interactive Videos

See Video 7.2

Watch the section lecture video and answer the following questions.

OBJECTIVE 1

6. Would you say a person needs to be quite comfortable with factoring polynomials in order to be successful with multiplying rational expressions? Explain, referencing Example 2 in your answer.

OBJECTIVE 2

7. Based on the lecture before Example 3, complete the following statements. Dividing rational expressions is exactly like dividing _____ . Therefore, to divide by a rational expression, multiply by its _____.

OBJECTIVE 3

8. In ▭ Examples 4 and 5, determining the operation is the first step in deciding how to simplify. Why do you think this is so?

OBJECTIVE 4

9. When converting between units of measurement, a unit fraction may be used. What units are used in the numerator and what units are used in the denominator of your unit fraction?

7.2   Exercise Set   MyMathLab®

Find each product and simplify if possible. See Examples 1 through 3.

1. $\dfrac{3x}{y^2} \cdot \dfrac{7y}{4x}$

2. $\dfrac{9x^2}{y} \cdot \dfrac{4y}{3x^3}$

3. $\dfrac{8x}{2} \cdot \dfrac{x^5}{4x^2}$

4. $\dfrac{6x^2}{10x^3} \cdot \dfrac{5x}{12}$

5. $-\dfrac{5a^2b}{30a^2b^2} \cdot b^3$

6. $-\dfrac{9x^3y^2}{18xy^5} \cdot y^3$

7. $\dfrac{x}{2x - 14} \cdot \dfrac{x^2 - 7x}{5}$

8. $\dfrac{4x - 24}{20x} \cdot \dfrac{5}{x - 6}$

9. $\dfrac{6x + 6}{5} \cdot \dfrac{10}{36x + 36}$

10. $\dfrac{x^2 + x}{8} \cdot \dfrac{16}{x + 1}$

11. $\dfrac{(m + n)^2}{m - n} \cdot \dfrac{m}{m^2 + mn}$

12. $\dfrac{(m - n)^2}{m + n} \cdot \dfrac{m}{m^2 - mn}$

13. $\dfrac{x^2 - 25}{x^2 - 3x - 10} \cdot \dfrac{x + 2}{x}$

14. $\dfrac{a^2 - 4a + 4}{a^2 - 4} \cdot \dfrac{a + 3}{a - 2}$

15. $\dfrac{x^2 + 6x + 8}{x^2 + x - 20} \cdot \dfrac{x^2 + 2x - 15}{x^2 + 8x + 16}$

16. $\dfrac{x^2 + 9x + 20}{x^2 - 15x + 44} \cdot \dfrac{x^2 - 11x + 28}{x^2 + 12x + 35}$

Find each quotient and simplify. See Examples 4 through 7.

17. $\dfrac{5x^7}{2x^5} \div \dfrac{15x}{4x^3}$

18. $\dfrac{9y^4}{6y} \div \dfrac{y^2}{3}$

19. $\dfrac{8x^2}{y^3} \div \dfrac{4x^2y^3}{6}$

20. $\dfrac{7a^2b}{3ab^2} \div \dfrac{21a^2b^2}{14ab}$

21. $\dfrac{(x - 6)(x + 4)}{4x} \div \dfrac{2x - 12}{8x^2}$

22. $\dfrac{(x + 3)^2}{5} \div \dfrac{5x + 15}{25}$

23. $\dfrac{3x^2}{x^2 - 1} \div \dfrac{x^5}{(x + 1)^2}$

24. $\dfrac{9x^5}{a^2 - b^2} \div \dfrac{27x^2}{3b - 3a}$

25. $\dfrac{m^2 - n^2}{m + n} \div \dfrac{m}{m^2 + nm}$

26. $\dfrac{(m - n)^2}{m + n} \div \dfrac{m^2 - mn}{m}$

27. $\dfrac{x + 2}{7 - x} \div \dfrac{x^2 - 5x + 6}{x^2 - 9x + 14}$

28. $\dfrac{x - 3}{2 - x} \div \dfrac{x^2 + 3x - 18}{x^2 + 2x - 8}$

29. $\dfrac{x^2 + 7x + 10}{x - 1} \div \dfrac{x^2 + 2x - 15}{x - 1}$

30. $\dfrac{x + 1}{(x + 1)(2x + 3)} \div \dfrac{20x + 100}{2x + 3}$

MIXED PRACTICE

Multiply or divide as indicated. See Examples 1 through 8.

31. $\dfrac{5x - 10}{12} \div \dfrac{4x - 8}{8}$

32. $\dfrac{6x + 6}{5} \div \dfrac{9x + 9}{10}$

33. $\dfrac{x^2 + 5x}{8} \cdot \dfrac{9}{3x + 15}$

34. $\dfrac{3x^2 + 12x}{6} \cdot \dfrac{9}{2x + 8}$

35. $\dfrac{7}{6p^2 + q} \div \dfrac{14}{18p^2 + 3q}$

36. $\dfrac{3x + 6}{20} \div \dfrac{4x + 8}{8}$

37. $\dfrac{3x + 4y}{x^2 + 4xy + 4y^2} \cdot \dfrac{x + 2y}{2}$

38. $\dfrac{x^2 - y^2}{3x^2 + 3xy} \cdot \dfrac{3x^2 + 6x}{3x^2 - 2xy - y^2}$

39. $\dfrac{(x + 2)^2}{x - 2} \div \dfrac{x^2 - 4}{2x - 4}$

40. $\dfrac{x + 3}{x^2 - 9} \div \dfrac{5x + 15}{(x - 3)^2}$

41. $\dfrac{x^2 - 4}{24x} \div \dfrac{2 - x}{6xy}$

42. $\dfrac{3y}{3 - x} \div \dfrac{12xy}{x^2 - 9}$

43. $\dfrac{a^2 + 7a + 12}{a^2 + 5a + 6} \cdot \dfrac{a^2 + 8a + 15}{a^2 + 5a + 4}$

44. $\dfrac{b^2 + 2b - 3}{b^2 + b - 2} \cdot \dfrac{b^2 - 4}{b^2 + 6b + 8}$

45. $\dfrac{5x - 20}{3x^2 + x} \cdot \dfrac{3x^2 + 13x + 4}{x^2 - 16}$

46. $\dfrac{9x + 18}{4x^2 - 3x} \cdot \dfrac{4x^2 - 11x + 6}{x^2 - 4}$

47. $\dfrac{8n^2 - 18}{2n^2 - 5n + 3} \div \dfrac{6n^2 + 7n - 3}{n^2 - 9n + 8}$

48. $\dfrac{36n^2 - 64}{3n^2 + 10n + 8} \div \dfrac{3n^2 - 13n + 12}{n^2 - 5n - 14}$

49. Find the quotient of $\dfrac{x^2 - 9}{2x}$ and $\dfrac{x + 3}{8x^4}$.

50. Find the quotient of $\dfrac{4x^2 + 4x + 1}{4x + 2}$ and $\dfrac{4x + 2}{16}$.

Multiply or divide as indicated. Some of these expressions contain 4-term polynomials and sums and differences of cubes. See Examples 1 through 8.

51. $\dfrac{a^2 + ac + ba + bc}{a - b} \div \dfrac{a + c}{a + b}$

52. $\dfrac{x^2 + 2x - xy - 2y}{x^2 - y^2} \div \dfrac{2x + 4}{x + y}$

53. $\dfrac{3x^2 + 8x + 5}{x^2 + 8x + 7} \cdot \dfrac{x + 7}{x^2 + 4}$

54. $\dfrac{16x^2 + 2x}{16x^2 + 10x + 1} \cdot \dfrac{1}{4x^2 + 2x}$

55. $\dfrac{x^3 + 8}{x^2 - 2x + 4} \cdot \dfrac{4}{x^2 - 4}$

56. $\dfrac{9y}{3y - 3} \cdot \dfrac{y^3 - 1}{y^3 + y^2 + y}$

57. $\dfrac{a^2 - ab}{6a^2 + 6ab} \div \dfrac{a^3 - b^3}{a^2 - b^2}$

58. $\dfrac{x^3 + 27y^3}{6x} \div \dfrac{x^2 - 9y^2}{x^2 - 3xy}$

Convert as indicated. See Examples 9 through 12.

59. 10 square feet = _____ square inches.

60. 1008 square inches = _____ square feet.

61. 45 square feet = _____ square yards.

62. 2 square yards = _____ square inches.

63. 3 cubic yards = _____ cubic feet.

64. 2 cubic yards = _____ cubic inches.

65. 50 miles per hour = _____ feet per second (round to the nearest whole).

66. 10 feet per second = _____ miles per hour (round to the nearest tenth).

67. 6.3 square yards = _____ square feet.

68. 3.6 square yards = _____ square feet.

69. In January 2010, the Burj Khalifa Tower officially became the tallest building in the world. This tower has a curtain wall (the exterior skin of the building) that is approximately 133,500 square yards. Convert this to square feet. (*Source:* Burj Khalifa)

70. The Pentagon, headquarters for the Department of Defense, contains 3,705,793 square feet of office and storage space. Convert this to square yards. Round to the nearest square yard. (*Source:* U.S. Department of Defense)

71. On October 9, 2007, Russ Wicks set a new stock car world speed record of 359.2 feet/second on the Bonneville Salt Flats in Utah. Convert this speed to miles/hour. Round to the nearest tenth. (*Source:* RussWicks.com)

72. On October 4, 2004, the rocket plane *SpaceShipOne* shot to an altitude of more than 100 km for the second time inside a week to claim the $10 million Ansari X-Prize. At one point in its flight, *SpaceShipOne* was traveling past Mach 1, about 930 miles per hour. Find this speed in feet per second. (*Source:* Space.com)

REVIEW AND PREVIEW

Perform each indicated operation. See Section 1.3.

73. $\dfrac{1}{5} + \dfrac{4}{5}$

74. $\dfrac{3}{15} + \dfrac{6}{15}$

75. $\dfrac{9}{9} - \dfrac{19}{9}$

76. $\dfrac{4}{3} - \dfrac{8}{3}$

77. $\dfrac{6}{5} + \left(\dfrac{1}{5} - \dfrac{8}{5}\right)$

78. $-\dfrac{3}{2} + \left(\dfrac{1}{2} - \dfrac{3}{2}\right)$

Graph each linear equation. See Section 3.2.

79. $x - 2y = 6$

80. $5x - y = 10$

CONCEPT EXTENSIONS

Identify each statement as true or false. If false, correct the multiplication. See the Concept Check in this section.

81. $\dfrac{4}{a} \cdot \dfrac{1}{b} = \dfrac{4}{ab}$

82. $\dfrac{2}{3} \cdot \dfrac{2}{4} = \dfrac{2}{7}$

83. $\dfrac{x}{5} \cdot \dfrac{x+3}{4} = \dfrac{2x+3}{20}$

84. $\dfrac{7}{a} \cdot \dfrac{3}{a} = \dfrac{21}{a}$

85. Find the area of the rectangle.

$\dfrac{2x}{x^2 - 25}$ feet

$\dfrac{x+5}{9x}$ feet

86. Find the area of the square.

$\dfrac{2x}{5x+3}$ meters

Multiply or divide as indicated.

87. $\left(\dfrac{x^2 - y^2}{x^2 + y^2} \div \dfrac{x^2 - y^2}{3x} \right) \cdot \dfrac{x^2 + y^2}{6}$

88. $\left(\dfrac{x^2 - 9}{x^2 - 1} \cdot \dfrac{x^2 + 2x + 1}{2x^2 + 9x + 9} \right) \div \dfrac{2x + 3}{1 - x}$

89. $\left(\dfrac{2a + b}{b^2} \cdot \dfrac{3a^2 - 2ab}{ab + 2b^2} \right) \div \dfrac{a^2 - 3ab + 2b^2}{5ab - 10b^2}$

90. $\left(\dfrac{x^2 y^2 - xy}{4x - 4y} \div \dfrac{3y - 3x}{8x - 8y} \right) \cdot \dfrac{y - x}{8}$

91. In your own words, explain how you multiply rational expressions.

92. Explain how dividing rational expressions is similar to dividing rational numbers.

7.3 Adding and Subtracting Rational Expressions with Common Denominators and Least Common Denominator

OBJECTIVES

1. Add and Subtract Rational Expressions with the Same Denominator.

2. Find the Least Common Denominator of a List of Rational Expressions.

3. Write a Rational Expression as an Equivalent Expression Whose Denominator Is Given.

OBJECTIVE

1 Adding and Subtracting Rational Expressions with the Same Denominator

Like multiplication and division, addition and subtraction of rational expressions is similar to addition and subtraction of rational numbers. In this section, we add and subtract rational expressions with a common (or the same) denominator.

Add: $\dfrac{6}{5} + \dfrac{2}{5}$

Add: $\dfrac{9}{x+2} + \dfrac{3}{x+2}$

Add the numerators and place the sum over the common denominator.

$\dfrac{6}{5} + \dfrac{2}{5} = \dfrac{6+2}{5}$

$\qquad = \dfrac{8}{5}$ Simplify.

$\dfrac{9}{x+2} + \dfrac{3}{x+2} = \dfrac{9+3}{x+2}$

$\qquad = \dfrac{12}{x+2}$ Simplify.

Adding and Subtracting Rational Expressions with Common Denominators

If $\dfrac{P}{R}$ and $\dfrac{Q}{R}$ are rational expressions, then

$$\dfrac{P}{R} + \dfrac{Q}{R} = \dfrac{P + Q}{R} \qquad \text{and} \qquad \dfrac{P}{R} - \dfrac{Q}{R} = \dfrac{P - Q}{R}$$

To add or subtract rational expressions, add or subtract the numerators and place the sum or difference over the common denominator.

EXAMPLE 1 Add: $\dfrac{5m}{2n} + \dfrac{m}{2n}$

Solution $\dfrac{5m}{2n} + \dfrac{m}{2n} = \dfrac{5m + m}{2n}$ Add the numerators.

$= \dfrac{6m}{2n}$ Simplify the numerator by combining like terms.

$= \dfrac{3m}{n}$ Simplify by applying the fundamental principle.   ☐

PRACTICE 1   Add: $\dfrac{7a}{4b} + \dfrac{a}{4b}$

EXAMPLE 2 Subtract: $\dfrac{2y}{2y - 7} - \dfrac{7}{2y - 7}$

Solution $\dfrac{2y}{2y - 7} - \dfrac{7}{2y - 7} = \dfrac{2y - 7}{2y - 7}$ Subtract the numerators.

$= \dfrac{1}{1}$ or   1   Simplify.   ☐

PRACTICE 2   Subtract: $\dfrac{3x}{3x - 2} - \dfrac{2}{3x - 2}$

EXAMPLE 3 Subtract: $\dfrac{3x^2 + 2x}{x - 1} - \dfrac{10x - 5}{x - 1}$

Solution $\dfrac{3x^2 + 2x}{x - 1} - \dfrac{10x - 5}{x - 1} = \dfrac{(3x^2 + 2x) - (10x - 5)}{x - 1}$ Subtract the numerators. Notice the parentheses.

$= \dfrac{3x^2 + 2x - 10x + 5}{x - 1}$ Use the distributive property.

$= \dfrac{3x^2 - 8x + 5}{x - 1}$ Combine like terms.

$= \dfrac{(x - 1)(3x - 5)}{x - 1}$ Factor.

$= 3x - 5$ Simplify.   ☐

> ▌ **Helpful Hint**
> Parentheses are inserted so that the entire numerator, $10x - 5$, is subtracted.

PRACTICE 3   Subtract: $\dfrac{4x^2 + 15x}{x + 3} - \dfrac{8x + 15}{x + 3}$

> ▌ **Helpful Hint**
> Notice how the numerator $10x - 5$ has been subtracted in Example 3.
>
> This $-$ sign applies to the entire numerator of $\underline{10x - 5}$.   So parentheses are inserted here to indicate this.
>
> $$\dfrac{3x^2 + 2x}{x - 1} - \dfrac{10x - 5}{x - 1} = \dfrac{3x^2 + 2x - (10x - 5)}{x - 1}$$

OBJECTIVE

2 Finding the Least Common Denominator

To add and subtract fractions with **unlike** denominators, first find a least common denominator (LCD) and then write all fractions as equivalent fractions with the LCD.

For example, suppose we add $\frac{8}{3}$ and $\frac{2}{5}$. The LCD of denominators 3 and 5 is 15, since 15 is the least common multiple (LCM) of 3 and 5. That is, 15 is the smallest number that both 3 and 5 divide into evenly.

Next, rewrite each fraction so that its denominator is 15.

$$\frac{8}{3} + \frac{2}{5} = \frac{8(5)}{3(5)} + \frac{2(3)}{5(3)} = \frac{40}{15} + \frac{6}{15} = \frac{40 + 6}{15} = \frac{46}{15}$$

We are multiplying by 1.

To add or subtract rational expressions with unlike denominators, we also first find an LCD and then write all rational expressions as equivalent expressions with the LCD. The **least common denominator (LCD) of a list of rational expressions** is a polynomial of least degree whose factors include all the factors of the denominators in the list.

Finding the Least Common Denominator (LCD)

Step 1. Factor each denominator completely.

Step 2. The least common denominator (LCD) is the product of all unique factors found in Step 1, each raised to a power equal to the greatest number of times that the factor appears in any one factored denominator.

EXAMPLE 4 Find the LCD for each pair.

a. $\frac{1}{8}, \frac{3}{22}$ 　　　　**b.** $\frac{7}{5x}, \frac{6}{15x^2}$

Solution

a. Start by finding the prime factorization of each denominator.

$$8 = 2 \cdot 2 \cdot 2 = 2^3 \quad \text{and}$$
$$22 = 2 \cdot 11$$

Next, write the product of all the unique factors, each raised to a power equal to the greatest number of times that the factor appears in any denominator.

The greatest number of times that the factor 2 appears is 3.

The greatest number of times that the factor 11 appears is 1.

$$LCD = 2^3 \cdot 11^1 = 8 \cdot 11 = 88$$

b. Factor each denominator.

$$5x = 5 \cdot x \quad \text{and}$$
$$15x^2 = 3 \cdot 5 \cdot x^2$$

The greatest number of times that the factor 5 appears is 1.

The greatest number of times that the factor 3 appears is 1.

The greatest number of times that the factor x appears is 2.

$$LCD = 3^1 \cdot 5^1 \cdot x^2 = 15x^2$$

PRACTICE

4 Find the LCD for each pair.

a. $\frac{3}{14}, \frac{5}{21}$ 　　　　**b.** $\frac{4}{9y}, \frac{11}{15y^3}$

EXAMPLE 5   Find the LCD of

a. $\dfrac{7x}{x+2}$ and $\dfrac{5x^2}{x-2}$ **b.** $\dfrac{3}{x}$ and $\dfrac{6}{x+4}$

Solution

a. The denominators $x + 2$ and $x - 2$ are completely factored already. The factor $x + 2$ appears once and the factor $x - 2$ appears once.

$$\text{LCD} = (x+2)(x-2)$$

b. The denominators x and $x + 4$ cannot be factored further. The factor x appears once and the factor $x + 4$ appears once.

$$\text{LCD} = x(x+4)$$

PRACTICE
5   Find the LCD of

a. $\dfrac{16}{y-5}$ and $\dfrac{3y^3}{y-4}$ **b.** $\dfrac{8}{a}$ and $\dfrac{5}{a+2}$

EXAMPLE 6   Find the LCD of $\dfrac{6m^2}{3m+15}$ and $\dfrac{2}{(m+5)^2}$.

Solution   We factor each denominator. $\dfrac{6m^2}{3(m+5)}$ $\dfrac{2}{(m+5)^2}$

$$3m + 15 = 3(m + 5)$$
$$(m+5)^2 = (m+5)^2 \quad \text{This denominator is already factored.}$$

The greatest number of times that the factor 3 appears is 1.

The greatest number of times that the factor $m + 5$ appears *in any one denominator* is 2.

$$\text{LCD} = 3(m+5)^2$$

PRACTICE
6   Find the LCD of $\dfrac{2x^3}{(2x-1)^2}$ and $\dfrac{5x}{6x-3}$.

✓**CONCEPT CHECK**

Choose the correct LCD of $\dfrac{x}{(x+1)^2}$ and $\dfrac{5}{x+1}$.

a. $x + 1$ **b.** $(x+1)^2$ **c.** $(x+1)^3$ **d.** $5x(x+1)^2$

EXAMPLE 7   Find the LCD of $\dfrac{t-10}{t^2-t-6}$ and $\dfrac{t+5}{t^2+3t+2}$.

Solution   Start by factoring each denominator.

$$t^2 - t - 6 = (t-3)(t+2)$$
$$t^2 + 3t + 2 = (t+1)(t+2)$$
$$\text{LCD} = (t-3)(t+2)(t+1)$$

PRACTICE
7   Find the LCD of $\dfrac{x-5}{x^2+5x+4}$ and $\dfrac{x+8}{x^2-16}$.

EXAMPLE 8 Find the LCD of $\dfrac{2}{x-2}$ and $\dfrac{10}{2-x}$.

Solution The denominators $x-2$ and $2-x$ are opposites. That is, $2-x=-1(x-2)$. Use $x-2$ or $2-x$ as the LCD.

$$\text{LCD} = x-2 \quad \text{or} \quad \text{LCD} = 2-x$$

PRACTICE
8 Find the LCD of $\dfrac{5}{3-x}$ and $\dfrac{4}{x-3}$.

OBJECTIVE
3 Writing Equivalent Rational Expressions

Next we practice writing a rational expression as an equivalent rational expression with a given denominator. To do this, we multiply by a form of 1. Recall that multiplying an expression by 1 produces an equivalent expression. In other words,

$$\frac{P}{Q} = \frac{P}{Q}\cdot 1 = \frac{P}{Q}\cdot\frac{R}{R} = \frac{PR}{QR}.$$

EXAMPLE 9 Write each rational expression as an equivalent rational expression with the given denominator.

a. $\dfrac{4b}{9a} = \dfrac{}{27a^2b}$ **b.** $\dfrac{7x}{2x+5} = \dfrac{}{6x+15}$

Solution

a. We can ask ourselves: "What do we multiply $9a$ by to get $27a^2b$?" The answer is $3ab$, since $9a(3ab) = 27a^2b$. So we multiply by 1 in the form of $\dfrac{3ab}{3ab}$.

$$\frac{4b}{9a} = \frac{4b}{9a}\cdot 1$$

$$= \frac{4b}{9a}\cdot\frac{3ab}{3ab}$$

$$= \frac{4b(3ab)}{9a(3ab)} = \frac{12ab^2}{27a^2b}$$

b. First, factor the denominator on the right.

$$\frac{7x}{2x+5} = \frac{}{3(2x+5)}$$

To obtain the denominator on the right from the denominator on the left, we multiply by 1 in the form of $\dfrac{3}{3}$.

$$\frac{7x}{2x+5} = \frac{7x}{2x+5}\cdot\frac{3}{3} = \frac{7x\cdot 3}{(2x+5)\cdot 3} = \frac{21x}{3(2x+5)} \text{ or } \frac{21x}{6x+15}$$

PRACTICE
9 Write each rational expression as an equivalent fraction with the given denominator.

a. $\dfrac{3x}{5y} = \dfrac{}{35xy^2}$ **b.** $\dfrac{9x}{4x+7} = \dfrac{}{8x+14}$

EXAMPLE 10   Write the rational expression as an equivalent rational expression with the given denominator.

$$\frac{5}{x^2 - 4} = \frac{}{(x - 2)(x + 2)(x - 4)}$$

Solution   First, factor the denominator $x^2 - 4$ as $(x - 2)(x + 2)$.

If we multiply the original denominator $(x - 2)(x + 2)$ by $x - 4$, the result is the new denominator $(x - 2)(x + 2)(x - 4)$. Thus, we multiply by 1 in the form of $\frac{x - 4}{x - 4}$.

$$\frac{5}{\underbrace{x^2 - 4}_{\substack{\text{Factored}\\\text{denominator}}}} = \frac{5}{(x - 2)(x + 2)} = \frac{5}{(x - 2)(x + 2)} \cdot \frac{x - 4}{x - 4}$$

$$= \frac{5(x - 4)}{(x - 2)(x + 2)(x - 4)}$$

$$= \frac{5x - 20}{(x - 2)(x + 2)(x - 4)}$$

PRACTICE
10   Write the rational expression as an equivalent rational expression with the given denominator.

$$\frac{3}{x^2 - 2x - 15} = \frac{}{(x - 2)(x + 3)(x - 5)}$$

Vocabulary, Readiness & Video Check

Use the choices below to fill in each blank. Not all choices will be used.

$$\frac{9}{22} \qquad \frac{5}{22} \qquad \frac{9}{11} \qquad \frac{5}{11} \qquad \frac{ac}{b} \qquad \frac{a - c}{b} \qquad \frac{a + c}{b} \qquad \frac{5 - 6 + x}{x} \qquad \frac{5 - (6 + x)}{x}$$

1. $\dfrac{7}{11} + \dfrac{2}{11} =$ _____

2. $\dfrac{7}{11} - \dfrac{2}{11} =$ _____

3. $\dfrac{a}{b} + \dfrac{c}{b} =$ _____

4. $\dfrac{a}{b} - \dfrac{c}{b} =$ _____

5. $\dfrac{5}{x} - \dfrac{6 + x}{x} =$ _____

Martin-Gay Interactive Videos

See Video 7.3

Watch the section lecture video and answer the following questions.

OBJECTIVE 1
6. In ▦ Example 3, why is it important to place parentheses around the second numerator when writing as one expression?

OBJECTIVE 2
7. In ▦ Examples 4 and 5, we factor the denominators completely. How does this help determine the LCD?

OBJECTIVE 3
8. Based on ▦ Example 6, complete the following statements. To write an equivalent rational expression, you multiply the _____ of a rational expression by the same expression as the denominator. This means you're multiplying the original rational expression by a factor of _____ and therefore not changing the _____ of the original expression.

7.3   Exercise Set   MyMathLab®

Add or subtract as indicated. Simplify the result if possible. See Examples 1 through 3.

1. $\dfrac{a+1}{13} + \dfrac{8}{13}$

2. $\dfrac{x+1}{7} + \dfrac{6}{7}$

3. $\dfrac{4m}{3n} + \dfrac{5m}{3n}$

4. $\dfrac{3p}{2q} + \dfrac{11p}{2q}$

5. $\dfrac{4m}{m-6} - \dfrac{24}{m-6}$

6. $\dfrac{8y}{y-2} - \dfrac{16}{y-2}$

7. $\dfrac{9}{3+y} + \dfrac{y+1}{3+y}$

8. $\dfrac{9}{y+9} + \dfrac{y-5}{y+9}$

9. $\dfrac{5x^2+4x}{x-1} - \dfrac{6x+3}{x-1}$

10. $\dfrac{x^2+9x}{x+7} - \dfrac{4x+14}{x+7}$

11. $\dfrac{4a}{a^2+2a-15} - \dfrac{12}{a^2+2a-15}$

12. $\dfrac{3y}{y^2+3y-10} - \dfrac{6}{y^2+3y-10}$

13. $\dfrac{2x+3}{x^2-x-30} - \dfrac{x-2}{x^2-x-30}$

14. $\dfrac{3x-1}{x^2+5x-6} - \dfrac{2x-7}{x^2+5x-6}$

15. $\dfrac{2x+1}{x-3} + \dfrac{3x+6}{x-3}$

16. $\dfrac{4p-3}{2p+7} + \dfrac{3p+8}{2p+7}$

17. $\dfrac{2x^2}{x-5} - \dfrac{25+x^2}{x-5}$

18. $\dfrac{6x^2}{2x-5} - \dfrac{25+2x^2}{2x-5}$

19. $\dfrac{5x+4}{x-1} - \dfrac{2x+7}{x-1}$

20. $\dfrac{7x+1}{x-4} - \dfrac{2x+21}{x-4}$

Find the LCD for each list of rational expressions. See Examples 4 through 8.

21. $\dfrac{19}{2x}, \quad \dfrac{5}{4x^3}$

22. $\dfrac{17x}{4y^5}, \quad \dfrac{2}{8y}$

23. $\dfrac{9}{8x}, \quad \dfrac{3}{2x+4}$

24. $\dfrac{1}{6y}, \quad \dfrac{3x}{4y+12}$

25. $\dfrac{2}{x+3}, \quad \dfrac{5}{x-2}$

26. $\dfrac{-6}{x-1}, \quad \dfrac{4}{x+5}$

27. $\dfrac{x}{x+6}, \quad \dfrac{10}{3x+18}$

28. $\dfrac{12}{x+5}, \quad \dfrac{x}{4x+20}$

29. $\dfrac{8x^2}{(x-6)^2}, \quad \dfrac{13x}{5x-30}$

30. $\dfrac{9x^2}{7x-14}, \quad \dfrac{6x}{(x-2)^2}$

31. $\dfrac{1}{3x+3}, \quad \dfrac{8}{2x^2+4x+2}$

32. $\dfrac{19x+5}{4x-12}, \quad \dfrac{3}{2x^2-12x+18}$

33. $\dfrac{5}{x-8}, \quad \dfrac{3}{8-x}$

34. $\dfrac{2x+5}{3x-7}, \quad \dfrac{5}{7-3x}$

35. $\dfrac{5x+1}{x^2+3x-4}, \quad \dfrac{3x}{x^2+2x-3}$

36. $\dfrac{4}{x^2+4x+3}, \quad \dfrac{4x-2}{x^2+10x+21}$

37. $\dfrac{2x}{3x^2+4x+1}, \quad \dfrac{7}{2x^2-x-1}$

38. $\dfrac{3x}{4x^2+5x+1}, \quad \dfrac{5}{3x^2-2x-1}$

39. $\dfrac{1}{x^2-16}, \quad \dfrac{x+6}{2x^3-8x^2}$

40. $\dfrac{5}{x^2-25}, \quad \dfrac{x+9}{3x^3-15x^2}$

Rewrite each rational expression as an equivalent rational expression with the given denominator. See Examples 9 and 10.

41. $\dfrac{3}{2x} = \dfrac{}{4x^2}$

42. $\dfrac{3}{9y^5} = \dfrac{}{72y^9}$

43. $\dfrac{6}{3a} = \dfrac{}{12ab^2}$

44. $\dfrac{5}{4y^2x} = \dfrac{}{32y^3x^2}$

45. $\dfrac{9}{2x+6} = \dfrac{}{2y(x+3)}$

46. $\dfrac{4x+1}{3x+6} = \dfrac{}{3y(x+2)}$

47. $\dfrac{9a+2}{5a+10} = \dfrac{}{5b(a+2)}$

48. $\dfrac{5+y}{2x^2+10} = \dfrac{}{4(x^2+5)}$

49. $\dfrac{x}{x^3+6x^2+8x} = \dfrac{}{x(x+4)(x+2)(x+1)}$

50. $\dfrac{5x}{x^3+2x^2-3x} = \dfrac{}{x(x-1)(x-5)(x+3)}$

51. $\dfrac{9y-1}{15x^2-30} = \dfrac{}{30x^2-60}$

52. $\dfrac{6m-5}{3x^2-9} = \dfrac{}{12x^2-36}$

MIXED PRACTICE

Perform the indicated operations.

53. $\dfrac{5x}{7} + \dfrac{9x}{7}$

54. $\dfrac{5x}{7} \cdot \dfrac{9x}{7}$

55. $\dfrac{x+3}{4} \div \dfrac{2x-1}{4}$

56. $\dfrac{x+3}{4} - \dfrac{2x-1}{4}$

57. $\dfrac{x^2}{x-6} - \dfrac{5x+6}{x-6}$

58. $\dfrac{x^2+5x}{x^2-25} \cdot \dfrac{3x-15}{x^2}$

59. $\dfrac{-2x}{x^3 - 8x} + \dfrac{3x}{x^3 - 8x}$ **60.** $\dfrac{-2x}{x^3 - 8x} \div \dfrac{3x}{x^3 - 8x}$

61. $\dfrac{12x - 6}{x^2 + 3x} \cdot \dfrac{4x^2 + 13x + 3}{4x^2 - 1}$ **62.** $\dfrac{x^3 + 7x^2}{3x^3 - x^2} \div \dfrac{5x^2 + 36x + 7}{9x^2 - 1}$

REVIEW AND PREVIEW

Perform each indicated operation. See Section 1.3.

63. $\dfrac{2}{3} + \dfrac{5}{7}$ **64.** $\dfrac{9}{10} - \dfrac{3}{5}$ **65.** $\dfrac{1}{6} - \dfrac{3}{4}$

66. $\dfrac{11}{15} + \dfrac{5}{9}$ **67.** $\dfrac{1}{12} + \dfrac{3}{20}$ **68.** $\dfrac{7}{30} + \dfrac{3}{18}$

CONCEPT EXTENSIONS

For Exercises 69 and 70, see the Concept Check in this section.

69. Choose the correct LCD of $\dfrac{11a^3}{4a - 20}$ and $\dfrac{15a^3}{(a - 5)^2}$.

    a. $4a(a - 5)(a + 5)$ **b.** $a - 5$ **c.** $(a - 5)^2$

    d. $4(a - 5)^2$ **e.** $(4a - 20)(a - 5)^2$

70. Choose the correct LCD of $\dfrac{5}{14x^2}$ and $\dfrac{y}{6x^3}$.

    a. $84x^5$ **b.** $84x^3$

    c. $42x^3$ **d.** $42x^5$

For Exercises 71 and 72, an algebra student approaches you with each incorrect solution. Find the error and correct the work shown below.

71. $\dfrac{2x - 6}{x - 5} - \dfrac{x + 4}{x - 5}$

    $= \dfrac{2x - 6 - x + 4}{x - 5}$

    $= \dfrac{x - 2}{x - 5}$

72. $\dfrac{x}{x + 3} + \dfrac{2}{x + 3}$

    $= \dfrac{x + 2}{x + 3}$

    $= \dfrac{2}{3}$

Multiple choice. Select the correct result.

73. $\dfrac{3}{x} + \dfrac{y}{x} =$

    a. $\dfrac{3 + y}{x^2}$ **b.** $\dfrac{3 + y}{2x}$ **c.** $\dfrac{3 + y}{x}$

74. $\dfrac{3}{x} - \dfrac{y}{x} =$

    a. $\dfrac{3 - y}{x^2}$ **b.** $\dfrac{3 - y}{2x}$ **c.** $\dfrac{3 - y}{x}$

75. $\dfrac{3}{x} \cdot \dfrac{y}{x} =$

    a. $\dfrac{3y}{x}$ **b.** $\dfrac{3y}{x^2}$ **c.** $3y$

76. $\dfrac{3}{x} \div \dfrac{y}{x} =$

    a. $\dfrac{3}{y}$ **b.** $\dfrac{y}{3}$ **c.** $\dfrac{3}{x^2 y}$

Write each rational expression as an equivalent expression with a denominator of $x - 2$.

77. $\dfrac{5}{2 - x}$ **78.** $\dfrac{8y}{2 - x}$

79. $-\dfrac{7 + x}{2 - x}$ **80.** $\dfrac{x - 3}{-(x - 2)}$

△ **81.** A square has a side of length $\dfrac{5}{x - 2}$ meters. Express its perimeter as a rational expression.

$\dfrac{5}{x - 2}$ meters

△ **82.** A trapezoid has sides of the indicated lengths. Find its perimeter.

$\dfrac{x + 4}{x + 3}$ inches

$\dfrac{5}{x + 3}$ inches $\dfrac{5}{x + 3}$ inches

$\dfrac{x + 1}{x + 3}$ inches

83. Write two rational expressions with the same denominator whose sum is $\dfrac{5}{3x - 1}$.

84. Write two rational expressions with the same denominator whose difference is $\dfrac{x - 7}{x^2 + 1}$.

85. The planet Mercury revolves around the sun in 88 Earth days. It takes Jupiter 4332 Earth days to make one revolution around the sun. (*Source:* National Space Science Data Center) If the two planets are aligned as shown in the figure, how long will it take for them to align again?

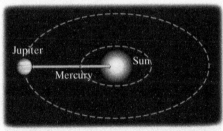

86. You are throwing a barbecue and you want to make sure that you purchase the same number of hot dogs as hot dog buns. Hot dogs come 8 to a package and hot dog buns come 12 to a package. What is the least number of each type of package you should buy?

87. Write some instructions to help a friend who is having difficulty finding the LCD of two rational expressions.

88. Explain why the LCD of the rational expressions $\dfrac{7}{x + 1}$ and $\dfrac{9x}{(x + 1)^2}$ is $(x + 1)^2$ and not $(x + 1)^3$.

89. In your own words, describe how to add or subtract two rational expressions with the same denominators.

90. Explain the similarities between subtracting $\dfrac{3}{8}$ from $\dfrac{7}{8}$ and subtracting $\dfrac{6}{x + 3}$ from $\dfrac{9}{x + 3}$.

7.4 Adding and Subtracting Rational Expressions with Unlike Denominators

OBJECTIVE

1   Adding and Subtracting Rational Expressions with Unlike Denominators

Let's add $\frac{3}{8}$ and $\frac{1}{6}$. From the previous section, the LCD of 8 and 6 is 24. Now let's write equivalent fractions with denominator 24 by multiplying by different forms of 1.

$$\frac{3}{8} = \frac{3}{8} \cdot 1 = \frac{3}{8} \cdot \frac{3}{3} = \frac{3 \cdot 3}{8 \cdot 3} = \frac{9}{24}$$

$$\frac{1}{6} = \frac{1}{6} \cdot 1 = \frac{1}{6} \cdot \frac{4}{4} = \frac{1 \cdot 4}{6 \cdot 4} = \frac{4}{24}$$

Now that the denominators are the same, we may add.

$$\frac{3}{8} + \frac{1}{6} = \frac{9}{24} + \frac{4}{24} = \frac{9 + 4}{24} = \frac{13}{24}$$

We add or subtract rational expressions the same way. You may want to use the steps below.

Adding or Subtracting Rational Expressions with Unlike Denominators

Step 1. Find the LCD of the rational expressions.

Step 2. Rewrite each rational expression as an equivalent expression whose denominator is the LCD found in Step 1.

Step 3. Add or subtract numerators and write the sum or difference over the common denominator.

Step 4. Simplify or write the rational expression in simplest form.

EXAMPLE 1   Perform each indicated operation.

a. $\dfrac{a}{4} - \dfrac{2a}{8}$ **b.** $\dfrac{3}{10x^2} + \dfrac{7}{25x}$

Solution

a. First, we must find the LCD. Since $4 = 2^2$ and $8 = 2^3$, the LCD $= 2^3 = 8$. Next we write each fraction as an equivalent fraction with the denominator 8, then we subtract.

$$\frac{a}{4} - \frac{2a}{8} = \frac{a(2)}{4(2)} - \frac{2a}{8} = \frac{2a}{8} - \frac{2a}{8} = \frac{2a - 2a}{8} = \frac{0}{8} = 0$$

Multiplying the numerator and denominator by 2 is the same as multiplying by $\frac{2}{2}$ or 1.

b. Since $10x^2 = 2 \cdot 5 \cdot x \cdot x$ and $25x = 5 \cdot 5 \cdot x$, the LCD $= 2 \cdot 5^2 \cdot x^2 = 50x^2$. We write each fraction as an equivalent fraction with a denominator of $50x^2$.

$$\frac{3}{10x^2} + \frac{7}{25x} = \frac{3(5)}{10x^2(5)} + \frac{7(2x)}{25x(2x)}$$

$$= \frac{15}{50x^2} + \frac{14x}{50x^2}$$

$$= \frac{15 + 14x}{50x^2} \qquad \text{Add numerators. Write the sum over the common denominator.} \qquad \square$$

1   Perform each indicated operation.

a. $\dfrac{2x}{5} - \dfrac{6x}{15}$

b. $\dfrac{7}{8a} + \dfrac{5}{12a^2}$

EXAMPLE 2   Subtract: $\dfrac{6x}{x^2 - 4} - \dfrac{3}{x + 2}$

Solution   Since $x^2 - 4 = (x + 2)(x - 2)$, the LCD $= (x - 2)(x + 2)$. We write equivalent expressions with the LCD as denominators.

$$\frac{6x}{x^2 - 4} - \frac{3}{x + 2} = \frac{6x}{(x - 2)(x + 2)} - \frac{3(x - 2)}{(x + 2)(x - 2)}$$

$$= \frac{6x - 3(x - 2)}{(x + 2)(x - 2)} \qquad \text{Subtract numerators. Write the difference over the common denominator.}$$

$$= \frac{6x - 3x + 6}{(x + 2)(x - 2)} \qquad \text{Apply the distributive property in the numerator.}$$

$$= \frac{3x + 6}{(x + 2)(x - 2)} \qquad \text{Combine like terms in the numerator.}$$

Next we factor the numerator to see if this rational expression can be simplified.

$$= \frac{3(x + 2)}{(x + 2)(x - 2)} \qquad \text{Factor.}$$

$$= \frac{3}{x - 2} \qquad \text{Divide out common factors to simplify.} \quad \square$$

2   Subtract: $\dfrac{12x}{x^2 - 25} - \dfrac{6}{x + 5}$

EXAMPLE 3   Add: $\dfrac{2}{3t} + \dfrac{5}{t + 1}$

Solution   The LCD is $3t(t + 1)$. We write each rational expression as an equivalent rational expression with a denominator of $3t(t + 1)$.

$$\frac{2}{3t} + \frac{5}{t + 1} = \frac{2(t + 1)}{3t(t + 1)} + \frac{5(3t)}{(t + 1)(3t)}$$

$$= \frac{2(t + 1) + 5(3t)}{3t(t + 1)} \qquad \text{Add numerators. Write the sum over the common denominator.}$$

$$= \frac{2t + 2 + 15t}{3t(t + 1)} \qquad \text{Apply the distributive property in the numerator.}$$

$$= \frac{17t + 2}{3t(t + 1)} \qquad \text{Combine like terms in the numerator.} \quad \square$$

3   Add: $\dfrac{3}{5y} + \dfrac{2}{y + 1}$

EXAMPLE 4   Subtract: $\dfrac{7}{x - 3} - \dfrac{9}{3 - x}$

Solution   To find a common denominator, we notice that $x - 3$ and $3 - x$ are opposites. That is, $3 - x = -(x - 3)$. We write the denominator $3 - x$ as $-(x - 3)$ and simplify.

(Continued on next page)

$$\frac{7}{x-3} - \frac{9}{3-x} = \frac{7}{x-3} - \frac{9}{-(x-3)}$$

$$= \frac{7}{x-3} - \frac{-9}{x-3} \qquad \text{Apply } \frac{a}{-b} = \frac{-a}{b}.$$

$$= \frac{7-(-9)}{x-3} \qquad \text{Subtract numerators. Write the difference over the common denominator.}$$

$$= \frac{16}{x-3}$$

PRACTICE
4   Subtract: $\dfrac{6}{x-5} - \dfrac{7}{5-x}$

EXAMPLE 5   Add: $1 + \dfrac{m}{m+1}$

Solution   Recall that 1 is the same as $\dfrac{1}{1}$. The LCD of $\dfrac{1}{1}$ and $\dfrac{m}{m+1}$ is $m+1$.

$$1 + \frac{m}{m+1} = \frac{1}{1} + \frac{m}{m+1} \qquad \text{Write 1 as } \frac{1}{1}.$$

$$= \frac{1(m+1)}{1(m+1)} + \frac{m}{m+1} \qquad \text{Multiply both the numerator and the denominator of } \frac{1}{1} \text{ by } m+1.$$

$$= \frac{m+1+m}{m+1} \qquad \text{Add numerators. Write the sum over the common denominator.}$$

$$= \frac{2m+1}{m+1} \qquad \text{Combine like terms in the numerator.}$$

PRACTICE
5   Add: $2 + \dfrac{b}{b+3}$

EXAMPLE 6   Subtract: $\dfrac{3}{2x^2+x} - \dfrac{2x}{6x+3}$

Solution   First, we factor the denominators.

$$\frac{3}{2x^2+x} - \frac{2x}{6x+3} = \frac{3}{x(2x+1)} - \frac{2x}{3(2x+1)}$$

The LCD is $3x(2x+1)$. We write equivalent expressions with denominators of $3x(2x+1)$.

$$= \frac{3(3)}{x(2x+1)(3)} - \frac{2x(x)}{3(2x+1)(x)}$$

$$= \frac{9-2x^2}{3x(2x+1)} \qquad \text{Subtract numerators. Write the difference over the common denominator.}$$

PRACTICE
6   Subtract: $\dfrac{5}{2x^2+3x} - \dfrac{3x}{4x+6}$

EXAMPLE 7   Add: $\dfrac{2x}{x^2 + 2x + 1} + \dfrac{x}{x^2 - 1}$

Solution   First we factor the denominators.

$$\frac{2x}{x^2 + 2x + 1} + \frac{x}{x^2 - 1} = \frac{2x}{(x + 1)(x + 1)} + \frac{x}{(x + 1)(x - 1)}$$

Now we write the rational expressions as equivalent expressions with denominators of $(x + 1)(x + 1)(x - 1)$, the LCD.

$$= \frac{2x(x - 1)}{(x + 1)(x + 1)(x - 1)} + \frac{x(x + 1)}{(x + 1)(x - 1)(x + 1)}$$

$$= \frac{2x(x - 1) + x(x + 1)}{(x + 1)^2(x - 1)} \quad \text{Add numerators. Write the sum over the common denominator.}$$

$$= \frac{2x^2 - 2x + x^2 + x}{(x + 1)^2(x - 1)} \quad \text{Apply the distributive property in the numerator.}$$

$$= \frac{3x^2 - x}{(x + 1)^2(x - 1)} \quad \text{or} \quad \frac{x(3x - 1)}{(x + 1)^2(x - 1)}$$

PRACTICE
7   Add: $\dfrac{2x}{x^2 + 7x + 12} + \dfrac{3x}{x^2 - 9}$

The numerator was factored as a last step to see if the rational expression could be simplified further. Since there are no factors common to the numerator and the denominator, we can't simplify further.

Vocabulary, Readiness & Video Check

Match each exercise with the first step needed to perform the operation. Do not actually perform the operation.

1. $\dfrac{3}{4} - \dfrac{y}{4}$ **2.** $\dfrac{2}{a} \cdot \dfrac{3}{(a + 6)}$ **3.** $\dfrac{x + 1}{x} \div \dfrac{x - 1}{x}$ **4.** $\dfrac{9}{x - 2} - \dfrac{x}{x + 2}$

   a. Multiply the first rational expression by the reciprocal of the second rational expression.
   b. Find the LCD. Write each expression as an equivalent expression with the LCD as denominator.
   c. Multiply numerators and multiply denominators.
   d. Subtract numerators. Place the difference over a common denominator.

Martin-Gay Interactive Videos

See Video 7.4

Watch the section lecture video and answer the following question.

OBJECTIVE
1   **5.** What special case is shown in ⊟ Example 2 and what's the purpose of presenting it?

7.4 Exercise Set

MyMathLab®

MIXED PRACTICE

Perform each indicated operation. Simplify if possible. See Examples 1 through 7.

1. $\dfrac{4}{2x} + \dfrac{9}{3x}$ **2.** $\dfrac{15}{7a} + \dfrac{8}{6a}$

3. $\dfrac{15a}{b} - \dfrac{6b}{5}$ **4.** $\dfrac{4c}{d} - \dfrac{8d}{5}$

5. $\dfrac{3}{x} + \dfrac{5}{2x^2}$ **6.** $\dfrac{14}{3x^2} + \dfrac{6}{x}$

7. $\dfrac{6}{x + 1} + \dfrac{10}{2x + 2}$ **8.** $\dfrac{8}{x + 4} - \dfrac{3}{3x + 12}$

9. $\dfrac{3}{x + 2} - \dfrac{2x}{x^2 - 4}$

10. $\dfrac{5}{x - 4} + \dfrac{4x}{x^2 - 16}$

11. $\dfrac{3}{4x} + \dfrac{8}{x - 2}$

12. $\dfrac{5}{y^2} - \dfrac{y}{2y + 1}$

13. $\dfrac{6}{x - 3} + \dfrac{8}{3 - x}$

14. $\dfrac{15}{y - 4} + \dfrac{20}{4 - y}$

15. $\dfrac{9}{x - 3} + \dfrac{9}{3 - x}$

16. $\dfrac{5}{a - 7} + \dfrac{5}{7 - a}$

17. $\dfrac{-8}{x^2 - 1} - \dfrac{7}{1 - x^2}$

18. $\dfrac{-9}{25x^2 - 1} + \dfrac{7}{1 - 25x^2}$

19. $\dfrac{5}{x} + 2$

20. $\dfrac{7}{x^2} - 5x$

21. $\dfrac{5}{x - 2} + 6$

22. $\dfrac{6y}{y + 5} + 1$

23. $\dfrac{y + 2}{y + 3} - 2$

24. $\dfrac{7}{2x - 3} - 3$

25. $\dfrac{-x + 2}{x} - \dfrac{x - 6}{4x}$

26. $\dfrac{-y + 1}{y} - \dfrac{2y - 5}{3y}$

27. $\dfrac{5x}{x + 2} - \dfrac{3x - 4}{x + 2}$

28. $\dfrac{7x}{x - 3} - \dfrac{4x + 9}{x - 3}$

29. $\dfrac{3x^4}{7} - \dfrac{4x^2}{21}$

30. $\dfrac{5x}{6} + \dfrac{11x^2}{2}$

31. $\dfrac{1}{x + 3} - \dfrac{1}{(x + 3)^2}$

32. $\dfrac{5x}{(x - 2)^2} - \dfrac{3}{x - 2}$

33. $\dfrac{4}{5b} + \dfrac{1}{b - 1}$

34. $\dfrac{1}{y + 5} + \dfrac{2}{3y}$

35. $\dfrac{2}{m} + 1$

36. $\dfrac{6}{x} - 1$

37. $\dfrac{2x}{x - 7} - \dfrac{x}{x - 2}$

38. $\dfrac{9x}{x - 10} - \dfrac{x}{x - 3}$

39. $\dfrac{6}{1 - 2x} - \dfrac{4}{2x - 1}$

40. $\dfrac{10}{3n - 4} - \dfrac{5}{4 - 3n}$

41. $\dfrac{7}{(x + 1)(x - 1)} + \dfrac{8}{(x + 1)^2}$

42. $\dfrac{5}{(x + 1)(x + 5)} - \dfrac{2}{(x + 5)^2}$

43. $\dfrac{x}{x^2 - 1} - \dfrac{2}{x^2 - 2x + 1}$

44. $\dfrac{x}{x^2 - 4} - \dfrac{5}{x^2 - 4x + 4}$

45. $\dfrac{3a}{2a + 6} - \dfrac{a - 1}{a + 3}$

46. $\dfrac{1}{x + y} - \dfrac{y}{x^2 - y^2}$

47. $\dfrac{y - 1}{2y + 3} + \dfrac{3}{(2y + 3)^2}$

48. $\dfrac{x - 6}{5x + 1} + \dfrac{6}{(5x + 1)^2}$

49. $\dfrac{5}{2 - x} + \dfrac{x}{2x - 4}$

50. $\dfrac{-1}{a - 2} + \dfrac{4}{4 - 2a}$

51. $\dfrac{15}{x^2 + 6x + 9} + \dfrac{2}{x + 3}$

52. $\dfrac{2}{x^2 + 4x + 4} + \dfrac{1}{x + 2}$

53. $\dfrac{13}{x^2 - 5x + 6} - \dfrac{5}{x - 3}$

54. $\dfrac{-7}{y^2 - 3y + 2} - \dfrac{2}{y - 1}$

55. $\dfrac{70}{m^2 - 100} + \dfrac{7}{2(m + 10)}$

56. $\dfrac{27}{y^2 - 81} + \dfrac{3}{2(y + 9)}$

▶ 57. $\dfrac{x + 8}{x^2 - 5x - 6} + \dfrac{x + 1}{x^2 - 4x - 5}$

58. $\dfrac{x + 4}{x^2 + 12x + 20} + \dfrac{x + 1}{x^2 + 8x - 20}$

59. $\dfrac{5}{4n^2 - 12n + 8} - \dfrac{3}{3n^2 - 6n}$

60. $\dfrac{6}{5y^2 - 25y + 30} - \dfrac{2}{4y^2 - 8y}$

MIXED PRACTICE

Perform the indicated operations. Addition, subtraction, multiplication, and division of rational expressions are included here.

61. $\dfrac{15x}{x + 8} \cdot \dfrac{2x + 16}{3x}$

62. $\dfrac{9z + 5}{15} \cdot \dfrac{5z}{81z^2 - 25}$

63. $\dfrac{8x + 7}{3x + 5} - \dfrac{2x - 3}{3x + 5}$

64. $\dfrac{2z^2}{4z - 1} - \dfrac{z - 2z^2}{4z - 1}$

65. $\dfrac{5a + 10}{18} \div \dfrac{a^2 - 4}{10a}$

66. $\dfrac{9}{x^2 - 1} \div \dfrac{12}{3x + 3}$

67. $\dfrac{5}{x^2 - 3x + 2} + \dfrac{1}{x - 2}$

68. $\dfrac{4}{2x^2 + 5x - 3} + \dfrac{2}{x + 3}$

REVIEW AND PREVIEW

Solve the following linear and quadratic equations. See Sections 2.3 and 6.6.

69. $3x + 5 = 7$

70. $5x - 1 = 8$

71. $2x^2 - x - 1 = 0$

72. $4x^2 - 9 = 0$

73. $4(x + 6) + 3 = -3$

74. $2(3x + 1) + 15 = -7$

CONCEPT EXTENSIONS

Perform each indicated operation.

75. $\dfrac{3}{x} - \dfrac{2x}{x^2 - 1} + \dfrac{5}{x + 1}$

76. $\dfrac{5}{x - 2} + \dfrac{7x}{x^2 - 4} - \dfrac{11}{x}$

77. $\dfrac{5}{x^2 - 4} + \dfrac{2}{x^2 - 4x + 4} - \dfrac{3}{x^2 - x - 6}$

78. $\dfrac{8}{x^2 + 6x + 5} - \dfrac{3x}{x^2 + 4x - 5} + \dfrac{2}{x^2 - 1}$

79. $\dfrac{9}{x^2 + 9x + 14} - \dfrac{3x}{x^2 + 10x + 21} + \dfrac{x + 4}{x^2 + 5x + 6}$

80. $\dfrac{x + 10}{x^2 - 3x - 4} - \dfrac{8}{x^2 + 6x + 5} - \dfrac{9}{x^2 + x - 20}$

81. A board of length $\dfrac{3}{x + 4}$ inches was cut into two pieces. If one piece is $\dfrac{1}{x - 4}$ inches, express the length of the other piece as a rational expression.

△ 82. The length of a rectangle is $\dfrac{3}{y - 5}$ feet, while its width is $\dfrac{2}{y}$ feet. Find its perimeter and then find its area.

83. In ice hockey, penalty killing percentage is a statistic calculated as $1 - \dfrac{G}{P}$, where G = opponent's power play goals and P = opponent's power play opportunities. Simplify this expression.

84. The dose of medicine prescribed for a child depends on the child's age A in years and the adult dose D for the medication. Two expressions that give a child's dose are Young's Rule, $\dfrac{DA}{A + 12}$, and Cowling's Rule, $\dfrac{D(A + 1)}{24}$. Find an expression for the difference in the doses given by these expressions.

85. Explain when the LCD of the rational expressions in a sum is the product of the denominators.

86. Explain when the LCD is the same as one of the denominators of a rational expression to be added or subtracted.

△ **87.** Two angles are said to be complementary if the sum of their measures is 90°. If one angle measures $\frac{40}{x}$ degrees, find the measure of its complement.

△ **88.** Two angles are said to be supplementary if the sum of their measures is 180°. If one angle measures $\frac{x+2}{x}$ degrees, find the measure of its supplement.

✎ **89.** In your own words, explain how to add two rational expressions with different denominators.

✎ **90.** In your own words, explain how to subtract two rational expressions with different denominators.

7.5 Solving Equations Containing Rational Expressions

OBJECTIVES

1 Solve Equations Containing Rational Expressions.

2 Solve Equations Containing Rational Expressions for a Specified Variable.

OBJECTIVE

1 Solving Equations Containing Rational Expressions

In Chapter 2, we solved equations containing fractions. In this section, we continue the work we began in Chapter 2 by solving equations containing rational expressions.

Examples of Equations Containing Rational Expressions

$$\frac{x}{2} + \frac{8}{3} = \frac{1}{6} \quad \text{and} \quad \frac{4x}{x^2 + x - 30} + \frac{2}{x-5} = \frac{1}{x+6}$$

To solve equations such as these, use the multiplication property of equality to clear the equation of fractions by multiplying both sides of the equation by the LCD.

EXAMPLE 1 Solve: $\dfrac{x}{2} + \dfrac{8}{3} = \dfrac{1}{6}$

Solution The LCD of denominators 2, 3, and 6 is 6, so we multiply both sides of the equation by 6.

$$6\left(\frac{x}{2} + \frac{8}{3}\right) = 6\left(\frac{1}{6}\right)$$

> **Helpful Hint**
> Make sure that *each* term is multiplied by the LCD, 6.

$$6\left(\frac{x}{2}\right) + 6\left(\frac{8}{3}\right) = 6\left(\frac{1}{6}\right) \quad \text{Use the distributive property.}$$

$$3 \cdot x + 16 = 1 \quad \text{Multiply and simplify.}$$

$$3x = -15 \quad \text{Subtract 16 from both sides.}$$

$$x = -5 \quad \text{Divide both sides by 3.}$$

Check: To check, we replace x with -5 in the original equation.

$$\frac{x}{2} + \frac{8}{3} = \frac{1}{6}$$

$$\frac{-5}{2} + \frac{8}{3} \stackrel{?}{=} \frac{1}{6} \quad \text{Replace } x \text{ with } -5$$

$$\frac{1}{6} = \frac{1}{6} \quad \text{True}$$

This number checks, so the solution is -5. □

PRACTICE
1 Solve: $\dfrac{x}{3} + \dfrac{4}{5} = \dfrac{2}{15}$

EXAMPLE 2 Solve: $\dfrac{t-4}{2} - \dfrac{t-3}{9} = \dfrac{5}{18}$

Solution The LCD of denominators 2, 9, and 18 is 18, so we multiply both sides of the equation by 18.

$$18\left(\dfrac{t-4}{2} - \dfrac{t-3}{9}\right) = 18\left(\dfrac{5}{18}\right)$$

$$18\left(\dfrac{t-4}{2}\right) - 18\left(\dfrac{t-3}{9}\right) = 18\left(\dfrac{5}{18}\right) \qquad \text{Use the distributive property.}$$

> **Helpful Hint**
> Multiply *each* term by 18.

$$9(t-4) - 2(t-3) = 5 \qquad \text{Simplify.}$$

$$9t - 36 - 2t + 6 = 5 \qquad \text{Use the distributive property.}$$

$$7t - 30 = 5 \qquad \text{Combine like terms.}$$

$$7t = 35$$

$$t = 5 \qquad \text{Solve for } t.$$

Check:

$$\dfrac{t-4}{2} - \dfrac{t-3}{9} = \dfrac{5}{18}$$

$$\dfrac{5-4}{2} - \dfrac{5-3}{9} \stackrel{?}{=} \dfrac{5}{18} \qquad \text{Replace } t \text{ with 5.}$$

$$\dfrac{1}{2} - \dfrac{2}{9} \stackrel{?}{=} \dfrac{5}{18} \qquad \text{Simplify.}$$

$$\dfrac{5}{18} = \dfrac{5}{18} \qquad \text{True}$$

The solution is 5.

PRACTICE
2 Solve: $\dfrac{x+4}{4} - \dfrac{x-3}{3} = \dfrac{11}{12}$

Recall from Section 7.1 that a rational expression is defined for all real numbers except those that make the denominator of the expression 0. This means that if an equation contains *rational expressions with variables in the denominator*, we must be certain that the proposed solution does not make the denominator 0. If replacing the variable with the proposed solution makes the denominator 0, the rational expression is undefined and this proposed solution must be rejected.

EXAMPLE 3 Solve: $3 - \dfrac{6}{x} = x + 8$

Solution In this equation, 0 cannot be a solution because if x is 0, the rational expression $\dfrac{6}{x}$ is undefined. The LCD is x, so we multiply both sides of the equation by x.

$$x\left(3 - \dfrac{6}{x}\right) = x(x + 8)$$

> **Helpful Hint**
> Multiply *each* term by x.

$$x(3) - x\left(\dfrac{6}{x}\right) = x \cdot x + x \cdot 8 \qquad \text{Use the distributive property.}$$

$$3x - 6 = x^2 + 8x \qquad \text{Simplify.}$$

Now we write the quadratic equation in standard form and solve for x.

$$0 = x^2 + 5x + 6$$

$$0 = (x+3)(x+2) \qquad \text{Factor.}$$

$$x + 3 = 0 \quad \text{or} \quad x + 2 = 0 \qquad \text{Set each factor equal to 0 and solve.}$$

$$x = -3 \qquad\qquad x = -2$$

(Continued on next page)

Notice that neither -3 nor -2 makes the denominator in the original equation equal to 0.

Check: To check these solutions, we replace x in the original equation by -3, and then by -2.

If $x = -3$:

$$3 - \frac{6}{x} = x + 8$$

$$3 - \frac{6}{-3} \stackrel{?}{=} -3 + 8$$

$$3 - (-2) \stackrel{?}{=} 5$$

$$5 = 5 \qquad \text{True}$$

If $x = -2$:

$$3 - \frac{6}{x} = x + 8$$

$$3 - \frac{6}{-2} \stackrel{?}{=} -2 + 8$$

$$3 - (-3) \stackrel{?}{=} 6$$

$$6 = 6 \qquad \text{True} \qquad \square$$

Both -3 and -2 are solutions.

PRACTICE
3   Solve: $8 + \dfrac{7}{x} = x + 2$

The following steps may be used to solve an equation containing rational expressions.

Solving an Equation Containing Rational Expressions

Step 1. Multiply both sides of the equation by the LCD of all rational expressions in the equation.

Step 2. Remove any grouping symbols and solve the resulting equation.

Step 3. Check the solution in the original equation.

EXAMPLE 4   Solve: $\dfrac{4x}{x^2 + x - 30} + \dfrac{2}{x - 5} = \dfrac{1}{x + 6}$

Solution   The denominator $x^2 + x - 30$ factors as $(x + 6)(x - 5)$. The LCD is then $(x + 6)(x - 5)$, so we multiply both sides of the equation by this LCD.

$$(x + 6)(x - 5)\left(\frac{4x}{x^2 + x - 30} + \frac{2}{x - 5}\right) = (x + 6)(x - 5)\left(\frac{1}{x + 6}\right) \quad \text{Multiply by the LCD.}$$

$$(x + 6)(x - 5) \cdot \frac{4x}{x^2 + x - 30} + (x + 6)(x - 5) \cdot \frac{2}{x - 5} \quad \text{Apply the distributive property.}$$

$$= (x + 6)(x - 5) \cdot \frac{1}{x + 6}$$

$$4x + 2(x + 6) = x - 5 \quad \text{Simplify.}$$

$$4x + 2x + 12 = x - 5 \quad \text{Apply the distributive property.}$$

$$6x + 12 = x - 5 \quad \text{Combine like terms.}$$

$$5x = -17$$

$$x = -\frac{17}{5} \quad \text{Divide both sides by 5.}$$

Check: Check by replacing x with $-\dfrac{17}{5}$ in the original equation. The solution is $-\dfrac{17}{5}$.

$\square$

PRACTICE
4   Solve: $\dfrac{6x}{x^2 - 5x - 14} - \dfrac{3}{x + 2} = \dfrac{1}{x - 7}$

EXAMPLE 5   Solve: $\dfrac{2x}{x-4} = \dfrac{8}{x-4} + 1$

Solution   Multiply both sides by the LCD, $x - 4$.

$$(x-4)\left(\dfrac{2x}{x-4}\right) = (x-4)\left(\dfrac{8}{x-4} + 1\right)$$ Multiply by the LCD. Notice that 4 cannot be a solution.

$$(x-4)\cdot\dfrac{2x}{x-4} = (x-4)\cdot\dfrac{8}{x-4} + (x-4)\cdot 1$$ Use the distributive property.

$$2x = 8 + (x-4)$$ Simplify.

$$2x = 4 + x$$

$$x = 4$$

Notice that 4 makes the denominators 0 in the original equation. Therefore, 4 is *not* a solution.

This equation has *no solution*.   □

PRACTICE
5   Solve: $\dfrac{7}{x-2} = \dfrac{3}{x-2} + 4$

> ▶ Helpful Hint
>
> As we can see from Example 5, it is important to check the proposed solution(s) in the *original* equation.

✓**CONCEPT CHECK**
When can we clear fractions by multiplying through by the LCD?
a. When adding or subtracting rational expressions
b. When solving an equation containing rational expressions
c. Both of these
d. Neither of these

EXAMPLE 6   Solve: $x + \dfrac{14}{x-2} = \dfrac{7x}{x-2} + 1$

Solution   Notice the denominators in this equation. We can see that 2 can't be a solution. The LCD is $x - 2$, so we multiply both sides of the equation by $x - 2$.

$$(x-2)\left(x + \dfrac{14}{x-2}\right) = (x-2)\left(\dfrac{7x}{x-2} + 1\right)$$

$$(x-2)(x) + (x-2)\left(\dfrac{14}{x-2}\right) = (x-2)\left(\dfrac{7x}{x-2}\right) + (x-2)(1)$$

$$x^2 - 2x + 14 = 7x + x - 2$$ Simplify.

$$x^2 - 2x + 14 = 8x - 2$$ Combine like terms.

$$x^2 - 10x + 16 = 0$$ Write the quadratic equation in standard form.

$$(x-8)(x-2) = 0$$ Factor.

$$x - 8 = 0 \quad \text{or} \quad x - 2 = 0$$ Set each factor equal to 0.

$$x = 8 \qquad\qquad x = 2$$ Solve.

(Continued on next page)

As we have already noted, 2 can't be a solution of the original equation. So we need only replace x with 8 in the original equation. We find that 8 is a solution; the only solution is 8.   □

PRACTICE
6   Solve: $x + \dfrac{x}{x-5} = \dfrac{5}{x-5} - 7$

OBJECTIVE
2   Solving Equations for a Specified Variable

The last example in this section is an equation containing several variables, and we are directed to solve for one of the variables. The steps used in the preceding examples can be applied to solve equations for a specified variable as well.

EXAMPLE 7   Solve $\dfrac{1}{a} + \dfrac{1}{b} = \dfrac{1}{x}$ for x.

Solution   (This type of equation often models a work problem, as we shall see in Section 7.6.) The LCD is abx, so we multiply both sides by abx.

$$abx\left(\dfrac{1}{a} + \dfrac{1}{b}\right) = abx\left(\dfrac{1}{x}\right)$$

$$abx\left(\dfrac{1}{a}\right) + abx\left(\dfrac{1}{b}\right) = abx \cdot \dfrac{1}{x}$$

$$bx + ax = ab \qquad \text{Simplify.}$$

$$x(b + a) = ab \qquad \text{Factor out } x \text{ from each term on the left side.}$$

$$\dfrac{x(b + a)}{b + a} = \dfrac{ab}{b + a} \qquad \text{Divide both sides by } b + a.$$

$$x = \dfrac{ab}{b + a} \qquad \text{Simplify.}$$

This equation is now solved for x.   □

PRACTICE
7   Solve: $\dfrac{1}{a} + \dfrac{1}{b} = \dfrac{1}{x}$ for b

---

Graphing Calculator Explorations

A graphing calculator may be used to check solutions of equations containing rational expressions. For example, to check the solution of Example 1, $\dfrac{x}{2} + \dfrac{8}{3} = \dfrac{1}{6}$, graph $y_1 = \dfrac{x}{2} + \dfrac{8}{3}$ and $y_2 = \dfrac{1}{6}$.

Use TRACE and ZOOM, or use INTERSECT, to find the point of intersection. The point of intersection has an x-value of -5, so the solution of the equation is -5.

Use a graphing calculator to check the examples of this section.

1. Example 2   **2.** Example 3

3. Example 5   **4.** Example 6

Vocabulary, Readiness & Video Check

Multiple choice. Choose the correct response.

1. Multiply both sides of the equation $\dfrac{3x}{2} + 5 = \dfrac{1}{4}$ by 4. The result is:

    a. $3x + 5 = 1$ **b.** $6x + 5 = 1$ **c.** $6x + 20 = 1$ **d.** $6x + 9 = 1$

2. Multiply both sides of the equation $\dfrac{1}{x} - \dfrac{3}{5x} = 2$ by $5x$. The result is:

    a. $1 - 3 = 10x$ **b.** $5 - 3 = 10x$ **c.** $1 - 3 = 7x$ **d.** $5 - 3 = 7x$

Choose the correct LCD for the fractions in each equation.

3. Equation: $\dfrac{9}{x} + \dfrac{3}{4} = \dfrac{1}{12}$; LCD: _____

    a. $4x$ **b.** $12x$ **c.** $48x$ **d.** x

4. Equation: $\dfrac{8}{3x} - \dfrac{1}{x} = \dfrac{7}{9}$; LCD: _____

    a. x **b.** $3x$ **c.** $27x$ **d.** $9x$

5. Equation: $\dfrac{9}{x-1} = \dfrac{7}{(x-1)^2}$; LCD: _____

    a. $(x-1)^2$ **b.** $x-1$ **c.** $(x-1)^3$ **d.** 63

6. Equation: $\dfrac{1}{x-2} - \dfrac{3}{x^2-4} = 8$; LCD: _____

    a. $(x-2)$ **b.** $x+2$ **c.** x^2-4 **d.** $(x-2)(x^2-4)$

Martin-Gay Interactive Videos

See Video 7.5

Watch the section lecture video and answer the following questions.

OBJECTIVE 1
7. After multiplying through by the LCD and then simplifying, why is it important to take a moment and determine whether you have a linear or a quadratic equation before you finish solving the problem?

OBJECTIVE 1
8. From ▭ Examples 2–5, what extra step is needed when checking solutions to an equation containing rational expressions?

OBJECTIVE 2
9. The steps for solving ▭ Example 6 for a specified variable are the same as what other steps? How do you treat this specified variable?

7.5 Exercise Set

MyMathLab®

Solve each equation and check each solution. See Examples 1 through 3.

1. $\dfrac{x}{5} + 3 = 9$

2. $\dfrac{x}{5} - 2 = 9$

3. $\dfrac{x}{2} + \dfrac{5x}{4} = \dfrac{x}{12}$

4. $\dfrac{x}{6} + \dfrac{4x}{3} = \dfrac{x}{18}$

5. $2 - \dfrac{8}{x} = 6$

6. $5 + \dfrac{4}{x} = 1$

7. $2 + \dfrac{10}{x} = x + 5$

8. $6 + \dfrac{5}{y} = y - \dfrac{2}{y}$

9. $\dfrac{a}{5} = \dfrac{a-3}{2}$

10. $\dfrac{b}{5} = \dfrac{b+2}{6}$

11. $\dfrac{x-3}{5} + \dfrac{x-2}{2} = \dfrac{1}{2}$

12. $\dfrac{a+5}{4} + \dfrac{a+5}{2} = \dfrac{a}{8}$

Solve each equation and check each proposed solution. See Examples 4 through 6.

13. $\dfrac{3}{2a-5} = -1$

14. $\dfrac{6}{4-3x} = -3$

15. $\dfrac{4y}{y-4} + 5 = \dfrac{5y}{y-4}$

16. $\dfrac{2a}{a+2} - 5 = \dfrac{7a}{a+2}$

17. $2 + \dfrac{3}{a-3} = \dfrac{a}{a-3}$

18. $\dfrac{2y}{y-2} - \dfrac{4}{y-2} = 4$

19. $\dfrac{1}{x+3} + \dfrac{6}{x^2-9} = 1$

20. $\dfrac{1}{x+2} + \dfrac{4}{x^2-4} = 1$

21. $\dfrac{2y}{y+4} + \dfrac{4}{y+4} = 3$

22. $\dfrac{5y}{y+1} - \dfrac{3}{y+1} = 4$

23. $\dfrac{2x}{x+2} - 2 = \dfrac{x-8}{x-2}$

24. $\dfrac{4y}{y-3} - 3 = \dfrac{3y-1}{y+3}$

MIXED PRACTICE

Solve each equation. See Examples 1 through 6.

25. $\dfrac{2}{y} + \dfrac{1}{2} = \dfrac{5}{2y}$

26. $\dfrac{6}{3y} + \dfrac{3}{y} = 1$

27. $\dfrac{a}{a-6} = \dfrac{-2}{a-1}$

28. $\dfrac{5}{x-6} = \dfrac{x}{x-2}$

29. $\dfrac{11}{2x} + \dfrac{2}{3} = \dfrac{7}{2x}$

30. $\dfrac{5}{3} - \dfrac{3}{2x} = \dfrac{3}{2}$

31. $\dfrac{2}{x-2} + 1 = \dfrac{x}{x+2}$

32. $1 + \dfrac{3}{x+1} = \dfrac{x}{x-1}$

33. $\dfrac{x+1}{3} - \dfrac{x-1}{6} = \dfrac{1}{6}$

34. $\dfrac{3x}{5} - \dfrac{x-6}{3} = -\dfrac{2}{5}$

35. $\dfrac{t}{t-4} = \dfrac{t+4}{6}$

36. $\dfrac{15}{x+4} = \dfrac{x-4}{x}$

37. $\dfrac{y}{2y+2} + \dfrac{2y-16}{4y+4} = \dfrac{2y-3}{y+1}$

38. $\dfrac{1}{x+2} = \dfrac{4}{x^2-4} - \dfrac{1}{x-2}$

39. $\dfrac{4r-4}{r^2+5r-14} + \dfrac{2}{r+7} = \dfrac{1}{r-2}$

40. $\dfrac{3}{x+3} = \dfrac{12x+19}{x^2+7x+12} - \dfrac{5}{x+4}$

41. $\dfrac{x+1}{x+3} = \dfrac{x^2-11x}{x^2+x-6} - \dfrac{x-3}{x-2}$

42. $\dfrac{2t+3}{t-1} - \dfrac{2}{t+3} = \dfrac{5-6t}{t^2+2t-3}$

Solve each equation for the indicated variable. See Example 7.

43. $R = \dfrac{E}{I}$ for I (Electronics: resistance of a circuit)

44. $T = \dfrac{V}{Q}$ for Q (Water purification: settling time)

45. $T = \dfrac{2U}{B+E}$ for B (Merchandising: stock turnover rate)

46. $i = \dfrac{A}{t+B}$ for t (Hydrology: rainfall intensity)

47. $B = \dfrac{705w}{h^2}$ for w (Health: body-mass index)

48. $\dfrac{A}{W} = L$ for W (Geometry: area of a rectangle)

49. $N = R + \dfrac{V}{G}$ for G (Urban forestry: tree plantings per year)

50. $C = \dfrac{D(A+1)}{24}$ for A (Medicine: Cowling's Rule for child's dose)

51. $\dfrac{C}{\pi r} = 2$ for r (Geometry: circumference of a circle)

52. $W = \dfrac{CE^2}{2}$ for C (Electronics: energy stored in a capacitor)

53. $\dfrac{1}{y} + \dfrac{1}{3} = \dfrac{1}{x}$ for x

54. $\dfrac{1}{5} + \dfrac{2}{y} = \dfrac{1}{x}$ for x

REVIEW AND PREVIEW

TRANSLATING

Write each phrase as an expression.

55. The reciprocal of x

56. The reciprocal of $x + 1$

57. The reciprocal of x, added to the reciprocal of 2

58. The reciprocal of x, subtracted from the reciprocal of 5

Answer each question.

59. If a tank is filled in 3 hours, what fractional part of the tank is filled in 1 hour?

60. If a strip of beach is cleaned in 4 hours, what fractional part of the beach is cleaned in 1 hour?

Identify the x- and y-intercepts. See Section 3.3.

61.

62.

63.

64.

CONCEPT EXTENSIONS

65. Explain the difference between solving an equation such as $\dfrac{x}{2} + \dfrac{3}{4} = \dfrac{x}{4}$ for x and performing an operation such as adding $\dfrac{x}{2} + \dfrac{3}{4}$.

66. When solving an equation such as $\dfrac{y}{4} = \dfrac{y}{2} - \dfrac{1}{4}$, we may multiply all terms by 4. When subtracting two rational expressions such as $\dfrac{y}{2} - \dfrac{1}{4}$, we may not. Explain why.

Determine whether each of the following is an equation or an expression. If it is an equation, then solve it for its variable. If it is an expression, perform the indicated operation.

△ **67.** $\dfrac{1}{x} + \dfrac{5}{9}$ **68.** $\dfrac{1}{x} + \dfrac{5}{9} = \dfrac{2}{3}$

69. $\dfrac{5}{x-1} - \dfrac{2}{x} = \dfrac{5}{x(x-1)}$

70. $\dfrac{5}{x-1} - \dfrac{2}{x}$

Recall that two angles are supplementary if the sum of their measures is 180°. Find the measures of the following supplementary angles.

△ **71.**

△ **72.**

Recall that two angles are complementary if the sum of their measures is 90°. Find the measures of the following complementary angles.

△ **73.**

△ **74.**

Solve each equation.

75. $\dfrac{5}{a^2 + 4a + 3} + \dfrac{2}{a^2 + a - 6} - \dfrac{3}{a^2 - a - 2} = 0$

76. $\dfrac{-2}{a^2 + 2a - 8} + \dfrac{1}{a^2 + 9a + 20} = \dfrac{-4}{a^2 + 3a - 10}$

Integrated Review SUMMARY ON RATIONAL EXPRESSIONS

Sections 7.1–7.5

It is important to know the difference between performing operations with rational expressions and solving an equation containing rational expressions. Study the examples below.

Performing Operations with Rational Expressions

Adding: $\quad \dfrac{1}{x} + \dfrac{1}{x+5} = \dfrac{1 \cdot (x+5)}{x(x+5)} + \dfrac{1 \cdot x}{x(x+5)} = \dfrac{x+5+x}{x(x+5)} = \dfrac{2x+5}{x(x+5)}$

Subtracting: $\quad \dfrac{3}{x} - \dfrac{5}{x^2 y} = \dfrac{3 \cdot xy}{x \cdot xy} - \dfrac{5}{x^2 y} = \dfrac{3xy - 5}{x^2 y}$

Multiplying: $\quad \dfrac{2}{x} \cdot \dfrac{5}{x-1} = \dfrac{2 \cdot 5}{x(x-1)} = \dfrac{10}{x(x-1)}$

Dividing: $\quad \dfrac{4}{2x+1} \div \dfrac{x-3}{x} = \dfrac{4}{2x+1} \cdot \dfrac{x}{x-3} = \dfrac{4x}{(2x+1)(x-3)}$

Solving an Equation Containing Rational Expressions

To solve an equation containing rational expressions, we clear the equation of fractions by multiplying both sides by the LCD.

$$\dfrac{3}{x} - \dfrac{5}{x-1} = \dfrac{1}{x(x-1)} \qquad \text{\small Note that } x \text{ can't be 0 or 1.}$$

$$x(x-1)\left(\dfrac{3}{x}\right) - x(x-1)\left(\dfrac{5}{x-1}\right) = x(x-1) \cdot \dfrac{1}{x(x-1)} \qquad \text{\small Multiply both sides by the LCD.}$$

$$3(x-1) - 5x = 1 \qquad \text{\small Simplify.}$$

$$3x - 3 - 5x = 1 \qquad \text{\small Use the distributive property.}$$

$$-2x - 3 = 1 \qquad \text{\small Combine like terms.}$$

$$-2x = 4 \qquad \text{\small Add 3 to both sides.}$$

$$x = -2 \qquad \text{\small Divide both sides by } -2.$$

Determine whether each of the following is an equation or an expression. If it is an equation, solve it for its variable.
If it is an expression, perform the indicated operation.

1. $\dfrac{1}{x} + \dfrac{2}{3}$

2. $\dfrac{3}{a} + \dfrac{5}{6}$

3. $\dfrac{1}{x} + \dfrac{2}{3} = \dfrac{3}{x}$

4. $\dfrac{3}{a} + \dfrac{5}{6} = 1$

5. $\dfrac{2}{x-1} - \dfrac{1}{x}$

6. $\dfrac{4}{x-3} - \dfrac{1}{x}$

7. $\dfrac{2}{x+1} - \dfrac{1}{x} = 1$

8. $\dfrac{4}{x-3} - \dfrac{1}{x} = \dfrac{6}{x(x-3)}$

9. $\dfrac{15x}{x+8} \cdot \dfrac{2x+16}{3x}$

10. $\dfrac{9z+5}{15} \cdot \dfrac{5z}{81z^2 - 25}$

11. $\dfrac{2x+1}{x-3} + \dfrac{3x+6}{x-3}$

12. $\dfrac{4p-3}{2p+7} + \dfrac{3p+8}{2p+7}$

13. $\dfrac{x+5}{7} = \dfrac{8}{2}$

14. $\dfrac{1}{2} = \dfrac{x-1}{8}$

15. $\dfrac{5a+10}{18} \div \dfrac{a^2-4}{10a}$

16. $\dfrac{9}{x^2-1} + \dfrac{12}{3x+3}$

17. $\dfrac{x+2}{3x-1} + \dfrac{5}{(3x-1)^2}$

18. $\dfrac{4}{(2x-5)^2} + \dfrac{x+1}{2x-5}$

19. $\dfrac{x-7}{x} - \dfrac{x+2}{5x}$

20. $\dfrac{10x-9}{x} - \dfrac{x-4}{3x}$

21. $\dfrac{3}{x+3} = \dfrac{5}{x^2-9} - \dfrac{2}{x-3}$

22. $\dfrac{9}{x^2-4} + \dfrac{2}{x+2} = \dfrac{-1}{x-2}$

23. Explain the difference between solving an equation such as $\dfrac{x}{5} + \dfrac{3}{10} = \dfrac{x}{10}$, for x and performing an operation such as adding $\dfrac{x}{5} + \dfrac{3}{10}$.

24. When solving an equation such as $\dfrac{y}{10} = \dfrac{y}{5} - \dfrac{1}{10}$, we may multiply all terms by 4. When subtracting two rational expressions such as $\dfrac{y}{5} - \dfrac{1}{10}$, we may not. Explain why.

7.6 Proportion and Problem Solving with Rational Equations

OBJECTIVES

1. Solve Proportions.
2. Use Proportions to Solve Problems.
3. Solve Problems About Numbers.
4. Solve Problems About Work.
5. Solve Problems About Distance.

OBJECTIVE

1 Solving Proportions

A **ratio** is the quotient of two numbers or two quantities. For example, the ratio of 2 to 5 can be written as $\dfrac{2}{5}$, the quotient of 2 and 5.

If two ratios are equal, we say the ratios are **in proportion** to each other. A **proportion** is a mathematical statement that two ratios are equal.

For example, the equation $\dfrac{1}{2} = \dfrac{4}{8}$ is a proportion, as is $\dfrac{x}{5} = \dfrac{8}{10}$, because both sides of the equations are ratios. When we want to emphasize the equation as a proportion, we

> read the proportion $\dfrac{1}{2} = \dfrac{4}{8}$ as "one is to two as four is to eight"

In a proportion, cross products are equal. To understand cross products, let's start with the proportion

$$\frac{a}{b} = \frac{c}{d}$$

and multiply both sides by the LCD, bd.

$$bd\left(\frac{a}{b}\right) = bd\left(\frac{c}{d}\right) \quad \text{Multiply both sides by the LCD, } bd.$$

$$\underbrace{ad} = \underbrace{bc} \quad \text{Simplify.}$$

Cross product   Cross product

Notice why ad and bc are called cross products.

$$ad \qquad\qquad bc$$

$$\frac{a}{b} = \frac{c}{d}$$

Cross Products

If $\dfrac{a}{b} = \dfrac{c}{d}$, then $ad = bc$.

For example, if

$$\frac{1}{2} = \frac{4}{8}, \text{ then } 1 \cdot 8 = 2 \cdot 4 \text{ or}$$

$$8 = 8$$

Notice that a proportion contains four numbers (or expressions). If any three numbers are known, we can solve and find the fourth number.

EXAMPLE 1   Solve for x: $\dfrac{45}{x} = \dfrac{5}{7}$

Solution   This is an equation with rational expressions, and also a proportion. Below are two ways to solve.

Since this is a rational equation, we can use the methods of the previous section.

$$\frac{45}{x} = \frac{5}{7}$$

$$7x \cdot \frac{45}{x} = 7x \cdot \frac{5}{7} \quad \begin{array}{l}\text{Multiply both sides}\\\text{by the LCD } 7x.\end{array}$$

$$7 \cdot 45 = x \cdot 5 \quad \text{Divide out common factors.}$$

$$315 = 5x \quad \text{Multiply.}$$

$$\frac{315}{5} = \frac{5x}{5} \quad \text{Divide both sides by 5.}$$

$$63 = x \quad \text{Simplify.}$$

Since this is also a proportion, we may set cross products equal.

$$\frac{45}{x} = \frac{5}{7}$$

$$45 \cdot 7 = x \cdot 5 \quad \text{Set cross products equal.}$$

$$315 = 5x \quad \text{Multiply.}$$

$$\frac{315}{5} = \frac{5x}{5} \quad \text{Divide both sides by 5.}$$

$$63 = x \quad \text{Simplify.}$$

Check: Both methods give us a solution of 63. To check, substitute 63 for x in the original proportion. The solution is 63.   □

PRACTICE
1   Solve for x: $\dfrac{36}{x} = \dfrac{4}{11}$

In this section, if the rational equation is a proportion, we will use cross products to solve.

EXAMPLE 2   Solve for x: $\dfrac{x-5}{3} = \dfrac{x+2}{5}$

Solution

$$\frac{x-5}{3} = \frac{x+2}{5}$$

$$
\begin{aligned}
5(x-5) &= 3(x+2) &&\text{Set cross products equal.}\\
5x - 25 &= 3x + 6 &&\text{Multiply.}\\
5x &= 3x + 31 &&\text{Add 25 to both sides.}\\
2x &= 31 &&\text{Subtract } 3x \text{ from both sides.}\\
\frac{2x}{2} &= \frac{31}{2} &&\text{Divide both sides by 2.}\\
x &= \frac{31}{2}
\end{aligned}
$$

Check: Verify that $\dfrac{31}{2}$ is the solution.

PRACTICE
2   Solve for x: $\dfrac{3x+2}{9} = \dfrac{x-1}{2}$

OBJECTIVE
2   Using Proportions to Solve Problems

Proportions can be used to model and solve many real-life problems. When using proportions in this way, it is important to judge whether the solution is reasonable. Doing so helps us decide if the proportion has been formed correctly. We use the same problem-solving steps that were introduced in Section 2.4.

EXAMPLE 3   Calculating the Cost of Recordable Compact Discs

Three boxes of CD-Rs (recordable compact discs) cost $37.47. How much should 5 boxes cost?

Solution

1. UNDERSTAND. Read and reread the problem. We know that the cost of 5 boxes is more than the cost of 3 boxes, or $37.47, and less than the cost of 6 boxes, which is double the cost of 3 boxes, or 2($37.47) = $74.94. Let's suppose that 5 boxes cost $60.00. To check, we see if 3 boxes is to 5 boxes as the *price* of 3 boxes is to the *price* of 5 boxes. In other words, we see if

$$\frac{3 \text{ boxes}}{5 \text{ boxes}} = \frac{\text{price of 3 boxes}}{\text{price of 5 boxes}}$$

or

$$\frac{3}{5} = \frac{37.47}{60.00}$$

or

$$3(60.00) = 5(37.47) \qquad \text{Set cross products equal.}$$

$$180.00 = 187.35 \qquad \text{Not a true statement.}$$

(Continued on next page)

Thus, $60 is not correct, but we now have a better understanding of the problem.

Let x = price of 5 boxes of CD-Rs.(Continued on next page)

2. TRANSLATE.

$$\frac{3 \text{ boxes}}{5 \text{ boxes}} = \frac{\text{price of 3 boxes}}{\text{price of 5 boxes}}$$

$$\frac{3}{5} = \frac{37.47}{x}$$

3. SOLVE.

$$\frac{3}{5} = \frac{37.47}{x}$$

$3x = 5(37.47)$ Set cross products equal.

$3x = 187.35$

$x = 62.45$ Divide both sides by **3**.

4. INTERPRET.

Check: Verify that 3 boxes is to 5 boxes as $37.47 is to $62.45. Also, notice that our solution is a reasonable one as discussed in Step 1.

State: Five boxes of CD-Rs cost $62.45.   ☐

PRACTICE

3   Four 2-liter bottles of Diet Pepsi cost $5.16. How much will seven 2-liter bottles cost?

▶ **Helpful Hint**

The proportion $\dfrac{5 \text{ boxes}}{3 \text{ boxes}} = \dfrac{\text{price of 5 boxes}}{\text{price of 3 boxes}}$ could also have been used to solve Example 3.

Notice that the cross products are the same.

Similar triangles have the same shape but not necessarily the same size. In similar triangles, the measures of corresponding angles are equal, and corresponding sides are in proportion.

If triangle ABC and triangle XYZ shown are similar, then we know that the measure of angle A = the measure of angle X, the measure of angle B = the measure of angle Y, and the measure of angle C = the measure of angle Z. We also know that corresponding sides are in proportion: $\dfrac{a}{x} = \dfrac{b}{y} = \dfrac{c}{z}$.

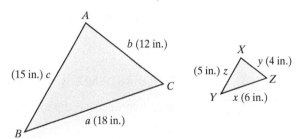

In this section, we will position similar triangles so that they have the same orientation.

To show that corresponding sides are in proportion for the triangles above, we write the ratios of the corresponding sides.

$$\frac{a}{x} = \frac{18}{6} = 3 \qquad \frac{b}{y} = \frac{12}{4} = 3 \qquad \frac{c}{z} = \frac{15}{5} = 3$$

⚠️ **EXAMPLE 4** **Finding the Length of a Side of a Triangle**

If the following two triangles are similar, find the missing length x.

10 yards
2 yards
3 yards
x yards

Solution

1. UNDERSTAND. Read the problem and study the figure.

2. TRANSLATE. Since the triangles are similar, their corresponding sides are in proportion and we have

$$\frac{2}{3} = \frac{10}{x}$$

3. SOLVE. To solve, we multiply both sides by the LCD, $3x$, or cross multiply.

$$2x = 30$$
$$x = 15 \quad \text{Divide both sides by 2.}$$

4. INTERPRET.

Check: To check, replace x with 15 in the original proportion and see that a true statement results.

State: The missing length is 15 yards. ☐

PRACTICE
4 If the following two triangles are similar, find x.

15 meters
20 meters
x meters
8 meters

OBJECTIVE
3 Solving Problems About Numbers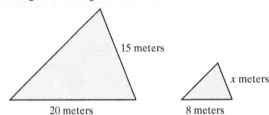

Let's continue to solve problems. The remaining problems are all modeled by rational equations.

EXAMPLE 5 **Finding an Unknown Number**

The quotient of a number and 6, minus $\frac{5}{3}$, is the quotient of the number and 2. Find the number.

Solution

1. UNDERSTAND. Read and reread the problem. Suppose that the unknown number is 2, then we see if the quotient of 2 and 6, or $\frac{2}{6}$, minus $\frac{5}{3}$ is equal to the quotient of 2 and 2, or $\frac{2}{2}$.

$$\frac{2}{6} - \frac{5}{3} = \frac{1}{3} - \frac{5}{3} = -\frac{4}{3}, \text{not } \frac{2}{2}$$

Don't forget that the purpose of a proposed solution is to better understand the problem.

Let $x =$ the unknown number.

2. TRANSLATE.

In words:	the quotient of x and 6	minus	$\frac{5}{3}$	is	the quotient of x and 2
	$\downarrow$	$\downarrow$	$\downarrow$	$\downarrow$	$\downarrow$
Translate:	$\frac{x}{6}$	$-$	$\frac{5}{3}$	$=$	$\frac{x}{2}$

3. SOLVE. Here, we solve the equation $\frac{x}{6} - \frac{5}{3} = \frac{x}{2}$. We begin by multiplying both sides of the equation by the LCD, 6.

$$6\left(\frac{x}{6} - \frac{5}{3}\right) = 6\left(\frac{x}{2}\right)$$

$$6\left(\frac{x}{6}\right) - 6\left(\frac{5}{3}\right) = 6\left(\frac{x}{2}\right) \quad \text{Apply the distributive property.}$$

$$x - 10 = 3x \quad \text{Simplify.}$$

$$-10 = 2x \quad \text{Subtract } x \text{ from both sides.}$$

$$\frac{-10}{2} = \frac{2x}{2} \quad \text{Divide both sides by 2.}$$

$$-5 = x \quad \text{Simplify.}$$

4. INTERPRET.

Check: To check, we verify that "the quotient of -5 and 6 minus $\frac{5}{3}$ is the quotient of -5 and 2," or $-\frac{5}{6} - \frac{5}{3} = -\frac{5}{2}$.

State: The unknown number is -5.   □

PRACTICE
5   The quotient of a number and 5, minus $\frac{3}{2}$, is the quotient of the number and 10. Find the number.

OBJECTIVE
4   Solving Problems About Work

The next example is often called a work problem. Work problems usually involve people or machines doing a certain task.

EXAMPLE 6   **Finding Work Rates**

Sam Waterton and Frank Schaffer work in a plant that manufactures automobiles. Sam can complete a quality control tour of the plant in 3 hours, while his assistant, Frank, needs 7 hours to complete the same job. The regional manager is coming to inspect the plant facilities, so both Sam and Frank are directed to complete a quality control tour together. How long will this take?

Solution

1. UNDERSTAND. Read and reread the problem. The key idea here is the relationship between the **time** (hours) it takes to complete the job and the **part of the job** completed in 1 unit of time (hour). For example, if the **time** it takes Sam to complete the job is 3 hours, the **part of the job** he can complete in 1 hour is $\frac{1}{3}$. Similarly, Frank can complete $\frac{1}{7}$ of the job in 1 hour.

Let $x =$ the **time** in hours it takes Sam and Frank to complete the job together. Then $\frac{1}{x} =$ the **part of the job** they complete in 1 hour.

(Continued on next page)

	Hours to Complete Total Job	*Part of Job Completed in 1 Hour*
Sam	3	$\frac{1}{3}$
Frank	7	$\frac{1}{7}$
Together	x	$\frac{1}{x}$

2. TRANSLATE.

In words:

part of job Sam completes in 1 hour	added to	part of job Frank completes in 1 hour	is equal to	part of job they complete together in 1 hour
↓	↓	↓	↓	↓

Translate: $\frac{1}{3}$ + $\frac{1}{7}$ = $\frac{1}{x}$

3. SOLVE. Here, we solve the equation $\frac{1}{3} + \frac{1}{7} = \frac{1}{x}$. We begin by multiplying both sides of the equation by the LCD, $21x$.

$$21x\left(\frac{1}{3}\right) + 21x\left(\frac{1}{7}\right) = 21x\left(\frac{1}{x}\right)$$

$$7x + 3x = 21 \qquad \text{Simplify.}$$

$$10x = 21$$

$$x = \frac{21}{10} \quad \text{or} \quad 2\frac{1}{10}\ \text{hours}$$

4. INTERPRET.

Check: Our proposed solution is $2\frac{1}{10}$ hours. This proposed solution is reasonable since $2\frac{1}{10}$ hours is more than half of Sam's time and less than half of Frank's time.

Check this solution in the originally *stated* problem.

State: Sam and Frank can complete the quality control tour in $2\frac{1}{10}$ hours. □

PRACTICE

6 Cindy Liu and Mary Beckwith own a landscaping company. Cindy can complete a certain garden planting in 3 hours, while Mary takes 4 hours to complete the same job. If both of them work together, how long will it take to plant the garden?

✓CONCEPT CHECK
Solve $E = mc^2$
a. for m.   **b.** for c^2.

Answers to Concept Check:
a. $m = \dfrac{E}{c^2}$ **b.** $c^2 = \dfrac{E}{m}$

OBJECTIVE
5 **Solving Problems About Distance** ▶

Next we look at a problem solved by the distance formula,

$$d = r \cdot t$$

EXAMPLE 7   **Finding Speeds of Vehicles**

A car travels 180 miles in the same time that a truck travels 120 miles. If the car's speed is 20 miles per hour faster than the truck's, find the car's speed and the truck's speed.

Solution

1. UNDERSTAND. Read and reread the problem. Suppose that the truck's speed is 45 miles per hour. Then the car's speed is 20 miles per hour more, or 65 miles per hour.

   We are given that the car travels 180 miles in the same time that the truck travels 120 miles. To find the time it takes the car to travel 180 miles, remember that since $d = rt$, we know that $\dfrac{d}{r} = t$.

Car's Time	*Truck's Time*
$t = \dfrac{d}{r} = \dfrac{180}{65} = 2\dfrac{50}{65} = 2\dfrac{10}{13}$ hours	$t = \dfrac{d}{r} = \dfrac{120}{45} = 2\dfrac{30}{45} = 2\dfrac{2}{3}$ hours

   Since the times are not the same, our proposed solution is not correct. But we have a better understanding of the problem.

   Let x = the speed of the truck.

   Since the car's speed is 20 miles per hour faster than the truck's, then

   $$x + 20 = \text{the speed of the car}$$

   Use the formula $d = r \cdot t$ or **d**istance = **r**ate $\cdot$ **t**ime. Prepare a chart to organize the information in the problem.

   ▶ Helpful Hint
   If $d = r \cdot t$,
   then $t = \dfrac{d}{r}$
   or $time = \dfrac{distance}{rate}.$

	Distance	=	*Rate*	$\cdot$	*Time*
Truck	120		x		$\begin{cases} 120 \leftarrow \text{distance} \\ x \leftarrow \text{rate} \end{cases}$
Car	180		$x + 20$		$\begin{cases} 180 \leftarrow \text{distance} \\ x + 20 \leftarrow \text{rate} \end{cases}$

2. TRANSLATE. Since the car and the truck travel the same amount of time, we have that

   In words: car's time   =   truck's time
                   ↓   ↓
   Translate: $\dfrac{180}{x + 20}$ = $\dfrac{120}{x}$

3. SOLVE. We begin by multiplying both sides of the equation by the LCD, $x(x + 20)$, or cross multiplying.

   $$\frac{180}{x + 20} = \frac{120}{x}$$

   $$180x = 120(x + 20)$$

   $$180x = 120x + 2400 \quad \text{Use the distributive property.}$$

   $$60x = 2400 \quad \text{Subtract } 120x \text{ from both sides.}$$

   $$x = 40 \quad \text{Divide both sides by 60.}$$

(Continued on next page)

4. INTERPRET. The speed of the truck is 40 miles per hour. The speed of the car must then be $x + 20$ or 60 miles per hour.

Check: Find the time it takes the car to travel 180 miles and the time it takes the truck to travel 120 miles.

$$\text{\emph{Car's Time}} \qquad\qquad \text{\emph{Truck's Time}}$$
$$t = \frac{d}{r} = \frac{180}{60} = 3 \text{ hours} \qquad t = \frac{d}{r} = \frac{120}{40} = 3 \text{ hours}$$

Since both travel the same amount of time, the proposed solution is correct.

State: The car's speed is 60 miles per hour and the truck's speed is 40 miles per hour. ☐

PRACTICE

7 A bus travels 180 miles in the same time that a car travels 240 miles. If the car's speed is 15 mph faster than the speed of the bus, find the speed of the car and the speed of the bus.

Vocabulary, Readiness & Video Check

Without solving algebraically, select the best choice for each exercise.

1. One person can complete a job in 7 hours. A second person can complete the same job in 5 hours. How long will it take them to complete the job if they work together?
  a. more than 7 hours
  b. between 5 and 7 hours
  c. less than 5 hours

2. One inlet pipe can fill a pond in 30 hours. A second inlet pipe can fill the same pond in 25 hours. How long before the pond is filled if both inlet pipes are on?
  a. less than 25 hours
  b. between 25 and 30 hours
  c. more than 30 hours

TRANSLATING

Given the variable in the first column, use the phrase in the second column to translate to an expression and then continue to the phrase in the third column to translate to another expression.

3.	A number: x	The reciprocal of the number:	The reciprocal of the number, decreased by 3:
4.	A number: y	The reciprocal of the number:	The reciprocal of the number, increased by 2:
5.	A number: z	The sum of the number and 5:	The reciprocal of the sum of the number and 5:
6.	A number: x	The difference of the number and 1:	The reciprocal of the difference of the number and 1:
7.	A number: y	Twice the number:	Eleven divided by twice the number:
8.	A number: z	Triple the number:	Negative ten divided by triple the number:

Martin-Gay Interactive Videos

See Video 7.6

Watch the section lecture video and answer the following questions.

OBJECTIVE 1
9. Based on 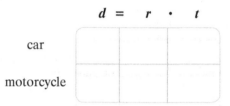 Examples 1 and 2, can proportions only be solved by using cross products? Explain.

OBJECTIVE 2
10. In Example 3 we are told there are many ways to set up a correct proportion. Why does this fact make it even more important to check that your solution is reasonable?

OBJECTIVE 3
11. What words or phrases in Example 5 told you to translate to an equation containing rational expressions?

OBJECTIVE 4
12. From Example 6, how can you determine a somewhat reasonable answer to a work problem before you even begin to solve it?

OBJECTIVE 5
13. The following problem is worded like Example 7 in the video, but using different quantities.

A car travels 325 miles in the same time that a motorcycle travels 290 miles. If the car's speed is 7 miles per hour more than the motorcycle's, find the speed of the car and the speed of the motorcycle. Fill in the table and set up an equation based on this problem (do not solve). Use Example 7 in the video as a model for your work.

	d	$=$	r	$\cdot$	t
car					
motorcycle					

7.6 Exercise Set   MyMathLab®

Solve each proportion. See Examples 1 and 2.

1. $\dfrac{2}{3} = \dfrac{x}{6}$

2. $\dfrac{x}{2} = \dfrac{16}{6}$

3. $\dfrac{x}{10} = \dfrac{5}{9}$

4. $\dfrac{9}{4x} = \dfrac{6}{2}$

5. $\dfrac{x+1}{2x+3} = \dfrac{2}{3}$

6. $\dfrac{x+1}{x+2} = \dfrac{5}{3}$

7. $\dfrac{9}{5} = \dfrac{12}{3x+2}$

8. $\dfrac{6}{11} = \dfrac{27}{3x-2}$

Solve. See Example 3.

9. The ratio of the weight of an object on Earth to the weight of the same object on Pluto is 100 to 3. If an elephant weighs 4100 pounds on Earth, find the elephant's weight on Pluto.

10. If a 170-pound person weighs approximately 65 pounds on Mars, about how much does a 9000-pound satellite weigh? Round your answer to the nearest pound.

11. There are 110 calories per 28.8 grams of Frosted Flakes cereal. Find how many calories are in 43.2 grams of this cereal.

12. On an architect's blueprint, 1 inch corresponds to 4 feet. Find the length of a wall represented by a line that is $3\dfrac{7}{8}$ inches long on the blueprint.

Find the unknown length x or y in the following pairs of similar triangles. See Example 4.

13.

14.

15.

16.

Solve the following. See Example 5.

17. Three times the reciprocal of a number equals 9 times the reciprocal of 6. Find the number.

18. Twelve divided by the sum of x and 2 equals the quotient of 4 and the difference of x and 2. Find x.

19. If twice a number added to 3 is divided by the number plus 1, the result is three halves. Find the number.

20. A number added to the product of 6 and the reciprocal of the number equals -5. Find the number.

See Example 6.

21. Smith Engineering found that an experienced surveyor surveys a roadbed in 4 hours. An apprentice surveyor needs 5 hours to survey the same stretch of road. If the two work together, find how long it takes them to complete the job.

22. An experienced bricklayer constructs a small wall in 3 hours. The apprentice completes the job in 6 hours. Find how long it takes if they work together.

23. In 2 minutes, a conveyor belt moves 300 pounds of recyclable aluminum from the delivery truck to a storage area. A smaller belt moves the same quantity of cans the same distance in 6 minutes. If both belts are used, find how long it takes to move the cans to the storage area.

24. Find how long it takes the conveyor belts described in Exercise 23 to move 1200 pounds of cans. (*Hint:* Think of 1200 pounds as four 300-pound jobs.)

See Example 7.

25. A jogger begins her workout by jogging to the park, a distance of 12 miles. She then jogs home at the same speed but along a different route. This return trip is 18 miles and her time is one hour longer. Find her jogging speed. Complete the accompanying chart and use it to find her jogging speed.

	Distance	=	Rate	·	Time
Trip to Park	12				
Return Trip	18				

26. A boat can travel 9 miles upstream in the same amount of time it takes to travel 11 miles downstream. If the current of the river is 3 miles per hour, complete the chart below and use it to find the speed of the boat in still water.

	Distance	=	Rate	·	Time
Upstream	9		$r-3$		
Downstream	11		$r+3$		

27. A cyclist rode the first 20-mile portion of his workout at a constant speed. For the 16-mile cooldown portion of his workout, he reduced his speed by 2 miles per hour. Each portion of the workout took the same time. Find the cyclist's speed during the first portion and find his speed during the cooldown portion.

28. A semi-truck travels 300 miles through the flatland in the same amount of time that it travels 180 miles through mountains. The rate of the truck is 20 miles per hour slower in the mountains than in the flatland. Find both the flatland rate and mountain rate.

MIXED PRACTICE

Solve the following. See Examples 1 through 7. (Note: Some exercises can be modeled by equations without rational expressions.)

29. A human factors expert recommends that there be at least 9 square feet of floor space in a college classroom for every student in the class. Find the minimum floor space that 40 students need.

30. Due to space problems at a local university, a 20-foot by 12-foot conference room is converted into a classroom. Find the maximum number of students the room can accommodate. (See Exercise 29.)

31. One-fourth equals the quotient of a number and 8. Find the number.

32. Four times a number added to 5 is divided by 6. The result is $\frac{7}{2}$. Find the number.

33. Marcus and Tony work for Lombardo's Pipe and Concrete. Mr. Lombardo is preparing an estimate for a customer. He knows that Marcus lays a slab of concrete in 6 hours. Tony lays the same size slab in 4 hours. If both work on the job and the cost of labor is $45.00 per hour, decide what the labor estimate should be.

34. Mr. Dodson can paint his house by himself in 4 days. His son needs an additional day to complete the job if he works by himself. If they work together, find how long it takes to paint the house.

35. A pilot can travel 400 miles with the wind in the same amount of time as 336 miles against the wind. Find the speed of the wind if the pilot's speed in still air is 230 miles per hour.

36. A fisherman on Pearl River rows 9 miles downstream in the same amount of time he rows 3 miles upstream. If the current is 6 miles per hour, find how long it takes him to cover the 12 miles.

37. Find the unknown length y.

38. Find the unknown length y.

39. Suppose two trains leave Holbrook, Arizona, at the same time, traveling in opposite directions. One train travels 10 mph faster than the other. In 3.5 hours, the trains are 322 miles apart. Find the speed of each train.

40. Suppose two cars leave Brinkley, Arkansas, at the same time, traveling in opposite directions. One car travels 8 mph faster than the other car. In 2.5 hours, the cars are 280 miles apart. Find the speed of each car.

41. Two divided by the difference of a number and 3, minus 4 divided by the number plus 3, equals 8 times the reciprocal of the difference of the number squared and 9. What is the number?

42. If 15 times the reciprocal of a number is added to the ratio of 9 times the number minus 7 and the number plus 2, the result is 9. What is the number?

43. A pilot flies 630 miles with a tailwind of 35 miles per hour. Against the wind, he flies only 455 miles in the same amount of time. Find the rate of the plane in still air.

44. A marketing manager travels 1080 miles in a corporate jet and then an additional 240 miles by car. If the car ride takes one hour longer than the jet ride takes, and if the rate of the jet is 6 times the rate of the car, find the time the manager travels by jet and find the time the manager travels by car.

45. To mix weed killer with water correctly, it is necessary to mix 8 teaspoons of weed killer with 2 gallons of water. Find how many gallons of water are needed to mix with the entire box if it contains 36 teaspoons of weed killer.

46. The directions for a certain bug spray concentrate is to mix 3 ounces of concentrate with 2 gallons of water. How many ounces of concentrate are needed to mix with 5 gallons of water?

47. A boater travels 16 miles per hour on the water on a still day. During one particular windy day, he finds that he travels 48 miles with the wind behind him in the same amount of time that he travels 16 miles into the wind. Find the rate of the wind.

Let x be the rate of the wind.

	r	×	t	=	d
with wind	$16 + x$				48
into wind	$16 - x$				16

48. The current on a portion of the Mississippi River is 3 miles per hour. A barge can go 6 miles upstream in the same amount of time it takes to go 10 miles downstream. Find the speed of the boat in still water.

Let x be the speed of the boat in still water.

	r	×	t	=	d
upstream	$x - 3$				6
downstream	$x + 3$				10

49. Two hikers are 11 miles apart and walking toward each other. They meet in 2 hours. Find the rate of each hiker if one hiker walks 1.1 mph faster than the other.

50. On a 255-mile trip, Gary Alessandrini traveled at an average speed of 70 mph, got a speeding ticket, and then traveled at 60 mph for the remainder of the trip. If the entire trip took 4.5 hours and the speeding ticket stop took 30 minutes, how long did Gary speed before getting stopped?

51. One custodian cleans a suite of offices in 3 hours. When a second worker is asked to join the regular custodian, the job takes only $1\frac{1}{2}$ hours. How long does it take the second worker to do the same job alone?

52. One person proofreads a copy for a small newspaper in 4 hours. If a second proofreader is also employed, the job can be done in $2\frac{1}{2}$ hours. How long does it take for the second proofreader to do the same job alone?

53. An architect is completing the plans for a triangular deck. Use the diagram below to find the missing dimension.

54. A student wishes to make a small model of a triangular mainsail to study the effects of wind on the sail. The smaller model will be the same shape as a regular-size sailboat's mainsail. Use the following diagram to find the missing dimensions.

55. The manufacturers of cans of salted mixed nuts state that the ratio of peanuts to other nuts is 3 to 2. If 324 peanuts are in a can, find how many other nuts should also be in the can.

56. There are 1280 calories in a 14-ounce portion of Eagle Brand Milk. Find how many calories are in 2 ounces of Eagle Brand Milk.

57. A jet plane traveling at 500 mph overtakes a propeller plane traveling at 200 mph that had a 2-hour head start. How far from the starting point are the planes?

58. How long will it take a bus traveling at 60 miles per hour to overtake a car traveling at 40 mph if the car had a 1.5-hour head start?

59. One pipe fills a storage pool in 20 hours. A second pipe fills the same pool in 15 hours. When a third pipe is added and all three are used to fill the pool, it takes only 6 hours. Find how long it takes the third pipe to do the job.

60. One pump fills a tank in 9 hours. A second pump fills the same tank in 6 hours. When a third pump is added and all three are used to fill the tank, it takes only 3 hours. Find how long it takes the third pump to fill the tank.

▶ **61.** A car travels 280 miles in the same time that a motorcycle travels 240 miles. If the car's speed is 10 miles per hour more than the motorcycle's, find the speed of the car and the speed of the motorcycle.

62. A bus traveled on a level road for 3 hours at an average speed 20 miles per hour faster than it traveled on a winding road. The time spent on the winding road was 4 hours. Find the average speed on the level road if the entire trip was 305 miles.

63. In 6 hours, an experienced cook prepares enough pies to supply a local restaurant's daily order. Another cook prepares the same number of pies in 7 hours. Together with a third cook, they prepare the pies in 2 hours. Find how long it takes the third cook to prepare the pies alone.

64. Mrs. Smith balances the company books in 8 hours. It takes her assistant 12 hours to do the same job. If they work together, find how long it takes them to balance the books.

65. The quotient of a number and 3, minus 1, equals $\frac{5}{3}$. Find the number.

66. The quotient of a number and 5, minus 1, equals $\frac{7}{5}$. Find the number.

67. Currently, the Toyota Corolla is the best-selling car in the world. Suppose that during a test drive of two Corollas, one car travels 224 miles in the same time that the second car travels 175 miles. If the speed of the first car is 14 miles per hour faster than the speed of the second car, find the speed of both cars. (*Source: Top Ten of Everything*)

68. The second best-selling car is the Volkswagen Golf. A driver of this car took a day trip around the California coastline driving at two speeds. He drove 70 miles at a slower speed and 300 miles at a speed 40 miles per hour faster. If the time spent driving the faster speed was twice that spent at the slower speed, find the two speeds during the trip. (*Source: Top Ten of Everything*)

69. A pilot can fly an MD-11 2160 miles with the wind in the same time she can fly 1920 miles against the wind. If the speed of the wind is 30 mph, find the speed of the plane in still air. (*Source*: Air Transport Association of America)

70. A pilot can fly a DC-10 1365 miles against the wind in the same time he can fly 1575 miles with the wind. If the speed of the plane in still air is 490 miles per hour, find the speed of the wind. (*Source*: Air Transport Association of America)

Given that the following pairs of triangles are similar, find each missing length.

△ **71.**

△ **72.**

△ **73.**

△ **74.**

REVIEW AND PREVIEW

Find the slope of the line through each pair of points. Use the slope to determine whether the line is vertical, horizontal, or moves upward or downward from left to right. See Section 3.4.

75. $(-2, 5), (4, -3)$

76. $(0, 4), (2, 10)$

77. $(-3, -6), (1, 5)$

78. $(-2, 7), (3, -2)$

79. $(3, 7), (3, -2)$

80. $(0, -4), (2, -4)$

CONCEPT EXTENSIONS

The following bar graph shows the capacity of the United States to generate electricity from the wind in the years shown. Use this graph for Exercises 81 and 82.

81. Find the approximate megawatt capacity in 2010.

82. Find the approximate megawatt capacity in 2009.

📱 *In general, 1000 megawatts will serve the average electricity needs of 560,000 people. Use this fact and the preceding graph to answer Exercises 83 and 84.*

83. In 2010, the number of megawatts that were generated from wind served the electricity needs of how many people? (Round to the nearest ten-thousand.)

84. How many megawatts of electricity are needed to serve the city or town in which you live?

For Exercises 85 and 86 decide whether we can immediately use cross products to solve for x. Do not actually solve.

85. $\dfrac{2 - x}{5} = \dfrac{1 + x}{3}$ **86.** $\dfrac{2}{5} - x = \dfrac{1 + x}{3}$

Solve.

87. One pump fills a tank 3 times as fast as another pump. If the pumps work together, they fill the tank in 21 minutes. How long does it take for each pump to fill the tank?

88. It takes 9 hours for pump A to fill a tank alone. Pump B takes 15 hours to fill the same tank alone. If pumps A, B, and C are used, the tank fills in 5 hours. How long does it take pump C to fill the tank alone?

89. For what value of x is $\dfrac{x}{x - 1}$ in proportion to $\dfrac{x + 1}{x}$? Explain your result.

90. If x is 10, is $\dfrac{2}{x}$ in proportion to $\dfrac{x}{50}$? Explain why or why not.

91. Person A can complete a job in 5 hours, and person B can complete the same job in 3 hours. Without solving algebraically, discuss reasonable and unreasonable answers for how long it would take them to complete the job together.

92. A hyena spots a giraffe 0.5 mile away and begins running toward it. The giraffe starts running away from the hyena just as the hyena begins running toward it. A hyena can run at a speed of 40 mph and a giraffe can run at 32 mph. How long will it take for the hyena to overtake the giraffe? (*Source: World Almanac and Book of Facts*)

Solve. See the Concept Check in this section.

Solve D = RT

93. for R **94.** for T

More on Functions and Graphs

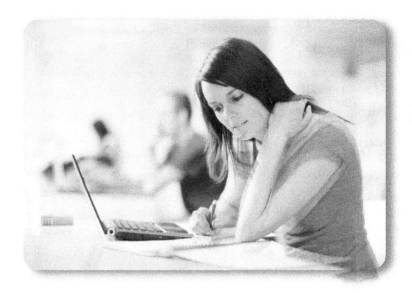

In Section 3.6, we introduced the notion of relation and the notion of function, perhaps the single most important and useful concepts in all of mathematics. In this chapter, we explore the concept of functions further.

We define online courses as courses in which at least 80% of the content is delivered online. Although there are many types of course delivery used by instructors, the bar graph below shows the increase in percent of students taking at least one online course. Notice that the two functions, $f(x)$ and $g(x)$, both approximate the percent of students taking at least one online course. Also, for both functions, x is the number of years since 2000. In Section 8.1, Exercises 69–74, we use these functions to predict the growth of online courses.

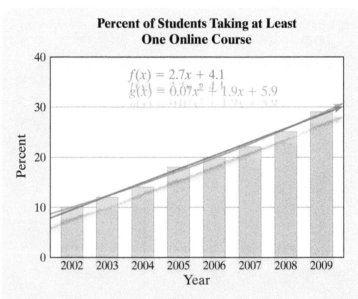

Percent of Students Taking at Least One Online Course

$f(x) = 2.7x + 4.1$
$g(x) = 0.07x^2 + 1.9x + 5.9$

Source: The College Board: Trends in Higher Education Series

8.1 Graphing and Writing Linear Functions

OBJECTIVE

1 Graphing Linear Functions

In this section, we identify and graph linear functions. By the vertical line test, Section 3.6, we know that all linear equations except those whose graphs are vertical lines are functions. Thus, all linear equations except those of the form $x = c$ (vertical lines) are linear functions. For example, we know from Section 3.2 that $y = 2x$ is a linear equation in two variables. Its graph is shown.

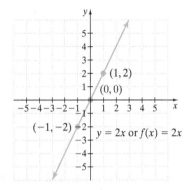

Because this graph passes the vertical line test, we know that $y = 2x$ is a function. If we want to emphasize that this equation describes a function, we may write $y = 2x$ as $f(x) = 2x$.

EXAMPLE 1 Graph $g(x) = 2x + 1$. Compare this graph with the graph of $f(x) = 2x$.

Solution To graph $g(x) = 2x + 1$, find three ordered pair solutions.

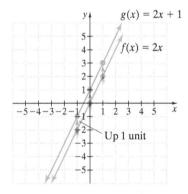

Notice that y-values for the graph of $g(x) = 2x + 1$ are obtained by adding 1 to each y-value of each corresponding point of the graph of $f(x) = 2x$. The graph of $g(x) = 2x + 1$ is the same as the graph of $f(x) = 2x$ shifted upward 1 unit. ☐

PRACTICE

1 Graph $g(x) = 4x - 3$ and $f(x) = 4x$ on the same axes. See graphing answer section.

If a linear function is solved for y, we can easily use function notation to describe it by replacing y with $f(x)$. Recall the slope-intercept form of a linear equation, $y = mx + b$, where m is the slope of the line and $(0, b)$ is the y-intercept. Since this form is solved for y, we use it to define a linear function.

In general, a **linear function** is a function that can be written in the form $f(x) = mx + b$. For example, $g(x) = 2x + 1$ is in this form, with $m = 2$ and $b = 1$. Thus, the slope of the linear function $g(x)$ is 2 and the y-intercept is $(0, 1)$.

EXAMPLE 2 Graph the linear functions $f(x) = -3x$ and $g(x) = -3x - 6$ on the same set of axes.

Solution To graph $f(x)$ and $g(x)$, find ordered pair solutions.

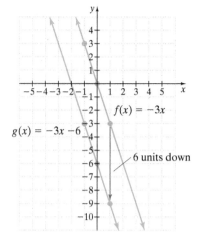

x	$f(x) = -3x$	$g(x) = -3x - 6$
0	0	−6
1	−3	−9
−1	3	−3
−2	6	0

subtract 6

subtract 6

Each y-value for the graph of $g(x) = -3x - 6$ is obtained by subtracting 6 from the y-value of the corresponding point of the graph of $f(x) = -3x$. The graph of $g(x) = -3x - 6$ is the same as the graph of $f(x) = -3x$ shifted down 6 units. ☐

PRACTICE

2 Graph the linear functions $f(x) = -2x$ and $g(x) = -2x + 5$ on the same set of axes.

OBJECTIVE

2 Writing Equations of Lines Using Function Notation

We now practice writing linear functions.

This means the graph is a line that passes the vertical line test.

Below is a review of some tools we can use.

$y = mx + b$	**Slope-intercept form** of a linear equation. The slope is m, and the y-intercept is $(0, b)$.
$y - y_1 = m(x - x_1)$	**Point-slope form** of a linear equation. The slope is m, and (x_1, y_1) is a point on the line.
$y = c$	**Horizontal line** The slope is 0, and the y-intercept is $(0, c)$.

Note: $x = c$, whose graph is a vertical line, is not included above, as these equations do **not** define functions.

EXAMPLE 3 Find an equation of the line with slope -3 and y-intercept $(0, -5)$. Write the equation using function notation.

Solution Because we know the slope and the y-intercept, we use the slope-intercept form with $m = -3$ and $b = -5$.

$$y = mx + b \qquad \text{Slope-intercept form}$$
$$y = -3 \cdot x + (-5) \qquad \text{Let } m = -3 \text{ and } b = -5.$$
$$y = -3x - 5 \qquad \text{Simplify.}$$

This equation is solved for y. To write using function notation, we replace y with $f(x)$.

$$f(x) = -3x - 5 \qquad ☐$$

PRACTICE

3 Find an equation of the line with slope -4 and y-intercept $(0, -3)$. Write the equation using function notation.

EXAMPLE 4 Find an equation of the line through points $(4, 0)$ and $(-4, -5)$. Write the equation using function notation.

Solution First, find the slope of the line.

$$m = \frac{-5 - 0}{-4 - 4} = \frac{-5}{-8} = \frac{5}{8}$$

Next, make use of the point-slope form. Replace (x_1, y_1) by either $(4, 0)$ or $(-4, -5)$ in the point-slope equation. We will choose the point $(4, 0)$. The line through $(4, 0)$ with slope $\frac{5}{8}$ is

$$y - y_1 = m(x - x_1) \quad \text{Point-slope form.}$$

$$y - 0 = \frac{5}{8}(x - 4) \quad \text{Let } m = \frac{5}{8} \text{ and } (x_1, y_1) = (4, 0).$$

$$8y = 5(x - 4) \quad \text{Multiply both sides by 8.}$$

$$8y = 5x - 20 \quad \text{Apply the distributive property.}$$

To write the equation using function notation, we solve for y, then replace y with $f(x)$.

$$8y = 5x - 20$$

$$y = \frac{5}{8}x - \frac{20}{8} \quad \text{Divide both sides by 8.}$$

$$f(x) = \frac{5}{8}x - \frac{5}{2} \quad \text{Write using function notation.} \qquad \square$$

PRACTICE
4 Find an equation of the line through points $(-1, 2)$ and $(2, 0)$. Write the equation using function notation.

> ▶ Helpful Hint
> If two points of a line are given, either one may be used with the point-slope form to write an equation of the line.

EXAMPLE 5 Find an equation of the horizontal line containing the point $(2, 3)$. Write the equation using function notation.

Solution A horizontal line has an equation of the form $y = c$. Since the line contains the point $(2, 3)$, the equation is $y = 3$, as shown to the right.
    Using function notation, the equation is

$$f(x) = 3.$$

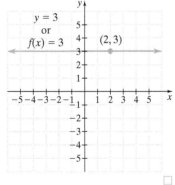

$\square$

PRACTICE
5 Find the equation of the horizontal line containing the point $(6, -2)$. Use function notation.

OBJECTIVE

3 **Finding Equations of Parallel and Perpendicular Lines**

Next, we find equations of parallel and perpendicular lines.

△ **EXAMPLE 6** Find an equation of the line containing the point $(4, 4)$ and parallel to the line $2x + 3y = -6$. Write the equation in standard form.

Solution Because the line we want to find is *parallel* to the line $2x + 3y = -6$, the two lines must have equal slopes. Find the slope of $2x + 3y = -6$ by writing it in the form $y = mx + b$. In other words, solve the equation for y.

$$2x + 3y = -6$$

$$3y = -2x - 6 \quad \text{Subtract } 2x \text{ from both sides.}$$

$$y = \frac{-2x}{3} - \frac{6}{3} \quad \text{Divide by 3.}$$

$$y = -\frac{2}{3}x - 2 \quad \text{Write in slope-intercept form.}$$

The slope of this line is $-\frac{2}{3}$. Thus, a line parallel to this line will also have a slope of $-\frac{2}{3}$. The equation we are asked to find describes a line containing the point $(4, 4)$ with a slope of $-\frac{2}{3}$. We use the point-slope form.

$$y - y_1 = m(x - x_1)$$

$$y - 4 = -\frac{2}{3}(x - 4) \quad \text{Let } m = -\frac{2}{3}, x_1 = 4, \text{ and } y_1 = 4.$$

$$3(y - 4) = -2(x - 4) \quad \text{Multiply both sides by 3.}$$

$$3y - 12 = -2x + 8 \quad \text{Apply the distributive property.}$$

$$2x + 3y = 20 \quad \text{Write in standard form.} \qquad \square$$

> ▶ **Helpful Hint**
>
> Multiply both sides of the equation $2x + 3y = 20$ by -1 and it becomes $-2x - 3y = -20$. Both equations are in standard form, and their graphs are the same line.

PRACTICE

6 Find an equation of the line containing the point $(8, -3)$ and parallel to the line $3x + 4y = 1$. Write the equation in standard form.

EXAMPLE 7 Write a function that describes the line containing the point $(4, 4)$ and perpendicular to the line $2x + 3y = -6$.

Solution In the previous example, we found that the slope of the line $2x + 3y = -6$ is $-\frac{2}{3}$. A line perpendicular to this line will have a slope that is the negative reciprocal of $-\frac{2}{3}$, or $\frac{3}{2}$. From the point-slope equation, we have

$$y - y_1 = m(x - x_1)$$

$$y - 4 = \frac{3}{2}(x - 4) \quad \text{Let } x_1 = 4, y_1 = 4 \text{ and } m = \frac{3}{2}.$$

$$2(y - 4) = 3(x - 4) \quad \text{Multiply both sides by 2.}$$

$$2y - 8 = 3x - 12 \quad \text{Apply the distributive property.}$$

$$2y = 3x - 4 \quad \text{Add 8 to both sides.}$$

$$y = \frac{3}{2}x - 2 \quad \text{Divide both sides by 2.}$$

$$f(x) = \frac{3}{2}x - 2 \quad \text{Write using function notation.} \qquad \square$$

PRACTICE
7   Write a function that describes the line containing the point $(8, -3)$ and perpendicular to the line $3x + 4y = 1$.

Graphing Calculator Explorations

You may have noticed by now that to use the $\boxed{Y =}$ key on a graphing calculator to graph an equation, the equation must be solved for y.

Graph each function by first solving the function for y.

1. $x = 3.5y$

2. $-2.7y = x$

3. $5.78x + 2.31y = 10.98$

4. $-7.22x + 3.89y = 12.57$

5. $y - |x| = 3.78$

6. $3y - 5x^2 = 6x - 4$

7. $y - 5.6x^2 = 7.7x + 1.5$

8. $y + 2.6|x| = -3.2$

Vocabulary, Readiness & Video Check

Use the choices given to fill in each blank. Some choices may not be used.

linear $(0, b)$ m

quadratic $(b, 0)$ mx

1. A _____ function can be written in the form $f(x) = mx + b$.

2. In the form $f(x) = mx + b$, the y-intercept is _____ and the slope is _____.

State the slope and the y-intercept of the graph of each function.

3. $f(x) = -4x + 12$

4. $g(x) = \dfrac{2}{3}x - \dfrac{7}{2}$

5. $g(x) = 5x$

6. $f(x) = -x$

Decide whether the lines are parallel, perpendicular, or neither.

7. $y = 12x + 6$
  $y = 12x - 2$

8. $y = -5x + 8$
  $y = -5x - 8$

9. $y = -9x + 3$
  $y = \dfrac{3}{2}x - 7$

10. $y = 2x - 12$
  $y = \dfrac{1}{2}x - 6$

Martin-Gay Interactive Videos

See Video 8.1

Watch the section lecture video and answer the following questions.

OBJECTIVE
1

11. Based on the lecture before Example 1, in what form can a linear function be written?

OBJECTIVE
2

12. From Example 2, given a *y*-intercept, how do you know which value to use for *b* in the slope-intercept form?

OBJECTIVE
2

13. Example 4 discusses how to find an equation of a line given two points. Under what circumstances might the slope-intercept form be chosen over the point-slope form to find an equation?

OBJECTIVE
3

14. Solve Example 6 again, this time writing the equation of the line in function notation *parallel* to the given line through the given point.

8.1 Exercise Set MyMathLab®

Graph each linear function. See Examples 1 and 2.

1. $f(x) = -2x$

2. $f(x) = 2x$

3. $f(x) = -2x + 3$

4. $f(x) = 2x + 6$

5. $f(x) = \frac{1}{2}x$

6. $f(x) = \frac{1}{3}x$

7. $f(x) = \frac{1}{2}x - 4$

8. $f(x) = \frac{1}{3}x - 2$

The graph of $f(x) = 5x$ follows. Use this graph to match each linear function with its graph. See Examples 1 and 2.

A

B

C

D

9. $f(x) = 5x - 3$

10. $f(x) = 5x - 2$

11. $f(x) = 5x + 1$

12. $f(x) = 5x + 3$

Use function notation to write the equation of each line with the given slope and y-intercept. See Example 3.

13. Slope -1; *y*-intercept $(0, 1)$

14. Slope $\frac{1}{2}$; *y*-intercept $(0, -6)$

15. Slope 2; *y*-intercept $\left(0, \frac{3}{4}\right)$

16. Slope -3; *y*-intercept $\left(0, -\frac{1}{5}\right)$

17. Slope $\frac{2}{7}$; *y*-intercept $(0, 0)$

18. Slope $-\frac{4}{5}$; *y*-intercept $(0, 0)$

Find an equation of the line with the given slope and containing the given point. Write the equation using function notation. See Example 3.

19. Slope 3; through $(1, 2)$

20. Slope 4; through $(5, 1)$

21. Slope -2; through $(1, -3)$

22. Slope -4; through $(2, -4)$

23. Slope $\frac{1}{2}$; through $(-6, 2)$

24. Slope $\frac{2}{3}$; through $(-9, 4)$

25. Slope $-\frac{9}{10}$; through $(-3, 0)$

26. Slope $-\frac{1}{5}$; through $(4, -6)$

Find an equation of the line passing through the given points. Use function notation to write the equation. See Example 4.

27. $(2, 0), (4, 6)$

28. $(3, 0), (7, 8)$

29. $(-2, 5), (-6, 13)$

30. $(7, -4), (2, 6)$

31. $(-2, -4), (-4, -3)$

32. $(-9, -2), (-3, 10)$

▶ **33.** $(-3, -8), (-6, -9)$

34. $(8, -3), (4, -8)$

35. $\left(\dfrac{3}{5}, \dfrac{2}{5}\right)$ and $\left(-\dfrac{1}{5}, \dfrac{7}{10}\right)$

36. $\left(\dfrac{1}{2}, -\dfrac{1}{4}\right)$ and $\left(\dfrac{3}{2}, \dfrac{3}{4}\right)$

Write an equation of each line using function notation. See Example 5.

▶ **37.** Slope 0; through $(-2, -4)$

38. Horizontal; through $(-3, 1)$

39. Horizontal; through $(0, 5)$

40. Slope 0; through $(-10, 23)$

Find an equation of each line. Write the equation using function notation. See Examples 6 and 7.

△ **41.** Through $(3, 8)$; parallel to $f(x) = 4x - 2$

△ **42.** Through $(1, 5)$; parallel to $f(x) = 3x - 4$

▶ **43.** Through $(2, -5)$; perpendicular to $3y = x - 6$

△ **44.** Through $(-4, 8)$; perpendicular to $2x - 3y = 1$

△ **45.** Through $(-2, -3)$; parallel to $3x + 2y = 5$

△ **46.** Through $(-2, -3)$; perpendicular to $3x + 2y = 5$

MIXED PRACTICE

Find the equation of each line. Write the equation using standard notation unless indicated otherwise. See Examples 3 through 7.

47. Slope 2; through $(-2, 3)$

48. Slope 3; through $(-4, 2)$

49. Through $(1, 6)$ and $(5, 2)$; use function notation

50. Through $(2, 9)$ and $(8, 6)$; use function notation

51. With slope $-\dfrac{1}{2}$; y-intercept 11; use function notation

52. With slope -4; y-intercept $\dfrac{2}{9}$; use function notation

53. Through $(-7, -4)$ and $(0, -6)$

54. Through $(2, -8)$ and $(-4, -3)$

55. Slope $-\dfrac{4}{3}$; through $(-5, 0)$

56. Slope $-\dfrac{3}{5}$; through $(4, -1)$

57. Horizontal line; through $(-2, -10)$; use function notation

58. Horizontal line; through $(1, 0)$; use function notation

△ **59.** Through $(6, -2)$; parallel to the line $2x + 4y = 9$

△ **60.** Through $(8, -3)$; parallel to the line $6x + 2y = 5$

61. Slope 0; through $(-9, 12)$; use function notation

62. Slope 0; through $(10, -8)$; use function notation

△ **63.** Through $(6, 1)$; parallel to the line $8x - y = 9$

△ **64.** Through $(3, 5)$; perpendicular to the line $2x - y = 8$

△ **65.** Through $(5, -6)$; perpendicular to $y = 9$

△ **66.** Through $(-3, -5)$; parallel to $y = 9$

67. Through $(2, -8)$ and $(-6, -5)$; use function notation

68. Through $(-4, -2)$ and $(-6, 5)$; use function notation

REVIEW AND PREVIEW

From the Chapter 8 opener, we have two functions to describe the percent of college students taking at least one online course. For both functions, x is the number of years since 2000 and y (or f(x) or g(x)) is the percent of students taking at least one online course.

$$f(x) = 2.7x + 4.1 \quad \text{or} \quad g(x) = 0.07x^2 + 1.9x + 5.9$$

Use this for Exercises 69–74. See Section 3.6.

69. Find $f(9)$ and describe in words what this means.

70. Find $g(9)$ and describe in words what this means.

71. Assume the trend of $g(x)$ continues. Find $g(16)$ and describe in words what this means.

72. Assume the trend of $f(x)$ continues. Find $f(16)$ and describe in words what this means.

73. Use Exercises 69–72 and compare $f(9)$ and $g(9)$, then $f(16)$ and $g(16)$. As x increases, are the function values staying about the same or not? Explain your answer.

74. Use the Chapter 8 opener graph and study the graphs of $f(x)$ and $g(x)$. Use these graphs to answer Exercise 73. Explain your answer.

CONCEPT EXTENSIONS

Find an equation of each line graphed. Write the equation using function notation. (Hint: Use each graph to write 2 ordered pair solutions. Find the slope of each line, then refer to Examples 3 or 4 to complete.)

75.   **76.**

77.   **78.**

Solve.

79. A rock is dropped from the top of a 400-foot building. After 1 second, the rock is traveling 32 feet per second. After 3 seconds, the rock is traveling 96 feet per second. Let y be the rate of descent and x be the number of seconds since the rock was dropped.

   a. Write a linear equation that relates time x to rate y. [*Hint:* Use the ordered pairs $(1, 32)$ and $(3, 96)$.]

   b. Use this equation to determine the rate of travel of the rock 4 seconds after it was dropped.

80. A fruit company recently released a new applesauce. By the end of its first year, profits on this product amounted to $30,000. The anticipated profit for the end of the fourth year is $66,000. The ratio of change in time to change in profit is constant. Let x be years and y be profit.

   a. Write a linear equation that relates profit and time. [*Hint:* Use the ordered pairs $(1, 30,000)$ and $(4, 66,000)$.]

   b. Use this equation to predict the company's profit at the end of the seventh year.

   c. Predict when the profit should reach $126,000.

81. The Whammo Company has learned that by pricing a newly released Frisbee at $6, sales will reach 2000 per day. Raising the price to $8 will cause the sales to fall to 1500 per day. Assume that the ratio of change in price to change in daily sales is constant and let x be the price of the Frisbee and y be number of sales.

   a. Find the linear equation that models the price–sales relationship for this Frisbee. [*Hint:* The line must pass through $(6, 2000)$ and $(8, 1500)$.]

   b. Use this equation to predict the daily sales of Frisbees if the price is set at $7.50.

82. The Pool Fun Company has learned that, by pricing a newly released Fun Noodle at $3, sales will reach 10,000 Fun Noodles per day during the summer. Raising the price to $5 will cause the sales to fall to 8000 Fun Noodles per day. Let x be price and y be the number sold.

   a. Assume that the relationship between sales price and number of Fun Noodles sold is linear and write an equation describing this relationship. [*Hint:* The line must pass through $(3, 10,000)$ and $(5, 8000)$.]

   b. Use this equation to predict the daily sales of Fun Noodles if the price is $3.50.

83. The number of people employed in the United States as registered nurses was 2619 thousand in 2008. By 2018, this number is expected to rise to 3200 thousand. Let y be the number of registered nurses (in thousands) employed in the United States in the year x, where $x = 0$ represents 2008. (*Source:* U.S. Bureau of Labor Statistics)

   a. Write a linear equation that models the number of people (in thousands) employed as registered nurses in year x.

   b. Use this equation to estimate the number of people employed as registered nurses in 2012.

84. In 2008, IBM had 398,500 employees worldwide. By 2010, this number had increased to 426,751. Let y be the number of IBM employees worldwide in the year x, where $x = 0$ represents 2008. (*Source:* IBM Corporation)

   a. Write a linear equation that models the growth in the number of IBM employees worldwide, in terms of the year x.

   b. Use this equation to predict the number of IBM employees worldwide in 2013.

85. In 2010, the average price of a new home sold in the United States was $272,900. In 2005, the average price of a new home in the United States was $297,000. Let y be the average price of a new home in the year x, where $x = 0$ represents the year 2005. (*Source:* Based on data from U.S. census)

   a. Write a linear equation that models the average price of a new home in terms of the year x. [*Hint:* The line must pass through the points $(0, 297,000)$ and $(5, 272,900)$.]

   b. Use this equation to predict the average price of a new home in 2013.

86. The number of McDonald's restaurants worldwide in 2010 was 32,737. In 2005, there were 31,046 McDonald's restaurants worldwide. Let y be the number of McDonald's restaurants in the year x, where $x = 0$ represents the year 2005. (*Source:* McDonald's Corporation)

   a. Write a linear equation that models the growth in the number of McDonald's restaurants worldwide in terms of the year x. [*Hint:* The line must pass through the points $(0, 31,046)$ and $(5, 32,737)$.]

   b. Use this equation to predict the number of McDonald's restaurants worldwide in 2013.

Example:

Find an equation of the perpendicular bisector of the line segment whose endpoints are $(2, 6)$ and $(0, -2)$.

Solution:

A perpendicular bisector is a line that contains the midpoint of the given segment and is perpendicular to the segment.

Step 1: The midpoint of the segment with endpoints $(2, 6)$ and $(0, -2)$ is $(1, 2)$.

Step 2: The slope of the segment containing points $(2, 6)$ and $(0, -2)$ is 4.

Step 3: A line perpendicular to this line segment will have slope of $-\dfrac{1}{4}$.

Step 4: The equation of the line through the midpoint $(1, 2)$ with a slope of $-\dfrac{1}{4}$ will be the equation of the perpendicular bisector. This equation in standard form is $x + 4y = 9$.

Find an equation of the perpendicular bisector of the line segment whose endpoints are given. See the previous example.

△ **87.** $(3, -1); (-5, 1)$

△ **88.** $(-6, -3); (-8, -1)$

△ **89.** $(-2, 6); (-22, -4)$

△ **90.** $(5, 8); (7, 2)$

△ **91.** $(2, 3); (-4, 7)$

△ **92.** $(-6, 8); (-4, -2)$

93. Describe how to check to see if the graph of $2x - 4y = 7$ passes through the points $(1.4, -1.05)$ and $(0, -1.75)$. Then follow your directions and check these points.

8.2 Reviewing Function Notation and Graphing Nonlinear Functions

OBJECTIVES

1 Review Function Notation.

2 Find Square Roots of Numbers.

3 Graph Nonlinear Functions.

In the previous section, we studied linear equations that described functions. Not all equations in two variables are linear equations, and not all graphs of equations in two variables are lines. In Chapter 3, we saw graphs of nonlinear equations, some of which were functions since they passed the vertical line test. In this section, we study the functions whose graphs may not be lines. First, let's review function notation.

OBJECTIVE

1 Reviewing Function Notation

Suppose we have a function f such that $f(2) = -1$. Recall this means that when $x = 2, f(x)$, or $y, = -1$. Thus, the graph of f passes through $(2, -1)$.

> ▶ **Helpful Hint**
>
> Remember that $f(x)$ is a special symbol in mathematics used to denote a function. The symbol $f(x)$ is read "f of x." It does *not* mean $f \cdot x$ (f times x).

✓**CONCEPT CHECK**

Suppose $y = f(x)$ and we are told that $f(3) = 9$. Which is not true?

a. When $x = 3, y = 9$.

b. A possible function is $f(x) = x^2$.

c. A point on the graph of the function is $(3, 9)$.

d. A possible function is $f(x) = 2x + 4$.

If it helps, think of a function, f, as a machine that has been programmed with a certain correspondence or rule. An input value (a member of the domain) is then fed into the machine, the machine does the correspondence or rule, and the result is the output (a member of the range).

EXAMPLE 1 Given the graphs of the functions f and g, find each function value by inspecting the graphs.

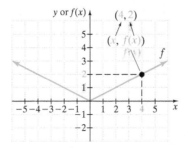

a. $f(4)$ **b.** $f(-2)$ **c.** $g(5)$ **d.** $g(0)$

e. Find all x-values such that $f(x) = 1$.   **f.** Find all x-values such that $g(x) = 0$.

(Continued on next page)

Solution

a. To find $f(4)$, find the y-value when $x = 4$. We see from the graph that when $x = 4$, y or $f(x) = 2$. Thus, $f(4) = 2$.

b. $f(-2) = 1$ from the ordered pair $(-2, 1)$.

c. $g(5) = 3$ from the ordered pair $(5, 3)$.

d. $g(0) = 0$ from the ordered pair $(0, 0)$.

e. To find x-values such that $f(x) = 1$, we are looking for any ordered pairs on the graph of f whose $f(x)$ or y-value is 1. They are $(2, 1)$ and $(-2, 1)$. Thus $f(2) = 1$ and $f(-2) = 1$. The x-values are 2 and -2.

f. Find ordered pairs on the graph of g whose $g(x)$ or y-value is 0. They are $(3, 0)$, $(0, 0)$, and $(-4, 0)$. Thus $g(3) = 0, g(0) = 0$, and $g(-4) = 0$. The x-values are 3, 0, and -4. □

PRACTICE

1 Given the graphs of the functions f and g, find each function value by inspecting the graphs.

a. $f(1)$ **b.** $f(0)$ **c.** $g(-2)$ **d.** $g(0)$

e. Find all x-values such that $f(x) = 1$.

f. Find all x-values such that $g(x) = -2$.

Many types of real-world paired data form functions. The broken-line graphs below and on the next page show the total and online enrollment in postsecondary institutions.

EXAMPLE 2 The following graph shows the total and online enrollments in postsecondary institutions as functions of time.

 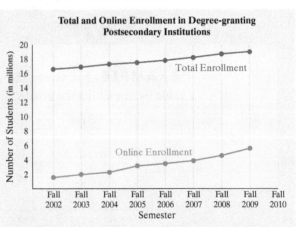

Source: Projections of Education Statistics to 2018, National Center for Education Statistics

a. Approximate the total enrollment in fall 2009.

b. In fall 2002, the total enrollment was 16.6 million students. Find the increase in total enrollment from fall 2002 to fall 2009.

Solution

a. Find the semester fall 2009 and move upward until you reach the top broken-line graph. From the point on the graph, move horizontally to the left until the vertical axis is reached. In fall 2009, approximately 19 million students, or 19,000,000 students, were enrolled in degree-granting postsecondary institutions.

b. The increase from fall 2002 to fall 2009 is 19 million − 16.6 million = 2.4 million or 2,400,000 students. □

PRACTICE
2   Use the graph in Example 2 and approximate the total enrollment in fall 2003.

Notice that each graph separately in Example 2 is the graph of a function since for each semester there is only one total enrollment and only one online enrollment. Also notice that each graph resembles the graph of a line. Often, businesses depend on equations that closely fit data-defined functions like this one to model the data and predict future trends. For example, by a method called **least squares,** the function $f(x) = 0.34x + 16$ approximates the data for the red graph, and the function $f(x) = 0.55x + 0.3$ approximates the data for the blue graph. For each function, x is the number of years since 2000, and $f(x)$ is the number of students (in millions). The graphs and the data functions are shown next.

> ▶ **Helpful Hint**
> Each function graphed is the graph of a function and passes the vertical line test.

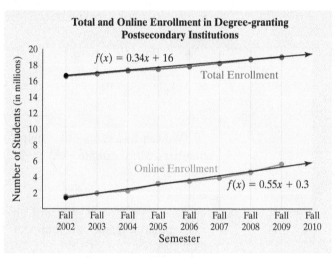

Total and Online Enrollment in Degree-granting Postsecondary Institutions

Source: Projections of Education Statistics to 2018, National Center for Education Statistics

EXAMPLE 3   Use the function $f(x) = 0.34x + 16$ and the discussion following Example 2 to estimate the total enrollment in degree-granting postsecondary institutions for fall 2010.

Solution   To estimate the total enrollment in fall 2010, remember that x represents the number of years since 2000, so $x = 2010 - 2000 = 10$. Use $f(x) = 0.34x + 16$ and find $f(10)$.

$$f(x) = 0.34x + 16$$
$$f(10) = 0.34(10) + 16$$
$$= 19.4$$

We estimate that in the fall 2010 semester, the total enrollment was 19.4 million, or 19,400,000 students. □

PRACTICE
3   Use $f(x) = 0.55x + 0.3$ to approximate the online enrollment in fall 2010.

OBJECTIVE

2   Finding Square Roots of Numbers

Later in this section, we graph the square root function, $f(x) = \sqrt{x}$. To prepare for this graph, let's review finding square roots of numbers.

The opposite of squaring a number is taking the **square root** of a number. For example, since the square of 4, or 4^2, is 16, we say that a square root of 16 is 4. The notation $\sqrt{a}$ is used to denote the **positive, or principal, square root** of a nonnegative number a. We then have in symbols that $\sqrt{16} = 4$. The negative square root of 16 is written $-\sqrt{16} = -4$. The square root of a negative number, such as $\sqrt{-16}$, is not a real number. Why? There is no real number that, when squared, gives a negative number.

EXAMPLE 4   Find the square roots.

a. $\sqrt{9}$ **b.** $\sqrt{25}$ **c.** $\sqrt{\dfrac{1}{4}}$ **d.** $-\sqrt{36}$ **e.** $\sqrt{-36}$ **f.** $\sqrt{0}$

Solution

a. $\sqrt{9} = 3$ since 3 is positive and $3^2 = 9$.   **b.** $\sqrt{25} = 5$ since $5^2 = 25$.

c. $\sqrt{\dfrac{1}{4}} = \dfrac{1}{2}$ since $\left(\dfrac{1}{2}\right)^2 = \dfrac{1}{4}$.   **d.** $-\sqrt{36} = -6$

e. $\sqrt{-36}$ is not a real number.   **f.** $\sqrt{0} = 0$ since $0^2 = 0$.   □

PRACTICE

4   Find the square roots.

a. $\sqrt{121}$ **b.** $\sqrt{\dfrac{1}{16}}$ **c.** $-\sqrt{64}$ **d.** $\sqrt{-64}$ **e.** $\sqrt{100}$

We can find roots other than square roots. Also, not all roots simplify to rational numbers. For example, $\sqrt{3} \approx 1.7$ using a calculator. We study radicals further in Chapter 10.

OBJECTIVE

3   Graphing Nonlinear Functions

Let's practice graphing nonlinear functions. In this section, we graph by plotting enough ordered pair solutions until we see a pattern. In the next section, we learn about shifting and reflecting of graphs.

EXAMPLE 5   Graph $f(x) = x^2$.

Solution   This equation is not linear because the x^2 term does not allow us to write it in the form $Ax + By = C$. Its graph is not a line. We begin by finding ordered pair solutions. Because $f(x) = y$, feel free to think of this equation as $f(x) = x^2$ or $y = x^2$. This graph is solved for y, so we choose x-values and find corresponding y-values.

If $x = -3$, then $f(-3) = (-3)^2$, or 9.

If $x = -2$, then $f(-2) = (-2)^2$, or 4.

If $x = -1$, then $f(-1) = (-1)^2$, or 1.

If $x = 0$, then $f(0) = 0^2$, or 0.

If $x = 1$, then $f(1) = 1^2$, or 1.

If $x = 2$, then $f(2) = 2^2$, or 4.

If $x = 3$, then $f(3) = 3^2$, or 9.

x	y or $f(x)$
-3	9
-2	4
-1	1
0	0
1	1
2	4
3	9

Study the table a moment and look for patterns. Notice that the ordered pair solution $(0, 0)$ contains the smallest y-value because any other x-value squared will give a positive result. This means that the point $(0, 0)$ will be the lowest point on the graph.

Also notice that all other *y*-values correspond to two different *x*-values. For example, $3^2 = 9$ and also $(-3)^2 = 9$. This means that the graph will be a mirror image of itself across the *y*-axis. Connect the plotted points with a smooth curve to sketch the graph.

This curve is given a special name, a **parabola.** We will study more about parabolas in later chapters.   ☐

PRACTICE
5   Graph $f(x) = 2x^2$.

EXAMPLE 6   Graph the nonlinear function $f(x) = |x|$.

Solution   This is not a linear equation since it cannot be written in the form $Ax + By = C$. Its graph is not a line. Because we do not know the shape of this graph, we find many ordered pair solutions. We will choose *x*-values and substitute to find corresponding *y*-values.

If $x = -3$, then $f(-3) = |-3|$, or 3.

If $x = -2$, then $f(-2) = |-2|$, or 2.

If $x = -1$, then $f(-1) = |-1|$, or 1.

If $x = 0$, then $f(0) = |0|$, or 0.

If $x = 1$, then $f(1) = |1|$, or 1.

If $x = 2$, then $f(2) = |2|$, or 2.

If $x = 3$, then $f(3) = |3|$, or 3.

x	y or f(x)
−3	3
−2	2
−1	1
0	0
1	1
2	2
3	3

Again, study the table of values for a moment and notice any patterns.

From the plotted ordered pairs, we see that the graph of this absolute value equation is V-shaped.   ☐

PRACTICE
6   Graph $f(x) = -|x|$.

EXAMPLE 7   Graph the nonlinear function $f(x) = \sqrt{x}$.

Solution   To graph this square root function, we identify the domain, evaluate the function for several values of *x*, plot the resulting points, and connect the points with a smooth curve. Since $\sqrt{x}$ represents the nonnegative square root of *x*, the domain of this function is the set of all nonnegative numbers, $\{x | x \geq 0\}$, or $[0, \infty)$. We have approximated $\sqrt{3}$ below to help us locate the point corresponding to $(3, \sqrt{3})$.

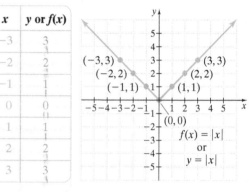

If $x = 0$, then $f(0) = \sqrt{0}$, or 0.

If $x = 1$, then $f(1) = \sqrt{1}$, or 1.

If $x = 3$, then $f(3) = \sqrt{3}$, or 1.7.

If $x = 4$, then $f(4) = \sqrt{4}$, or 2.

If $x = 9$, then $f(9) = \sqrt{9}$, or 3.

x	y or f(x)
0	0
1	1
3	$\sqrt{3} \approx 1.7$
4	2
9	3

PRACTICE
7   Graph $f(x) = \sqrt{x} + 1$.

Graphing Calculator Explorations

It is possible to use a graphing calculator to sketch the graph of more than one equation on the same set of axes. For example, graph the functions $f(x) = x^2$ and $g(x) = x^2 + 4$ on the same set of axes.

To graph on the same set of axes, press the $\boxed{Y =}$ key and enter the equations on the first two lines.

$$Y_1 = x^2$$

$$Y_2 = x^2 + 4$$

Then press the $\boxed{\text{GRAPH}}$ key as usual. The screen should look like this.

Notice that the graph of y or $g(x) = x^2 + 4$ is the graph of $y = x^2$ moved 4 units upward.

Graph each pair of functions on the same set of axes.

1. $f(x) = |x|$ **2.** $f(x) = x^2$

   $g(x) = |x| + 1$ $h(x) = x^2 - 5$

3. $f(x) = x$ **4.** $f(x) = |x|$

   $H(x) = x - 6$ $G(x) = |x| + 3$

5. $f(x) = -x^2$ **6.** $f(x) = x$

   $F(x) = -x^2 + 7$ $F(x) = x + 2$

Vocabulary, Readiness & Video Check

Use the choices below to fill in each blank. Some choices may not be used.

(1.7, −2)	line	parabola	−6	−9
(−2, 1.7)	V-shaped	6	9	

1. The graph of $y = |x|$ looks _____ .

2. The graph of $y = x^2$ is a _____ .

3. If $f(-2) = 1.7$, the corresponding ordered pair is _____ .

4. If $f(x) = x^2$, then $f(-3) =$ _____ .

Martin-Gay Interactive Videos

See Video 8.2

Watch the section lecture video and answer the following questions.

OBJECTIVE
1

5. From Examples 1 and 2, what is the connection between function notation to evaluate a function at certain values and ordered pair solutions of the function?

OBJECTIVE
2

6. Explain why Example 6 does not simplify to a real number.

OBJECTIVE
3

7. Based on Examples 7, 8, and 9, complete the following statements. When graphing a nonlinear equation, first recognize it as a nonlinear equation and know that the graph is _____ a line. If you don't know the _____ of the graph, plot enough points until you see a pattern.

8.2   Exercise Set   MyMathLab®

Use the graph of the following function f(x) to find each value. See Examples 1 and 2.

1. $f(1)$

2. $f(0)$

3. $f(-1)$

4. $f(2)$

5. Find x such that $f(x) = 4$.

6. Find x such that $f(x) = -6$.

Use the graph of the functions below to answer Exercises 7 through 18. See Examples 1 and 2.

7. If $f(1) = -10$, write the corresponding ordered pair.

8. If $f(-5) = -10$, write the corresponding ordered pair.

9. If $g(4) = 56$, write the corresponding ordered pair.

10. If $g(-2) = 8$, write the corresponding ordered pair.

11. Find $f(-1)$.

12. Find $f(-2)$.

13. Find $g(2)$.

14. Find $g(-4)$.

15. Find all values of x such that $f(x) = -5$.

16. Find all values of x such that $f(x) = -2$.

17. Find all positive values of x such that $g(x) = 4$.

18. Find all values of x such that $g(x) = 0$.

Find the following roots. See Example 4.

19. $\sqrt{49}$

20. $\sqrt{144}$

21. $-\sqrt{\dfrac{4}{9}}$

22. $-\sqrt{\dfrac{4}{25}}$

23. $\sqrt{64}$

24. $\sqrt{4}$

25. $\sqrt{81}$

26. $\sqrt{1}$

27. $\sqrt{-100}$

28. $\sqrt{-25}$

MIXED PRACTICE

Graph each function by finding and plotting ordered pair solutions. See Examples 5 through 7.

29. $f(x) = x^2 + 3$

30. $g(x) = (x + 2)^2$

31. $h(x) = |x| - 2$

32. $f(x) = |x - 2|$

33. $g(x) = 2x^2$

34. $h(x) = 5x^2$

35. $f(x) = 5x - 1$

36. $g(x) = -3x + 2$

37. $f(x) = \sqrt{x + 1}$

38. $f(x) = \sqrt{x} - 1$

39. $g(x) = -2|x|$

40. $g(x) = -3|x|$

41. $h(x) = \sqrt{x} + 2$

42. $h(x) = \sqrt{x + 2}$

Use the graph on page 520 to answer the following. Also see Example 3.

43. a. Use the graph to approximate the online enrollment in fall 2009.

   b. The function $f(x) = 0.55x + 0.3$ approximates the online enrollment (in millions). Use this function to approximate the online enrollment in fall 2009.

44. a. Use the graph to approximate the total enrollment in fall 2008.

   b. The function $f(x) = 0.34x + 16$ approximates the total enrollment (in millions). Use this function to approximate the total enrollment in fall 2008.

The function $f(x) = 0.42x + 10.5$ can be used to predict diamond production. For this function, x is the number of years after 2000, and f(x) is the value (in billions of dollars) of diamond production.

45. Use the function in the directions above to estimate diamond production in 2012.

46. Use the function in the directions above to predict diamond production in 2015.

The function $A(r) = \pi r^2$ may be used to find the area of a circle if we are given its radius.

△ **47.** Find the area of a circle whose radius is 5 centimeters. (Do not approximate π.)

△ **48.** Find the area of a circular garden whose radius is 8 feet. (Do not approximate π.)

The function $V(x) = x^3$ may be used to find the volume of a cube if we are given the length x of a side.

49. Find the volume of a cube whose side is 14 inches.

50. Find the volume of a die whose side is 1.7 centimeters.

Forensic scientists use the following functions to find the height of a woman if they are given the height of her femur bone f or her tibia bone t in centimeters.

$$H(f) = 2.59f + 47.24$$

$$H(t) = 2.72t + 61.28$$

46 cm Femur   35 cm Tibia

51. Find the height of a woman whose femur measures 46 centimeters.

52. Find the height of a woman whose tibia measures 35 centimeters.

The dosage in milligrams D of Ivermectin, a heartworm preventive, for a dog who weighs x pounds is given by

$$D(x) = \frac{136}{25}x$$

53. Find the proper dosage for a dog that weighs 30 pounds.

54. Find the proper dosage for a dog that weighs 50 pounds.

55. What is the greatest number of x-intercepts that a function may have? Explain your answer.

56. What is the greatest number of y-intercepts that a function may have? Explain your answer.

REVIEW AND PREVIEW

Solve the following equations. See Section 2.3.

57. $3(x - 2) + 5x = 6x - 16$

58. $5 + 7(x + 1) = 12 + 10x$

59. $3x + \frac{2}{5} = \frac{1}{10}$

60. $\frac{1}{6} + 2x = \frac{2}{3}$

CONCEPT EXTENSIONS

For Exercises 61 through 64, match each description with the graph that best illustrates it.

61. Moe worked 40 hours per week until the fall semester started. He quit and didn't work again until he worked 60 hours a week during the holiday season starting mid-December.

62. Kawana worked 40 hours a week for her father during the summer. She slowly cut back her hours to not working at all during the fall semester. During the holiday season in December, she started working again and increased her hours to 60 hours per week.

63. Wendy worked from July through February, never quitting. She worked between 10 and 30 hours per week.

64. Bartholomew worked from July through February. During the holiday season between mid-November and the beginning of January, he worked 40 hours per week. The rest of the time, he worked between 10 and 40 hours per week.

a. **b.** **c.** **d.**

This broken-line graph shows the hourly minimum wage and the years it increased. Use this graph for Exercises 65 through 68.

The Federal Hourly Minimum Wage

Source: U.S. Department of Labor

65. What was the first year that the minimum hourly wage rose above $5.00?

66. What was the first year that the minimum hourly wage rose above $6.00?

67. Why do you think that this graph is shaped the way it is?

68. The federal hourly minimum wage started in 1938 at $0.25. How much has it increased by 2011?

69. Graph $y = x^2 - 4x + 7$. Let $x = 0, 1, 2, 3, 4$ to generate ordered pair solutions.

70. Graph $y = x^2 + 2x + 3$. Let $x = -3, -2, -1, 0, 1$ to generate ordered pair solutions.

71. The function $f(x) = [x]$ is called the greatest integer function and its graph is similar to the graph above. The value of $[x]$ is the greatest integer less than or equal to x. For example, $f(1.5) = [1.5] = 1$ since the greatest integer ≤ 1.5 is 1. Sketch the graph of $f(x) = [x]$.

Integrated Review   SUMMARY ON FUNCTIONS AND EQUATIONS OF LINES

Sections 8.1–8.2

Find the slope and y-intercept of the graph of each function.

1. $f(x) = 3x - 5$

2. $f(x) = \dfrac{5}{2}x - \dfrac{7}{2}$

Determine whether each pair of lines is parallel, perpendicular, or neither.

3. $f(x) = 8x - 6$
$g(x) = 8x + 6$

4. $f(x) = \dfrac{2}{3}x + 1$
$2y + 3x = 1$

Find the equation of each line. Write the equation using function notation.

5. Through $(1, 6)$ and $(5, 2)$

6. Through $(2, -8)$ and $(-6, -5)$

7. Through $(-1, -5)$; parallel to $3x - y = 5$

8. Through $(0, 4)$; perpendicular to $4x - 5y = 10$

9. Through $(2, -3)$; perpendicular to $4x + y = \dfrac{2}{3}$

10. Through $(-1, 0)$; parallel to $5x + 2y = 2$

Determine whether each function is linear or not. Then graph the function.

11. $f(x) = 4x - 2$

12. $f(x) = 6x - 5$

13. $g(x) = |x| + 3$

14. $h(x) = |x| + 2$

15. $f(x) = 2x^2$

16. $F(x) = 3x^2$

17. $h(x) = x^2 - 3$

18. $G(x) = x^2 + 3$

19. $F(x) = -2x$

20. $H(x) = -3x$

21. $G(x) = |x + 2|$

22. $g(x) = |x - 1|$

23. $f(x) = \dfrac{1}{3}x - 1$

24. $f(x) = \dfrac{1}{2}x - 3$

25. $g(x) = -\dfrac{3}{2}x + 1$

26. $G(x) = -\dfrac{2}{3}x + 1$

Inequalities and Absolute Value

Today, it seems that most people in the world want to stay connected most of the time. In fact, 86% of U.S. citizens own cell phones. Also, computers with Internet access are just as important in our lives. Thus, the merging of these two into Wi-Fi-enabled cell phones might be the next big technological explosion. In Section 9.3, Exercises 83 and 84, you will find the projected increase in the number of Wi-Fi-enabled cell phones in the United States as well as the percent increase. (*Source:* Techcrunchies.com)

Mathematics is a tool for solving problems in such diverse fields as transportation, engineering, economics, medicine, business, and biology. We solve problems using mathematics by modeling real-world phenomena with mathematical equations or inequalities. Our ability to solve problems using mathematics, then, depends in part on our ability to solve different types of equations and inequalities. This chapter includes solving absolute value equations and inequalities and other types of inequalities.

Projected Growth of Wi-Fi-Enabled Cell Phones in the U.S.

Compound Inequalities

Two inequalities joined by the words **and** or **or** are called **compound inequalities.**

Compound Inequalities

$$x + 3 < 8 \quad and \quad x > 2$$

$$\frac{2x}{3} \geq 5 \quad or \quad -x + 10 < 7$$

OBJECTIVE

1 Finding the Intersection of Two Sets

The solution set of a compound inequality formed by the word **and** is the **intersection** of the solution sets of the two inequalities. We use the symbol ∩ to represent "intersection."

Intersection of Two Sets

The intersection of two sets, A and B, is the set of all elements common to both sets. A intersect B is denoted by A ∩ B.

EXAMPLE 1   If $A = \{x \mid x$ is an even number greater than 0 and less than 10$\}$ and $B = \{3, 4, 5, 6\}$, find $A \cap B$.

Solution   Let's list the elements in set A.

$$A = \{2, 4, 6, 8\}$$

The numbers 4 and 6 are in sets A and B. The intersection is $\{4, 6\}$.

PRACTICE

1   If $A = \{x \mid x$ is an odd number greater than 0 and less than 10$\}$ and $B = \{1, 2, 3, 4\}$, find $A \cap B$.

OBJECTIVE

2 Solving Compound Inequalities Containing "and"

A value is a solution of a compound inequality formed by the word **and** if it is a solution of *both* inequalities. For example, the solution set of the compound inequality $x \leq 5$ and $x \geq 3$ contains all values of x that make the inequality $x \leq 5$ a true statement **and** the inequality $x \geq 3$ a true statement. The first graph shown below is the graph of $x \leq 5$, the second graph is the graph of $x \geq 3$, and the third graph shows the intersection of the two graphs. The third graph is the graph of $x \leq 5$ **and** $x \geq 3$.

$\{x \mid x \leq 5\}$ $(-\infty, 5]$

$\{x \mid x \geq 3\}$ $[3, \infty)$

$\{x \mid x \leq 5 \text{ and } x \geq 3\}$ $[3, 5]$
also $\{x \mid 3 \leq x \leq 5\}$
(see below)

Since $x \geq 3$ is the same as $3 \leq x$, the compound inequality $3 \leq x$ and $x \leq 5$ can be written in a more compact form as $3 \leq x \leq 5$. The solution set $\{x \mid 3 \leq x \leq 5\}$ includes all numbers that are greater than or equal to 3 and at the same time less than or equal to 5.

In interval notation, the set $\{x \mid x \leq 5 \text{ and } x \geq 3\}$ or the set $\{x \mid 3 \leq x \leq 5\}$ is written as $[3, 5]$.

> ▶ Helpful Hint
>
> Don't forget that some compound inequalities containing "and" can be written in a more compact form.

Compound Inequality	Compact Form	Interval Notation
$2 \leq x \text{ and } x \leq 6$	$2 \leq x \leq 6$	$[2, 6]$

Graph:

EXAMPLE 2   Solve: $x - 7 < 2 \text{ and } 2x + 1 < 9$

Solution   First we solve each inequality separately.

$$x - 7 < 2 \quad \text{and} \quad 2x + 1 < 9$$
$$x < 9 \quad \text{and} \quad 2x < 8$$
$$x < 9 \quad \text{and} \quad x < 4$$

Now we can graph the two intervals on two number lines and find their intersection. Their intersection is shown on the third number line.

$\{x \,|\, x < 9\}$ $(-\infty, 9)$

$\{x \,|\, x < 4\}$ $(-\infty, 4)$

$\{x \,|\, x < 9 \text{ and } x < 4\} = \{x \,|\, x < 4\}$ $(-\infty, 4)$

The solution set is $(-\infty, 4)$.

PRACTICE

2   Solve: $x + 3 < 8 \text{ and } 2x - 1 < 3$. Write the solution set in interval notation.

EXAMPLE 3   Solve: $2x \geq 0 \text{ and } 4x - 1 \leq -9$.

Solution   First we solve each inequality separately.

$$2x \geq 0 \quad \text{and} \quad 4x - 1 \leq -9$$
$$x \geq 0 \quad \text{and} \quad 4x \leq -8$$
$$x \geq 0 \quad \text{and} \quad x \leq -2$$

Now we can graph the two intervals and find their intersection.

$\{x \,|\, x \geq 0\}$ $[0, \infty)$

$\{x \,|\, x \leq -2\}$ $(-\infty, -2]$

$\{x \,|\, x \geq 0 \text{ and } x \leq -2\} = \varnothing$ $\varnothing$

There is no number that is greater than or equal to 0 *and* less than or equal to -2. The solution set is $\varnothing$.

PRACTICE

3   Solve: $4x \leq 0 \text{ and } 3x + 2 > 8$. Write the solution set in interval notation.

> ▶ Helpful Hint
>
> Example 3 shows that some compound inequalities have no solution. Also, some have all real numbers as solutions.

To solve a compound inequality written in a compact form, such as $2 < 4 - x < 7$, we get x alone in the "middle part." Since a compound inequality is really two inequalities in one statement, we must perform the same operations on all three parts of the inequality. For example:

$$2 < 4 - x < 7 \quad \text{means} \quad 2 < 4 - x \quad and \quad 4 - x < 7.$$

EXAMPLE 4 Solve: $2 < 4 - x < 7$

Solution To get x alone, we first subtract 4 from all three parts.

$$2 < 4 - x < 7$$

$$2 - 4 < 4 - x - 4 < 7 - 4 \qquad \text{Subtract 4 from all three parts.}$$

$$-2 < -x < 3 \qquad\qquad\qquad \text{Simplify.}$$

$$\frac{-2}{-1} > \frac{-x}{-1} > \frac{3}{-1} \qquad\qquad \text{Divide all three parts by } -1 \text{ and reverse the inequality symbols.}$$

$$2 > x > -3$$

> **Helpful Hint**
> Don't forget to reverse both inequality symbols.

This is equivalent to $-3 < x < 2$.

The solution set in interval notation is $(-3, 2)$, and its graph is shown.

PRACTICE
4 Solve: $3 < 5 - x < 9$. Write the solution set in interval notation.

EXAMPLE 5 Solve: $-1 \leq \dfrac{2x}{3} + 5 \leq 2$.

Solution First, clear the inequality of fractions by multiplying all three parts by the LCD 3.

$$-1 \leq \frac{2x}{3} + 5 \leq 2$$

$$3(-1) \leq 3\left(\frac{2x}{3} + 5\right) \leq 3(2) \qquad \text{Multiply all three parts by the LCD 3.}$$

$$-3 \leq 2x + 15 \leq 6 \qquad\qquad \text{Use the distributive property and multiply.}$$

$$-3 - 15 \leq 2x + 15 - 15 \leq 6 - 15 \qquad \text{Subtract 15 from all three parts.}$$

$$-18 \leq 2x \leq -9 \qquad\qquad \text{Simplify.}$$

$$\frac{-18}{2} \leq \frac{2x}{2} \leq \frac{-9}{2} \qquad\qquad \text{Divide all three parts by 2.}$$

$$-9 \leq x \leq -\frac{9}{2} \qquad\qquad \text{Simplify.}$$

The graph of the solution is shown.

The solution set in interval notation is $\left[-9, -\dfrac{9}{2}\right]$.

PRACTICE
5 Solve: $-4 \leq \dfrac{x}{2} - 1 \leq 3$. Write the solution set in interval notation.

OBJECTIVE
3   Finding the Union of Two Sets

The solution set of a compound inequality formed by the word **or** is the **union** of the solution sets of the two inequalities. We use the symbol $\cup$ to denote "union."

> ▶ Helpful Hint
>
> The word *either* in this definition means "one or the other or both."

Union of Two Sets

The **union** of two sets, A and B, is the set of elements that belong to *either* of the sets. A union B is denoted by $A \cup B$.

$$A \quad B$$
$$\underbrace{}$$
$$A \cup B$$

EXAMPLE 6   If $A = \{x \mid x \text{ is an even number greater than 0 and less than 10}\}$ and $B = \{3, 4, 5, 6\}$, find $A \cup B$.

Solution   Recall from Example 1 that $A = \{2, 4, 6, 8\}$. The numbers that are in either set or both sets are $\{2, 3, 4, 5, 6, 8\}$. This set is the union. □

PRACTICE
6   If $A = \{x \mid x \text{ is an odd number greater than 0 and less than 10}\}$ and $B = \{2, 3, 4, 5, 6\}$, find $A \cup B$.

OBJECTIVE
4   Solving Compound Inequalities Containing "or"

A value is a solution of a compound inequality formed by the word **or** if it is a solution of **either** inequality. For example, the solution set of the compound inequality $x \leq 1$ **or** $x \geq 3$ contains all numbers that make the inequality $x \leq 1$ a true statement **or** the inequality $x \geq 3$ a true statement.

$\{x \mid x \leq 1\}$		$(-\infty, 1]$
$\{x \mid x \geq 3\}$		$[3, \infty)$
$\{x \mid x \leq 1 \text{ or } x \geq 3\}$		$(-\infty, 1] \cup [3, \infty)$

In interval notation, the set $\{x \mid x \leq 1 \text{ or } x \geq 3\}$ is written as $(-\infty, 1] \cup [3, \infty)$.

EXAMPLE 7   Solve: $5x - 3 \leq 10 \text{ or } x + 1 \geq 5$.

Solution   First we solve each inequality separately.

$$5x - 3 \leq 10 \quad \text{or} \quad x + 1 \geq 5$$
$$5x \leq 13 \quad \text{or} \quad x \geq 4$$
$$x \leq \frac{13}{5} \quad \text{or} \quad x \geq 4$$

Now we can graph each interval and find their union.

$\left\{x \mid x \leq \dfrac{13}{5}\right\}$		$\left(-\infty, \dfrac{13}{5}\right]$
$\{x \mid x \geq 4\}$		$[4, \infty)$
$\left\{x \mid x \leq \dfrac{13}{5} \text{ or } x \geq 4\right\}$		$\left(-\infty, \dfrac{13}{5}\right] \cup [4, \infty)$

(Continued on next page)

The solution set is $\left(-\infty, \dfrac{13}{5}\right] \cup [4, \infty)$.

PRACTICE
7 Solve: $8x + 5 \le 8 \text{ or } x - 1 \ge 2$. Write the solution set in interval notation.

EXAMPLE 8 Solve: $-2x - 5 < -3 \text{ or } 6x < 0$.

Solution First we solve each inequality separately.

$$-2x - 5 < -3 \quad \text{or} \quad 6x < 0$$
$$-2x < 2 \quad \text{or} \quad x < 0$$
$$x > -1 \quad \text{or} \quad x < 0$$

Now we can graph each interval and find their union.

$\{x \mid x > -1\}$ $(-1, \infty)$

$\{x \mid x < 0\}$ $(-\infty, 0)$

$\{x \mid x > -1 \text{ or } x < 0\}$ $(-\infty, \infty)$

= all real numbers

The solution set is $(-\infty, \infty)$.

PRACTICE
8 Solve: $-3x - 2 > -8 \text{ or } 5x > 0$. Write the solution set in interval notation.

✓CONCEPT CHECK
Which of the following is *not* a correct way to represent the set of all numbers between -3 and 5?
a. $\{x \mid -3 < x < 5\}$ **b.** $-3 < x \text{ or } x < 5$
c. $(-3, 5)$ **d.** $x > -3 \text{ and } x < 5$

Answer to Concept Check:
b is not correct

Vocabulary, Readiness & Video Check

Use the choices below to fill in each blank.

or	$\cup$	$\varnothing$
and	$\cap$	compound

1. Two inequalities joined by the words "and" or "or" are called _____ inequalities.
2. The word _____ means intersection.
3. The word _____ means union.
4. The symbol _____ represents intersection.
5. The symbol _____ represents union.
6. The symbol _____ is the empty set.

Martin-Gay Interactive Videos

See Video 9.1

Watch the section lecture video and answer the following questions.

OBJECTIVE 1

7. Based on Example 1 and the lecture before, complete the following statement. For an element to be in the intersection of sets A and B, the element must be in set A ——————— in set B.

OBJECTIVE 2

8. In Example 2, how can using three number lines help us find the solution to this "and" compound inequality?

OBJECTIVE 3

9. Based on Example 4 and the lecture before, complete the following statement. For an element to be in the union of sets A and B, the element must be in set A ——————— in set B.

OBJECTIVE 4

10. In Example 5, how can using three number lines help us find the solution to this "or" compound inequality?

9.1   Exercise Set   MyMathLab®

MIXED PRACTICE

If $A = \{x \mid x$ is an even integer$\}$, $B = \{x \mid x$ is an odd integer$\}$, $C = \{2, 3, 4, 5\}$, and $D = \{4, 5, 6, 7\}$, list the elements of each set. See Examples 1 and 6.

1. $C \cup D$
2. $C \cap D$
3. $A \cap D$
4. $A \cup D$
5. $A \cup B$
6. $A \cap B$
7. $B \cap D$
8. $B \cup D$
9. $B \cup C$
10. $B \cap C$
11. $A \cap C$
12. $A \cup C$

Solve each compound inequality. Graph the solution set and write it in interval notation. See Examples 2 and 3.

13. $x < 1$ and $x > -3$
14. $x \leq 0$ and $x \geq -2$
15. $x \leq -3$ and $x \geq -2$
16. $x < 2$ and $x > 4$
17. $x < -1$ and $x < 1$
18. $x \geq -4$ and $x > 1$

Solve each compound inequality. Write solutions in interval notation. See Examples 2 and 3.

19. $x + 1 \geq 7$ and $3x - 1 \geq 5$
20. $x + 2 \geq 3$ and $5x - 1 \geq 9$
21. $4x + 2 \leq -10$ and $2x \leq 0$
22. $2x + 4 > 0$ and $4x > 0$
23. $-2x < -8$ and $x - 5 < 5$
24. $-7x \leq -21$ and $x - 20 \leq -15$

Solve each compound inequality. See Examples 4 and 5.

25. $5 < x - 6 < 11$
26. $-2 \leq x + 3 \leq 0$
27. $-2 \leq 3x - 5 \leq 7$
28. $1 < 4 + 2x < 7$
29. $1 \leq \frac{2}{3}x + 3 \leq 4$
30. $-2 < \frac{1}{2}x - 5 < 1$

31. $-5 \leq \frac{-3x + 1}{4} \leq 2$
32. $-4 \leq \frac{-2x + 5}{3} \leq 1$

Solve each compound inequality. Graph the solution set and write it in interval notation. See Examples 7 and 8.

33. $x < 4$ or $x < 5$
34. $x \geq -2$ or $x \leq 2$
35. $x \leq -4$ or $x \geq 1$
36. $x < 0$ or $x < 1$
37. $x > 0$ or $x < 3$
38. $x \geq -3$ or $x \leq -4$

Solve each compound inequality. Write solutions in interval notation. See Examples 7 and 8.

39. $-2x \leq -4$ or $5x - 20 \geq 5$
40. $-5x \leq 10$ or $3x - 5 \geq 1$
41. $x + 4 < 0$ or $6x > -12$
42. $x + 9 < 0$ or $4x > -12$
43. $3(x - 1) < 12$ or $x + 7 > 10$
44. $5(x - 1) \geq -5$ or $5 + x \leq 11$

MIXED PRACTICE

Solve each compound inequality. Write solutions in interval notation. See Examples 1 through 8.

45. $x < \frac{2}{3}$ and $x > -\frac{1}{2}$
46. $x < \frac{5}{7}$ and $x < 1$
47. $x < \frac{2}{3}$ or $x > -\frac{1}{2}$
48. $x < \frac{5}{7}$ or $x < 1$
49. $0 \leq 2x - 3 \leq 9$
50. $3 < 5x + 1 < 11$

51. $\frac{1}{2} < x - \frac{3}{4} < 2$

52. $\frac{2}{3} < x + \frac{1}{2} < 4$

53. $x + 3 \geq 3$ and $x + 3 \leq 2$

54. $2x - 1 \geq 3$ and $-x > 2$

55. $3x \geq 5$ or $-\frac{5}{8}x - 6 > 1$

56. $\frac{3}{8}x + 1 \leq 0$ or $-2x < -4$

57. $0 < \frac{5 - 2x}{3} < 5$

58. $-2 < \frac{-2x - 1}{3} < 2$

59. $-6 < 3(x - 2) \leq 8$

60. $-5 < 2(x + 4) < 8$

61. $-x + 5 > 6$ and $1 + 2x \leq -5$

62. $5x \leq 0$ and $-x + 5 < 8$

63. $3x + 2 \leq 5$ or $7x > 29$

64. $-x < 7$ or $3x + 1 < -20$

65. $5 - x > 7$ and $2x + 3 \geq 13$

66. $-2x < -6$ or $1 - x > -2$

67. $-\frac{1}{2} \leq \frac{4x - 1}{6} < \frac{5}{6}$

68. $-\frac{1}{2} \leq \frac{3x - 1}{10} < \frac{1}{2}$

69. $\frac{1}{15} < \frac{8 - 3x}{15} < \frac{4}{5}$

70. $-\frac{1}{4} < \frac{6 - x}{12} < -\frac{1}{6}$

71. $0.3 < 0.2x - 0.9 < 1.5$

72. $-0.7 \leq 0.4x + 0.8 < 0.5$

REVIEW AND PREVIEW

Evaluate the following. See Sections 1.5 and 1.6.

73. $|-7| - |19|$

74. $|-7 - 19|$

75. $-(-6) - |-10|$

76. $|-4| - (-4) + |-20|$

Find by inspection all values for x that make each equation true.

77. $|x| = 7$

78. $|x| = 5$

79. $|x| = 0$

80. $|x| = -2$

CONCEPT EXTENSIONS

Use the graph to answer Exercises 81 and 82.

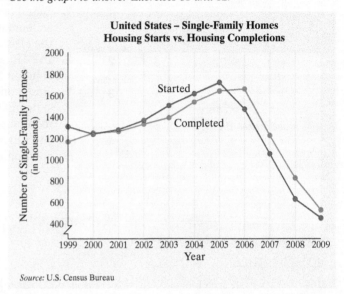

Source: U.S. Census Bureau

81. For which years were the number of single-family housing starts greater than 1500 and the number of single-family home completions greater than 1500?

82. For which years were the number of single-family housing starts less than 1000 or the number of single-family housing completions greater than 1500?

83. In your own words, describe how to find the union of two sets.

84. In your own words, describe how to find the intersection of two sets.

*Solve each compound inequality for x. See the example below. To solve $x - 6 < 3x < 2x + 5$, notice that this inequality contains a variable not only in the middle but also on the left and the right. When this occurs, we solve by rewriting the inequality using the word **and**.*

$$x - 6 < 3x \quad \text{and} \quad 3x < 2x + 5$$
$$-6 < 2x \quad \text{and} \quad x < 5$$
$$-3 < x$$
$$x > -3 \quad \text{and} \quad x < 5$$

$x > -3$

$x < 5$

$$-3 < x < 5 \text{ or } (-3, 5)$$

85. $2x - 3 < 3x + 1 < 4x - 5$

86. $x + 3 < 2x + 1 < 4x + 6$

87. $-3(x - 2) \leq 3 - 2x \leq 10 - 3x$

88. $7x - 1 \leq 7 + 5x \leq 3(1 + 2x)$

89. $5x - 8 < 2(2 + x) < -2(1 + 2x)$

90. $1 + 2x < 3(2 + x) < 1 + 4x$

The formula for converting Fahrenheit temperatures to Celsius temperatures is $C = \dfrac{5}{9}(F - 32)$. Use this formula for Exercises 91 and 92.

91. During a recent year, the temperatures in Chicago ranged from $-29°$C to $35°$C. Use a compound inequality to convert these temperatures to Fahrenheit temperatures.

92. In Oslo, the average temperature ranges from $-10°$ to $18°$ Celsius. Use a compound inequality to convert these temperatures to the Fahrenheit scale.

Solve.

93. Christian D'Angelo has scores of 68, 65, 75, and 78 on his algebra tests. Use a compound inequality to find the scores he can make on his final exam to receive a C in the course. The final exam counts as two tests, and a C is received if the final course average is from 70 to 79.

94. Wendy Wood has scores of 80, 90, 82, and 75 on her chemistry tests. Use a compound inequality to find the range of scores she can make on her final exam to receive a B in the course. The final exam counts as two tests, and a B is received if the final course average is from 80 to 89.

9.2 Absolute Value Equations

OBJECTIVE

1 Solve Absolute Value Equations.

OBJECTIVE

1 Solving Absolute Value Equations

In Chapter 1, we defined the absolute value of a number as its distance from 0 on a number line.

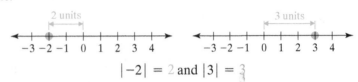

$$|-2| = 2 \text{ and } |3| = 3$$

In this section, we concentrate on solving equations containing the absolute value of a variable or a variable expression. Examples of absolute value equations are

$$|x| = 3 \qquad -5 = |2y + 7| \qquad |z - 6.7| = |3z + 1.2|$$

Since distance and absolute value are so closely related, absolute value equations and inequalities (see Section 9.3) are extremely useful in solving distance-type problems such as calculating the possible error in a measurement.

For the absolute value equation $|x| = 3$, its solution set will contain all numbers whose distance from 0 is 3 units. Two numbers are 3 units away from 0 on the number line: 3 and -3.

Thus, the solution set of the equation $|x| = 3$ is $\{3, -3\}$. This suggests the following:

Solving Equations of the Form $|X| = a$

If a is a positive number, then $|X| = a$ is equivalent to $X = a$ or $X = -a$.

EXAMPLE 1   Solve: $|p| = 2$.

Solution   Since 2 is positive, $|p| = 2$ is equivalent to $p = 2$ or $p = -2$.

To check, let $p = 2$ and then $p = -2$ in the original equation.

$|p| = 2$	Original equation		$|p| = 2$	Original equation
$|2| = 2$	Let $p = 2$.		$|-2| = 2$	Let $p = -2$.
$2 = 2$	True		$2 = 2$	True

The solutions are 2 and -2 or the solution set is $\{2, -2\}$.

PRACTICE

1   Solve: $|q| = 3$.

If the expression inside the absolute value bars is more complicated than a single variable, we can still apply the absolute value property.

> ▶ **Helpful Hint**
> For the equation $|X| = a$ in the box on the previous page, X can be a single variable or a variable expression.

EXAMPLE 2 Solve: $|5w + 3| = 7$.

Solution Here the expression inside the absolute value bars is $5w + 3$. If we think of the expression $5w + 3$ as X in the absolute value property, we see that $|X| = 7$ is equivalent to

$$X = 7 \quad \text{or} \quad X = -7$$

Then substitute $5w + 3$ for X, and we have

$$5w + 3 = 7 \quad \text{or} \quad 5w + 3 = -7$$

Solve these two equations for w.

$$
\begin{array}{rcl}
5w + 3 = 7 & \text{or} & 5w + 3 = -7 \\
5w = 4 & \text{or} & 5w = -10 \\
w = \dfrac{4}{5} & \text{or} & w = -2
\end{array}
$$

Check: To check, let $w = -2$ and then $w = \dfrac{4}{5}$ in the original equation.

$$
\begin{array}{cc}
\text{Let } w = -2 & \text{Let } w = \dfrac{4}{5} \\[2mm]
|5(-2) + 3| = 7 & \left|5\left(\dfrac{4}{5}\right) + 3\right| = 7 \\[2mm]
|-10 + 3| = 7 & |4 + 3| = 7 \\[1mm]
|-7| = 7 & |7| = 7 \\[1mm]
7 = 7 \quad \text{True} & 7 = 7 \quad \text{True}
\end{array}
$$

Both solutions check, and the solutions are -2 and $\dfrac{4}{5}$ or the solution set is $\left\{-2, \dfrac{4}{5}\right\}$. ☐

PRACTICE
2 Solve: $|2x - 3| = 5$.

EXAMPLE 3 Solve: $\left|\dfrac{x}{2} - 1\right| = 11$.

Solution $\left|\dfrac{x}{2} - 1\right| = 11$ is equivalent to

$$\dfrac{x}{2} - 1 = 11 \quad \text{or} \quad \dfrac{x}{2} - 1 = -11$$

$$2\left(\dfrac{x}{2} - 1\right) = 2(11) \quad \text{or} \quad 2\left(\dfrac{x}{2} - 1\right) = 2(-11) \quad \text{Clear fractions.}$$

$$x - 2 = 22 \quad \text{or} \quad x - 2 = -22 \quad \text{Apply the distributive property.}$$

$$x = 24 \quad \text{or} \quad x = -20$$

The solutions are 24 and -20. ☐

PRACTICE
3 Solve: $\left|\dfrac{x}{5} + 1\right| = 15$.

To apply the absolute value property, first make sure that the absolute value expression is isolated.

> ▶ Helpful Hint
>
> If the equation has a single absolute value expression containing variables, isolate the absolute value expression first.

EXAMPLE 4   Solve: $|2x| + 5 = 7$.

Solution   We want the absolute value expression alone on one side of the equation, so begin by subtracting 5 from both sides. Then apply the absolute value property.

$$|2x| + 5 = 7$$
$$|2x| = 2 \qquad \text{Subtract 5 from both sides.}$$
$$2x = 2 \quad \text{or} \quad 2x = -2$$
$$x = 1 \quad \text{or} \quad x = -1$$

The solutions are -1 and 1.

PRACTICE
4   Solve: $|3x| + 8 = 14$.

EXAMPLE 5   Solve: $|y| = 0$.

Solution   We are looking for all numbers whose distance from 0 is zero units. The only number is 0. The solution is 0.

PRACTICE
5   Solve: $|z| = 0$.

The next two examples illustrate a special case for absolute value equations. This special case occurs when an isolated absolute value is equal to a negative number.

EXAMPLE 6   Solve: $2|x| + 25 = 23$.

Solution   First, isolate the absolute value.

$$2|x| + 25 = 23$$
$$2|x| = -2 \quad \text{Subtract 25 from both sides.}$$
$$|x| = -1 \quad \text{Divide both sides by 2.}$$

The absolute value of a number is never negative, so this equation has no solution. The solution set is $\{\ \}$ or $\varnothing$.

PRACTICE
6   Solve: $3|z| + 9 = 7$.

EXAMPLE 7   Solve: $\left|\dfrac{3x + 1}{2}\right| = -2$.

Solution   Again, the absolute value of any expression is never negative, so no solution exists. The solution set is $\{\ \}$ or $\varnothing$.

PRACTICE
7   Solve: $\left|\dfrac{5x + 3}{4}\right| = -8$.

Given two absolute value expressions, we might ask, when are the absolute values of two expressions equal? To see the answer, notice that

$$|2| = |2|, \quad |-2| = |-2|, \quad |-2| = |2|, \quad \text{and} \quad |2| = |-2|$$

same   same   opposites   opposites

Two absolute value expressions are equal when the expressions inside the absolute value bars are equal to or are opposites of each other.

EXAMPLE 8   Solve: $|3x + 2| = |5x - 8|$.

Solution   This equation is true if the expressions inside the absolute value bars are equal to or are opposites of each other.

$$3x + 2 = 5x - 8 \quad \text{or} \quad 3x + 2 = -(5x - 8)$$

Next, solve each equation.

$$
\begin{aligned}
3x + 2 &= 5x - 8 &\quad \text{or} \quad 3x + 2 &= -5x + 8 \\
-2x + 2 &= -8 &\quad \text{or} \quad 8x + 2 &= 8 \\
-2x &= -10 &\quad \text{or} \quad 8x &= 6 \\
x &= 5 &\quad \text{or} \quad x &= \frac{3}{4}
\end{aligned}
$$

The solutions are $\frac{3}{4}$ and 5.

PRACTICE
8   Solve: $|2x + 4| = |3x - 1|$.

EXAMPLE 9   Solve: $|x - 3| = |5 - x|$.

Solution

$$
\begin{aligned}
x - 3 &= 5 - x &\quad \text{or} \quad x - 3 &= -(5 - x) \\
2x - 3 &= 5 &\quad \text{or} \quad x - 3 &= -5 + x \\
2x &= 8 &\quad \text{or} \quad x - 3 - x &= -5 + x - x \\
x &= 4 &\quad \text{or} \quad -3 &= -5 \quad \text{False}
\end{aligned}
$$

Recall from Section 2.3 that when an equation simplifies to a false statement, the equation has no solution. Thus, the only solution for the original absolute value equation is 4.

PRACTICE
9   Solve: $|x - 2| = |8 - x|$.

✓CONCEPT CHECK
True or false? Absolute value equations always have two solutions. Explain your answer.

The following box summarizes the methods shown for solving absolute value equations.

Absolute Value Equations

$|X| = a$
$\begin{cases} \text{If } a \text{ is positive, then solve } X = a \text{ or } X = -a. \\ \text{If } a \text{ is 0, solve } X = 0. \\ \text{If } a \text{ is negative, the equation } |X| = a \text{ has no solution.} \end{cases}$

$|X| = |Y|$ Solve $X = Y$ or $X = -Y$.

Vocabulary, Readiness & Video Check

Match each absolute value equation with an equivalent statement.

1. $|x - 2| = 5$
2. $|x - 2| = 0$
3. $|x - 2| = |x + 3|$
4. $|x + 3| = 5$
5. $|x + 3| = -5$

A. $x - 2 = 0$
B. $x - 2 = x + 3$ or $x - 2 = -(x + 3)$
C. $x - 2 = 5$ or $x - 2 = -5$
D. $\varnothing$
E. $x + 3 = 5$ or $x + 3 = -5$

Martin-Gay Interactive Videos

Watch the section lecture videos and answer the following question.

OBJECTIVE
1

6. As explained in Example 3, why is *a* positive in the rule "$|X| = a$ is equivalent to $X = a$ or $X = -a$"?

See Video 9.2

 9.2   Exercise Set   MyMathLab®

Solve each absolute value equation. See Examples 1 through 7.

1. $|x| = 7$
2. $|y| = 15$
3. $|3x| = 12.6$
4. $|6n| = 12.6$
5. $|2x - 5| = 9$
6. $|6 + 2n| = 4$
7. $\left|\dfrac{x}{2} - 3\right| = 1$
8. $\left|\dfrac{n}{3} + 2\right| = 4$
9. $|z| + 4 = 9$
10. $|x| + 1 = 3$
11. $|3x| + 5 = 14$
12. $|2x| - 6 = 4$
13. $|2x| = 0$
14. $|7z| = 0$
15. $|4n + 1| + 10 = 4$
16. $|3z - 2| + 8 = 1$
17. $|5x - 1| = 0$
18. $|3y + 2| = 0$

Solve. See Examples 8 and 9.

19. $|5x - 7| = |3x + 11|$
20. $|9y + 1| = |6y + 4|$
21. $|z + 8| = |z - 3|$
22. $|2x - 5| = |2x + 5|$

MIXED PRACTICE

Solve each absolute value equation. See Examples 1 through 9.

23. $|x| = 4$
24. $|x| = 1$
25. $|y| = 0$
26. $|y| = 8$
27. $|z| = -2$
28. $|y| = -9$
29. $|7 - 3x| = 7$
30. $|4m + 5| = 5$
31. $|6x| - 1 = 11$
32. $|7z| + 1 = 22$
33. $|4p| = -8$
34. $|5m| = -10$

35. $|x - 3| + 3 = 7$
36. $|x + 4| - 4 = 1$
37. $\left|\dfrac{z}{4} + 5\right| = -7$
38. $\left|\dfrac{c}{5} - 1\right| = -2$
39. $|9v - 3| = -8$
40. $|1 - 3b| = -7$
41. $|8n + 1| = 0$
42. $|5x - 2| = 0$
43. $|1 + 6c| - 7 = -3$
44. $|2 + 3m| - 9 = -7$
45. $|5x + 1| = 11$
46. $|8 - 6c| = 1$
47. $|4x - 2| = |-10|$
48. $|3x + 5| = |-4|$
49. $|5x + 1| = |4x - 7|$
50. $|3 + 6n| = |4n + 11|$
51. $|6 + 2x| = -|-7|$
52. $|4 - 5y| = -|-3|$
53. $|2x - 6| = |10 - 2x|$
54. $|4n + 5| = |4n + 3|$
55. $\left|\dfrac{2x - 5}{3}\right| = 7$
56. $\left|\dfrac{1 + 3n}{4}\right| = 4$
57. $2 + |5n| = 17$
58. $8 + |4m| = 24$
59. $\left|\dfrac{2x - 1}{3}\right| = |-5|$
60. $\left|\dfrac{5x + 2}{2}\right| = |-6|$
61. $|2y - 3| = |9 - 4y|$
62. $|5z - 1| = |7 - z|$
63. $\left|\dfrac{3n + 2}{8}\right| = |-1|$
64. $\left|\dfrac{2r - 6}{5}\right| = |-2|$
65. $|x + 4| = |7 - x|$
66. $|8 - y| = |y + 2|$
67. $\left|\dfrac{8c - 7}{3}\right| = -|-5|$
68. $\left|\dfrac{5d + 1}{6}\right| = -|-9|$

REVIEW AND PREVIEW

The circle graph shows the types of cheese produced in the United States in 2010. Use this graph to answer Exercises 69 through 72. See Section 2.6.

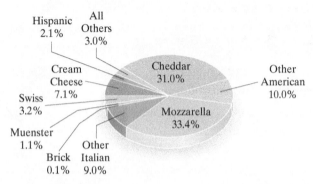

U.S. Cheese¹ Production by Variety, 2010

Hispanic 2.1%
All Others 3.0%
Cream Cheese 7.1%
Swiss 3.2%
Muenster 1.1%
Brick 0.1%
Other Italian 9.0%
Cheddar 31.0%
Mozzarella 33.4%
Other American 10.0%

¹Excludes Cottage Cheese

Source: USDA, *Dairy Products Annual Survey*

69. In 2010, cheddar cheese made up what percent of U.S. cheese production?

70. Which cheese had the highest U.S. production in 2010?

71. A circle contains 360°. Find the number of degrees found in the 9% sector for Other Italian Cheese.

72. In 2010, the total production of cheese in the United States was 10,109,293,000 pounds. Find the amount of cream cheese produced during that year.

List five integer solutions of each inequality. See Sections 1.2 and 1.4.

73. $|x| \leq 3$

74. $|x| \geq -2$

75. $|y| > -10$

76. $|y| < 0$

CONCEPT EXTENSIONS

Without going through a solution procedure, determine the solution of each absolute value equation or inequality.

77. $|x - 7| = -4$

78. $|x - 7| < -4$

79. Write an absolute value equation representing all numbers x whose distance from 0 is 5 units.

80. Write an absolute value equation representing all numbers x whose distance from 0 is 2 units.

81. Explain why some absolute value equations have two solutions.

82. Explain why some absolute value equations have one solution.

83. Write an absolute value equation representing all numbers x whose distance from 1 is 5 units.

84. Write an absolute value equation representing all numbers x whose distance from 7 is 2 units.

85. Describe how solving an absolute value equation such as $|2x - 1| = 3$ is similar to solving an absolute value equation such as $|2x - 1| = |x - 5|$.

86. Describe how solving an absolute value equation such as $|2x - 1| = 3$ is different from solving an absolute value equation such as $|2x - 1| = |x - 5|$.

Write each as an equivalent absolute value equation.

87. $x = 6$ or $x = -6$

88. $2x - 1 = 4$ or $2x - 1 = -4$

89. $x - 2 = 3x - 4$ or $x - 2 = -(3x - 4)$

90. For what value(s) of c will an absolute value equation of the form $|ax + b| = c$ have

a. one solution?

b. no solution?

c. two solutions?

9.3 | **Absolute Value Inequalities**

OBJECTIVES

1 Solve Absolute Value Inequalities of the Form $|X| < a$.

2 Solve Absolute Value Inequalities of the Form $|X| > a$.

OBJECTIVE

1 Solving Absolute Value Inequalities of the Form $|X| < a$

The solution set of an absolute value inequality such as $|x| < 2$ contains all numbers whose distance from 0 is less than 2 units, as shown below.

Distance from 0: less than 2 units
Distance from 0: less than 2 units

-3 -2 -1 0 1 2 3

The solution set is $\{x | -2 < x < 2\}$, or $(-2, 2)$ in interval notation.

EXAMPLE 1 Solve: $|x| \leq 3$ and graph the solution set.

Solution The solution set of this inequality contains all numbers whose distance from 0 is less than or equal to 3. Thus 3, -3, and all numbers between 3 and -3 are in the solution set.

The solution set is $[-3, 3]$.

PRACTICE
   1   Solve: $|x| < 5$ and graph the solution set.

In general, we have the following.

Solving Absolute Value Inequalities of the Form $|X| < a$

If a is a positive number, then $|X| < a$ is equivalent to $-a < X < a$.

This property also holds true for the inequality symbol $\leq$.

EXAMPLE 2   Solve for m: $|m - 6| < 2$. Graph the solution set.

Solution   Replace X with $m - 6$ and a with 2 in the preceding property, and we see that

$$|m - 6| < 2 \quad \text{is equivalent to} \quad -2 < m - 6 < 2$$

Solve this compound inequality for m by adding 6 to all three parts.

$$-2 < m - 6 < 2$$
$$-2 + 6 < m - 6 + 6 < 2 + 6 \quad \text{Add 6 to all three parts.}$$
$$4 < m < 8 \quad \text{Simplify.}$$

The solution set is $(4, 8)$, and its graph is shown.

PRACTICE
   2   Solve for b: $|b + 1| < 3$. Graph the solution set.

▶ **Helpful Hint**

Before using an absolute value inequality property, isolate the absolute value expression on one side of the inequality.

EXAMPLE 3   Solve for x: $|5x + 1| + 1 \leq 10$. Graph the solution set.

Solution   First, isolate the absolute value expression by subtracting 1 from both sides.

$$|5x + 1| + 1 \leq 10$$
$$|5x + 1| \leq 10 - 1 \quad \text{Subtract 1 from both sides.}$$
$$|5x + 1| \leq 9 \quad \text{Simplify.}$$

Since 9 is positive, we apply the absolute value property for $|X| \leq a$.

$$-9 \leq 5x + 1 \leq 9$$
$$-9 - 1 \leq 5x + 1 - 1 \leq 9 - 1 \quad \text{Subtract 1 from all three parts.}$$
$$-10 \leq 5x \leq 8 \quad \text{Simplify.}$$
$$-2 \leq x \leq \frac{8}{5} \quad \text{Divide all three parts by 5.}$$

The solution set is $\left[-2, \frac{8}{5}\right]$, and the graph is shown above.

PRACTICE
   3   Solve for x: $|3x - 2| + 5 \leq 9$. Graph the solution set.

EXAMPLE 4 Solve for x: $\left| 2x - \dfrac{1}{10} \right| < -13$.

Solution The absolute value of a number is always nonnegative and can never be less than -13. Thus this absolute value inequality has no solution. The solution set is $\{\ \}$ or $\varnothing$.

PRACTICE
4 Solve for x: $\left| 3x + \dfrac{5}{8} \right| < -4$.

EXAMPLE 5 Solve for x: $\left| \dfrac{2(x + 1)}{3} \right| \leq 0$.

Solution Recall that "$\leq$" means "is less than or equal to." The absolute value of any expression will never be less than 0, but it may be equal to 0. Thus, to solve $\left| \dfrac{2(x + 1)}{3} \right| \leq 0$, we solve $\left| \dfrac{2(x + 1)}{3} \right| = 0$

$$\frac{2(x + 1)}{3} = 0$$

$$3\left[\frac{2(x + 1)}{3} \right] = 3(0) \quad \text{Clear the equation of fractions.}$$

$$2x + 2 = 0 \quad \text{Apply the distributive property.}$$

$$2x = -2 \quad \text{Subtract 2 from both sides.}$$

$$x = -1 \quad \text{Divide both sides by 2.}$$

The solution set is $\{-1\}$.

PRACTICE
5 Solve for x: $\left| \dfrac{3(x - 2)}{5} \right| \leq 0$.

OBJECTIVE
2 Solving Absolute Value Inequalities of the Form $|X| > a$

Let us now solve an absolute value inequality of the form $|X| > a$, such as $|x| \geq 3$. The solution set contains all numbers whose distance from 0 is 3 or more units. Thus the graph of the solution set contains 3 and all points to the right of 3 on the number line or -3 and all points to the left of -3 on the number line.

Distance from 0: greater than or equal to 3 units

Distance from 0: greater than or equal to 3 units

$-3\ -2\ -1\ \ 0\ \ 1\ \ 2\ \ 3$

This solution set is written as $\{x | x \leq -3 \text{ or } x \geq 3\}$. In interval notation, the solution is $(-\infty, -3] \cup [3, \infty)$, since "or" means "union." In general, we have the following.

> **Solving Absolute Value Inequalities of the Form $|X| > a$**
>
> If a is a positive number, then $|X| > a$ is equivalent to $X < -a$ or $X > a$.

This property also holds true for the inequality symbol $\geq$.

EXAMPLE 6 Solve for y: $|y - 3| > 7$.

Solution Since 7 is positive, we apply the property for $|X| > a$.

$$|y - 3| > 7 \text{ is equivalent to } y - 3 < -7 \text{ or } y - 3 > 7$$

Next, solve the compound inequality.

$$y - 3 < -7 \qquad \text{or} \qquad y - 3 > 7$$
$$y - 3 + 3 < -7 + 3 \quad \text{or} \quad y - 3 + 3 > 7 + 3 \qquad \text{Add 3 to both sides.}$$
$$y < -4 \qquad \text{or} \qquad y > 10 \qquad \text{Simplify.}$$

The solution set is $(-\infty, -4) \cup (10, \infty)$, and its graph is shown.

PRACTICE
6   Solve for y: $|y + 4| \geq 6$.

Example 7 illustrates another special case of absolute value inequalities when an isolated absolute value expression is less than, less than or equal to, greater than, or greater than or equal to a negative number or 0.

EXAMPLE 7   Solve: $|2x + 9| + 5 > 3$.

Solution   First isolate the absolute value expression by subtracting 5 from both sides.

$$|2x + 9| + 5 > 3$$
$$|2x + 9| + 5 - 5 > 3 - 5 \qquad \text{Subtract 5 from both sides.}$$
$$|2x + 9| > -2 \qquad \text{Simplify.}$$

The absolute value of any number is always nonnegative and thus is always greater than -2. This inequality and the original inequality are true for all values of x. The solution set is $\{x \mid x \text{ is a real number}\}$ or $(-\infty, \infty)$, and its graph is shown.

PRACTICE
7   Solve: $|4x + 3| + 5 > 3$. Graph the solution set.

✓**CONCEPT CHECK**
Without taking any solution steps, how do you know that the absolute value inequality $|3x - 2| > -9$ has a solution? What is its solution?

EXAMPLE 8   Solve: $\left|\dfrac{x}{3} - 1\right| - 7 \geq -5$.

Solution   First, isolate the absolute value expression by adding 7 to both sides.

$$\left|\frac{x}{3} - 1\right| - 7 \geq -5$$

$$\left|\frac{x}{3} - 1\right| - 7 + 7 \geq -5 + 7 \qquad \text{Add 7 to both sides.}$$

$$\left|\frac{x}{3} - 1\right| \geq 2 \qquad \text{Simplify.}$$

Next, write the absolute value inequality as an equivalent compound inequality and solve.

$$\frac{x}{3} - 1 \leq -2 \qquad \text{or} \qquad \frac{x}{3} - 1 \geq 2$$

$$3\left(\frac{x}{3} - 1\right) \leq 3(-2) \qquad \text{or} \qquad 3\left(\frac{x}{3} - 1\right) \geq 3(2) \qquad \text{Clear the inequalities of fractions.}$$

$$x - 3 \leq -6 \qquad \text{or} \qquad x - 3 \geq 6 \qquad \text{Apply the distributive property.}$$

$$x \leq -3 \qquad \text{or} \qquad x \geq 9 \qquad \text{Add 3 to both sides.}$$

(Continued on next page)

Answer to Concept Check:
$(-\infty, \infty)$ since the absolute value is always nonnegative

The solution set is $(-\infty, -3] \cup [9, \infty)$, and its graph is shown.

PRACTICE
8   Solve: $\left| \dfrac{x}{2} - 3 \right| - 5 > -2$. Graph the solution set.

The following box summarizes the types of absolute value equations and inequalities.

Solving Absolute Value Equations and Inequalities with $a > 0$

Algebraic Solution | **Solution Graph**

$|X| = a$ is equivalent to $X = a$ or $X = -a$.

$|X| < a$ is equivalent to $-a < X < a$.

$|X| > a$ is equivalent to $X < -a$ or $X > a$.

Vocabulary, Readiness & Video Check

Match each absolute value statement with an equivalent statement.

1. $|2x + 1| = 3$
2. $|2x + 1| \le 3$
3. $|2x + 1| < 3$
4. $|2x + 1| \ge 3$
5. $|2x + 1| > 3$

A. $2x + 1 > 3$ or $2x + 1 < -3$
B. $2x + 1 \ge 3$ or $2x + 1 \le -3$
C. $-3 < 2x + 1 < 3$
D. $2x + 1 = 3$ or $2x + 1 = -3$
E. $-3 \le 2x + 1 \le 3$

Martin-Gay Interactive Videos

See Video 9.3

Watch the section lecture video and answer the following questions.

OBJECTIVE
1
6. In ▭ Example 3, how can you reason that the inequality has no solution even if you don't know the rule?

OBJECTIVE
2
7. In ▭ Example 4, why is the union symbol used when the solution is written in interval notation?

9.3   Exercise Set   MyMathLab®

Solve each inequality. Then graph the solution set and write it in interval notation. See Examples 1 through 4.

1. $|x| \le 4$
2. $|x| < 6$
3. $|x - 3| < 2$
4. $|y - 7| \le 5$
5. $|x + 3| < 2$
6. $|x + 4| < 6$
7. $|2x + 7| \le 13$
8. $|5x - 3| \le 18$
9. $|x| + 7 \le 12$
10. $|x| + 6 \le 7$
11. $|3x - 1| < -5$
12. $|8x - 3| < -2$
13. $|x - 6| - 7 \le -1$
14. $|z + 2| - 7 < -3$

Solve each inequality. Graph the solution set and write it in interval notation. See Examples 6 through 8.

15. $|x| > 3$
16. $|y| \ge 4$
17. $|x + 10| \ge 14$
18. $|x - 9| \ge 2$
19. $|x| + 2 > 6$
20. $|x| - 1 > 3$
21. $|5x| > -4$
22. $|4x - 11| > -1$
23. $|6x - 8| + 3 > 7$
24. $|10 + 3x| + 1 > 2$

Solve each inequality. Graph the solution set and write it in interval notation. See Example 5.

25. $|x| \leq 0$ **26.** $|x| \geq 0$

27. $|8x + 3| > 0$

28. $|5x - 6| < 0$

MIXED PRACTICE

Solve each inequality. Graph the solution set and write it in interval notation. See Examples 1 through 8.

▶ **29.** $|x| \leq 2$ **30.** $|z| < 8$

31. $|y| > 1$ **32.** $|x| \geq 10$

33. $|x - 3| < 8$ **34.** $|-3 + x| \leq 10$

35. $|0.6x - 3| > 0.6$ **36.** $|1 + 0.3x| \geq 0.1$

37. $5 + |x| \leq 2$ **38.** $8 + |x| < 1$

39. $|x| > -4$ **40.** $|x| \leq -7$

41. $|2x - 7| \leq 11$ **42.** $|5x + 2| < 8$

43. $|x + 5| + 2 \geq 8$ **44.** $|-1 + x| - 6 > 2$

45. $|x| > 0$ **46.** $|x| < 0$

47. $9 + |x| > 7$ **48.** $5 + |x| \geq 4$

49. $6 + |4x - 1| \leq 9$ **50.** $-3 + |5x - 2| \leq 4$

51. $\left|\dfrac{2}{3}x + 1\right| > 1$ **52.** $\left|\dfrac{3}{4}x - 1\right| \geq 2$

53. $|5x + 3| < -6$ **54.** $|4 + 9x| \geq -6$

55. $\left|\dfrac{8x - 3}{4}\right| \leq 0$ **56.** $\left|\dfrac{5x + 6}{2}\right| \leq 0$

57. $|1 + 3x| + 4 < 5$ **58.** $|7x - 3| - 1 \leq 10$

▶ **59.** $\left|\dfrac{x + 6}{3}\right| > 2$

60. $\left|\dfrac{7 + x}{2}\right| \geq 4$

▶ **61.** $-15 + |2x - 7| \leq -6$

62. $-9 + |3 + 4x| < -4$

63. $\left|2x + \dfrac{3}{4}\right| - 7 \leq -2$

64. $\left|\dfrac{3}{5} + 4x\right| - 6 < -1$

MIXED PRACTICE

Solve each equation or inequality for x. (Sections 9.2, 9.3)

65. $|2x - 3| < 7$ **66.** $|2x - 3| > 7$

67. $|2x - 3| = 7$ **68.** $|5 - 6x| = 29$

69. $|x - 5| \geq 12$ **70.** $|x + 4| \geq 20$

71. $|9 + 4x| = 0$ **72.** $|9 + 4x| \geq 0$

73. $|2x + 1| + 4 < 7$

74. $8 + |5x - 3| \geq 11$

75. $|3x - 5| + 4 = 5$

76. $|5x - 3| + 2 = 4$

77. $|x + 11| = -1$

78. $|4x - 4| = -3$

79. $\left|\dfrac{2x - 1}{3}\right| = 6$

80. $\left|\dfrac{6 - x}{4}\right| = 5$

81. $\left|\dfrac{3x - 5}{6}\right| > 5$

82. $\left|\dfrac{4x - 7}{5}\right| < 2$

MIXED PRACTICE

Solve. See Section 2.4.

Many companies predict the growth or decline of various technologies. The following data is based on information from Techcrunchies, a technological information site. Notice that the first table is the estimated increase in the number of Wi-Fi-enabled cell phones (in millions), and the second is the estimated percent increase in the number of Wi-Fi-enabled cell phones in the United States.

83. Use the middle column in the table to find the estimated number of Wi-Fi-enabled cell phones for each year.

Year	*Increase in Wi-Fi-Enabled Cell Phones*	*Estimated Number*
2010	$2x - 21$	
2012	$\dfrac{5}{2}x + 2$	
2014	$3x + 24$	
Total	290 million	

84. Use the middle column in the table to find the estimated percent increase in the number of Wi-Fi-enabled cell phones for each year.

Year	*Percent Increase in Wi-Fi-Enabled Cell Phones since 2009*	*Estimated Percent Increase*
2010	x	
2011	$2x + 10$	
2012	$4x - 25$	
	300%	

Consider the equation $3x - 4y = 12$. For each value of x or y given, find the corresponding value of the other variable that makes the statement true. See Section 3.1.

85. If $x = 2$, find y.

86. If $y = -1$, find x.

87. If $y = -3$, find x.

88. If $x = 4$, find y.

CONCEPT EXTENSIONS

89. Write an absolute value inequality representing all numbers x whose distance from 0 is less than 7 units.

90. Write an absolute value inequality representing all numbers x whose distance from 0 is greater than 4 units.

91. Write $-5 \leq x \leq 5$ as an equivalent inequality containing an absolute value.

92. Write $x > 1$ or $x < -1$ as an equivalent inequality containing an absolute value.

93. Describe how solving $|x - 3| = 5$ is different from solving $|x - 3| < 5$.

94. Describe how solving $|x + 4| = 0$ is similar to solving $|x + 4| \leq 0$.

The expression $|x_T - x|$ is defined to be the absolute error in x, where x_T is the true value of a quantity and x is the measured value or value as stored in a computer.

95. If the true value of a quantity is 3.5 and the absolute error must be less than 0.05, find the acceptable measured values.

96. If the true value of a quantity is 0.2 and the approximate value stored in a computer is $\frac{51}{256}$, find the absolute error.

Integrated Review SOLVING COMPOUND INEQUALITIES AND ABSOLUTE VALUE EQUATIONS AND INEQUALITIES

Solve each equation or inequality. Write inequality solution sets in interval rotation. For inequalities containing "and" or "or", also graph the solution set and write it in interval rotation.

1. $x < 7$ and $x > -5$

2. $x < 7$ or $x > -5$

3. $|4x - 3| = 1$

4. $|2x + 1| < 5$

5. $|6x| - 9 \geq -3$

6. $|x - 7| = |2x + 11|$

7. $-5 \leq \dfrac{3x - 8}{2} \leq 2$

8. $|9x - 1| = -3$

9. $3x + 2 \leq 5$ or $-3x \geq 0$

10. $3x + 2 \leq 5$ and $-3x \geq 0$

11. $|3 - x| - 5 \leq -2$

12. $\left| \dfrac{4x + 1}{5} \right| = |-1|$

Match each equation or inequality on the left with an equivalent statement on the right.

13. $|2x + 1| = 5$

14. $|2x + 1| < 5$

15. $|2x + 1| > 5$

16. $x < 3$ or $x < 5$

17. $x < 3$ and $x < 5$

A. $2x + 1 > 5$ or $2x + 1 < -5$

B. $2x + 1 = 5$ or $2x + 1 = -5$

C. $x < 5$

D. $x < 3$

E. $-5 < 2x + 1 < 5$

9.4 **Graphing Linear Inequalities in Two Variables and Systems of Linear Inequalities** ⊘

OBJECTIVE

1 Graph a Linear Inequality in Two Variables. ⊘

2 Solve a System of Linear Inequalities. ⊘

In this section, we first learn to graph a single linear inequality in two variables. Then we solve systems of linear inequalities.

Recall that a linear equation in two variables is an equation that can be written in the form $Ax + By = C$ where A, B, and C are real numbers and A and B are not both 0. The definition of a linear inequality is the same except that the equal sign is replaced with an inequality sign.

A **linear inequality in two variables** is an inequality that can be written in one of the forms:

$$Ax + By < C \qquad Ax + By \leq C$$
$$Ax + By > C \qquad Ax + By \geq C$$

where A, B, and C are real numbers and A and B are not both 0. Just as for linear equations in x and y, an ordered pair is a **solution** of an inequality in x and y if replacing the variables by coordinates of the ordered pair results in a true statement.

OBJECTIVE
1   Graphing Linear Inequalities in Two Variables

The linear equation $x - y = 1$ is graphed next. Recall that all points on the line correspond to ordered pairs that satisfy the equation $x - y = 1$.

Notice the line defined by $x - y = 1$ divides the rectangular coordinate system plane into 2 sides. All points on one side of the line satisfy the inequality $x - y < 1$ and all points on the other side satisfy the inequality $x - y > 1$. The graph below shows a few examples of this.

Check	$x - y < 1$
$(1, 3)$	$1 - 3 < 1$ True
$(-2, 1)$	$-2 - 1 < 1$ True
$(-4, -4)$	$-4 - (-4) < 1$ True

Check	$x - y > 1$
$(4, 1)$	$4 - 1 > 1$ True
$(2, -2)$	$2 - (-2) > 1$ True
$(0, -4)$	$0 - (-4) > 1$ True

The graph of $x - y < 1$ is the region shaded blue, and the graph of $x - y > 1$ is the region shaded red below.

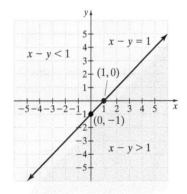

The region to the left of the line and the region to the right of the line are called **half-planes.** Every line divides the plane (similar to a sheet of paper extending indefinitely in all directions) into two half-planes; the line is called the **boundary.**

Recall that the inequality $x - y \leq 1$ means

$$x - y = 1 \quad \text{or} \quad x - y < 1$$

Thus, the graph of $x - y \leq 1$ is the half-plane $x - y < 1$ along with the boundary line $x - y = 1$.

Graphing a Linear Inequality in Two Variables

Step 1. Graph the boundary line found by replacing the inequality sign with an equal sign. If the inequality sign is $>$ or $<$, graph a dashed boundary line (indicating that the points on the line are not solutions of the inequality). If the inequality sign is $\geq$ or $\leq$, graph a solid boundary line (indicating that the points on the line are solutions of the inequality).

Step 2. Choose a point, *not* on the boundary line, as a test point. Substitute the coordinates of this test point into the *original* inequality.

Step 3. If a true statement is obtained in Step 2, shade the half-plane that contains the test point. If a false statement is obtained, shade the half-plane that does not contain the test point.

EXAMPLE 1   Graph: $x + y < 7$

Solution

Step 1. First we graph the boundary line by graphing the equation $x + y = 7$. We graph this boundary as a dashed line because the inequality sign is $<$, and thus the points on the line are not solutions of the inequality $x + y < 7$.

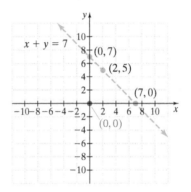

Step 2. Next, we choose a test point, being careful not to choose a point on the boundary line. We choose $(0, 0)$. Substitute the coordinates of $(0, 0)$ into $x + y < 7$.

$$x + y < 7 \quad \text{Original inequality}$$
$$0 + 0 \stackrel{?}{<} 7 \quad \text{Replace } x \text{ with 0 and } y \text{ with 0.}$$
$$0 < 7 \quad \text{True}$$

Step 3. Since the result is a true statement, $(0, 0)$ is a solution of $x + y < 7$, and every point in the same half-plane as $(0, 0)$ is also a solution. To indicate this, shade the entire half-plane containing $(0, 0)$, as shown.

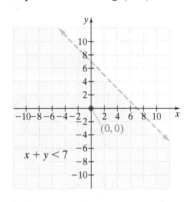

PRACTICE

1   Graph: $x + y > 5$

✓CONCEPT CHECK
Determine whether $(0, 0)$ is included in the graph of
a. $y \geq 2x + 3$ **b.** $x < 7$ **c.** $2x - 3y < 6$

EXAMPLE 2   Graph: $2x - y \geq 3$

Solution

Step 1. We graph the boundary line by graphing $2x - y = 3$. We draw this line as a solid line because the inequality sign is $\geq$, and thus the points on the line are solutions of $2x - y \geq 3$.

Step 2. Once again, $(0, 0)$ is a convenient test point since it is not on the boundary line. We substitute 0 for x and 0 for y into the original inequality.

$$2x - y \geq 3$$
$$2(0) - 0 \geq 3 \quad \text{Let } x = 0 \text{ and } y = 0.$$
$$0 \geq 3 \quad \text{False}$$

Step 3. Since the statement is false, no point in the half-plane containing $(0, 0)$ is a solution. Therefore, we shade the half-plane that does not contain $(0, 0)$. Every point in the shaded half-plane and every point on the boundary line is a solution of $2x - y \geq 3$.

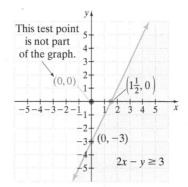

PRACTICE

2   Graph: $3x - y \geq 4$

▶ Helpful Hint

When graphing an inequality, make sure the test point is substituted into the **original inequality.** For Example 2, we substituted the test point $(0, 0)$ into the **original inequality** $2x - y \geq 3$, *not* $2x - y = 3$.

EXAMPLE 3   Graph: $x > 2y$

Solution

Step 1. We find the boundary line by graphing $x = 2y$. The boundary line is a dashed line since the inequality symbol is $>$.

Step 2. We cannot use $(0, 0)$ as a test point because it is a point on the boundary line. We choose instead $(0, 2)$.

$$x > 2y$$
$$0 > 2(2) \quad \text{Let } x = 0 \text{ and } y = 2.$$
$$0 > 4 \quad \text{False}$$

Answers to Concept Check:
a. no   **b.** yes   **c.** yes

(Continued on next page)

Step 3. Since the statement is false, we shade the half-plane that does not contain the test point $(0, 2)$, as shown.

PRACTICE
3 Graph: $x > 3y$

EXAMPLE 4 Graph: $5x + 4y \leq 20$

Solution We graph the solid boundary line $5x + 4y = 20$ and choose $(0, 0)$ as the test point.

$$5x + 4y \leq 20$$
$$5(0) + 4(0) \overset{?}{\leq} 20 \quad \text{Let } x = 0 \text{ and } y = 0.$$
$$0 \leq 20 \quad \text{True}$$

We shade the half-plane that contains $(0, 0)$, as shown.

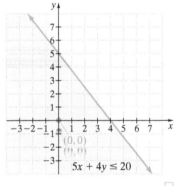

PRACTICE
4 Graph: $3x + 4y \geq 12$

EXAMPLE 5 Graph: $y > 3$

Solution We graph the dashed boundary line $y = 3$ and choose $(0, 0)$ as the test point. (Recall that the graph of $y = 3$ is a horizontal line with y-intercept 3.)

$$y > 3$$
$$0 \overset{?}{>} 3 \quad \text{Let } y = 0.$$
$$0 > 3 \quad \text{False}$$

We shade the half-plane that does not contain $(0, 0)$, as shown.

PRACTICE
5 Graph: $x > 3$

OBJECTIVE

2   **Solving Systems of Linear Inequalities**

Just as two linear equations make a system of linear equations, two linear inequalities make a **system of linear inequalities.** Systems of inequalities are very important in a process called linear programming. Many businesses use linear programming to find the most profitable way to use limited resources such as employees, machines, or buildings.

A **solution of a system of linear inequalities** is an ordered pair that satisfies each inequality in the system. The set of all such ordered pairs is the solution set of the system. Graphing this set gives us a picture of the solution set. We can graph a system of inequalities by graphing each inequality in the system and identifying the region of overlap.

EXAMPLE 6   Graph the solution of the system: $\begin{cases} 3x \geq y \\ x + 2y \leq 8 \end{cases}$

Solution   We begin by graphing each inequality on the same set of axes. The graph of the solution region of the system is the region contained in the graphs of both inequalities. It is their intersection.

First, graph $3x \geq y$. The boundary line is the graph of $3x = y$. Sketch a solid boundary line since the inequality $3x \geq y$ means $3x > y$ or $3x = y$. The test point $(1, 0)$ satisfies the inequality, so shade the half-plane that includes $(1, 0)$.

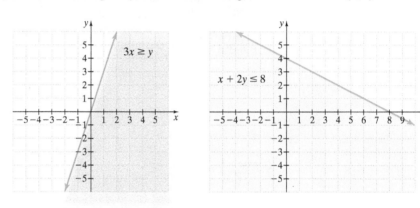

Next, sketch a solid boundary line $x + 2y = 8$ on the same set of axes. The test point $(0, 0)$ satisfies the inequality $x + 2y \leq 8$, so shade the half-plane that includes $(0, 0)$. (For clarity, the graph of $x + 2y \leq 8$ is shown on a separate set of axes.)

An ordered pair solution of the system must satisfy both inequalities. These solutions are points that lie in both shaded regions. The solution region of the system is the purple shaded region as seen below. This solution region includes parts of both boundary lines.

PRACTICE

6   Graph the solution of the system: $\begin{cases} 4x \leq y \\ x + 3y \geq 9 \end{cases}$

In linear programming, it is sometimes necessary to find the coordinates of the **corner point:** the point at which the two boundary lines intersect. To find the point of intersection, solve the related linear system

$$\begin{cases} 3x = y \\ x + 2y = 8 \end{cases}$$

by the substitution method or the addition method. The lines intersect at $\left(\dfrac{8}{7}, \dfrac{24}{7}\right)$, the corner point of the graph.

Graphing the Solution Region of a System of Linear Inequalities

Step 1. Graph each inequality in the system on the same set of axes.

Step 2. The solutions (or solution region) of the system are the points common to the graphs of all the inequalities in the system.

EXAMPLE 7 Graph the solution of the system: $\begin{cases} x - y < 2 \\ x + 2y > -1 \end{cases}$

Solution Graph both inequalities on the same set of axes. Both boundary lines are dashed lines since the inequality symbols are $<$ and $>$. The solution region of the system is the region shown by the purple shading. In this example, the boundary lines are not a part of the solution.

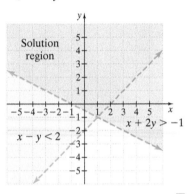

PRACTICE
7 Graph the solution of the system: $\begin{cases} x - y > 4 \\ x + 3y < -4 \end{cases}$

EXAMPLE 8 Graph the solution of the system: $\begin{cases} -3x + 4y < 12 \\ x \geq 2 \end{cases}$

Solution Graph both inequalities on the same set of axes.

The solution region of the system is the purple shaded region, including a portion of the line $x = 2$.

PRACTICE
8 Graph the solution of the system: $\begin{cases} y \leq 6 \\ -2x + 5y > 10 \end{cases}$

Vocabulary, Readiness & Video Check

Use the choices below to fill in each blank. Some choices may be used more than once and some not at all.

true	$x < 3$	$y < 3$	half-planes	yes
false	$x \leq 3$	$y \leq 3$	linear inequality in two variables	no

1. The statement $5x - 6y < 7$ is an example of a(n) _____.
2. A boundary line divides a plane into two regions called _____.
3. True or false: The graph of $5x - 6y < 7$ includes its corresponding boundary line. _____
4. True or false: When graphing a linear inequality, to determine which side of the boundary line to shade, choose a point *not* on the boundary line. _____
5. True or false: The boundary line for the inequality $5x - 6y < 7$ is the graph of $5x - 6y = 7$.
   _____
6. The graph of _____ is

State whether the graph of each inequality includes its corresponding boundary line. Answer yes or no.

7. $y \geq x + 4$ **8.** $x - y > -7$ **9.** $y \geq x$ **10.** $x > 0$

Martin-Gay Interactive Videos

See Video 9.4

Watch the section lecture video and answer the following questions.

OBJECTIVE
1
11. From Example 1, how do you find the equation of the boundary line? How do you determine if the points on the boundary line are solutions of the inequality?

OBJECTIVE
2
12. In Example 2, did the graph of the first inequality of the system limit where we could choose the test point for the second inequality? Why or why not?

9.4 Exercise Set   MyMathLab®

Determine whether the ordered pairs given are solutions of the linear inequality in two variables.

1. $x - y > 3; (2, -1), (5, 1)$
2. $y - x < -2; (2, 1), (5, -1)$
3. $3x - 5y \leq -4; (-1, -1), (4, 0)$
4. $2x + y \geq 10; (-1, -4), (5, 0)$
5. $x < -y; (0, 2), (-5, 1)$
6. $y > 3x; (0, 0), (-1, -4)$

MIXED PRACTICE

Graph each inequality. See Examples 1 through 5.

7. $x + y \leq 1$
8. $x + y \geq -2$
9. $2x + y > -4$
10. $x + 3y \leq 3$
11. $x + 6y \leq -6$
12. $7x + y > -14$
13. $2x + 5y > -10$
14. $5x + 2y \leq 10$
15. $x + 2y \leq 3$
16. $2x + 3y > -5$

17. $2x + 7y > 5$

18. $3x + 5y \leq -2$

19. $x - 2y \geq 3$

20. $4x + y \leq 2$

21. $5x + y < 3$

22. $x + 2y > -7$

23. $4x + y < 8$

24. $9x + 2y \geq -9$

25. $y \geq 2x$ **26.** $x < 5y$ **27.** $x \geq 0$

28. $y \leq 0$ **29.** $y \leq -3$ **30.** $x > -\dfrac{2}{3}$

31. $2x - 7y > 0$ **32.** $5x + 2y \leq 0$ **33.** $3x - 7y \geq 0$

34. $-2x - 9y > 0$ **35.** $x > y$ **36.** $x \leq -y$

37. $x - y \leq 6$ **38.** $x - y > 10$ **39.** $-\dfrac{1}{4}y + \dfrac{1}{3}x > 1$

40. $\dfrac{1}{2}x - \dfrac{1}{3}y \leq -1$ **41.** $-x < 0.4y$ **42.** $0.3x \geq 0.1y$

In Exercises 43 through 48, match each inequality with its graph.

   a. $x > 2$ **b.** $y < 2$ **c.** $y < 2x$

   d. $y \leq -3x$ **e.** $2x + 3y < 6$ **f.** $3x + 2y > 6$

43.

44.

45.

46.

47.

48.

Graph the solution of each system of linear inequalities. See Examples 6 through 8.

49. $\begin{cases} y \geq x + 1 \\ y \geq 3 - x \end{cases}$ **50.** $\begin{cases} y \geq x - 3 \\ y \geq -1 - x \end{cases}$

51. $\begin{cases} y < 3x - 4 \\ y \leq x + 2 \end{cases}$ **52.** $\begin{cases} y \leq 2x + 1 \\ y > x + 2 \end{cases}$

53. $\begin{cases} y \leq -2x - 2 \\ y \geq x + 4 \end{cases}$ **54.** $\begin{cases} y \leq 2x + 4 \\ y \geq -x - 5 \end{cases}$

55. $\begin{cases} y \geq -x + 2 \\ y \leq 2x + 5 \end{cases}$ **56.** $\begin{cases} y \geq x - 5 \\ y \leq -3x + 3 \end{cases}$

57. $\begin{cases} x \geq 3y \\ x + 3y \leq 6 \end{cases}$ **58.** $\begin{cases} -2x < y \\ x + 2y < 3 \end{cases}$

59. $\begin{cases} y + 2x \geq 0 \\ 5x - 3y \leq 12 \end{cases}$ **60.** $\begin{cases} y + 2x \leq 0 \\ 5x + 3y \geq -2 \end{cases}$

61. $\begin{cases} 3x - 4y \geq -6 \\ 2x + y \leq 7 \end{cases}$ **62.** $\begin{cases} 4x - y \geq -2 \\ 2x + 3y \leq -8 \end{cases}$

63. $\begin{cases} x \leq 2 \\ y \geq -3 \end{cases}$ **64.** $\begin{cases} x \geq -3 \\ y \geq -2 \end{cases}$

65. $\begin{cases} y \geq 1 \\ x < -3 \end{cases}$ **66.** $\begin{cases} y > 2 \\ x \geq -1 \end{cases}$

67. $\begin{cases} 2x + 3y < -8 \\ x \geq -4 \end{cases}$ **68.** $\begin{cases} 3x + 2y \leq 6 \\ x < 2 \end{cases}$

69. $\begin{cases} 2x - 5y \leq 9 \\ y \leq -3 \end{cases}$ **70.** $\begin{cases} 2x + 5y \leq -10 \\ y \geq 1 \end{cases}$

71. $\begin{cases} y \geq \dfrac{1}{2}x + 2 \\ y \leq \dfrac{1}{2}x - 3 \end{cases}$ **72.** $\begin{cases} y \geq -\dfrac{3}{2}x + 3 \\ y < -\dfrac{3}{2}x + 6 \end{cases}$

REVIEW AND PREVIEW

Evaluate each expression for the given replacement value. See Section 5.1.

73. x^2 if x is -5 **74.** x^3 if x is -5

75. $2x^3$ if x is -1 **76.** $3x^2$ if x is -1

CONCEPT EXTENSIONS

Determine whether $(1,1)$ is included in each graph. See the Concept Check in this section.

77. $3x + 4y < 8$ **78.** $y > 5x$

79. $y \geq -\dfrac{1}{2}x$ **80.** $x > 3$

81. Write an inequality whose solutions are all pairs of numbers x and y whose sum is at least 13. Graph the inequality.

82. Write an inequality whose solutions are all the pairs of numbers x and y whose sum is at most -4. Graph the inequality.

83. Explain why a point on the boundary line should not be chosen as the test point.

84. Describe the graph of a linear inequality.

85. The price for a taxi cab in a small city is $2.50 per mile, x, while traveling, and $0.25 every minute, y, while waiting. If you have $20 to spend on a cab ride, the inequality

$$2.5x + 0.25y \leq 20$$

represents your situation. Graph this inequality in the first quadrant only.

86. A word processor charges $22 per hour, x, for typing a first draft, and $15 per hour, y, for making changes and typing a second draft. If you need a document typed and have $100, the inequality

$$22x + 15y \leq 100$$

represents your situation. Graph the inequality in the first quadrant only.

87. In Exercises 85 and 86, why were you instructed to graph each inequality in the first quadrant only?

88. Scott Sambracci and Sara Thygeson are planning their wedding. They have calculated that they want the cost of their wedding ceremony, x, plus the cost of their reception, y, to be no more than $5000.

  a. Write an inequality describing this relationship.

  b. Graph this inequality.

  c. Why should we be interested in only quadrant I of this graph?

89. It's the end of the budgeting period for Dennis Fernandes, and he has $500 left in his budget for car rental expenses. He plans to spend this budget on a sales trip throughout southern Texas. He will rent a car that costs $30 per day and $0.15 per mile, and he can spend no more than $500.

  a. Write an inequality describing this situation. Let x = number of days and let y = number of miles.

  b. Graph this inequality.

  c. Why should we be interested in only quadrant I of this graph?

90. Explain how to decide which region to shade to show the solution region of the following system.

$$\begin{cases} x \geq 3 \\ y \geq -2 \end{cases}$$

For each system of inequalities, choose the corresponding graph.

91. $\begin{cases} y < 5 \\ x > 3 \end{cases}$ **92.** $\begin{cases} y > 5 \\ x < 3 \end{cases}$ **93.** $\begin{cases} y \leq 5 \\ x < 3 \end{cases}$

94. $\begin{cases} y > 5 \\ x \geq 3 \end{cases}$

A.   **B.**

C.   **D.**

95. Graph the solution of $\begin{cases} 2x - y \leq 6 \\ x \geq 3 \\ y > 2 \end{cases}$

96. Graph the solution of $\begin{cases} x + y < 5 \\ y < 2x \\ x \geq 0 \\ y \geq 0 \end{cases}$

97. Describe the location of the solution region of the system

$$\begin{cases} x > 0 \\ y > 0. \end{cases}$$

CHAPTER 10

Rational Exponents, Radicals, and Complex Numbers

In this chapter, radical notation is reviewed, and then rational exponents are introduced. As the name implies, rational exponents are exponents that are rational numbers. We present an interpretation of rational exponents that is consistent with the meaning and rules already established for integer exponents, and we present two forms of notation for roots: radical and exponent. We conclude this chapter with complex numbers, a natural extension of the real number system.

The Google Lunar X PRIZE is an international competition to safely land a robot on the surface of the moon, travel 500 meters over the lunar surface, and send images and data back to Earth. Teams needed to be registered by December 31, 2010. There are multiple prizes and bonuses, but the first team to land on the moon and complete the mission objectives by December 31, 2012, will be awarded $20 million. After this time, the first prize drops to $15 million. The deadline for winning the competition is December 31, 2014, and thus far, 20 teams are competing for the prize.

To reach the moon, these vehicles must first leave the gravity of Earth. In Exercises 115 and 116 of Section 10.1, you will calculate the escape velocity of Earth and the moon, the minimum speed an object must reach to escape the pull of a planet's gravity. (*Source:* X PRIZE Foundation)

Composition of the Moon

Oxygen 42%

Silicon 21%

Other 17%

Aluminum 7%

Iron 13%

Why the moon? To name a few reasons:

- It is closest to Earth (1.3 seconds for light or radio) so that lunar machines can be directly controlled from Earth.

- It is also the closest source of materials to use for any other space project, and it is 22 times easier to launch from the moon than from Earth.

- The moon is 42% oxygen by weight (see the circle graph to the left) and oxygen is the main ingredient of rocket fuel.

- We can collect energy from the moon's surface and transmit it to Earth.

10.1 | Radicals and Radical Functions

OBJECTIVES

1 Find Square Roots.

2 Approximate Roots.

3 Find Cube Roots.

4 Find *n*th Roots.

5 Find $\sqrt[n]{a^n}$ Where *a* Is a Real Number.

6 Graph Square and Cube Root Functions.

OBJECTIVE

1   Finding Square Roots

Recall from Section 8.2 that to find a **square root** of a number *a*, we find a number that was squared to get *a*.

Thus, because

$$5^2 = 25 \quad \text{and} \quad (-5)^2 = 25,$$

both 5 and -5 are square roots of 25.

Recall that we denote the **nonnegative, or principal, square root** with the **radical sign.**

$$\sqrt{25} = 5$$

We denote the **negative square root** with the **negative radical sign.**

$$-\sqrt{25} = -5$$

An expression containing a radical sign is called a **radical expression.** An expression within, or "under," a radical sign is called a **radicand.**

radical expression:

Principal and Negative Square Roots

If *a* is a nonnegative number, then

$\sqrt{a}$ is the **principal, or nonnegative, square root** of *a*

$-\sqrt{a}$ is the **negative square root** of *a*

EXAMPLE 1   Simplify. Assume that all variables represent positive numbers.

a. $\sqrt{36}$ **b.** $\sqrt{0}$ **c.** $\sqrt{\dfrac{4}{49}}$ **d.** $\sqrt{0.25}$

e. $\sqrt{x^6}$ **f.** $\sqrt{9x^{12}}$ **g.** $-\sqrt{81}$ **h.** $\sqrt{-81}$

Solution

a. $\sqrt{36} = 6$ because $6^2 = 36$ and 6 is not negative.

b. $\sqrt{0} = 0$ because $0^2 = 0$ and 0 is not negative.

c. $\sqrt{\dfrac{4}{49}} = \dfrac{2}{7}$ because $\left(\dfrac{2}{7}\right)^2 = \dfrac{4}{49}$ and $\dfrac{2}{7}$ is not negative.

d. $\sqrt{0.25} = 0.5$ because $(0.5)^2 = 0.25$.

e. $\sqrt{x^6} = x^3$ because $(x^3)^2 = x^6$.

f. $\sqrt{9x^{12}} = 3x^6$ because $(3x^6)^2 = 9x^{12}$.

g. $-\sqrt{81} = -9$. The negative in front of the radical indicates the negative square root of 81.

h. $\sqrt{-81}$ is not a real number.

PRACTICE

1   Simplify. Assume that all variables represent positive numbers.

a. $\sqrt{49}$ **b.** $\sqrt{\dfrac{0}{1}}$ **c.** $\sqrt{\dfrac{16}{81}}$ **d.** $\sqrt{0.64}$

e. $\sqrt{z^8}$ **f.** $\sqrt{16b^4}$ **g.** $-\sqrt{36}$ **h.** $\sqrt{-36}$

Recall from Section 8.2 our discussion of the square root of a negative number. For example, can we simplify $\sqrt{-4}$? That is, can we find a real number whose square is -4? No, there is no real number whose square is -4, and we say that $\sqrt{-4}$ is not a real number. In general:

The square root of a negative number is not a real number.

▶ Helpful Hint

- Remember: $\sqrt{0} = 0$.
- Don't forget that the square root of a negative number is not a real number. For example,

$$\sqrt{-9} \text{ is not a real number}$$

because there is no real number that when multiplied by itself would give a product of -9. In Section 10.7, we will see what kind of a number $\sqrt{-9}$ is.

OBJECTIVE

2 Approximating Roots

Recall that numbers such as 1, 4, 9, and 25 are called **perfect squares,** since $1 = 1^2, 4 = 2^2, 9 = 3^2$, and $25 = 5^2$. Square roots of perfect square radicands simplify to rational numbers. What happens when we try to simplify a root such as $\sqrt{3}$? Since there is no rational number whose square is 3, $\sqrt{3}$ is not a rational number. It is called an **irrational number,** and we can find a decimal **approximation** of it. To find decimal approximations, use a calculator. For example, an approximation for $\sqrt{3}$ is

$$\sqrt{3} \approx 1.732$$

approximation symbol

To see if the approximation is reasonable, notice that since

$$1 < 3 < 4,$$
$$\sqrt{1} < \sqrt{3} < \sqrt{4}, \text{ or}$$
$$1 < \sqrt{3} < 2.$$

We found $\sqrt{3} \approx 1.732$, a number between 1 and 2, so our result is reasonable.

EXAMPLE 2 Use a calculator to approximate $\sqrt{20}$. Round the approximation to 3 decimal places and check to see that your approximation is reasonable.

$$\sqrt{20} \approx 4.472$$

Solution Is this reasonable? Since $16 < 20 < 25$, $\sqrt{16} < \sqrt{20} < \sqrt{25}$, or $4 < \sqrt{20} < 5$. The approximation is between 4 and 5 and thus is reasonable. □

PRACTICE

2 Use a calculator to approximate $\sqrt{45}$. Round the approximation to three decimal places and check to see that your approximation is reasonable.

OBJECTIVE

3 Finding Cube Roots

Finding roots can be extended to other roots such as cube roots. For example, since $2^3 = 8$, we call 2 the **cube root** of 8. In symbols, we write

$$\sqrt[3]{8} = 2$$

Cube Root

The **cube root** of a real number a is written as $\sqrt[3]{a}$, and

$$\sqrt[3]{a} = b \text{ only if } b^3 = a$$

From this definition, we have

$$\sqrt[3]{64} = 4 \text{ since } 4^3 = 64$$
$$\sqrt[3]{-27} = -3 \text{ since } (-3)^3 = -27$$
$$\sqrt[3]{x^3} = x \text{ since } x^3 = x^3$$

Notice that, unlike with square roots, *it is possible to have a negative radicand when finding a cube root.* This is so because the *cube* of a negative number is a negative number. Therefore, the *cube root* of a negative number is a negative number.

EXAMPLE 3   Find the cube roots.

a. $\sqrt[3]{1}$ **b.** $\sqrt[3]{-64}$ **c.** $\sqrt[3]{\dfrac{8}{125}}$ **d.** $\sqrt[3]{x^6}$ **e.** $\sqrt[3]{-27x^9}$

Solution

a. $\sqrt[3]{1} = 1$ because $1^3 = 1$.

b. $\sqrt[3]{-64} = -4$ because $(-4)^3 = -64$.

c. $\sqrt[3]{\dfrac{8}{125}} = \dfrac{2}{5}$ because $\left(\dfrac{2}{5}\right)^3 = \dfrac{8}{125}$.

d. $\sqrt[3]{x^6} = x^2$ because $(x^2)^3 = x^6$.

e. $\sqrt[3]{-27x^9} = -3x^3$ because $(-3x^3)^3 = -27x^9$.

PRACTICE
3   Find the cube roots.

a. $\sqrt[3]{-1}$ **b.** $\sqrt[3]{27}$ **c.** $\sqrt[3]{\dfrac{27}{64}}$ **d.** $\sqrt[3]{x^{12}}$ **e.** $\sqrt[3]{-8x^3}$

OBJECTIVE
4   Finding *n*th Roots

Just as we can raise a real number to powers other than 2 or 3, we can find roots other than square roots and cube roots. In fact, we can find the **nth root** of a number, where n is any natural number. In symbols, the *n*th root of a is written as $\sqrt[n]{a}$, where n is called the **index.** The index 2 is usually omitted for square roots.

> ▶ **Helpful Hint**
>
> If the index is even, such as $\sqrt{}$, $\sqrt[4]{}$, $\sqrt[6]{}$, and so on, the radicand must be nonnegative for the root to be a real number. For example,
>
> $$\sqrt[4]{16} = 2, \text{ but } \sqrt[4]{-16} \text{ is not a real number.}$$
> $$\sqrt[6]{64} = 2, \text{ but } \sqrt[6]{-64} \text{ is not a real number.}$$
>
> If the index is odd, such as $\sqrt[3]{}$, $\sqrt[5]{}$, and so on, the radicand may be any real number. For example,
>
> $$\sqrt[3]{64} = 4 \quad \text{and} \quad \sqrt[3]{-64} = -4$$
> $$\sqrt[5]{32} = 2 \quad \text{and} \quad \sqrt[5]{-32} = -2$$

✓ CONCEPT CHECK
Which one is not a real number?

a. $\sqrt[3]{-15}$ **b.** $\sqrt[4]{-15}$ **c.** $\sqrt[5]{-15}$ **d.** $\sqrt{(-15)^2}$

EXAMPLE 4 Simplify the following expressions.

a. $\sqrt[4]{81}$ b. $\sqrt[5]{-243}$ c. $-\sqrt{25}$ d. $\sqrt[4]{-81}$ e. $\sqrt[3]{64x^3}$

Solution

a. $\sqrt[4]{81} = 3$ because $3^4 = 81$ and 3 is positive.

b. $\sqrt[5]{-243} = -3$ because $(-3)^5 = -243$.

c. $-\sqrt{25} = -5$ because -5 is the opposite of $\sqrt{25}$.

d. $\sqrt[4]{-81}$ is not a real number. There is no real number that, when raised to the fourth power, is -81.

e. $\sqrt[3]{64x^3} = 4x$ because $(4x)^3 = 64x^3$.

PRACTICE

4 Simplify the following expressions.

a. $\sqrt[4]{10,000}$ b. $\sqrt[5]{-1}$ c. $-\sqrt{81}$ d. $\sqrt[4]{-625}$ e. $\sqrt[3]{27x^9}$

OBJECTIVE

5 Finding $\sqrt[n]{a^n}$ Where *a* Is a Real Number

Recall that the notation $\sqrt{a^2}$ indicates the positive square root of a^2 only. For example,

$$\sqrt{(-7)^2} = \sqrt{49} = 7$$

When variables are present in the radicand and it is *unclear whether the variable represents a positive number or a negative number*, absolute value bars are sometimes needed to ensure that the result is a positive number. For example,

$$\sqrt{x^2} = |x|$$

This ensures that the result is positive. This same situation may occur when the index is any *even* positive integer. When the index is any *odd* positive integer, absolute value bars are not necessary.

Finding $\sqrt[n]{a^n}$

If *n* is an *even* positive integer, then $\sqrt[n]{a^n} = |a|$.

If *n* is an *odd* positive integer, then $\sqrt[n]{a^n} = a$.

EXAMPLE 5 Simplify.

a. $\sqrt{(-3)^2}$ b. $\sqrt{x^2}$ c. $\sqrt[4]{(x-2)^4}$ d. $\sqrt[3]{(-5)^3}$

e. $\sqrt[5]{(2x-7)^5}$ f. $\sqrt{25x^2}$ g. $\sqrt{x^2 + 2x + 1}$

Solution

a. $\sqrt{(-3)^2} = |-3| = 3$ When the index is even, the absolute value bars ensure that our result is not negative.

b. $\sqrt{x^2} = |x|$

c. $\sqrt[4]{(x-2)^4} = |x-2|$

d. $\sqrt[3]{(-5)^3} = -5$

e. $\sqrt[5]{(2x-7)^5} = 2x - 7$ Absolute value bars are not needed when the index is odd.

f. $\sqrt{25x^2} = 5|x|$

g. $\sqrt{x^2 + 2x + 1} = \sqrt{(x+1)^2} = |x+1|$

PRACTICE
5   Simplify.

a. $\sqrt{(-4)^2}$ **b.** $\sqrt{x^{14}}$ **c.** $\sqrt[4]{(x+7)^4}$ **d.** $\sqrt[3]{(-7)^3}$

e. $\sqrt[5]{(3x-5)^5}$ **f.** $\sqrt{49x^2}$ **g.** $\sqrt{x^2+16x+64}$

OBJECTIVE
6   **Graphing Square and Cube Root Functions**

Recall that an equation in x and y describes a function if each x-value is paired with exactly one y-value. With this in mind, does the equation

$$y = \sqrt{x}$$

describe a function? First, notice that replacement values for x must be nonnegative real numbers, since $\sqrt{x}$ is not a real number if $x < 0$. The notation $\sqrt{x}$ denotes the principal square root of x, so for every nonnegative number x, there is exactly one number, $\sqrt{x}$. Therefore, $y = \sqrt{x}$ describes a function, and we may write it as

$$f(x) = \sqrt{x}$$

In general, radical functions are functions of the form

$$f(x) = \sqrt[n]{x}.$$

Recall that the domain of a function in x is the set of all possible replacement values of x. This means that if n is even, the domain is the set of all nonnegative numbers, or $\{x \mid x \geq 0\}$ or $[0, \infty)$. If n is odd, the domain is the set of all real numbers, or $(-\infty, \infty)$. Keep this in mind as we find function values.

EXAMPLE 6   If $f(x) = \sqrt{x-4}$ and $g(x) = \sqrt[3]{x+2}$, find each function value.

a. $f(8)$ **b.** $f(6)$ **c.** $g(-1)$ **d.** $g(1)$

Solution

a. $f(8) = \sqrt{8-4} = \sqrt{4} = 2$ **b.** $f(6) = \sqrt{6-4} = \sqrt{2}$

c. $g(-1) = \sqrt[3]{-1+2} = \sqrt[3]{1} = 1$ **d.** $g(1) = \sqrt[3]{1+2} = \sqrt[3]{3}$

PRACTICE
6   If $f(x) = \sqrt{x+5}$ and $g(x) = \sqrt[3]{x-3}$, find each function value.

a. $f(11)$ **b.** $f(-1)$ **c.** $g(11)$ **d.** $g(-6)$

> ▶ Helpful Hint
>
> Notice that for the function $f(x) = \sqrt{x-4}$, the domain includes all real numbers that make the radicand ≥ 0. To see what numbers these are, solve $x - 4 \geq 0$ and find that $x \geq 4$. The domain is $\{x \mid x \geq 4\}$, or $[4, \infty)$.
>   The domain of the cube root function $g(x) = \sqrt[3]{x+2}$ is the set of real numbers, or $(-\infty, \infty)$.

EXAMPLE 7   Graph the square root function $f(x) = \sqrt{x}$.

Solution   To graph, we identify the domain, evaluate the function for several values of x, plot the resulting points, and connect the points with a smooth curve. Since $\sqrt{x}$ represents the nonnegative square root of x, the domain of this function is the set of all nonnegative numbers, $\{x \mid x \geq 0\}$ or $[0, \infty)$. We have approximated $\sqrt{3}$ in the table on the next page to help us locate the point corresponding to $(3, \sqrt{3})$.

(Continued on next page)

x	$f(x) = \sqrt{x}$
0	0
1	1
3	$\sqrt{3} \approx 1.7$
4	2
9	3

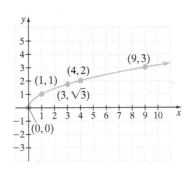

Notice that the graph of this function passes the vertical line test, as expected.

PRACTICE

7 Graph the square root function $h(x) = \sqrt{x + 2}$.

The equation $f(x) = \sqrt[3]{x}$ also describes a function. Here, x may be any real number, so the domain of this function is the set of all real numbers, or $(-\infty, \infty)$. A few function values are given next.

$$f(0) = \sqrt[3]{0} = 0$$
$$f(1) = \sqrt[3]{1} = 1$$
$$f(-1) = \sqrt[3]{-1} = -1$$
$$f(6) = \sqrt[3]{6}$$
$$f(-6) = \sqrt[3]{-6}$$
$$f(8) = \sqrt[3]{8} = 2$$
$$f(-8) = \sqrt[3]{-8} = -2$$

Here, there is no rational number whose cube is 6. Thus, the radicals do not simplify to rational numbers.

EXAMPLE 8 Graph the function $f(x) = \sqrt[3]{x}$.

Solution To graph, we identify the domain, plot points, and connect the points with a smooth curve. The domain of this function is the set of all real numbers. The table comes from the function values obtained earlier. We have approximated $\sqrt[3]{6}$ and $\sqrt[3]{-6}$ for graphing purposes.

x	$f(x) = \sqrt[3]{x}$
0	0
1	1
-1	-1
6	$\sqrt[3]{6} \approx 1.8$
-6	$\sqrt[3]{-6} \approx -1.8$
8	2
-8	-2

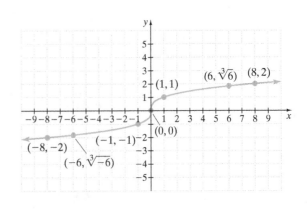

The graph of this function passes the vertical line test, as expected.

PRACTICE

8 Graph the function $f(x) = \sqrt[3]{x} - 4$.

Vocabulary, Readiness & Video Check

Use the choices below to fill in each blank. Not all choices will be used.

is	cubes	$-\sqrt{a}$	radical sign	index
is not	squares	$\sqrt{-a}$	radicand	

1. In the expression $\sqrt[n]{a}$, the n is called the _____, the $\sqrt{}$ is called the _____, and a is called the _____.
2. If $\sqrt{a}$ is the positive square root of $a, a \neq 0$, then _____ is the negative square root of a.
3. The square root of a negative number _____ a real number.
4. Numbers such as 1, 4, 9, and 25 are called perfect _____, whereas numbers such as 1, 8, 27, and 125 are called perfect _____.

Fill in the blank.

5. The domain of the function $f(x) = \sqrt{x}$ is _____.
6. The domain of the function $f(x) = \sqrt[3]{x}$ is _____.
7. If $f(16) = 4$, the corresponding ordered pair is _____.
8. If $g(-8) = -2$, the corresponding ordered pair is _____.

Martin-Gay Interactive Videos

See Video 10.1

Watch the section lecture video and answer the following questions.

OBJECTIVE 1
9. From Examples 5 and 6, when simplifying radicals containing variables with exponents, describe a shortcut you can use.

OBJECTIVE 2
10. From Example 9, how can you determine a reasonable approximation for a non-perfect square root without using a calculator?

OBJECTIVE 3
11. From Example 11, what is an important difference between the square root and the cube root of a negative number?

OBJECTIVE 4
12. From Example 12, what conclusion is made about the even root of a negative number?

OBJECTIVE 5
13. From the lecture before Example 17, why do you think no absolute value bars are used when n is odd?

OBJECTIVE 6
14. In Example 19, the domain is found by looking at the graph. How can the domain be found by looking at the function?

10.1 Exercise Set   MyMathLab®

Simplify. Assume that variables represent positive real numbers. See Example 1.

1. $\sqrt{100}$

2. $\sqrt{400}$

3. $\sqrt{\dfrac{1}{4}}$

4. $\sqrt{\dfrac{9}{25}}$

5. $\sqrt{0.0001}$

6. $\sqrt{0.04}$

7. $-\sqrt{36}$

8. $-\sqrt{9}$

9. $\sqrt{x^{10}}$

10. $\sqrt{x^{16}}$

11. $\sqrt{16y^6}$

12. $\sqrt{64y^{20}}$

Use a calculator to approximate each square root to 3 decimal places. Check to see that each approximation is reasonable. See Example 2.

13. $\sqrt{7}$

14. $\sqrt{11}$

▶ 15. $\sqrt{38}$

16. $\sqrt{56}$

17. $\sqrt{200}$

18. $\sqrt{300}$

Find each cube root. See Example 3.

19. $\sqrt[3]{64}$

20. $\sqrt[3]{27}$

▶ 21. $\sqrt[3]{\dfrac{1}{8}}$

22. $\sqrt[3]{\dfrac{27}{64}}$

23. $\sqrt[3]{-1}$

24. $\sqrt[3]{-125}$

25. $\sqrt[3]{x^{12}}$

26. $\sqrt[3]{x^{15}}$

▶ 27. $\sqrt[3]{-27x^9}$

28. $\sqrt[3]{-64x^6}$

Find each root. Assume that all variables represent nonnegative real numbers. See Example 4.

29. $-\sqrt[4]{16}$

30. $\sqrt[5]{-243}$

31. $\sqrt[4]{-16}$

32. $\sqrt{-16}$

33. $\sqrt[5]{-32}$

34. $\sqrt[5]{-1}$

35. $\sqrt[5]{x^{20}}$

36. $\sqrt[4]{x^{20}}$

37. $\sqrt[6]{64x^{12}}$

38. $\sqrt[5]{-32x^{15}}$

39. $\sqrt{81x^4}$

40. $\sqrt[4]{81x^4}$

41. $\sqrt[4]{256x^8}$

42. $\sqrt{256x^8}$

Simplify. Assume that the variables represent any real number. See Example 5.

43. $\sqrt{(-8)^2}$

44. $\sqrt{(-7)^2}$

45. $\sqrt[3]{(-8)^3}$

46. $\sqrt[5]{(-7)^5}$

47. $\sqrt{4x^2}$

48. $\sqrt[4]{16x^4}$

49. $\sqrt[3]{x^3}$

50. $\sqrt[5]{x^5}$

51. $\sqrt{(x-5)^2}$

52. $\sqrt{(y-6)^2}$

53. $\sqrt{x^2+4x+4}$
(*Hint:* Factor the polynomial first.)

54. $\sqrt{x^2-8x+16}$
(*Hint:* Factor the polynomial first.)

MIXED PRACTICE

Simplify each radical. Assume that all variables represent positive real numbers.

55. $-\sqrt{121}$

56. $-\sqrt[3]{125}$

57. $\sqrt[3]{8x^3}$

58. $\sqrt{16x^8}$

59. $\sqrt{y^{12}}$

60. $\sqrt[3]{y^{12}}$

61. $\sqrt{25a^2b^{20}}$

62. $\sqrt{9x^4y^6}$

63. $\sqrt[3]{-27x^{12}y^9}$

64. $\sqrt[3]{-8a^{21}b^6}$

65. $\sqrt[4]{a^{16}b^4}$

66. $\sqrt[4]{x^8y^{12}}$

67. $\sqrt[5]{-32x^{10}y^5}$

68. $\sqrt[5]{-243x^5z^{15}}$

69. $\sqrt{\dfrac{25}{49}}$

70. $\sqrt{\dfrac{4}{81}}$

71. $\sqrt{\dfrac{x^{20}}{4y^2}}$

72. $\sqrt{\dfrac{y^{10}}{9x^6}}$

73. $-\sqrt[3]{\dfrac{z^{21}}{27x^3}}$

74. $-\sqrt[3]{\dfrac{64a^3}{b^9}}$

75. $\sqrt[4]{\dfrac{x^4}{16}}$

76. $\sqrt[4]{\dfrac{y^4}{81x^4}}$

If $f(x) = \sqrt{2x+3}$ and $g(x) = \sqrt[3]{x-8}$, find the following function values. See Example 6.

77. $f(0)$

78. $g(0)$

79. $g(7)$

80. $f(-1)$

81. $g(-19)$

82. $f(3)$

83. $f(2)$

84. $g(1)$

Identify the domain and then graph each function. See Example 7.

85. $f(x) = \sqrt{x} + 2$

86. $f(x) = \sqrt{x} - 2$

87. $f(x) = \sqrt{x-3}$; use the following table.

x	$f(x)$
3	
4	
7	
12	

88. $f(x) = \sqrt{x+1}$; use the following table.

x	$f(x)$
-1	
0	
3	
8	

Identify the domain and then graph each function. See Example 8.

89. $f(x) = \sqrt[3]{x} + 1$

90. $f(x) = \sqrt[3]{x} - 2$

91. $g(x) = \sqrt[3]{x-1}$; use the following table.

x	$g(x)$
1	
2	
0	
9	
-7	

92. $g(x) = \sqrt[3]{x+1}$; use the following table.

x	$g(x)$
-1	
0	
-2	
7	
-9	

REVIEW AND PREVIEW

Simplify each exponential expression. See Sections 5.1 and 5.5.

93. $(-2x^3y^2)^5$

94. $(4y^6z^7)^3$

95. $(-3x^2y^3z^5)(20x^5y^7)$

96. $(-14a^5bc^2)(2abc^4)$

97. $\dfrac{7x^{-1}y}{14(x^5y^2)^{-2}}$

98. $\dfrac{(2a^{-1}b^2)^3}{(8a^2b)^{-2}}$

CONCEPT EXTENSIONS

Determine whether the following are real numbers. See the Concept Check in this section.

99. $\sqrt{-17}$

100. $\sqrt[3]{-17}$

101. $\sqrt[10]{-17}$

102. $\sqrt[15]{-17}$

Choose the correct letter or letters. No pencil is needed, just think your way through these.

103. Which radical is not a real number?

   a. $\sqrt{3}$ **b.** $-\sqrt{11}$ **c.** $\sqrt[3]{-10}$ **d.** $\sqrt{-10}$

104. Which radical(s) simplify to 3?

   a. $\sqrt{9}$ **b.** $\sqrt{-9}$ **c.** $\sqrt[3]{27}$ **d.** $\sqrt[3]{-27}$

105. Which radical(s) simplify to -3?

   a. $\sqrt{9}$ **b.** $\sqrt{-9}$ **c.** $\sqrt[3]{27}$ **d.** $\sqrt[3]{-27}$

106. Which radical does not simplify to a whole number?

   a. $\sqrt{64}$ **b.** $\sqrt[3]{64}$ **c.** $\sqrt{8}$ **d.** $\sqrt[3]{8}$

For Exercises 107 through 110, do not use a calculator.

107. $\sqrt{160}$ is closest to

   a. 10   **b.** 13   **c.** 20   **d.** 40

108. $\sqrt{1000}$ is closest to

   a. 10   **b.** 30   **c.** 100   **d.** 500

△ **109.** The perimeter of the triangle is closest to

   a. 12   **b.** 18

   c. 66   **d.** 132

110. The length of the bent wire is closest to

   a. 5   **b.** $\sqrt{28}$

   c. 7   **d.** 14

111. Explain why $\sqrt{-64}$ is not a real number.

112. Explain why $\sqrt[3]{-64}$ is a real number.

The Mosteller formula for calculating adult body surface area is $B = \sqrt{\dfrac{hw}{3131}}$, where B is an individual's body surface area in square meters, h is the individual's height in inches, and w is the individual's weight in pounds. Use this information to answer Exercises 113 and 114. Round answers to 2 decimal places.

△ **113.** Find the body surface area of an individual who is 66 inches tall and who weighs 135 pounds.

△ **114.** Find the body surface area of an individual who is 74 inches tall and who weighs 225 pounds.

115. Escape velocity is the minimum speed that an object must reach to escape the pull of a planet's gravity. Escape velocity v is given by the equation $v = \sqrt{\dfrac{2Gm}{r}}$, where m is the mass of the planet, r is its radius, and G is the universal gravitational constant, which has a value of $G = 6.67 \times 10^{-11} \, \text{m}^3/\text{kg} \cdot \text{s}^2$. The mass of Earth is 5.97×10^{24} kg, and its radius is 6.37×10^6 m. Use this information to find the escape velocity for Earth in meters per second. Round to the nearest whole number. (*Source*: National Space Science Data Center)

116. Use the formula from Exercise 115 to determine the escape velocity for the moon. The mass of the moon is 7.35×10^{22} kg, and its radius is 1.74×10^6 m. Round to the nearest whole number. (*Source*: National Space Science Data Center)

117. Suppose a classmate tells you that $\sqrt{13} \approx 5.7$. Without a calculator, how can you convince your classmate that he or she must have made an error?

118. Suppose a classmate tells you that $\sqrt[3]{10} \approx 3.2$. Without a calculator, how can you convince your friend that he or she must have made an error?

Use a graphing calculator to verify the domain of each function and its graph.

119. Exercise 85   **120.** Exercise 86

121. Exercise 89   **122.** Exercise 90

10.2 | Rational Exponents

OBJECTIVE

1   Understanding the Meaning of $a^{1/n}$

So far in this text, we have not defined expressions with rational exponents such as $3^{1/2}$, $x^{2/3}$, and $-9^{-1/4}$. We will define these expressions so that the rules for exponents will apply to these rational exponents as well.

Suppose that $x = 5^{1/3}$. Then

$$x^3 = (5^{1/3})^3 = 5^{1/3 \cdot 3} = 5^1 \text{ or } 5$$

using rules for exponents

Since $x^3 = 5$, x is the number whose cube is 5, or $x = \sqrt[3]{5}$. Notice that we also know that $x = 5^{1/3}$. This means

$$5^{1/3} = \sqrt[3]{5}$$

> **Definition of $a^{1/n}$**
>
> If n is a positive integer greater than 1 and $\sqrt[n]{a}$ is a real number, then
>
> $$a^{1/n} = \sqrt[n]{a}$$

Notice that the denominator of the rational exponent corresponds to the index of the radical.

EXAMPLE 1   Use radical notation to write the following. Simplify if possible.

a. $4^{1/2}$ **b.** $64^{1/3}$ **c.** $x^{1/4}$ **d.** $0^{1/6}$ **e.** $-9^{1/2}$ **f.** $(81x^8)^{1/4}$ **g.** $5y^{1/3}$

Solution

a. $4^{1/2} = \sqrt{4} = 2$ **b.** $64^{1/3} = \sqrt[3]{64} = 4$

c. $x^{1/4} = \sqrt[4]{x}$ **d.** $0^{1/6} = \sqrt[6]{0} = 0$

e. $-9^{1/2} = -\sqrt{9} = -3$ **f.** $(81x^8)^{1/4} = \sqrt[4]{81x^8} = 3x^2$

g. $5y^{1/3} = 5\sqrt[3]{y}$

PRACTICE

1   Use radical notation to write the following. Simplify if possible.

a. $36^{1/2}$ **b.** $1000^{1/3}$ **c.** $x^{1/3}$ **d.** $1^{1/4}$

e. $-64^{1/2}$ **f.** $(125x^9)^{1/3}$ **g.** $3x^{1/4}$

OBJECTIVE

2   Understanding the Meaning of $a^{m/n}$

As we expand our use of exponents to include $\dfrac{m}{n}$, we define their meaning so that rules for exponents still hold true. For example, by properties of exponents,

$$8^{2/3} = (8^{1/3})^2 = (\sqrt[3]{8})^2 \quad \text{or}$$
$$8^{2/3} = (8^2)^{1/3} = \sqrt[3]{8^2}$$

> **Definition of $a^{m/n}$**
>
> If m and n are positive integers greater than 1 with $\dfrac{m}{n}$ in simplest form, then
>
> $$a^{m/n} = \sqrt[n]{a^m} = (\sqrt[n]{a})^m$$
>
> as long as $\sqrt[n]{a}$ is a real number.

Notice that the denominator n of the rational exponent corresponds to the index of the radical. The numerator m of the rational exponent indicates that the base is to be raised to the mth power. This means

$$8^{2/3} = \sqrt[3]{8^2} = \sqrt[3]{64} = 4 \qquad \text{or}$$

$$8^{2/3} = \left(\sqrt[3]{8}\right)^2 = 2^2 = 4$$

From simplifying $8^{2/3}$, can you see that it doesn't matter whether you raise to a power first and then take the nth root or you take the nth root first and then raise to a power?

> ▶ Helpful Hint
>
> Most of the time, $\left(\sqrt[n]{a}\right)^m$ will be easier to calculate than $\sqrt[n]{a^m}$.

EXAMPLE 2   Use radical notation to write the following. Then simplify if possible.

a. $4^{3/2}$ **b.** $-16^{3/4}$ **c.** $(-27)^{2/3}$

d. $\left(\dfrac{1}{9}\right)^{3/2}$ **e.** $(4x - 1)^{3/5}$

Solution

a. $4^{3/2} = \left(\sqrt{4}\right)^3 = 2^3 = 8$ **b.** $-16^{3/4} = -\left(\sqrt[4]{16}\right)^3 = -(2)^3 = -8$

c. $(-27)^{2/3} = \left(\sqrt[3]{-27}\right)^2 = (-3)^2 = 9$ **d.** $\left(\dfrac{1}{9}\right)^{3/2} = \left(\sqrt{\dfrac{1}{9}}\right)^3 = \left(\dfrac{1}{3}\right)^3 = \dfrac{1}{27}$

e. $(4x - 1)^{3/5} = \sqrt[5]{(4x - 1)^3}$

PRACTICE

2   Use radical notation to write the following. Simplify if possible.

a. $16^{3/2}$ **b.** $-1^{3/5}$ **c.** $-(81)^{3/4}$

d. $\left(\dfrac{1}{25}\right)^{3/2}$ **e.** $(3x + 2)^{5/9}$

> ▶ Helpful Hint
>
> The *denominator* of a rational exponent is the index of the corresponding radical. For example, $x^{1/5} = \sqrt[5]{x}$ and $z^{2/3} = \sqrt[3]{z^2}$, or $z^{2/3} = \left(\sqrt[3]{z}\right)^2$.

OBJECTIVE

3   Understanding the Meaning of $a^{-m/n}$ ▶

The rational exponents we have given meaning to exclude negative rational numbers. To complete the set of definitions, we define $a^{-m/n}$.

> **Definition of $a^{-m/n}$**
>
> $$a^{-m/n} = \dfrac{1}{a^{m/n}}$$
>
> as long as $a^{m/n}$ is a nonzero real number.

EXAMPLE 3   Write each expression with a positive exponent, and then simplify.

a. $16^{-3/4}$ **b.** $(-27)^{-2/3}$

Solution

a. $16^{-3/4} = \dfrac{1}{16^{3/4}} = \dfrac{1}{\left(\sqrt[4]{16}\right)^3} = \dfrac{1}{2^3} = \dfrac{1}{8}$

b. $(-27)^{-2/3} = \dfrac{1}{(-27)^{2/3}} = \dfrac{1}{\left(\sqrt[3]{-27}\right)^2} = \dfrac{1}{(-3)^2} = \dfrac{1}{9}$

(Continued on next page)

PRACTICE

3 Write each expression with a positive exponent; then simplify.

a. $9^{-3/2}$

b. $(-64)^{-2/3}$

> ▶ Helpful Hint
>
> If an expression contains a negative rational exponent, such as $9^{-3/2}$, you may want to first write the expression with a positive exponent and then interpret the rational exponent. Notice that the sign of the base is not affected by the sign of its exponent. For example,
>
> $$9^{-3/2} = \frac{1}{9^{3/2}} = \frac{1}{(\sqrt{9})^3} = \frac{1}{27}$$
>
> Also,
>
> $$(-27)^{-1/3} = \frac{1}{(-27)^{1/3}} = -\frac{1}{3}$$

✓CONCEPT CHECK

Which one is correct?

a. $-8^{2/3} = \dfrac{1}{4}$

b. $8^{-2/3} = -\dfrac{1}{4}$

c. $8^{-2/3} = -4$

d. $-8^{-2/3} = -\dfrac{1}{4}$

OBJECTIVE

4 Using Rules for Exponents to Simplify Expressions

It can be shown that the properties of integer exponents hold for rational exponents. By using these properties and definitions, we can now simplify expressions that contain rational exponents.

These rules are repeated here for review.

Note: For the remainder of this chapter, we will assume that variables represent positive real numbers. Since this is so, we need not insert absolute value bars when we simplify even roots.

Summary of Exponent Rules

If m and n are rational numbers, and a, b, and c are numbers for which the expressions below exist, then

Product rule for exponents:	$a^m \cdot a^n = a^{m+n}$
Power rule for exponents:	$(a^m)^n = a^{m \cdot n}$
Power rules for products and quotients:	$(ab)^n = a^n b^n$ and
	$\left(\dfrac{a}{c}\right)^n = \dfrac{a^n}{c^n}, c \neq 0$
Quotient rule for exponents:	$\dfrac{a^m}{a^n} = a^{m-n}, a \neq 0$
Zero exponent:	$a^0 = 1, a \neq 0$
Negative exponent:	$a^{-n} = \dfrac{1}{a^n}, a \neq 0$

EXAMPLE 4 Use properties of exponents to simplify. Write results with only positive exponents.

a. $b^{1/3} \cdot b^{5/3}$

b. $x^{1/2} x^{1/3}$

c. $\dfrac{7^{1/3}}{7^{4/3}}$

d. $y^{-4/7} \cdot y^{6/7}$

e. $\dfrac{(2x^{2/5}y^{-1/3})^5}{x^2 y}$

Solution

a. $b^{1/3} \cdot b^{5/3} = b^{(1/3+5/3)} = b^{6/3} = b^2$

b. $x^{1/2} x^{1/3} = x^{(1/2+1/3)} = x^{3/6+2/6} = x^{5/6}$ Use the product rule.

c. $\dfrac{7^{1/3}}{7^{4/3}} = 7^{1/3-4/3} = 7^{-3/3} = 7^{-1} = \dfrac{1}{7}$ Use the quotient rule.

d. $y^{-4/7} \cdot y^{6/7} = y^{-4/7+6/7} = y^{2/7}$ Use the product rule.

e. We begin by using the power rule $(ab)^m = a^m b^m$ to simplify the numerator.

$$\frac{(2x^{2/5}y^{-1/3})^5}{x^2 y} = \frac{2^5(x^{2/5})^5(y^{-1/3})^5}{x^2 y} = \frac{32x^2 y^{-5/3}}{x^2 y}$$ Use the power rule and simplify

$$= 32x^{2-2}y^{-5/3-3/3}$$ Apply the quotient rule.

$$= 32x^0 y^{-8/3}$$

$$= \frac{32}{y^{8/3}}$$ □

PRACTICE
4   Use properties of exponents to simplify.

a. $y^{2/3} \cdot y^{8/3}$ **b.** $x^{3/5} \cdot x^{1/4}$ **c.** $\dfrac{9^{2/7}}{9^{9/7}}$

d. $b^{4/9} \cdot b^{-2/9}$ **e.** $\dfrac{(3x^{1/4}y^{-2/3})^4}{x^4 y}$

EXAMPLE 5   Multiply.

a. $z^{2/3}(z^{1/3} - z^5)$ **b.** $(x^{1/3} - 5)(x^{1/3} + 2)$

Solution

a. $z^{2/3}(z^{1/3} - z^5) = z^{2/3} z^{1/3} - z^{2/3} z^5$ Apply the distributive property.

$$= z^{(2/3+1/3)} - z^{(2/3+5)}$$ Use the product rule.

$$= z^{3/3} - z^{(2/3+15/3)}$$

$$= z - z^{17/3}$$

b. $(x^{1/3} - 5)(x^{1/3} + 2) = x^{2/3} + 2x^{1/3} - 5x^{1/3} - 10$ Think of $(x^{1/3} - 5)$ and $(x^{1/3} + 2)$ as 2 binomials, and FOIL.

$$= x^{2/3} - 3x^{1/3} - 10$$ □

PRACTICE
5   Multiply.

a. $x^{3/5}(x^{1/3} - x^2)$ **b.** $(x^{1/2} + 6)(x^{1/2} - 2)$

EXAMPLE 6   Factor $x^{-1/2}$ from the expression $3x^{-1/2} - 7x^{5/2}$. Assume that all variables represent positive numbers.

Solution

$$3x^{-1/2} - 7x^{5/2} = (x^{-1/2})(3) - (x^{-1/2})(7x^{6/2})$$

$$= x^{-1/2}(3 - 7x^3)$$

To check, multiply $x^{-1/2}(3 - 7x^3)$ to see that the product is $3x^{-1/2} - 7x^{5/2}$.   □

PRACTICE
6   Factor $x^{-1/5}$ from the expression $2x^{-1/5} - 7x^{4/5}$.

OBJECTIVE

5 Using Rational Exponents to Simplify Radical Expressions

Some radical expressions are easier to simplify when we first write them with rational exponents. Use properties of exponents to simplify, and then convert back to radical notation.

EXAMPLE 7 Use rational exponents to simplify. Assume that variables represent positive numbers.

a. $\sqrt[8]{x^4}$ **b.** $\sqrt[6]{25}$ **c.** $\sqrt[4]{r^2 s^6}$

Solution

a. $\sqrt[8]{x^4} = x^{4/8} = x^{1/2} = \sqrt{x}$

b. $\sqrt[6]{25} = 25^{1/6} = (5^2)^{1/6} = 5^{2/6} = 5^{1/3} = \sqrt[3]{5}$

c. $\sqrt[4]{r^2 s^6} = (r^2 s^6)^{1/4} = r^{2/4} s^{6/4} = r^{1/2} s^{3/2} = (rs^3)^{1/2} = \sqrt{rs^3}$

PRACTICE

7 Use rational exponents to simplify. Assume that the variables represent positive numbers.

a. $\sqrt[9]{x^3}$ **b.** $\sqrt[4]{36}$ **c.** $\sqrt[8]{a^4 b^2}$

EXAMPLE 8 Use rational exponents to write as a single radical.

a. $\sqrt{x} \cdot \sqrt[4]{x}$ **b.** $\dfrac{\sqrt{x}}{\sqrt[3]{x}}$ **c.** $\sqrt[3]{3} \cdot \sqrt{2}$

Solution

a. $\sqrt{x} \cdot \sqrt[4]{x} = x^{1/2} \cdot x^{1/4} = x^{1/2 + 1/4}$
$= x^{3/4} = \sqrt[4]{x^3}$

b. $\dfrac{\sqrt{x}}{\sqrt[3]{x}} = \dfrac{x^{1/2}}{x^{1/3}} = x^{1/2 - 1/3} = x^{3/6 - 2/6}$
$= x^{1/6} = \sqrt[6]{x}$

c. $\sqrt[3]{3} \cdot \sqrt{2} = 3^{1/3} \cdot 2^{1/2}$ Write with rational exponents.

$= 3^{2/6} \cdot 2^{3/6}$ Write the exponents so that they have the same denominator.

$= (3^2 \cdot 2^3)^{1/6}$ Use $a^n b^n = (ab)^n$

$= \sqrt[6]{3^2 \cdot 2^3}$ Write with radical notation.

$= \sqrt[6]{72}$ Multiply $3^2 \cdot 2^3$.

PRACTICE

8 Use rational expressions to write each of the following as a single radical.

a. $\sqrt[3]{x} \cdot \sqrt[4]{x}$ **b.** $\dfrac{\sqrt[3]{y}}{\sqrt[5]{y}}$ **c.** $\sqrt[3]{5} \cdot \sqrt{3}$

Vocabulary, Readiness & Video Check

Answer each true or false.

1. $9^{-1/2}$ is a positive number. _____

2. $9^{-1/2}$ is a whole number. _____

3. $\dfrac{1}{a^{-m/n}} = a^{m/n}$ (where $a^{m/n}$ is a nonzero real number). _____

Fill in the blank with the correct choice.

4. To simplify $x^{2/3} \cdot x^{1/5}$, _____ the exponents.
   a. add   **b.** subtract   **c.** multiply   **d.** divide

5. To simplify $(x^{2/3})^{1/5}$, _____ the exponents.
   a. add   **b.** subtract   **c.** multiply   **d.** divide

6. To simplify $\dfrac{x^{2/3}}{x^{1/5}}$, _____ the exponents.
   a. add   **b.** subtract   **c.** multiply   **d.** divide

---

Martin-Gay Interactive Videos

See Video 10.2

Watch the section lecture video and answer the following questions.

OBJECTIVE 1
7. From looking at Example 2, what is $-(3x)^{1/5}$ in radical notation?

OBJECTIVE 2
8. From Examples 3 and 4, in a fractional exponent, what do the numerator and denominator each represent in radical form?

OBJECTIVE 3
9. Based on Example 5, complete the following statements. A negative fractional exponent will move a base from the numerator to the _____ with the fractional exponent becoming _____.

OBJECTIVE 4
10. Based on Examples 7–9, complete the following statements. Assume you have an expression with fractional exponents. If applying the product rule of exponents, you _____ the exponents. If applying the quotient rule of exponents, you _____ the exponents. If applying the power rule of exponents, you _____ the exponents.

OBJECTIVE 5
11. From Example 10, describe a way to simplify a radical of a variable raised to a power if the index and the exponent have a common factor.

10.2 Exercise Set   MyMathLab®

Use radical notation to write each expression. Simplify if possible. See Example 1.

1. $49^{1/2}$ **2.** $64^{1/3}$

3. $27^{1/3}$ **4.** $8^{1/3}$

5. $\left(\dfrac{1}{16}\right)^{1/4}$ **6.** $\left(\dfrac{1}{64}\right)^{1/2}$

7. $169^{1/2}$ **8.** $81^{1/4}$

9. $2m^{1/3}$ **10.** $(2m)^{1/3}$

11. $(9x^4)^{1/2}$ **12.** $(16x^8)^{1/2}$

13. $(-27)^{1/3}$ **14.** $-64^{1/2}$

15. $-16^{1/4}$ **16.** $(-32)^{1/5}$

Use radical notation to write each expression. Simplify if possible. See Example 2.

17. $16^{3/4}$ **18.** $4^{5/2}$

19. $(-64)^{2/3}$ **20.** $(-8)^{4/3}$

21. $(-16)^{3/4}$ **22.** $(-9)^{3/2}$

23. $(2x)^{3/5}$ **24.** $2x^{3/5}$

25. $(7x + 2)^{2/3}$ **26.** $(x - 4)^{3/4}$

27. $\left(\dfrac{16}{9}\right)^{3/2}$ **28.** $\left(\dfrac{49}{25}\right)^{3/2}$

Write with positive exponents. Simplify if possible. See Example 3.

29. $8^{-4/3}$ **30.** $64^{-2/3}$

31. $(-64)^{-2/3}$ **32.** $(-8)^{-4/3}$

33. $(-4)^{-3/2}$ **34.** $(-16)^{-5/4}$

35. $x^{-1/4}$ **36.** $y^{-1/6}$

37. $\dfrac{1}{a^{-2/3}}$ **38.** $\dfrac{1}{n^{-8/9}}$

39. $\dfrac{5}{7x^{-3/4}}$ **40.** $\dfrac{2}{3y^{-5/7}}$

Use the properties of exponents to simplify each expression. Write with positive exponents. See Example 4.

41. $a^{2/3}a^{5/3}$ **42.** $b^{9/5}b^{8/5}$

43. $x^{-2/5} \cdot x^{7/5}$ **44.** $y^{4/3} \cdot y^{-1/3}$

45. $3^{1/4} \cdot 3^{3/8}$ **46.** $5^{1/2} \cdot 5^{1/6}$

47. $\dfrac{y^{1/3}}{y^{1/6}}$ **48.** $\dfrac{x^{3/4}}{x^{1/8}}$

49. $(4u^2)^{3/2}$ **50.** $(32^{1/5}x^{2/3})^3$

51. $\dfrac{b^{1/2}b^{3/4}}{-b^{1/4}}$ **52.** $\dfrac{a^{1/4}a^{-1/2}}{a^{2/3}}$

53. $\dfrac{(x^3)^{1/2}}{x^{7/2}}$ **54.** $\dfrac{y^{11/3}}{(y^5)^{1/3}}$

55. $\dfrac{(3x^{1/4})^3}{x^{1/12}}$

56. $\dfrac{(2x^{1/5})^4}{x^{3/10}}$

57. $\dfrac{(y^3z)^{1/6}}{y^{-1/2}z^{1/3}}$

58. $\dfrac{(m^2n)^{1/4}}{m^{-1/2}n^{5/8}}$

59. $\dfrac{(x^3y^2)^{1/4}}{(x^{-5}y^{-1})^{-1/2}}$

60. $\dfrac{(a^{-2}b^3)^{1/8}}{(a^{-3}b)^{-1/4}}$

Multiply. See Example 5.

61. $y^{1/2}(y^{1/2} - y^{2/3})$

62. $x^{1/2}(x^{1/2} + x^{3/2})$

63. $x^{2/3}(x - 2)$

64. $3x^{1/2}(x + y)$

65. $(2x^{1/3} + 3)(2x^{1/3} - 3)$

66. $(y^{1/2} + 5)(y^{1/2} + 5)$

Factor the given factor from the expression. See Example 6.

67. $x^{8/3}; x^{8/3} + x^{10/3}$

68. $x^{3/2}; x^{5/2} - x^{3/2}$

69. $x^{1/5}; x^{2/5} - 3x^{1/5}$

70. $x^{2/7}; x^{3/7} - 2x^{2/7}$

71. $x^{-1/3}; 5x^{-1/3} + x^{2/3}$

72. $x^{-3/4}; x^{-3/4} + 3x^{1/4}$

Use rational exponents to simplify each radical. Assume that all variables represent positive numbers. See Example 7.

73. $\sqrt[6]{x^3}$

74. $\sqrt[9]{a^3}$

75. $\sqrt[6]{4}$

76. $\sqrt[4]{36}$

77. $\sqrt[4]{16x^2}$

78. $\sqrt[8]{4y^2}$

79. $\sqrt[8]{x^4y^4}$

80. $\sqrt[9]{y^6z^3}$

81. $\sqrt[12]{a^8b^4}$

82. $\sqrt[10]{a^5b^5}$

83. $\sqrt[4]{(x + 3)^2}$

84. $\sqrt[8]{(y + 1)^4}$

Use rational expressions to write as a single radical expression. See Example 8.

85. $\sqrt[3]{y} \cdot \sqrt[5]{y^2}$

86. $\sqrt[3]{y^2} \cdot \sqrt[6]{y}$

87. $\dfrac{\sqrt[3]{b^2}}{\sqrt[4]{b}}$

88. $\dfrac{\sqrt[4]{a}}{\sqrt[5]{a}}$

89. $\sqrt[3]{x} \cdot \sqrt[4]{x} \cdot \sqrt[8]{x^3}$

90. $\sqrt[6]{y} \cdot \sqrt[3]{y} \cdot \sqrt[5]{y^2}$

91. $\dfrac{\sqrt[3]{a^2}}{\sqrt[6]{a}}$

92. $\dfrac{\sqrt[5]{b^2}}{\sqrt[10]{b^3}}$

93. $\sqrt{3} \cdot \sqrt[3]{4}$

94. $\sqrt[3]{5} \cdot \sqrt{2}$

95. $\sqrt[5]{7} \cdot \sqrt[3]{y}$

96. $3\sqrt[4]{5} \cdot \sqrt[3]{x}$

97. $\sqrt{5r} \cdot \sqrt[3]{s}$

98. $\sqrt[3]{b} \cdot \sqrt[5]{4a}$

REVIEW AND PREVIEW

Write each integer as a product of two integers such that one of the factors is a perfect square. For example, write 18 as $9 \cdot 2$ because 9 is a perfect square.

99. 75

100. 20

101. 48

102. 45

Write each integer as a product of two integers such that one of the factors is a perfect cube. For example, write 24 as $8 \cdot 3$ because 8 is a perfect cube.

103. 16

104. 56

105. 54

106. 80

CONCEPT EXTENSIONS

Choose the correct letter for each exercise. Letters will be used more than once. No pencil is needed. Just think about the meaning of each expression.

A = 2, B = −2, C = not a real number

107. $4^{1/2}$ _____

108. $-4^{1/2}$ _____

109. $(-4)^{1/2}$ _____

110. $8^{1/3}$ _____

111. $-8^{1/3}$ _____

112. $(-8)^{1/3}$ _____

Basal metabolic rate (BMR) is the number of calories per day a person needs to maintain life. A person's basal metabolic rate $B(w)$ in calories per day can be estimated with the function $B(w) = 70w^{3/4}$, where w is the person's weight in kilograms. Use this information to answer Exercises 113 and 114.

113. Estimate the BMR for a person who weighs 60 kilograms. Round to the nearest calorie. (*Note:* 60 kilograms is approximately 132 pounds.)

114. Estimate the BMR for a person who weighs 90 kilograms. Round to the nearest calorie. (*Note:* 90 kilograms is approximately 198 pounds.)

The number of cell telephone subscribers in the United States from 1995–2010 can be modeled by $f(x) = 25x^{23/25}$, where $f(x)$ is the number of cellular telephone subscriptions in millions, x years after 1995. (Source: CTIA-Wireless Association, 1995–2010) Use this information to answer Exercises 115 and 116.

115. Use this model to estimate the number of cellular subscriptions in 2010. Round to the nearest tenth of a million.

116. Predict the number of cellular telephone subscriptions in 2015. Round to the nearest tenth of a million.

117. Explain how writing x^{-7} with positive exponents is similar to writing $x^{-1/4}$ with positive exponents.

118. Explain how writing $2x^{-5}$ with positive exponents is similar to writing $2x^{-3/4}$ with positive exponents.

Fill in each box with the correct expression.

119. $\square \cdot a^{2/3} = a^{3/3}$, or a

120. $\square \cdot x^{1/8} = x^{4/8}$, or $x^{1/2}$

121. $\dfrac{\square}{x^{-2/5}} = x^{3/5}$

122. $\dfrac{\square}{y^{-3/4}} = y^{4/4}$, or y

Use a calculator to write a four-decimal-place approximation of each number.

123. $8^{1/4}$

124. $20^{1/5}$

125. $18^{3/5}$

126. $76^{5/7}$

127. In physics, the speed of a wave traveling over a stretched string with tension t and density u is given by the expression $\dfrac{\sqrt{t}}{\sqrt{u}}$. Write this expression with rational exponents.

128. In electronics, the angular frequency of oscillations in a certain type of circuit is given by the expression $(LC)^{-1/2}$. Use radical notation to write this expression.

10.3 Simplifying Radical Expressions

OBJECTIVES

1 Use the Product Rule for Radicals.

2 Use the Quotient Rule for Radicals.

3 Simplify Radicals.

4 Use the Distance and Midpoint Formulas.

OBJECTIVE

1 Using the Product Rule

It is possible to simplify some radicals that do not evaluate to rational numbers. To do so, we use a product rule and a quotient rule for radicals. To discover the product rule, notice the following pattern.

$$\sqrt{9} \cdot \sqrt{4} = 3 \cdot 2 = 6$$
$$\sqrt{9 \cdot 4} = \sqrt{36} = 6$$

Since both expressions simplify to 6, it is true that

$$\sqrt{9} \cdot \sqrt{4} = \sqrt{9 \cdot 4}$$

This pattern suggests the following product rule for radicals.

> **Product Rule for Radicals**
>
> If $\sqrt[n]{a}$ and $\sqrt[n]{b}$ are real numbers, then
> $$\sqrt[n]{a} \cdot \sqrt[n]{b} = \sqrt[n]{ab}$$

Notice that the product rule is the relationship $a^{1/n} \cdot b^{1/n} = (ab)^{1/n}$ stated in radical notation.

EXAMPLE 1 Multiply.

a. $\sqrt{3} \cdot \sqrt{5}$ **b.** $\sqrt{21} \cdot \sqrt{x}$ **c.** $\sqrt[3]{4} \cdot \sqrt[3]{2}$

d. $\sqrt[4]{5y^2} \cdot \sqrt[4]{2x^3}$ **e.** $\sqrt{\dfrac{2}{a}} \cdot \sqrt{\dfrac{b}{3}}$

Solution

a. $\sqrt{3} \cdot \sqrt{5} = \sqrt{3 \cdot 5} = \sqrt{15}$

b. $\sqrt{21} \cdot \sqrt{x} = \sqrt{21x}$

c. $\sqrt[3]{4} \cdot \sqrt[3]{2} = \sqrt[3]{4 \cdot 2} = \sqrt[3]{8} = 2$

d. $\sqrt[4]{5y^2} \cdot \sqrt[4]{2x^3} = \sqrt[4]{5y^2 \cdot 2x^3} = \sqrt[4]{10y^2x^3}$

e. $\sqrt{\dfrac{2}{a}} \cdot \sqrt{\dfrac{b}{3}} = \sqrt{\dfrac{2}{a} \cdot \dfrac{b}{3}} = \sqrt{\dfrac{2b}{3a}}$

PRACTICE

1 Multiply.

a. $\sqrt{5} \cdot \sqrt{7}$ **b.** $\sqrt{13} \cdot \sqrt{z}$ **c.** $\sqrt[4]{125} \cdot \sqrt[4]{5}$

d. $\sqrt[3]{5y} \cdot \sqrt[3]{3x^2}$ **e.** $\sqrt{\dfrac{5}{m}} \cdot \sqrt{\dfrac{t}{2}}$

OBJECTIVE

2   Using the Quotient Rule

To discover a quotient rule for radicals, notice the following pattern.

$$\sqrt{\frac{4}{9}} = \frac{2}{3}$$

$$\frac{\sqrt{4}}{\sqrt{9}} = \frac{2}{3}$$

Since both expressions simplify to $\frac{2}{3}$, it is true that

$$\sqrt{\frac{4}{9}} = \frac{\sqrt{4}}{\sqrt{9}}$$

This pattern suggests the following quotient rule for radicals.

Quotient Rule for Radicals

If $\sqrt[n]{a}$ and $\sqrt[n]{b}$ are real numbers and $\sqrt[n]{b}$ is not zero, then

$$\sqrt[n]{\frac{a}{b}} = \frac{\sqrt[n]{a}}{\sqrt[n]{b}}$$

Notice that the quotient rule is the relationship $\left(\dfrac{a}{b}\right)^{1/n} = \dfrac{a^{1/n}}{b^{1/n}}$ stated in radical notation. We can use the quotient rule to simplify radical expressions by reading the rule from left to right or to divide radicals by reading the rule from right to left.

For example,

$$\sqrt{\frac{x}{16}} = \frac{\sqrt{x}}{\sqrt{16}} = \frac{\sqrt{x}}{4} \qquad \text{Using } \sqrt[n]{\frac{a}{b}} = \frac{\sqrt[n]{a}}{\sqrt[n]{b}}$$

$$\frac{\sqrt{75}}{\sqrt{3}} = \sqrt{\frac{75}{3}} = \sqrt{25} = 5 \qquad \text{Using } \frac{\sqrt[n]{a}}{\sqrt[n]{b}} = \sqrt[n]{\frac{a}{b}}$$

Note: *Recall that from Section 10.2 on, we assume that variables represent positive real numbers. Since this is so, we need not insert absolute value bars when we simplify even roots.*

EXAMPLE 2   Use the quotient rule to simplify.

a. $\sqrt{\dfrac{25}{49}}$ **b.** $\sqrt{\dfrac{x}{9}}$ **c.** $\sqrt[3]{\dfrac{8}{27}}$ **d.** $\sqrt[4]{\dfrac{3}{16y^4}}$

Solution

a. $\sqrt{\dfrac{25}{49}} = \dfrac{\sqrt{25}}{\sqrt{49}} = \dfrac{5}{7}$ **b.** $\sqrt{\dfrac{x}{9}} = \dfrac{\sqrt{x}}{\sqrt{9}} = \dfrac{\sqrt{x}}{3}$

c. $\sqrt[3]{\dfrac{8}{27}} = \dfrac{\sqrt[3]{8}}{\sqrt[3]{27}} = \dfrac{2}{3}$ **d.** $\sqrt[4]{\dfrac{3}{16y^4}} = \dfrac{\sqrt[4]{3}}{\sqrt[4]{16y^4}} = \dfrac{\sqrt[4]{3}}{2y}$

PRACTICE

2   Use the quotient rule to simplify.

a. $\sqrt{\dfrac{36}{49}}$ **b.** $\sqrt{\dfrac{z}{16}}$ **c.** $\sqrt[3]{\dfrac{125}{8}}$ **d.** $\sqrt[4]{\dfrac{5}{81x^8}}$

OBJECTIVE

3   **Simplifying Radicals**

Both the product and quotient rules can be used to simplify a radical. If the product rule is read from right to left, we have that

$$\sqrt[n]{ab} = \sqrt[n]{a} \cdot \sqrt[n]{b}.$$

This is used to simplify the following radicals.

EXAMPLE 3   Simplify the following.

a. $\sqrt{50}$ **b.** $\sqrt[3]{24}$ **c.** $\sqrt{26}$ **d.** $\sqrt[4]{32}$

Solution

a. Factor 50 such that one factor is the largest perfect square that divides 50. The largest perfect square factor of 50 is 25, so we write 50 as $25 \cdot 2$ and use the product rule for radicals to simplify.

$$\sqrt{50} = \sqrt{25 \cdot 2} = \sqrt{25} \cdot \sqrt{2} = 5\sqrt{2}$$

The largest perfect square factor of 50

> **Helpful Hint**
> Don't forget that, for example, $5\sqrt{2}$ means $5 \cdot \sqrt{2}$.

b. $\sqrt[3]{24} = \sqrt[3]{8 \cdot 3} = \sqrt[3]{8} \cdot \sqrt[3]{3} = 2\sqrt[3]{3}$

The largest perfect cube factor of 24

c. $\sqrt{26}$ The largest perfect square factor of 26 is 1, so $\sqrt{26}$ cannot be simplified further.

d. $\sqrt[4]{32} = \sqrt[4]{16 \cdot 2} = \sqrt[4]{16} \cdot \sqrt[4]{2} = 2\sqrt[4]{2}$

The largest fourth power factor of 32

PRACTICE

3   Simplify the following.

a. $\sqrt{98}$ **b.** $\sqrt[3]{54}$ **c.** $\sqrt{35}$ **d.** $\sqrt[4]{243}$

After simplifying a radical such as a square root, always check the radicand to see that it contains no other perfect square factors. It may, if the largest perfect square factor of the radicand was not originally recognized. For example,

$$\sqrt{200} = \sqrt{4 \cdot 50} = \sqrt{4} \cdot \sqrt{50} = 2\sqrt{50}$$

Notice that the radicand 50 still contains the perfect square factor 25. This is because 4 is not the largest perfect square factor of 200. We continue as follows.

$$2\sqrt{50} = 2\sqrt{25 \cdot 2} = 2 \cdot \sqrt{25} \cdot \sqrt{2} = 2 \cdot 5 \cdot \sqrt{2} = 10\sqrt{2}$$

The radical is now simplified since 2 contains no perfect square factors (other than 1).

> **Helpful Hint**
> To help you recognize largest perfect power factors of a radicand, it will help if you are familiar with some perfect powers. A few are listed below.
>
> | Perfect Squares | 1, | 4, | 9, | 16, | 25, | 36, | 49, | 64, | 81, | 100, | 121, | 144 |
> |---|---|---|---|---|---|---|---|---|---|---|---|---|
> | | 1^2 | 2^2 | 3^2 | 4^2 | 5^2 | 6^2 | 7^2 | 8^2 | 9^2 | 10^2 | 11^2 | 12^2 |
>
> | Perfect Cubes | 1, | 8, | 27, | 64, | 125 |
> |---|---|---|---|---|---|
> | | 1^3 | 2^3 | 3^3 | 4^3 | 5^3 |
>
> | Perfect Fourth Powers | 1, | 16, | 81, | 256 |
> |---|---|---|---|---|
> | | 1^4 | 2^4 | 3^4 | 4^4 |

In general, we say that a radicand of the form $\sqrt[n]{a}$ is simplified when the radicand a contains no factors that are perfect nth powers (other than 1 or -1).

EXAMPLE 4 Use the product rule to simplify.

a. $\sqrt{25x^3}$ **b.** $\sqrt[3]{54x^6y^8}$ **c.** $\sqrt[4]{81z^{11}}$

Solution

a. $\sqrt{25x^3} = \sqrt{25x^2 \cdot x}$ Find the largest perfect square factor.

$\phantom{\sqrt{25x^3}} = \sqrt{25x^2} \cdot \sqrt{x}$ Apply the product rule.

$\phantom{\sqrt{25x^3}} = 5x\sqrt{x}$ Simplify.

b. $\sqrt[3]{54x^6y^8} = \sqrt[3]{27 \cdot 2 \cdot x^6 \cdot y^6 \cdot y^2}$ Factor the radicand and identify perfect cube factors.

$\phantom{\sqrt[3]{54x^6y^8}} = \sqrt[3]{27x^6y^6 \cdot 2y^2}$

$\phantom{\sqrt[3]{54x^6y^8}} = \sqrt[3]{27x^6y^6} \cdot \sqrt[3]{2y^2}$ Apply the product rule.

$\phantom{\sqrt[3]{54x^6y^8}} = 3x^2y^2\sqrt[3]{2y^2}$ Simplify.

c. $\sqrt[4]{81z^{11}} = \sqrt[4]{81 \cdot z^8 \cdot z^3}$ Factor the radicand and identify perfect fourth power factors.

$\phantom{\sqrt[4]{81z^{11}}} = \sqrt[4]{81z^8} \cdot \sqrt[4]{z^3}$ Apply the product rule.

$\phantom{\sqrt[4]{81z^{11}}} = 3z^2\sqrt[4]{z^3}$ Simplify.   □

PRACTICE

4 Use the product rule to simplify.

a. $\sqrt{36z^7}$ **b.** $\sqrt[3]{32p^4q^7}$ **c.** $\sqrt[4]{16x^{15}}$

EXAMPLE 5 Use the quotient rule to divide, and simplify if possible.

a. $\dfrac{\sqrt{20}}{\sqrt{5}}$ **b.** $\dfrac{\sqrt{50x}}{2\sqrt{2}}$ **c.** $\dfrac{7\sqrt[3]{48x^4y^8}}{\sqrt[3]{6y^2}}$ **d.** $\dfrac{2\sqrt[4]{32a^8b^6}}{\sqrt[4]{a^{-1}b^2}}$

Solution

a. $\dfrac{\sqrt{20}}{\sqrt{5}} = \sqrt{\dfrac{20}{5}}$ Apply the quotient rule.

$\phantom{\dfrac{\sqrt{20}}{\sqrt{5}}} = \sqrt{4}$ Simplify.

$\phantom{\dfrac{\sqrt{20}}{\sqrt{5}}} = 2$ Simplify.

b. $\dfrac{\sqrt{50x}}{2\sqrt{2}} = \dfrac{1}{2} \cdot \sqrt{\dfrac{50x}{2}}$ Apply the quotient rule.

$\phantom{\dfrac{\sqrt{50x}}{2\sqrt{2}}} = \dfrac{1}{2} \cdot \sqrt{25x}$ Simplify.

$\phantom{\dfrac{\sqrt{50x}}{2\sqrt{2}}} = \dfrac{1}{2} \cdot \sqrt{25} \cdot \sqrt{x}$ Factor $25x$.

$\phantom{\dfrac{\sqrt{50x}}{2\sqrt{2}}} = \dfrac{1}{2} \cdot 5 \cdot \sqrt{x}$ Simplify.

$\phantom{\dfrac{\sqrt{50x}}{2\sqrt{2}}} = \dfrac{5}{2}\sqrt{x}$

c. $\dfrac{7\sqrt[3]{48x^4y^8}}{\sqrt[3]{6y^2}} = 7 \cdot \sqrt[3]{\dfrac{48x^4y^8}{6y^2}}$ Apply the quotient rule.

$\phantom{\dfrac{7\sqrt[3]{48x^4y^8}}{\sqrt[3]{6y^2}}} = 7 \cdot \sqrt[3]{8x^4y^6}$ Simplify.

$\phantom{\dfrac{7\sqrt[3]{48x^4y^8}}{\sqrt[3]{6y^2}}} = 7\sqrt[3]{8x^3y^6 \cdot x}$ Factor.

$\phantom{\dfrac{7\sqrt[3]{48x^4y^8}}{\sqrt[3]{6y^2}}} = 7 \cdot \sqrt[3]{8x^3y^6} \cdot \sqrt[3]{x}$ Apply the product rule.

$$= 7 \cdot 2xy^2 \cdot \sqrt[3]{x} \quad \text{Simplify.}$$
$$= 14xy^2 \sqrt[3]{x}$$

d. $\dfrac{2\sqrt[4]{32a^8b^6}}{\sqrt[4]{a^{-1}b^2}} = 2\sqrt[4]{\dfrac{32a^8b^6}{a^{-1}b^2}} = 2\sqrt[4]{32a^9b^4} = 2\sqrt[4]{16 \cdot a^8 \cdot b^4 \cdot 2 \cdot a}$

$$= 2\sqrt[4]{16a^8b^4} \cdot \sqrt[4]{2a} = 2 \cdot 2a^2b \cdot \sqrt[4]{2a} = 4a^2b\sqrt[4]{2a}$$

PRACTICE

5   Use the quotient rule to divide and simplify.

a. $\dfrac{\sqrt{80}}{\sqrt{5}}$ **b.** $\dfrac{\sqrt{98z}}{3\sqrt{2}}$ **c.** $\dfrac{5\sqrt[3]{40x^5y^7}}{\sqrt[3]{5y}}$ **d.** $\dfrac{3\sqrt[5]{64x^9y^8}}{\sqrt[5]{x^{-1}y^2}}$

✓CONCEPT CHECK
Find and correct the error:

$$\cancel{\dfrac{\sqrt[3]{27}}{\sqrt{9}} = \sqrt[3]{\dfrac{27}{9}} = \sqrt[3]{3}}$$

OBJECTIVE

4   Using the Distance and Midpoint Formulas

Now that we know how to simplify radicals, we can derive and use the distance formula. The midpoint formula is often confused with the distance formula, so to clarify both, we will also review the midpoint formula.

The Cartesian coordinate system helps us visualize a distance between points. To find the distance between two points, we use the distance formula, which is derived from the Pythagorean theorem.

To find the distance d between two points (x_1, y_1) and (x_2, y_2) as shown to the left, notice that the length of leg a is $x_2 - x_1$ and that the length of leg b is $y_2 - y_1$.

Thus, the Pythagorean theorem tells us that

$$d^2 = a^2 + b^2$$

or

$$d^2 = (x_2 - x_1)^2 + (y_2 - y_1)^2$$

or

$$d = \sqrt{(x_2 - x_1)^2 + (y_2 - y_1)^2}$$

This formula gives us the distance between any two points on the real plane.

Distance Formula

The distance d between two points (x_1, y_1) and (x_2, y_2) is given by

$$d = \sqrt{(x_2 - x_1)^2 + (y_2 - y_1)^2}$$

EXAMPLE 6   Find the distance between $(2, -5)$ and $(1, -4)$. Give an exact distance and a three-decimal-place approximation.

Solution   To use the distance formula, it makes no difference which point we call (x_1, y_1) and which point we call (x_2, y_2). We will let $(x_1, y_1) = (2, -5)$ and $(x_2, y_2) = (1, -4)$.

(Continued on next page)

Answer to Concept Check:
$\dfrac{\sqrt[3]{27}}{\sqrt{9}} = \dfrac{3}{3} = 1$

$$d = \sqrt{(x_2 - x_1)^2 + (y_2 - y_1)^2}$$
$$= \sqrt{(1 - 2)^2 + [-4 - (-5)]^2}$$
$$= \sqrt{(-1)^2 + (1)^2}$$
$$= \sqrt{1 + 1}$$
$$= \sqrt{2} \approx 1.414$$

The distance between the two points is exactly $\sqrt{2}$ units, or approximately 1.414 units.

PRACTICE

6 Find the distance between $(-3, 7)$ and $(-2, 3)$. Give an exact distance and a three-decimal-place approximation.

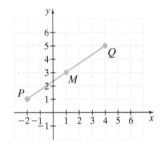

The **midpoint** of a line segment is the **point** located exactly halfway between the two endpoints of the line segment. On the graph to the left, the point M is the midpoint of line segment PQ. Thus, the distance between M and P equals the distance between M and Q.

Note: We usually need no knowledge of roots to calculate the midpoint of a line segment. We review midpoint here only because it is often confused with the distance between two points.

The x-coordinate of M is at half the distance between the x-coordinates of P and Q, and the y-coordinate of M is at half the distance between the y-coordinates of P and Q. That is, the x-coordinate of M is the average of the x-coordinates of P and Q; the y-coordinate of M is the average of the y-coordinates of P and Q.

Midpoint Formula

The midpoint of the line segment whose endpoints are (x_1, y_1) and (x_2, y_2) is the point with coordinates

$$\left(\frac{x_1 + x_2}{2}, \frac{y_1 + y_2}{2} \right)$$

EXAMPLE 7 Find the midpoint of the line segment that joins points $P(-3, 3)$ and $Q(1, 0)$.

Solution Use the midpoint formula. It makes no difference which point we call (x_1, y_1) or which point we call (x_2, y_2). Let $(x_1, y_1) = (-3, 3)$ and $(x_2, y_2) = (1, 0)$.

$$\text{midpoint} = \left(\frac{x_1 + x_2}{2}, \frac{y_1 + y_2}{2} \right)$$
$$= \left(\frac{-3 + 1}{2}, \frac{3 + 0}{2} \right)$$
$$= \left(\frac{-2}{2}, \frac{3}{2} \right)$$
$$= \left(-1, \frac{3}{2} \right)$$

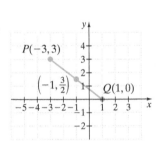

The midpoint of the segment is $\left(-1, \frac{3}{2} \right)$.

PRACTICE

7 Find the midpoint of the line segment that joins points $P(5, -2)$ and $Q(8, -6)$.

> ▶ Helpful Hint
>
> The distance between two points is a distance. The midpoint of a line segment is the point halfway between the endpoints of the segment.
>
> distance—measured in units
>
> midpoint—it is a point

Vocabulary, Readiness & Video Check

Use the choices below to fill in each blank. Some choices may be used more than once.

   distance   midpoint   point

1. The _____ of a line segment is a _____ exactly halfway between the two endpoints of the line segment.

2. The _____ between two points is a distance, measured in units.

3. The _____ formula is $d = \sqrt{(x_2 - x_1)^2 + (y_2 - y_1)^2}$.

4. The _____ formula is $\left(\dfrac{x_1 + x_2}{2}, \dfrac{y_1 + y_2}{2} \right)$.

Martin-Gay Interactive Videos

See Video 10.3 🍅

Watch the section lecture video and answer the following questions.

OBJECTIVE 1

5. From ▭ Example 1 and the lecture before, in order to apply the product rule for radicals, what must be true about the indexes of the radicals being multiplied?

OBJECTIVE 2

6. From ▭ Examples 2–6, when might you apply the quotient rule (in either direction) in order to simplify a fractional radical expression?

OBJECTIVE 3

7. From ▭ Example 8, we know that an even power of a variable is a perfect square factor of the variable, leaving no factor in the radicand once simplified. Therefore, what must be true about the power of any variable left in the radicand of a simplified square root? Explain.

OBJECTIVE 4

8. From ▭ Example 10, the formula uses the coordinates of two points similar to the slope formula. What caution should you take when replacing values in the formula?

OBJECTIVE 4

9. Based on ▭ Example 11, complete the following statement. The *x*-value of the midpoint is the _____ of the *x*-values of the endpoints and the *y*-value of the midpoint is the _____ of the *y*-values of the endpoints.

10.3 Exercise Set MyMathLab®

Use the product rule to multiply. See Example 1.

1. $\sqrt{7} \cdot \sqrt{2}$

2. $\sqrt{11} \cdot \sqrt{10}$

3. $\sqrt[4]{8} \cdot \sqrt[4]{2}$

4. $\sqrt[4]{27} \cdot \sqrt[4]{3}$

5. $\sqrt[3]{4} \cdot \sqrt[3]{9}$

6. $\sqrt[3]{10} \cdot \sqrt[3]{5}$

▶ 7. $\sqrt{2} \cdot \sqrt{3x}$

8. $\sqrt{3y} \cdot \sqrt{5x}$

9. $\sqrt{\dfrac{7}{x}} \cdot \sqrt{\dfrac{2}{y}}$

10. $\sqrt{\dfrac{6}{m}} \cdot \sqrt{\dfrac{n}{5}}$

11. $\sqrt[4]{4x^3} \cdot \sqrt[4]{5}$

12. $\sqrt[4]{ab^2} \cdot \sqrt[4]{27ab}$

Use the quotient rule to simplify. See Examples 2 and 3.

▶ 13. $\sqrt{\dfrac{6}{49}}$

14. $\sqrt{\dfrac{8}{81}}$

15. $\sqrt{\dfrac{2}{49}}$

16. $\sqrt{\dfrac{5}{121}}$

▶ 17. $\sqrt[4]{\dfrac{x^3}{16}}$

18. $\sqrt[4]{\dfrac{y}{81x^4}}$

19. $\sqrt[3]{\dfrac{4}{27}}$

20. $\sqrt[3]{\dfrac{3}{64}}$

21. $\sqrt[4]{\dfrac{8}{x^8}}$

22. $\sqrt[4]{\dfrac{a^3}{81}}$

23. $\sqrt[3]{\dfrac{2x}{81y^{12}}}$

24. $\sqrt[3]{\dfrac{3}{8x^6}}$

25. $\sqrt{\dfrac{x^2y}{100}}$

26. $\sqrt{\dfrac{y^2z}{36}}$

27. $\sqrt{\dfrac{5x^2}{4y^2}}$

28. $\sqrt{\dfrac{y^{10}}{9x^6}}$

29. $-\sqrt[3]{\dfrac{z^7}{27x^3}}$

30. $-\sqrt[3]{\dfrac{64a}{b^9}}$

Simplify. See Examples 3 and 4.

31. $\sqrt{32}$ **32.** $\sqrt{27}$

33. $\sqrt[3]{192}$ **34.** $\sqrt[3]{108}$

35. $5\sqrt{75}$ **36.** $3\sqrt{8}$

37. $\sqrt{24}$ **38.** $\sqrt{20}$

39. $\sqrt{100x^5}$ **40.** $\sqrt{64y^9}$

41. $\sqrt[3]{16y^7}$ **42.** $\sqrt[3]{64y^9}$

43. $\sqrt[4]{a^8b^7}$ **44.** $\sqrt[5]{32z^{12}}$

45. $\sqrt{y^5}$ **46.** $\sqrt[3]{y^5}$

47. $\sqrt{25a^2b^3}$ **48.** $\sqrt{9x^5y^7}$

49. $\sqrt[5]{-32x^{10}y}$ **50.** $\sqrt[5]{-243z^9}$

51. $\sqrt[3]{50x^{14}}$ **52.** $\sqrt[3]{40y^{10}}$

53. $-\sqrt{32a^8b^7}$ **54.** $-\sqrt{20ab^6}$

55. $\sqrt{9x^7y^9}$ **56.** $\sqrt{12r^9s^{12}}$

57. $\sqrt[3]{125r^9s^{12}}$ **58.** $\sqrt[3]{8a^6b^9}$

59. $\sqrt[4]{32x^{12}y^5}$ **60.** $\sqrt[4]{162x^7y^{20}}$

Use the quotient rule to divide. Then simplify if possible. See Example 5.

61. $\dfrac{\sqrt{14}}{\sqrt{7}}$ **62.** $\dfrac{\sqrt{45}}{\sqrt{9}}$

63. $\dfrac{\sqrt[3]{24}}{\sqrt[3]{3}}$ **64.** $\dfrac{\sqrt[3]{10}}{\sqrt[3]{2}}$

65. $\dfrac{5\sqrt[4]{48}}{\sqrt[4]{3}}$ **66.** $\dfrac{7\sqrt[4]{162}}{\sqrt[4]{2}}$

67. $\dfrac{\sqrt{x^5y^3}}{\sqrt{xy}}$ **68.** $\dfrac{\sqrt{a^7b^6}}{\sqrt{a^3b^2}}$

69. $\dfrac{8\sqrt[3]{54m^7}}{\sqrt[3]{2m}}$ **70.** $\dfrac{\sqrt[3]{128x^3}}{-3\sqrt[3]{2x}}$

71. $\dfrac{3\sqrt{100x^2}}{2\sqrt{2x^{-1}}}$ **72.** $\dfrac{\sqrt{270y^2}}{5\sqrt{3y^{-4}}}$

73. $\dfrac{\sqrt[4]{96a^{10}b^3}}{\sqrt[4]{3a^2b^3}}$ **74.** $\dfrac{\sqrt[4]{160x^{10}y^5}}{\sqrt[4]{2x^2y^2}}$

75. $\dfrac{\sqrt[5]{64x^{10}y^3}}{\sqrt[5]{2x^3y^{-7}}}$ **76.** $\dfrac{\sqrt[5]{192x^6y^{12}}}{\sqrt[5]{2x^{-1}y^{-3}}}$

Find the distance between each pair of points. Give an exact distance and a three-decimal-place approximation. See Example 6.

77. $(5,1)$ and $(8,5)$ **78.** $(2,3)$ and $(14,8)$

79. $(-3,2)$ and $(1,-3)$

80. $(3,-2)$ and $(-4,1)$

81. $(-9,4)$ and $(-8,1)$

82. $(-5,-2)$ and $(-6,-6)$

83. $(0,-\sqrt{2})$ and $(\sqrt{3},0)$

84. $(-\sqrt{5},0)$ and $(0,\sqrt{7})$

85. $(1.7,-3.6)$ and $(-8.6,5.7)$

86. $(9.6,2.5)$ and $(-1.9,-3.7)$

Find the midpoint of the line segment whose endpoints are given. See Example 7.

87. $(6,-8),(2,4)$ **88.** $(3,9),(7,11)$

89. $(-2,-1),(-8,6)$ **90.** $(-3,-4),(6,-8)$

91. $(7,3),(-1,-3)$ **92.** $(-2,5),(-1,6)$

93. $\left(\dfrac{1}{2},\dfrac{3}{8}\right),\left(-\dfrac{3}{2},\dfrac{5}{8}\right)$ **94.** $\left(-\dfrac{2}{5},\dfrac{7}{15}\right),\left(-\dfrac{2}{5},-\dfrac{4}{15}\right)$

95. $(\sqrt{2},3\sqrt{5}),(\sqrt{2},-2\sqrt{5})$

96. $(\sqrt{8},-\sqrt{12}),(3\sqrt{2},7\sqrt{3})$

97. $(4.6,-3.5),(7.8,-9.8)$

98. $(-4.6,2.1),(-6.7,1.9)$

REVIEW AND PREVIEW

Perform each indicated operation. See Sections 2.1, 5.3 and 5.4.

99. $6x+8x$ **100.** $(6x)(8x)$

101. $(2x+3)(x-5)$ **102.** $(2x+3)+(x-5)$

103. $9y^2-8y^2$ **104.** $(9y^2)(-8y^2)$

105. $-3(x+5)$ **106.** $-3+x+5$

107. $(x-4)^2$ **108.** $(2x+1)^2$

CONCEPT EXTENSIONS

Answer true or false. Assume all radicals represent nonzero real numbers.

109. $\sqrt[n]{a}\cdot\sqrt[n]{b}=\sqrt[n]{ab},$ _____   **110.** $\sqrt[3]{7}\cdot\sqrt[3]{11}=\sqrt[3]{18},$ _____

111. $\sqrt[3]{7}\cdot\sqrt{11}=\sqrt{77},$ _____

112. $\sqrt{x^7y^8}=\sqrt{x^7}\cdot\sqrt{y^8},$ _____

113. $\dfrac{\sqrt[n]{a}}{\sqrt[n]{b}}=\sqrt[n]{\dfrac{a}{b}},$ _____   **114.** $\dfrac{\sqrt[3]{12}}{\sqrt[3]{4}}=\sqrt[3]{8},$ _____

Find and correct the error. See the Concept Check in this section.

115. $\dfrac{\sqrt[3]{64}}{\sqrt{64}} = \sqrt[3]{\dfrac{64}{64}} = \sqrt[3]{1} = 1$

116. $\dfrac{\sqrt[4]{16}}{\sqrt{4}} = \sqrt[4]{\dfrac{16}{4}} = \sqrt[4]{4}$

Simplify. See the Concept Check in this section. Assume variables represent positive numbers.

117. $\sqrt[5]{x^{35}}$

118. $\sqrt[6]{y^{48}}$

119. $\sqrt[4]{a^{12}b^4c^{20}}$

120. $\sqrt[3]{a^9b^{21}c^3}$

121. $\sqrt[3]{z^{32}}$

122. $\sqrt[5]{x^{49}}$

123. $\sqrt[7]{q^{17}r^{40}s^7}$

124. $\sqrt[4]{p^{11}q^4r^{45}}$

125. The formula for the radius r of a sphere with surface area A is given by $r = \sqrt{\dfrac{A}{4\pi}}$. Calculate the radius of a standard zorb, whose outside surface area is 32.17 sq m. Round to the nearest tenth. (A zorb is a large inflated ball within a ball in which a person, strapped inside, may choose to roll down a hill. *Source:* Zorb, Ltd.)

126. The owner of Knightime Classic Movie Rentals has determined that the demand equation for renting older released DVDs is $F(x) = 0.6\sqrt{49 - x^2}$, where x is the price in dollars per two-day rental and $F(x)$ is the number of times the DVD is demanded per week.

a. Approximate to one decimal place the demand per week of an older released DVD if the rental price is $3 per two-day rental.

b. Approximate to one decimal place the demand per week of an older released DVD if the rental price is $5 per two-day rental.

c. Explain how the owner of the store can use this equation to predict the number of copies of each DVD that should be in stock.

127. The formula for the lateral surface area A of a cone with height h and radius r is given by

$$A = \pi r \sqrt{r^2 + h^2}$$

a. Find the lateral surface area of a cone whose height is 3 centimeters and whose radius is 4 centimeters.

b. Approximate to two decimal places the lateral surface area of a cone whose height is 7.2 feet and whose radius is 6.8 feet.

128. Before Mount Vesuvius, a volcano in Italy, erupted violently in 79 C.E., its height was 4190 feet. Vesuvius was roughly cone-shaped, and its base had a radius of approximately 25,200 feet. Use the formula for the lateral surface area of a cone, given in Exercise 127, to approximate the surface area this volcano had before it erupted. (*Source:* Global Volcanism Network)

4190 ft

25,200 ft

10.4 Adding, Subtracting, and Multiplying Radical Expressions

OBJECTIVES

1 Add or Subtract Radical Expressions.

2 Multiply Radical Expressions.

OBJECTIVE

1 Adding or Subtracting Radical Expressions

We have learned that sums or differences of like terms can be simplified. To simplify these sums or differences, we use the distributive property. For example,

$$2x + 3x = (2 + 3)x = 5x \quad \text{and} \quad 7x^2y - 4x^2y = (7 - 4)x^2y = 3x^2y$$

The distributive property can also be used to add **like radicals.**

Like Radicals

Radicals with the same index and the same radicand are like radicals.

For example, $2\sqrt{7} + 3\sqrt{7} = (2 + 3)\sqrt{7} = 5\sqrt{7}$. Also,

Like radicals

$$5\sqrt{3x} - 7\sqrt{3x} = (5 - 7)\sqrt{3x} = -2\sqrt{3x}$$

The expression $2\sqrt{7} + 2\sqrt[3]{7}$ cannot be simplified further since $2\sqrt{7}$ and $2\sqrt[3]{7}$ are not like radicals.

Unlike radicals

EXAMPLE 1 Add or subtract as indicated. Assume all variables represent positive real numbers.

a. $4\sqrt{11} + 8\sqrt{11}$ **b.** $5\sqrt[3]{3x} - 7\sqrt[3]{3x}$ **c.** $4\sqrt{5} + 4\sqrt[3]{5}$

Solution

a. $4\sqrt{11} + 8\sqrt{11} = (4 + 8)\sqrt{11} = 12\sqrt{11}$
b. $5\sqrt[3]{3x} - 7\sqrt[3]{3x} = (5 - 7)\sqrt[3]{3x} = -2\sqrt[3]{3x}$
c. $4\sqrt{5} + 4\sqrt[3]{5}$
This expression cannot be simplified since $4\sqrt{5}$ and $4\sqrt[3]{5}$ do not contain like radicals.

PRACTICE

1 Add or subtract as indicated.

a. $3\sqrt{17} + 5\sqrt{17}$ **b.** $7\sqrt[3]{5z} - 12\sqrt[3]{5z}$ **c.** $3\sqrt{2} + 5\sqrt[3]{2}$

When adding or subtracting radicals, always check first to see whether any radicals can be simplified.

✓CONCEPT CHECK
True or false?

$$\sqrt{a} + \sqrt{b} = \sqrt{a + b}$$

Explain.

EXAMPLE 2 Add or subtract. Assume that variables represent positive real numbers.

a. $\sqrt{20} + 2\sqrt{45}$ **b.** $\sqrt[3]{54} - 5\sqrt[3]{16} + \sqrt[3]{2}$ **c.** $\sqrt{27x} - 2\sqrt{9x} + \sqrt{72x}$
d. $\sqrt[3]{98} + \sqrt{98}$ **e.** $\sqrt[3]{48y^4} + \sqrt[3]{6y^4}$

Solution First, simplify each radical. Then add or subtract any like radicals.

a. $\sqrt{20} + 2\sqrt{45} = \sqrt{4 \cdot 5} + 2\sqrt{9 \cdot 5}$ Factor 20 and 45.
$= \sqrt{4} \cdot \sqrt{5} + 2 \cdot \sqrt{9} \cdot \sqrt{5}$ Use the product rule.
$= 2 \cdot \sqrt{5} + 2 \cdot 3 \cdot \sqrt{5}$ Simplify $\sqrt{4}$ and $\sqrt{9}$.
$= 2\sqrt{5} + 6\sqrt{5}$
$= 8\sqrt{5}$ Add like radicals.

b. $\sqrt[3]{54} - 5\sqrt[3]{16} + \sqrt[3]{2}$
$= \sqrt[3]{27} \cdot \sqrt[3]{2} - 5 \cdot \sqrt[3]{8} \cdot \sqrt[3]{2} + \sqrt[3]{2}$ Factor and use the product rule.
$= 3 \cdot \sqrt[3]{2} - 5 \cdot 2 \cdot \sqrt[3]{2} + \sqrt[3]{2}$ Simplify $\sqrt[3]{27}$ and $\sqrt[3]{8}$.
$= 3\sqrt[3]{2} - 10\sqrt[3]{2} + \sqrt[3]{2}$ Write $5 \cdot 2$ as 10.
$= -6\sqrt[3]{2}$ Combine like radicals.

Answer to Concept Check:
false; answers may vary

c. $\sqrt{27x} - 2\sqrt{9x} + \sqrt{72x}$

$\qquad = \sqrt{9} \cdot \sqrt{3x} - 2 \cdot \sqrt{9} \cdot \sqrt{x} + \sqrt{36} \cdot \sqrt{2x}$ Factor and use the product rule.

$\qquad = 3 \cdot \sqrt{3x} - 2 \cdot 3 \cdot \sqrt{x} + 6 \cdot \sqrt{2x}$ Simplify $\sqrt{9}$ and $\sqrt{36}$.

$\qquad = 3\sqrt{3x} - 6\sqrt{x} + 6\sqrt{2x}$ Write $2 \cdot 3$ as 6.

> **Helpful Hint**
> None of these terms contain like radicals. We can simplify no further.

d. $\sqrt[3]{98} + \sqrt{98} = \sqrt[3]{98} + \sqrt{49} \cdot \sqrt{2}$ Factor and use the product rule.

$\qquad = \sqrt[3]{98} + 7\sqrt{2}$ No further simplification is possible.

e. $\sqrt[3]{48y^4} + \sqrt[3]{6y^4} = \sqrt[3]{8y^3} \cdot \sqrt[3]{6y} + \sqrt[3]{y^3} \cdot \sqrt[3]{6y}$ Factor and use the product rule.

$\qquad = 2y\sqrt[3]{6y} + y\sqrt[3]{6y}$ Simplify $\sqrt[3]{8y^3}$ and $\sqrt[3]{y^3}$.

$\qquad = 3y\sqrt[3]{6y}$ Combine like radicals.   □

PRACTICE
2 Add or subtract.

a. $\sqrt{24} + 3\sqrt{54}$ **b.** $\sqrt[3]{24} - 4\sqrt[3]{81} + \sqrt[3]{3}$ **c.** $\sqrt{75x} - 3\sqrt{27x} + \sqrt{12x}$
d. $\sqrt{40} + \sqrt[3]{40}$ **e.** $\sqrt[3]{81x^4} + \sqrt[3]{3x^4}$

Let's continue to assume that variables represent positive real numbers.

EXAMPLE 3   Add or subtract as indicated.

a. $\dfrac{\sqrt{45}}{4} - \dfrac{\sqrt{5}}{3}$ **b.** $\sqrt[3]{\dfrac{7x}{8}} + 2\sqrt[3]{7x}$

Solution

a. $\dfrac{\sqrt{45}}{4} - \dfrac{\sqrt{5}}{3} = \dfrac{3\sqrt{5}}{4} - \dfrac{\sqrt{5}}{3}$ To subtract, notice that the LCD is 12.

$\qquad = \dfrac{3\sqrt{5} \cdot 3}{4 \cdot 3} - \dfrac{\sqrt{5} \cdot 4}{3 \cdot 4}$ Write each expression as an equivalent expression with a denominator of 12.

$\qquad = \dfrac{9\sqrt{5}}{12} - \dfrac{4\sqrt{5}}{12}$ Multiply factors in the numerator and the denominator.

$\qquad = \dfrac{5\sqrt{5}}{12}$ Subtract.

b. $\sqrt[3]{\dfrac{7x}{8}} + 2\sqrt[3]{7x} = \dfrac{\sqrt[3]{7x}}{\sqrt[3]{8}} + 2\sqrt[3]{7x}$ Apply the quotient rule for radicals.

$\qquad = \dfrac{\sqrt[3]{7x}}{2} + 2\sqrt[3]{7x}$ Simplify.

$\qquad = \dfrac{\sqrt[3]{7x}}{2} + \dfrac{2\sqrt[3]{7x} \cdot 2}{2}$ Write each expression as an equivalent expression with a denominator of 2.

$\qquad = \dfrac{\sqrt[3]{7x}}{2} + \dfrac{4\sqrt[3]{7x}}{2}$

$\qquad = \dfrac{5\sqrt[3]{7x}}{2}$ Add.   □

PRACTICE
3 Add or subtract as indicated.

a. $\dfrac{\sqrt{28}}{3} - \dfrac{\sqrt{7}}{4}$ **b.** $\sqrt[3]{\dfrac{6y}{64}} + 3\sqrt[3]{6y}$

OBJECTIVE

2 Multiplying Radical Expressions

We can multiply radical expressions by using many of the same properties used to multiply polynomial expressions. For instance, to multiply $\sqrt{2}(\sqrt{6} - 3\sqrt{2})$, we use the distributive property and multiply $\sqrt{2}$ by each term inside the parentheses.

$$\sqrt{2}(\sqrt{6} - 3\sqrt{2}) = \sqrt{2}(\sqrt{6}) - \sqrt{2}(3\sqrt{2}) \quad \text{Use the distributive property.}$$
$$= \sqrt{2 \cdot 6} - 3\sqrt{2 \cdot 2}$$
$$= \sqrt{2 \cdot 2 \cdot 3} - 3 \cdot 2 \quad \text{Use the product rule for radicals.}$$
$$= 2\sqrt{3} - 6$$

EXAMPLE 4 Multiply.

a. $\sqrt{3}(5 + \sqrt{30})$ **b.** $(\sqrt{5} - \sqrt{6})(\sqrt{7} + 1)$ **c.** $(7\sqrt{x} + 5)(3\sqrt{x} - \sqrt{5})$

d. $(4\sqrt{3} - 1)^2$ **e.** $(\sqrt{2x} - 5)(\sqrt{2x} + 5)$ **f.** $(\sqrt{x - 3} + 5)^2$

Solution

a. $\sqrt{3}(5 + \sqrt{30}) = \sqrt{3}(5) + \sqrt{3}(\sqrt{30})$
$$= 5\sqrt{3} + \sqrt{3 \cdot 30}$$
$$= 5\sqrt{3} + \sqrt{3 \cdot 3 \cdot 10}$$
$$= 5\sqrt{3} + 3\sqrt{10}$$

b. To multiply, we can use the FOIL method.

$$\overset{\text{First}\qquad\text{Outer}\qquad\text{Inner}\qquad\text{Last}}{(\sqrt{5} - \sqrt{6})(\sqrt{7} + 1) = \sqrt{5} \cdot \sqrt{7} + \sqrt{5} \cdot 1 - \sqrt{6} \cdot \sqrt{7} - \sqrt{6} \cdot 1}$$
$$= \sqrt{35} + \sqrt{5} - \sqrt{42} - \sqrt{6}$$

c. $(7\sqrt{x} + 5)(3\sqrt{x} - \sqrt{5}) = 7\sqrt{x}(3\sqrt{x}) - 7\sqrt{x}(\sqrt{5}) + 5(3\sqrt{x}) - 5(\sqrt{5})$
$$= 21x - 7\sqrt{5x} + 15\sqrt{x} - 5\sqrt{5}$$

d. $(4\sqrt{3} - 1)^2 = (4\sqrt{3} - 1)(4\sqrt{3} - 1)$
$$= 4\sqrt{3}(4\sqrt{3}) - 4\sqrt{3}(1) - 1(4\sqrt{3}) - 1(-1)$$
$$= 16 \cdot 3 - 4\sqrt{3} - 4\sqrt{3} + 1$$
$$= 48 - 8\sqrt{3} + 1$$
$$= 49 - 8\sqrt{3}$$

e. $(\sqrt{2x} - 5)(\sqrt{2x} + 5) = \sqrt{2x} \cdot \sqrt{2x} + 5\sqrt{2x} - 5\sqrt{2x} - 5 \cdot 5$
$$= 2x - 25$$

f. $(\underbrace{\sqrt{x-3}}_{a} + \underbrace{5}_{b})^2 = \underbrace{(\sqrt{x-3})^2}_{a^2} + \underbrace{2 \cdot}_{+2 \cdot} \underbrace{\sqrt{x-3}}_{a} \cdot \underbrace{5}_{\cdot b} + \underbrace{5^2}_{+ b^2}$

$$= x - 3 + 10\sqrt{x-3} + 25 \quad \text{Simplify.}$$
$$= x + 22 + 10\sqrt{x-3} \quad \text{Combine like terms.} \quad \square$$

PRACTICE

4 Multiply.

a. $\sqrt{5}(2 + \sqrt{15})$ **b.** $(\sqrt{2} - \sqrt{5})(\sqrt{6} + 2)$

c. $(3\sqrt{z} - 4)(2\sqrt{z} + 3)$ **d.** $(\sqrt{6} - 3)^2$

e. $(\sqrt{5x} + 3)(\sqrt{5x} - 3)$ **f.** $(\sqrt{x + 2} + 3)^2$

Vocabulary, Readiness & Video Check

Complete the table with "Like" or "Unlike."

	Terms	Like or Unlike Radical Terms?
1.	$\sqrt{7}, \sqrt[3]{7}$	
2.	$\sqrt[3]{x^2y}, \sqrt[3]{yx^2}$	
3.	$\sqrt[3]{abc}, \sqrt[3]{cba}$	
4.	$2x\sqrt{5}, 2x\sqrt{10}$	

Simplify. Assume that all variables represent positive real numbers.

5. $2\sqrt{3} + 4\sqrt{3} =$ _____

6. $5\sqrt{7} + 3\sqrt{7} =$ _____

7. $8\sqrt{x} - \sqrt{x} =$ _____

8. $3\sqrt{y} - \sqrt{y} =$ _____

9. $7\sqrt[3]{x} + \sqrt[3]{x} =$ _____

10. $8\sqrt[3]{z} + \sqrt[3]{z} =$ _____

Martin-Gay Interactive Videos

See Video 10.4 🍎

Watch the section lecture video and answer the following questions.

OBJECTIVE
1

11. From Examples 1 and 2, why should you always check to see if all terms in your expression are simplified before attempting to add or subtract radicals?

OBJECTIVE
2

12. In Example 4, what are you told to remember about the square root of a positive number?

10.4 Exercise Set   MyMathLab®

Add or subtract. See Examples 1 through 3.

1. $\sqrt{8} - \sqrt{32}$

2. $\sqrt{27} - \sqrt{75}$

3. $2\sqrt{2x^3} + 4x\sqrt{8x}$

4. $3\sqrt{45x^3} + x\sqrt{5x}$

▶ **5.** $2\sqrt{50} - 3\sqrt{125} + \sqrt{98}$

6. $4\sqrt{32} - \sqrt{18} + 2\sqrt{128}$

7. $\sqrt[3]{16x} - \sqrt[3]{54x}$

8. $2\sqrt[3]{3a^4} - 3a\sqrt[3]{81a}$

9. $\sqrt{9b^3} - \sqrt{25b^3} + \sqrt{49b^3}$

10. $\sqrt{4x^7} + 9x^2\sqrt{x^3} - 5x\sqrt{x^5}$

11. $\dfrac{5\sqrt{2}}{3} + \dfrac{2\sqrt{2}}{5}$

12. $\dfrac{\sqrt{3}}{2} + \dfrac{4\sqrt{3}}{3}$

▶ **13.** $\sqrt[3]{\dfrac{11}{8}} - \dfrac{\sqrt[3]{11}}{6}$

14. $\dfrac{2\sqrt[3]{4}}{7} - \dfrac{\sqrt[3]{4}}{14}$

15. $\dfrac{\sqrt{20x}}{9} + \sqrt{\dfrac{5x}{9}}$

16. $\dfrac{3x\sqrt{7}}{5} + \sqrt{\dfrac{7x^2}{100}}$

17. $7\sqrt{9} - 7 + \sqrt{3}$

18. $\sqrt{16} - 5\sqrt{10} + 7$

19. $2 + 3\sqrt{y^2} - 6\sqrt{y^2} + 5$

20. $3\sqrt{7} - \sqrt[3]{x} + 4\sqrt{7} - 3\sqrt[3]{x}$

21. $3\sqrt{108} - 2\sqrt{18} - 3\sqrt{48}$

22. $-\sqrt{75} + \sqrt{12} - 3\sqrt{3}$

23. $-5\sqrt[3]{625} + \sqrt[3]{40}$

24. $-2\sqrt[3]{108} - \sqrt[3]{32}$

25. $a^3\sqrt{9ab^3} - \sqrt{25a^7b^3} + \sqrt{16a^7b^3}$

26. $\sqrt{4x^7y^5} + 9x^2\sqrt{x^3y^5} - 5xy\sqrt{x^5y^3}$

27. $5y\sqrt{8y} + 2\sqrt{50y^3}$

28. $3\sqrt{8x^2y^3} - 2x\sqrt{32y^3}$

29. $\sqrt[3]{54xy^3} - 5\sqrt[3]{2xy^3} + y\sqrt[3]{128x}$

30. $2\sqrt[3]{24x^3y^4} + 4x\sqrt[3]{81y^4}$

31. $6\sqrt[3]{11} + 8\sqrt{11} - 12\sqrt{11}$

32. $3\sqrt[3]{5} + 4\sqrt{5} - 8\sqrt{5}$

33. $-2\sqrt[4]{x^7} + 3\sqrt[4]{16x^7} - x\sqrt[4]{x^3}$

34. $6\sqrt[3]{24x^3} - 2\sqrt[3]{81x^3} - x\sqrt[3]{3}$

35. $\dfrac{4\sqrt{3}}{3} - \dfrac{\sqrt{12}}{3}$

36. $\dfrac{\sqrt{45}}{10} + \dfrac{7\sqrt{5}}{10}$

37. $\dfrac{\sqrt[3]{8x^4}}{7} + \dfrac{3x\sqrt[3]{x}}{7}$

38. $\dfrac{\sqrt[4]{48}}{5x} - \dfrac{2\sqrt[4]{3}}{10x}$

39. $\sqrt{\dfrac{28}{x^2}} + \sqrt{\dfrac{7}{4x^2}}$

40. $\dfrac{\sqrt{99}}{5x} - \sqrt{\dfrac{44}{x^2}}$

41. $\sqrt[3]{\dfrac{16}{27}} - \dfrac{\sqrt[3]{54}}{6}$

42. $\dfrac{\sqrt[3]{3}}{10} + \sqrt[3]{\dfrac{24}{125}}$

43. $-\dfrac{\sqrt[3]{2x^4}}{9} + \sqrt[3]{\dfrac{250x^4}{27}}$

44. $\dfrac{\sqrt[3]{y^5}}{8} + \dfrac{5y\sqrt[3]{y^2}}{4}$

△ **45.** Find the perimeter of the trapezoid.

$2\sqrt{12}$ in.

$3\sqrt{3}$ in. $\sqrt{12}$ in.

$2\sqrt{27}$ in.

△ **46.** Find the perimeter of the triangle.

$\sqrt{8}$ m $\sqrt{32}$ m

$\sqrt{45}$ m

Multiply and then simplify if possible. See Example 4.

47. $\sqrt{7}(\sqrt{5} + \sqrt{3})$

48. $\sqrt{5}(\sqrt{15} - \sqrt{35})$

49. $(\sqrt{5} - \sqrt{2})^2$

50. $(3x - \sqrt{2})(3x - \sqrt{2})$

51. $\sqrt{3x}(\sqrt{3} - \sqrt{x})$

52. $\sqrt{5y}(\sqrt{y} + \sqrt{5})$

53. $(2\sqrt{x} - 5)(3\sqrt{x} + 1)$

54. $(8\sqrt{y} + z)(4\sqrt{y} - 1)$

55. $(\sqrt[3]{a} - 4)(\sqrt[3]{a} + 5)$

56. $(\sqrt[3]{a} + 2)(\sqrt[3]{a} + 7)$

57. $6(\sqrt{2} - 2)$

58. $\sqrt{5}(6 - \sqrt{5})$

59. $\sqrt{2}(\sqrt{2} + x\sqrt{6})$

60. $\sqrt{3}(\sqrt{3} - 2\sqrt{5x})$

61. $(2\sqrt{7} + 3\sqrt{5})(\sqrt{7} - 2\sqrt{5})$

62. $(\sqrt{6} - 4\sqrt{2})(3\sqrt{6} + \sqrt{2})$

63. $(\sqrt{x} - y)(\sqrt{x} + y)$

64. $(\sqrt{3x} + 2)(\sqrt{3x} - 2)$

65. $(\sqrt{3} + x)^2$

66. $(\sqrt{y} - 3x)^2$

67. $(\sqrt{5x} - 2\sqrt{3x})(\sqrt{5x} - 3\sqrt{3x})$

68. $(5\sqrt{7x} - \sqrt{2x})(4\sqrt{7x} + 6\sqrt{2x})$

69. $(\sqrt[3]{4} + 2)(\sqrt[3]{2} - 1)$

70. $(\sqrt[3]{3} + \sqrt[3]{2})(\sqrt[3]{9} - \sqrt[3]{4})$

71. $(\sqrt[3]{x} + 1)(\sqrt[3]{x^2} - \sqrt[3]{x} + 1)$

72. $(\sqrt[3]{3x} + 2)(\sqrt[3]{9x^2} - 2\sqrt[3]{3x} + 4)$

73. $(\sqrt{x - 1} + 5)^2$

74. $(\sqrt{3x + 1} + 2)^2$

75. $(\sqrt{2x + 5} - 1)^2$

76. $(\sqrt{x - 6} - 7)^2$

REVIEW AND PREVIEW

Factor each numerator and denominator. Then simplify if possible. See Section 7.1.

77. $\dfrac{2x - 14}{2}$

78. $\dfrac{8x - 24y}{4}$

79. $\dfrac{7x - 7y}{x^2 - y^2}$

80. $\dfrac{x^3 - 8}{4x - 8}$

81. $\dfrac{6a^2b - 9ab}{3ab}$

82. $\dfrac{14r - 28r^2s^2}{7rs}$

83. $\dfrac{-4 + 2\sqrt{3}}{6}$

84. $\dfrac{-5 + 10\sqrt{7}}{5}$

CONCEPT EXTENSIONS

△ **85.** Find the perimeter and area of the rectangle.

$\sqrt{125}$ ft

$3\sqrt{20}$ ft

△ **86.** Find the area and perimeter of the trapezoid. (*Hint:* The area of a trapezoid is the product of half the height $6\sqrt{3}$ meters and the sum of the bases $2\sqrt{63}$ and $7\sqrt{7}$ meters.)

2√63 m

2√27 m   6√3 m

7√7 m

87. a. Add: $\sqrt{3} + \sqrt{3}$.

  b. Multiply: $\sqrt{3} \cdot \sqrt{3}$.

  c. Describe the differences in parts (a) and (b).

88. a. Add: $2\sqrt{5} + \sqrt{5}$

  b. Multiply: $2\sqrt{5} \cdot \sqrt{5}$

  c. Describe the differences in parts (a) and (b).

89. Multiply: $\left(\sqrt{2} + \sqrt{3} - 1\right)^2$.

90. Multiply: $\left(\sqrt{5} - \sqrt{2} + 1\right)^2$

91. Explain how simplifying $2x + 3x$ is similar to simplifying $2\sqrt{x} + 3\sqrt{x}$.

92. Explain how multiplying $(x - 2)(x + 3)$ is similar to multiplying $\left(\sqrt{x} - \sqrt{2}\right)\left(\sqrt{x} + 3\right)$.

10.5 Rationalizing Denominators and Numerators of Radical Expressions

OBJECTIVES

1 Rationalize Denominators.

2 Rationalize Denominators Having Two Terms.

3 Rationalize Numerators.

OBJECTIVE

1   Rationalizing Denominators of Radical Expressions

Often in mathematics, it is helpful to write a radical expression such as $\dfrac{\sqrt{3}}{\sqrt{2}}$ either without a radical in the denominator or without a radical in the numerator. The process of writing this expression as an equivalent expression but without a radical in the denominator is called **rationalizing the denominator.** To rationalize the denominator of $\dfrac{\sqrt{3}}{\sqrt{2}}$, we use the fundamental principle of fractions and multiply the numerator and the denominator by $\sqrt{2}$. Recall that this is the same as multiplying by $\dfrac{\sqrt{2}}{\sqrt{2}}$, which simplifies to 1.

$$\frac{\sqrt{3}}{\sqrt{2}} = \frac{\sqrt{3} \cdot \sqrt{2}}{\sqrt{2} \cdot \sqrt{2}} = \frac{\sqrt{6}}{\sqrt{4}} = \frac{\sqrt{6}}{2}$$

In this section, we continue to assume that variables represent positive real numbers.

EXAMPLE 1   Rationalize the denominator of each expression.

a. $\dfrac{2}{\sqrt{5}}$ **b.** $\dfrac{2\sqrt{16}}{\sqrt{9x}}$ **c.** $\sqrt[3]{\dfrac{1}{2}}$

Solution

a. To rationalize the denominator, we multiply the numerator and denominator by a factor that makes the radicand in the denominator a perfect square.

$$\frac{2}{\sqrt{5}} = \frac{2 \cdot \sqrt{5}}{\sqrt{5} \cdot \sqrt{5}} = \frac{2\sqrt{5}}{5} \quad \text{The denominator is now rationalized.}$$

b. First, we simplify the radicals and then rationalize the denominator.

$$\frac{2\sqrt{16}}{\sqrt{9x}} = \frac{2(4)}{3\sqrt{x}} = \frac{8}{3\sqrt{x}}$$

To rationalize the denominator, multiply the numerator and denominator by $\sqrt{x}$. Then

$$\frac{8}{3\sqrt{x}} = \frac{8 \cdot \sqrt{x}}{3\sqrt{x} \cdot \sqrt{x}} = \frac{8\sqrt{x}}{3x}$$

(Continued on next page)

c. $\sqrt[3]{\dfrac{1}{2}} = \dfrac{\sqrt[3]{1}}{\sqrt[3]{2}} = \dfrac{1}{\sqrt[3]{2}}$. Now we rationalize the denominator. Since $\sqrt[3]{2}$ is a cube root, we want to multiply by a value that will make the radicand 2 a perfect cube. If we multiply $\sqrt[3]{2}$ by $\sqrt[3]{2^2}$, we get $\sqrt[3]{2^3} = \sqrt[3]{8} = 2$.

$$\dfrac{1 \cdot \sqrt[3]{2^2}}{\sqrt[3]{2} \cdot \sqrt[3]{2^2}} = \dfrac{\sqrt[3]{4}}{\sqrt[3]{2^3}} = \dfrac{\sqrt[3]{4}}{2}$$ Multiply the numerator and denominator by $\sqrt[3]{2^2}$ and then simplify.

PRACTICE
1 Rationalize the denominator of each expression.

a. $\dfrac{5}{\sqrt{3}}$ b. $\dfrac{3\sqrt{25}}{\sqrt{4x}}$ c. $\sqrt[3]{\dfrac{2}{9}}$

✓CONCEPT CHECK
Determine by which number both the numerator and denominator can be multiplied to rationalize the denominator of the radical expression.

a. $\dfrac{1}{\sqrt[3]{7}}$ b. $\dfrac{1}{\sqrt[4]{8}}$

EXAMPLE 2   Rationalize the denominator of $\sqrt{\dfrac{7x}{3y}}$.

Solution $\sqrt{\dfrac{7x}{3y}} = \dfrac{\sqrt{7x}}{\sqrt{3y}}$ Use the quotient rule. No radical may be simplified further.

$\qquad = \dfrac{\sqrt{7x} \cdot \sqrt{3y}}{\sqrt{3y} \cdot \sqrt{3y}}$ Multiply numerator and denominator by $\sqrt{3y}$ so that the radicand in the denominator is a perfect square.

$\qquad = \dfrac{\sqrt{21xy}}{3y}$ Use the product rule in the numerator and denominator. Remember that $\sqrt{3y} \cdot \sqrt{3y} = 3y$.

PRACTICE
2 Rationalize the denominator of $\sqrt{\dfrac{3z}{5y}}$.

EXAMPLE 3   Rationalize the denominator of $\dfrac{\sqrt[4]{x}}{\sqrt[4]{81y^5}}$.

Solution   First, simplify each radical if possible.

$\dfrac{\sqrt[4]{x}}{\sqrt[4]{81y^5}} = \dfrac{\sqrt[4]{x}}{\sqrt[4]{81y^4} \cdot \sqrt[4]{y}}$ Use the product rule in the denominator.

$\qquad = \dfrac{\sqrt[4]{x}}{3y\sqrt[4]{y}}$ Write $\sqrt[4]{81y^4}$ as $3y$.

$\qquad = \dfrac{\sqrt[4]{x} \cdot \sqrt[4]{y^3}}{3y\sqrt[4]{y} \cdot \sqrt[4]{y^3}}$ Multiply numerator and denominator by $\sqrt[4]{y^3}$ so that the radicand in the denominator is a perfect fourth power.

$\qquad = \dfrac{\sqrt[4]{xy^3}}{3y\sqrt[4]{y^4}}$ Use the product rule in the numerator and denominator.

$\qquad = \dfrac{\sqrt[4]{xy^3}}{3y^2}$ In the denominator, $\sqrt[4]{y^4} = y$ and $3y \cdot y = 3y^2$.

PRACTICE
3 Rationalize the denominator of $\dfrac{\sqrt[3]{z^2}}{\sqrt[3]{27x^4}}$.

OBJECTIVE

2 Rationalizing Denominators Having Two Terms

Remember the product of the sum and difference of two terms?

$$(a + b)(a - b) = a^2 - b^2$$

These two expressions are called **conjugates** of each other.

To rationalize a numerator or denominator that is a sum or difference of two terms, we use conjugates. To see how and why this works, let's rationalize the denominator of the expression $\dfrac{5}{\sqrt{3} - 2}$. To do so, we multiply both the numerator and the denominator by $\sqrt{3} + 2$, the **conjugate** of the denominator $\sqrt{3} - 2$, and see what happens.

$$\frac{5}{\sqrt{3} - 2} = \frac{5(\sqrt{3} + 2)}{(\sqrt{3} - 2)(\sqrt{3} + 2)}$$

$$= \frac{5(\sqrt{3} + 2)}{(\sqrt{3})^2 - 2^2} \quad \text{Multiply the sum and difference of two terms: } (a + b)(a - b) = a^2 - b^2.$$

$$= \frac{5(\sqrt{3} + 2)}{3 - 4}$$

$$= \frac{5(\sqrt{3} + 2)}{-1}$$

$$= -5(\sqrt{3} + 2) \quad \text{or} \quad -5\sqrt{3} - 10$$

Notice in the denominator that the product of $(\sqrt{3} - 2)$ and its conjugate, $(\sqrt{3} + 2)$, is -1. In general, the product of an expression and its conjugate will contain no radical terms. This is why, when rationalizing a denominator or a numerator containing two terms, we multiply by its conjugate. Examples of conjugates are

$$\sqrt{a} - \sqrt{b} \quad \text{and} \quad \sqrt{a} + \sqrt{b}$$
$$x + \sqrt{y} \quad \text{and} \quad x - \sqrt{y}$$

EXAMPLE 4 Rationalize each denominator.

a. $\dfrac{2}{3\sqrt{2} + 4}$ **b.** $\dfrac{\sqrt{6} + 2}{\sqrt{5} - \sqrt{3}}$ **c.** $\dfrac{2\sqrt{m}}{3\sqrt{x} + \sqrt{m}}$

Solution

a. Multiply the numerator and denominator by the conjugate of the denominator, $3\sqrt{2} + 4$.

$$\frac{2}{3\sqrt{2} + 4} = \frac{2(3\sqrt{2} - 4)}{(3\sqrt{2} + 4)(3\sqrt{2} - 4)}$$

$$= \frac{2(3\sqrt{2} - 4)}{(3\sqrt{2})^2 - 4^2}$$

$$= \frac{2(3\sqrt{2} - 4)}{18 - 16}$$

$$= \frac{2(3\sqrt{2} - 4)}{2}, \quad \text{or} \quad 3\sqrt{2} - 4$$

It is often useful to leave a numerator in factored form to help determine whether the expression can be simplified.

(Continued on next page)

b. Multiply the numerator and denominator by the conjugate of $\sqrt{5} - \sqrt{3}$.

$$\frac{\sqrt{6} + 2}{\sqrt{5} - \sqrt{3}} = \frac{(\sqrt{6} + 2)(\sqrt{5} + \sqrt{3})}{(\sqrt{5} - \sqrt{3})(\sqrt{5} + \sqrt{3})}$$

$$= \frac{\sqrt{6}\sqrt{5} + \sqrt{6}\sqrt{3} + 2\sqrt{5} + 2\sqrt{3}}{(\sqrt{5})^2 - (\sqrt{3})^2}$$

$$= \frac{\sqrt{30} + \sqrt{18} + 2\sqrt{5} + 2\sqrt{3}}{5 - 3}$$

$$= \frac{\sqrt{30} + 3\sqrt{2} + 2\sqrt{5} + 2\sqrt{3}}{2}$$

c. Multiply by the conjugate of $3\sqrt{x} + \sqrt{m}$ to eliminate the radicals from the denominator.

$$\frac{2\sqrt{m}}{3\sqrt{x} + \sqrt{m}} = \frac{2\sqrt{m}(3\sqrt{x} - \sqrt{m})}{(3\sqrt{x} + \sqrt{m})(3\sqrt{x} - \sqrt{m})} = \frac{6\sqrt{mx} - 2m}{(3\sqrt{x})^2 - (\sqrt{m})^2}$$

$$= \frac{6\sqrt{mx} - 2m}{9x - m}$$

PRACTICE

4 Rationalize the denominator.

a. $\dfrac{5}{3\sqrt{5} + 2}$ **b.** $\dfrac{\sqrt{2} + 5}{\sqrt{3} - \sqrt{5}}$ **c.** $\dfrac{3\sqrt{x}}{2\sqrt{x} + \sqrt{y}}$

OBJECTIVE

3 **Rationalizing Numerators**

As mentioned earlier, it is also often helpful to write an expression such as $\dfrac{\sqrt{3}}{\sqrt{2}}$ as an equivalent expression without a radical in the numerator. This process is called **rationalizing the numerator.** To rationalize the numerator of $\dfrac{\sqrt{3}}{\sqrt{2}}$, we multiply the numerator and the denominator by $\sqrt{3}$.

$$\frac{\sqrt{3}}{\sqrt{2}} = \frac{\sqrt{3} \cdot \sqrt{3}}{\sqrt{2} \cdot \sqrt{3}} = \frac{\sqrt{9}}{\sqrt{6}} = \frac{3}{\sqrt{6}}$$

EXAMPLE 5 Rationalize the numerator of $\dfrac{\sqrt{7}}{\sqrt{45}}$.

Solution First we simplify $\sqrt{45}$.

$$\frac{\sqrt{7}}{\sqrt{45}} = \frac{\sqrt{7}}{\sqrt{9 \cdot 5}} = \frac{\sqrt{7}}{3\sqrt{5}}$$

Next we rationalize the numerator by multiplying the numerator and the denominator by $\sqrt{7}$.

$$\frac{\sqrt{7}}{3\sqrt{5}} = \frac{\sqrt{7} \cdot \sqrt{7}}{3\sqrt{5} \cdot \sqrt{7}} = \frac{7}{3\sqrt{5} \cdot 7} = \frac{7}{3\sqrt{35}}$$

PRACTICE

5 Rationalize the numerator of $\dfrac{\sqrt{32}}{\sqrt{80}}$.

EXAMPLE 6   Rationalize the numerator of $\dfrac{\sqrt[3]{2x^2}}{\sqrt[3]{5y}}$.

Solution   The numerator and the denominator of this expression are already simplified. To rationalize the numerator, $\sqrt[3]{2x^2}$, we multiply the numerator and denominator by a factor that will make the radicand a perfect cube. If we multiply $\sqrt[3]{2x^2}$ by $\sqrt[3]{4x}$, we get $\sqrt[3]{8x^3} = 2x$.

$$\frac{\sqrt[3]{2x^2}}{\sqrt[3]{5y}} = \frac{\sqrt[3]{2x^2} \cdot \sqrt[3]{4x}}{\sqrt[3]{5y} \cdot \sqrt[3]{4x}} = \frac{\sqrt[3]{8x^3}}{\sqrt[3]{20xy}} = \frac{2x}{\sqrt[3]{20xy}}$$

PRACTICE
6   Rationalize the numerator of $\dfrac{\sqrt[3]{5b}}{\sqrt[3]{2a}}$.

EXAMPLE 7   Rationalize the numerator of $\dfrac{\sqrt{x} + 2}{5}$.

Solution   We multiply the numerator and the denominator by the conjugate of the numerator, $\sqrt{x} + 2$.

$$\frac{\sqrt{x} + 2}{5} = \frac{(\sqrt{x} + 2)(\sqrt{x} - 2)}{5(\sqrt{x} - 2)} \quad \text{Multiply by } \sqrt{x} - 2, \text{ the conjugate of } \sqrt{x} + 2.$$

$$= \frac{(\sqrt{x})^2 - 2^2}{5(\sqrt{x} - 2)} \quad (a + b)(a - b) = a^2 - b^2$$

$$= \frac{x - 4}{5(\sqrt{x} - 2)}$$

PRACTICE
7   Rationalize the numerator of $\dfrac{\sqrt{x} - 3}{4}$.

Vocabulary, Readiness & Video Check

Use the choices below to fill in each blank. Not all choices will be used.

rationalizing the numerator   conjugate $\dfrac{\sqrt{3}}{\sqrt{3}}$

rationalizing the denominator $\dfrac{5}{5}$

1. The _____ of $a + b$ is $a - b$.

2. The process of writing an equivalent expression, but without a radical in the denominator, is called _____.

3. The process of writing an equivalent expression, but without a radical in the numerator, is called _____.

4. To rationalize the denominator of $\dfrac{5}{\sqrt{3}}$, we multiply by _____ .

Martin-Gay Interactive Videos

See Video 10.5

Watch the section lecture video and answer the following questions.

OBJECTIVE 1
5. From Examples 1–3, what is the goal of rationalizing a denominator?

OBJECTIVE 2
6. From Example 4, why will multiplying a denominator by its conjugate always rationalize the denominator?

OBJECTIVE 3
7. From Example 5, is the process of rationalizing a numerator any different from rationalizing a denominator?

10.5 Exercise Set MyMathLab®

Rationalize each denominator. See Examples 1 through 3.

1. $\dfrac{\sqrt{2}}{\sqrt{7}}$

2. $\dfrac{\sqrt{3}}{\sqrt{2}}$

3. $\sqrt{\dfrac{1}{5}}$

4. $\sqrt{\dfrac{1}{2}}$

5. $\sqrt{\dfrac{4}{x}}$

6. $\sqrt{\dfrac{25}{y}}$

7. $\dfrac{4}{\sqrt[3]{3}}$

8. $\dfrac{6}{\sqrt[3]{9}}$

9. $\dfrac{3}{\sqrt{8x}}$

10. $\dfrac{5}{\sqrt{27a}}$

11. $\dfrac{3}{\sqrt[3]{4x^2}}$

12. $\dfrac{5}{\sqrt[3]{3y}}$

13. $\dfrac{9}{\sqrt{3a}}$

14. $\dfrac{x}{\sqrt{5}}$

15. $\dfrac{3}{\sqrt[3]{2}}$

16. $\dfrac{5}{\sqrt[3]{9}}$

17. $\dfrac{2\sqrt{3}}{\sqrt{7}}$

18. $\dfrac{-5\sqrt{2}}{\sqrt{11}}$

19. $\sqrt{\dfrac{2x}{5y}}$

20. $\sqrt{\dfrac{13a}{2b}}$

21. $\sqrt[3]{\dfrac{3}{5}}$

22. $\sqrt[3]{\dfrac{7}{10}}$

23. $\sqrt{\dfrac{3x}{50}}$

24. $\sqrt{\dfrac{11y}{45}}$

25. $\dfrac{1}{\sqrt{12z}}$

26. $\dfrac{1}{\sqrt{32x}}$

27. $\dfrac{\sqrt[3]{2y^2}}{\sqrt[3]{9x^2}}$

28. $\dfrac{\sqrt[3]{3x}}{\sqrt[3]{4y^4}}$

29. $\sqrt[4]{\dfrac{81}{8}}$

30. $\sqrt[4]{\dfrac{1}{9}}$

31. $\sqrt[4]{\dfrac{16}{9x^7}}$

32. $\sqrt[5]{\dfrac{32}{m^6 n^{13}}}$

33. $\dfrac{5a}{\sqrt[5]{8a^9 b^{11}}}$

34. $\dfrac{9y}{\sqrt[4]{4y^9}}$

Write the conjugate of each expression.

35. $\sqrt{2} + x$

36. $\sqrt{3} + y$

37. $5 - \sqrt{a}$

38. $6 - \sqrt{b}$

39. $-7\sqrt{5} + 8\sqrt{x}$

40. $-9\sqrt{2} - 6\sqrt{y}$

Rationalize each denominator. See Example 4.

41. $\dfrac{6}{2 - \sqrt{7}}$

42. $\dfrac{3}{\sqrt{7} - 4}$

43. $\dfrac{-7}{\sqrt{x} - 3}$

44. $\dfrac{-8}{\sqrt{y} + 4}$

45. $\dfrac{\sqrt{2} - \sqrt{3}}{\sqrt{2} + \sqrt{3}}$

46. $\dfrac{\sqrt{3} + \sqrt{4}}{\sqrt{2} - \sqrt{3}}$

47. $\dfrac{\sqrt{a} + 1}{2\sqrt{a} - \sqrt{b}}$

48. $\dfrac{2\sqrt{a} - 3}{2\sqrt{a} + \sqrt{b}}$

49. $\dfrac{8}{1 + \sqrt{10}}$

50. $\dfrac{-3}{\sqrt{6} - 2}$

51. $\dfrac{\sqrt{x}}{\sqrt{x} + \sqrt{y}}$

52. $\dfrac{2\sqrt{a}}{2\sqrt{x} - \sqrt{y}}$

53. $\dfrac{2\sqrt{3} + \sqrt{6}}{4\sqrt{3} - \sqrt{6}}$

54. $\dfrac{4\sqrt{5} + \sqrt{2}}{2\sqrt{5} - \sqrt{2}}$

Rationalize each numerator. See Examples 5 and 6.

55. $\sqrt{\dfrac{5}{3}}$

56. $\sqrt{\dfrac{3}{2}}$

57. $\sqrt{\dfrac{18}{5}}$

58. $\sqrt{\dfrac{12}{7}}$

59. $\dfrac{\sqrt{4x}}{7}$

60. $\dfrac{\sqrt{3x^5}}{6}$

61. $\dfrac{\sqrt[3]{5y^2}}{\sqrt[3]{4x}}$

62. $\dfrac{\sqrt[3]{4x}}{\sqrt[3]{z^4}}$

63. $\sqrt{\dfrac{2}{5}}$

64. $\sqrt{\dfrac{3}{7}}$

65. $\dfrac{\sqrt{2x}}{11}$

66. $\dfrac{\sqrt{y}}{7}$

67. $\sqrt[3]{\dfrac{7}{8}}$

68. $\sqrt[3]{\dfrac{25}{2}}$

69. $\dfrac{\sqrt[3]{3x^5}}{10}$

70. $\sqrt[3]{\dfrac{9y}{7}}$

71. $\sqrt{\dfrac{18x^4 y^6}{3z}}$

72. $\sqrt{\dfrac{8x^5 y}{2z}}$

Rationalize each numerator. See Example 7.

73. $\dfrac{2 - \sqrt{11}}{6}$

74. $\dfrac{\sqrt{15} + 1}{2}$

75. $\dfrac{2 - \sqrt{7}}{-5}$

76. $\dfrac{\sqrt{5} + 2}{\sqrt{2}}$

77. $\dfrac{\sqrt{x} + 3}{\sqrt{x}}$

78. $\dfrac{5 + \sqrt{2}}{\sqrt{2x}}$

79. $\dfrac{\sqrt{2} - 1}{\sqrt{2} + 1}$

80. $\dfrac{\sqrt{8} - \sqrt{3}}{\sqrt{2} + \sqrt{3}}$

81. $\dfrac{\sqrt{x} + 1}{\sqrt{x} - 1}$

82. $\dfrac{\sqrt{x} + \sqrt{y}}{\sqrt{x} - \sqrt{y}}$

REVIEW AND PREVIEW

Solve each equation. See Sections 2.3 and 6.6.

83. $2x - 7 = 3(x - 4)$

84. $9x - 4 = 7(x - 2)$

85. $(x - 6)(2x + 1) = 0$

86. $(y + 2)(5y + 4) = 0$

87. $x^2 - 8x = -12$

88. $x^3 = x$

CONCEPT EXTENSIONS

△ **89.** The formula of the radius r of a sphere with surface area A is

$$r = \sqrt{\frac{A}{4\pi}}$$

Rationalize the denominator of the radical expression in this formula.

△ **90.** The formula for the radius r of a cone with height 7 centimeters and volume V is

$$r = \sqrt{\frac{3V}{7\pi}}$$

Rationalize the numerator of the radical expression in this formula.

7 cm

91. Given $\dfrac{\sqrt{5y^3}}{\sqrt{12x^3}}$, rationalize the denominator by following parts (a) and (b).

  a. Multiply the numerator and denominator by $\sqrt{12x^3}$.

  b. Multiply the numerator and denominator by $\sqrt{3x}$.

  c. What can you conclude from parts (a) and (b)?

92. Given $\dfrac{\sqrt[3]{5y}}{\sqrt[3]{4}}$, rationalize the denominator by following parts (a) and (b).

  a. Multiply the numerator and denominator by $\sqrt[3]{16}$.

  b. Multiply the numerator and denominator by $\sqrt[3]{2}$.

  c. What can you conclude from parts (a) and (b)?

Determine the smallest number both the numerator and denominator should be multiplied by to rationalize the denominator of the radical expression. See the Concept Check in this section.

93. $\dfrac{9}{\sqrt[3]{5}}$

94. $\dfrac{5}{\sqrt{27}}$

95. When rationalizing the denominator of $\dfrac{\sqrt{5}}{\sqrt{7}}$, explain why both the numerator and the denominator must be multiplied by $\sqrt{7}$.

96. When rationalizing the numerator of $\dfrac{\sqrt{5}}{\sqrt{7}}$, explain why both the numerator and the denominator must be multiplied by $\sqrt{5}$.

97. Explain why rationalizing the denominator does not change the value of the original expression.

98. Explain why rationalizing the numerator does not change the value of the original expression.

Integrated Review — RADICALS AND RATIONAL EXPONENTS

Sections 10.1–10.5

Throughout this review, assume that all variables represent positive real numbers.

Find each root.

1. $\sqrt{81}$

2. $\sqrt[3]{-8}$

3. $\sqrt[4]{\dfrac{1}{16}}$

4. $\sqrt{x^6}$

5. $\sqrt[3]{y^9}$

6. $\sqrt{4y^{10}}$

7. $\sqrt[5]{-32y^5}$

8. $\sqrt[4]{81b^{12}}$

Use radical notation to write each expression. Simplify if possible.

9. $36^{1/2}$

10. $(3y)^{1/4}$

11. $64^{-2/3}$

12. $(x + 1)^{3/5}$

Use the properties of exponents to simplify each expression. Write with positive exponents.

13. $y^{-1/6} \cdot y^{7/6}$

14. $\dfrac{(2x^{1/3})^4}{x^{5/6}}$

15. $\dfrac{x^{1/4}x^{3/4}}{x^{-1/4}}$

16. $4^{1/3} \cdot 4^{2/5}$

Use rational exponents to simplify each radical.

17. $\sqrt[3]{8x^6}$

18. $\sqrt[12]{a^9b^6}$

Use rational exponents to write each as a single radical expression.

19. $\sqrt[4]{x} \cdot \sqrt{x}$

20. $\sqrt{5} \cdot \sqrt[3]{2}$

Simplify.

21. $\sqrt{40}$

22. $\sqrt[4]{16x^7y^{10}}$

23. $\sqrt[3]{54x^4}$

24. $\sqrt[5]{-64b^{10}}$

Multiply or divide. Then simplify if possible.

25. $\sqrt{5} \cdot \sqrt{x}$

26. $\sqrt[3]{8x} \cdot \sqrt[3]{8x^2}$

27. $\dfrac{\sqrt{98y^6}}{\sqrt{2y}}$

28. $\dfrac{\sqrt[4]{48a^9b^3}}{\sqrt[4]{ab^3}}$

Perform each indicated operation.

29. $\sqrt{20} - \sqrt{75} + 5\sqrt{7}$

30. $\sqrt[3]{54y^4} - y\sqrt[3]{16y}$

31. $\sqrt{3}\left(\sqrt{5} - \sqrt{2}\right)$

32. $\left(\sqrt{7} + \sqrt{3}\right)^2$

33. $\left(2x - \sqrt{5}\right)\left(2x + \sqrt{5}\right)$

34. $\left(\sqrt{x+1} - 1\right)^2$

Rationalize each denominator.

35. $\sqrt{\dfrac{7}{3}}$

36. $\dfrac{5}{\sqrt[3]{2x^2}}$

37. $\dfrac{\sqrt{3} - \sqrt{7}}{2\sqrt{3} + \sqrt{7}}$

Rationalize each numerator.

38. $\sqrt{\dfrac{7}{3}}$

39. $\sqrt[3]{\dfrac{9y}{11}}$

40. $\dfrac{\sqrt{x} - 2}{\sqrt{x}}$

10.6 | Radical Equations and Problem Solving

OBJECTIVES

1 Solve Equations That Contain Radical Expressions.

2 Use the Pythagorean Theorem to Model Problems.

OBJECTIVE

1 Solving Equations That Contain Radical Expressions

In this section, we present techniques to solve equations containing radical expressions such as

$$\sqrt{2x - 3} = 9$$

We use the power rule to help us solve these radical equations.

> **Power Rule**
>
> If both sides of an equation are raised to the same power, **all** solutions of the original equation are **among** the solutions of the new equation.

This property *does not* say that raising both sides of an equation to a power yields an equivalent equation. A solution of the new equation *may or may not* be a solution of the original equation. For example, $(-2)^2 = 2^2$, but $-2 \neq 2$. Thus, *each solution of the new equation must be checked* to make sure it is a solution of the original equation. Recall that a proposed solution that is not a solution of the original equation is called an **extraneous solution**.

EXAMPLE 1   Solve: $\sqrt{2x - 3} = 9$.

Solution   We use the power rule to square both sides of the equation to eliminate the radical.

$$\sqrt{2x - 3} = 9$$
$$(\sqrt{2x - 3})^2 = 9^2$$
$$2x - 3 = 81$$
$$2x = 84$$
$$x = 42$$

Now we check the solution in the original equation.

Check:

$$\sqrt{2x - 3} = 9$$
$$\sqrt{2(42) - 3} \overset{?}{=} 9 \quad \text{Let } x = 42.$$
$$\sqrt{84 - 3} \overset{?}{=} 9$$
$$\sqrt{81} \overset{?}{=} 9$$
$$9 = 9 \quad \text{True}$$

The solution checks, so we conclude that the solution is 42, or the solution set is $\{42\}$. □

PRACTICE
1   Solve: $\sqrt{3x - 5} = 7$.

To solve a radical equation, first isolate a radical on one side of the equation.

EXAMPLE 2   Solve: $\sqrt{-10x - 1} + 3x = 0$.

Solution   First, isolate the radical on one side of the equation. To do this, we subtract $3x$ from both sides.

$$\sqrt{-10x - 1} + 3x = 0$$
$$\sqrt{-10x - 1} + 3x - 3x = 0 - 3x$$
$$\sqrt{-10x - 1} = -3x$$

Next we use the power rule to eliminate the radical.

$$(\sqrt{-10x - 1})^2 = (-3x)^2$$
$$-10x - 1 = 9x^2$$

Since this is a quadratic equation, we can set the equation equal to 0 and try to solve by factoring.

$$9x^2 + 10x + 1 = 0$$
$$(9x + 1)(x + 1) = 0 \quad \text{Factor.}$$
$$9x + 1 = 0 \quad \text{or} \quad x + 1 = 0 \quad \text{Set each factor equal to 0.}$$
$$x = -\frac{1}{9} \quad \text{or} \quad x = -1$$

Check: Let $x = -\frac{1}{9}$.   Let $x = -1$.

$$\sqrt{-10x - 1} + 3x = 0$$ $$\sqrt{-10x - 1} + 3x = 0$$
$$\sqrt{-10\left(-\frac{1}{9}\right) - 1} + 3\left(-\frac{1}{9}\right) \overset{?}{=} 0$$ $$\sqrt{-10(-1) - 1} + 3(-1) \overset{?}{=} 0$$
$$\sqrt{\frac{10}{9} - \frac{9}{9}} - \frac{3}{9} \overset{?}{=} 0$$ $$\sqrt{10 - 1} - 3 \overset{?}{=} 0$$
$$\sqrt{\frac{1}{9}} - \frac{1}{3} \overset{?}{=} 0$$ $$\sqrt{9} - 3 \overset{?}{=} 0$$
$$\frac{1}{3} - \frac{1}{3} = 0 \quad \text{True}$$ $$3 - 3 = 0 \quad \text{True}$$

Both solutions check. The solutions are $-\frac{1}{9}$ and -1, or the solution set is $\left\{-\frac{1}{9}, -1\right\}$. □

PRACTICE
2   Solve: $\sqrt{16x - 3} - 4x = 0$.

The following steps may be used to solve a radical equation.

> **Solving a Radical Equation**
>
> **Step 1.** Isolate one radical on one side of the equation.
>
> **Step 2.** Raise each side of the equation to a power equal to the index of the radical and simplify.
>
> **Step 3.** If the equation still contains a radical term, repeat Steps 1 and 2. If not, solve the equation.
>
> **Step 4.** Check all proposed solutions in the original equation.

EXAMPLE 3   Solve: $\sqrt[3]{x + 1} + 5 = 3$.

Solution   First we isolate the radical by subtracting 5 from both sides of the equation.

$$\sqrt[3]{x + 1} + 5 = 3$$
$$\sqrt[3]{x + 1} = -2$$

Next we raise both sides of the equation to the third power to eliminate the radical.

$$(\sqrt[3]{x + 1})^3 = (-2)^3$$
$$x + 1 = -8$$
$$x = -9$$

The solution checks in the original equation, so the solution is -9.   □

PRACTICE
3   Solve: $\sqrt[3]{x - 2} + 1 = 3$.

EXAMPLE 4   Solve: $\sqrt{4 - x} = x - 2$.

Solution

$$\sqrt{4 - x} = x - 2$$
$$(\sqrt{4 - x})^2 = (x - 2)^2$$
$$4 - x = x^2 - 4x + 4$$

$x^2 - 3x = 0$	Write the quadratic equation in standard form.
$x(x - 3) = 0$	Factor.
$x = 0 \quad \text{or} \quad x - 3 = 0$	Set each factor equal to 0.
$x = 3$	

Check:

$$\sqrt{4 - x} = x - 2 \qquad\qquad \sqrt{4 - x} = x - 2$$
$$\sqrt{4 - 0} \stackrel{?}{=} 0 - 2 \quad \text{Let } x = 0. \qquad \sqrt{4 - 3} \stackrel{?}{=} 3 - 2 \quad \text{Let } x = 3.$$
$$2 = -2 \quad \text{False} \qquad\qquad 1 = 1 \quad \text{True}$$

The proposed solution 3 checks, but 0 does not. Since 0 is an extraneous solution, the only solution is 3.   □

PRACTICE
4   Solve: $\sqrt{16 + x} = x - 4$.

> ▶ **Helpful Hint**
>
> In Example 4, notice that $(x - 2)^2 = x^2 - 4x + 4$. Make sure binomials are squared correctly.

✓CONCEPT CHECK

How can you immediately tell that the equation $\sqrt{2y + 3} = -4$ has no real solution?

EXAMPLE 5   Solve: $\sqrt{2x + 5} + \sqrt{2x} = 3$.

Solution   We get one radical alone by subtracting $\sqrt{2x}$ from both sides.

$$\sqrt{2x + 5} + \sqrt{2x} = 3$$
$$\sqrt{2x + 5} = 3 - \sqrt{2x}$$

Now we use the power rule to begin eliminating the radicals. First we square both sides.

$$\left(\sqrt{2x + 5}\right)^2 = \left(3 - \sqrt{2x}\right)^2$$
$$2x + 5 = 9 - 6\sqrt{2x} + 2x \quad \text{Multiply } (3 - \sqrt{2x})(3 - \sqrt{2x}).$$

There is still a radical in the equation, so we get a radical alone again. Then we square both sides.

$$2x + 5 = 9 - 6\sqrt{2x} + 2x$$
$$6\sqrt{2x} = 4 \qquad \text{Get the radical alone.}$$
$$36(2x) = 16 \qquad \text{Square both sides of the equation to eliminate the radical.}$$
$$72x = 16 \qquad \text{Multiply.}$$
$$x = \frac{16}{72} \qquad \text{Solve.}$$
$$x = \frac{2}{9} \qquad \text{Simplify.}$$

The proposed solution, $\frac{2}{9}$, checks in the original equation. The solution is $\frac{2}{9}$.   □

PRACTICE
5   Solve: $\sqrt{8x + 1} + \sqrt{3x} = 2$.

▶ Helpful Hint

Make sure expressions are squared correctly. In Example 5, we squared $(3 - \sqrt{2x})$ as
$$\left(3 - \sqrt{2x}\right)^2 = \left(3 - \sqrt{2x}\right)\left(3 - \sqrt{2x}\right)$$
$$= 3 \cdot 3 - 3\sqrt{2x} - 3\sqrt{2x} + \sqrt{2x} \cdot \sqrt{2x}$$
$$= 9 - 6\sqrt{2x} + 2x$$

✓CONCEPT CHECK

What is wrong with the following solution?
$$\sqrt{2x + 5} + \sqrt{4 - x} = 8$$
$$\left(\sqrt{2x + 5} + \sqrt{4 - x}\right)^2 = 8^2$$
$$(2x + 5) + (4 - x) = 64$$
$$x + 9 = 64$$
$$x = 55$$

Answers to Concept Checks:
answers may vary;
$\left(\sqrt{2x + 5} + \sqrt{4 - x}\right)^2$ is not
$(2x + 5) + (4 - x)$.

OBJECTIVE
2   **Using the Pythagorean Theorem**

Recall that the Pythagorean theorem states that in a right triangle, the length of the hypotenuse squared equals the sum of the lengths of each of the legs squared.

Pythagorean Theorem

If a and b are the lengths of the legs of a right triangle and c is the length of the hypotenuse, then $a^2 + b^2 = c^2$.

Hypotenuse

c

a

b

Legs

△ **EXAMPLE 6** Find the length of the unknown leg of the right triangle.

10 m

4 m

b

Solution In the formula $a^2 + b^2 = c^2$, c is the hypotenuse. Here, $c = 10$, the length of the hypotenuse, and $a = 4$. We solve for b. Then $a^2 + b^2 = c^2$ becomes

$$4^2 + b^2 = 10^2$$
$$16 + b^2 = 100$$
$$b^2 = 84 \quad \text{Subtract 16 from both sides.}$$
$$b = \pm\sqrt{84} = \pm\sqrt{4 \cdot 21} = \pm 2\sqrt{21}$$

Since b is a length and thus is positive, we will use the positive value only. The unknown leg of the triangle is $2\sqrt{21}$ meters long.

PRACTICE

6 Find the length of the unknown leg of the right triangle.

12 m

6 m

a

△ **EXAMPLE 7** **Calculating Placement of a Wire**

A 50-foot supporting wire is to be attached to a 75-foot antenna. Because of surrounding buildings, sidewalks, and roadways, the wire must be anchored exactly 20 feet from the base of the antenna.

75 ft

50 ft

←— 20 ft —→

a. How high from the base of the antenna is the wire attached?

b. Local regulations require that a supporting wire be attached at a height no less than $\frac{3}{5}$ of the total height of the antenna. From part (a), have local regulations been met?

Solution

50 ft

x ft

←—20 ft—→

1. UNDERSTAND. Read and reread the problem. From the diagram, we notice that a right triangle is formed with hypotenuse 50 feet and one leg 20 feet. Let x be the height from the base of the antenna to the attached wire.

2. TRANSLATE. Use the Pythagorean theorem.

$$a^2 + b^2 = c^2$$
$$20^2 + x^2 = 50^2 \quad a = 20, c = 50$$

3. SOLVE.

$$20^2 + x^2 = 50^2$$
$$400 + x^2 = 2500$$
$$x^2 = 2100 \quad \text{Subtract 400 from both sides.}$$
$$x = \pm\sqrt{2100}$$
$$= \pm 10\sqrt{21}$$

4. INTERPRET. *Check* the work and *state* the solution.

Check: We will use only the positive value, $x = 10\sqrt{21}$, because x represents length. The wire is attached exactly $10\sqrt{21}$ feet from the base of the pole, or approximately 45.8 feet.

State: The supporting wire must be attached at a height no less than $\frac{3}{5}$ of the total height of the antenna. This height is $\frac{3}{5}$ (75 feet), or 45 feet. Since we know from part (a) that the wire is to be attached at a height of approximately 45.8 feet, local regulations have been met. □

PRACTICE

7 Keith Robinson bought two Siamese fighting fish, but when he got home, he found he only had one rectangular tank that was 12 in. long, 7 in. wide, and 5 in. deep. Since the fish must be kept separated, he needed to insert a plastic divider in the diagonal of the tank. He already has a piece that is 5 in. in one dimension, but how long must it be to fit corner to corner in the tank?

Graphing Calculator Explorations

We can use a graphing calculator to solve radical equations. For example, to use a graphing calculator to approximate the solutions of the equation solved in Example 4, we graph the following.

$$Y_1 = \sqrt{4 - x} \quad \text{and} \quad Y_2 = x - 2$$

The x-value of the point of intersection is the solution. Use the Intersect feature or the Zoom and Trace features of your graphing calculator to see that the solution is 3.

Use a graphing calculator to solve each radical equation. Round all solutions to the nearest hundredth.

1. $\sqrt{x + 7} = x$ **2.** $\sqrt{3x + 5} = 2x$

3. $\sqrt{2x + 1} = \sqrt{2x + 2}$ **4.** $\sqrt{10x - 1} = \sqrt{-10x + 10} - 1$

5. $1.2x = \sqrt{3.1x + 5}$ **6.** $\sqrt{1.9x^2 - 2.2} = -0.8x + 3$

Vocabulary, Readiness & Video Check

Use the choices below to fill in each blank. Not all choices will be used.

hypotenuse   right $x^2 + 25$ $16 - 8\sqrt{7x} + 7x$

extraneous solution   legs $x^2 - 10x + 25$ $16 + 7x$

1. A proposed solution that is not a solution of the original equation is called a(n) _____.

2. The Pythagorean theorem states that $a^2 + b^2 = c^2$ where a and b are the lengths of the _____ of a(n) _____ triangle and c is the length of the _____.

3. The square of $x - 5$, or $(x - 5)^2 =$ _____.

4. The square of $4 - \sqrt{7x}$, or $(4 - \sqrt{7x})^2 =$ _____.

Martin-Gay Interactive Videos

Watch the section lecture video and answer the following questions.

OBJECTIVE
1

5. From ▯ Examples 1–4, why must you be careful and check your proposed solution(s) in the original equation?

OBJECTIVE
2

6. From ▯ Example 5, when solving problems using the Pythagorean theorem, what two things must you remember?

OBJECTIVE
2

7. What important reminder is given as the final answer to ▯ Example 5 is being found?

See Video 10.6

10.6 Exercise Set MyMathLab®

Solve. See Examples 1 and 2.

1. $\sqrt{2x} = 4$

2. $\sqrt{3x} = 3$

▶ **3.** $\sqrt{x - 3} = 2$

4. $\sqrt{x + 1} = 5$

5. $\sqrt{2x} = -4$

6. $\sqrt{5x} = -5$

7. $\sqrt{4x - 3} - 5 = 0$

8. $\sqrt{x - 3} - 1 = 0$

9. $\sqrt{2x - 3} - 2 = 1$

10. $\sqrt{3x + 3} - 4 = 8$

Solve. See Example 3.

11. $\sqrt[3]{6x} = -3$

12. $\sqrt[3]{4x} = -2$

13. $\sqrt[3]{x - 2} - 3 = 0$

14. $\sqrt[3]{2x - 6} - 4 = 0$

Solve. See Examples 4 and 5.

15. $\sqrt{13 - x} = x - 1$

16. $\sqrt{2x - 3} = 3 - x$

▶ **17.** $x - \sqrt{4 - 3x} = -8$

18. $2x + \sqrt{x + 1} = 8$

19. $\sqrt{y + 5} = 2 - \sqrt{y - 4}$

20. $\sqrt{x + 3} + \sqrt{x - 5} = 3$

21. $\sqrt{x - 3} + \sqrt{x + 2} = 5$

22. $\sqrt{2x - 4} - \sqrt{3x + 4} = -2$

MIXED PRACTICE

Solve. See Examples 1 through 5.

23. $\sqrt{3x - 2} = 5$

24. $\sqrt{5x - 4} = 9$

25. $-\sqrt{2x} + 4 = -6$

26. $-\sqrt{3x + 9} = -12$

27. $\sqrt{3x + 1} + 2 = 0$

28. $\sqrt{3x + 1} - 2 = 0$

29. $\sqrt[4]{4x + 1} - 2 = 0$

30. $\sqrt[4]{2x - 9} - 3 = 0$

31. $\sqrt{4x - 3} = 7$

32. $\sqrt{3x + 9} = 6$

33. $\sqrt[3]{6x - 3} - 3 = 0$

34. $\sqrt[3]{3x} + 4 = 7$

▶ **35.** $\sqrt[3]{2x - 3} - 2 = -5$

36. $\sqrt[3]{x - 4} - 5 = -7$

37. $\sqrt{x + 4} = \sqrt{2x - 5}$

38. $\sqrt{3y + 6} = \sqrt{7y - 6}$

39. $x - \sqrt{1 - x} = -5$

40. $x - \sqrt{x - 2} = 4$

41. $\sqrt[3]{-6x - 1} = \sqrt[3]{-2x - 5}$

42. $\sqrt[3]{-4x - 3} = \sqrt[3]{-x - 15}$

▶ **43.** $\sqrt{5x - 1} - \sqrt{x + 2} = 3$

44. $\sqrt{2x - 1} - 4 = -\sqrt{x - 4}$

45. $\sqrt{2x - 1} = \sqrt{1 - 2x}$

46. $\sqrt{7x - 4} = \sqrt{4 - 7x}$

47. $\sqrt{3x + 4} - 1 = \sqrt{2x + 1}$

48. $\sqrt{x - 2} + 3 = \sqrt{4x + 1}$

49. $\sqrt{y + 3} - \sqrt{y - 3} = 1$

50. $\sqrt{x + 1} - \sqrt{x - 1} = 2$

Find the length of the unknown side of each triangle. See Example 6.

▶ **51.**

△ **52.**

△ **53.**

△ **54.**

Find the length of the unknown side of each triangle. Give the exact length and a one-decimal-place approximation. See Example 6.

△ **55.**

△ **56.**

△ **57.**

△ **58.**

Solve. Give exact answers and two-decimal-place approximations where appropriate. For Exercises 59 and 60, the solutions have been started for you. See Example 7.

59. A wire is needed to support a vertical pole 15 feet tall. The cable will be anchored to a stake 8 feet from the base of the pole. How much cable is needed?

15 ft

8 ft

Start the solution:

1. UNDERSTAND the problem. Reread it as many times as needed. Notice that a right triangle is formed with legs of length 8 ft and 15 ft.
   Since we are looking for how much cable is needed, let

   $$x = \text{amount of cable needed}$$

2. TRANSLATE into an equation. We use the Pythagorean theorem. (Fill in the blanks below.)

$$\begin{array}{ccccc} a^2 & + & b^2 & = & c^2 \\ \downarrow & & \downarrow & & \\ \underline{\quad}^2 & + & \underline{\quad}^2 & = & x^2 \end{array}$$

   Finish with:

3. SOLVE and 4. INTERPRET

60. The tallest structure in the United States is a TV tower in Blanchard, North Dakota. Its height is 2063 feet. A 2382-foot length of wire is to be used as a guy wire attached to the top of the tower. Approximate to the nearest foot how far from the base of the tower the guy wire must be anchored. (*Source:* U.S. Geological Survey)

2382 ft   2063 ft

?

Start the solution:

1. UNDERSTAND the problem. Reread it as many times as needed. Notice that a right triangle is formed with hypotenuse 2382 ft and one leg 2063 ft.
   Since we are looking for how far from the base of the tower the guy wire is anchored, let

   $$x = \text{distance from base of tower to where guy wire is anchored.}$$

2. TRANSLATE into an equation. We use the Pythagorean theorem. (Fill in the blanks below.)

$$\begin{array}{ccccc} a^2 & + & b^2 & = & c^2 \\ \downarrow & & \downarrow & & \\ \underline{\quad}^2 & + & x^2 & = & \underline{\quad}^2 \end{array}$$

   Finish with:

3. SOLVE and 4. INTERPRET

61. A spotlight is mounted on the eaves of a house 12 feet above the ground. A flower bed runs between the house and the sidewalk, so the closest a ladder can be placed to the house is 5 feet. How long of a ladder is needed so that an electrician can reach the place where the light is mounted?

12 ft

5 ft

62. A wire is to be attached to support a telephone pole. Because of surrounding buildings, sidewalks, and roadways, the wire must be anchored exactly 15 feet from the base of the pole. Telephone company workers have only 30 feet of cable, and 2 feet of that must be used to attach the cable to the pole and to the stake on the ground. How high from the base of the pole can the wire be attached?

15 ft

63. The radius of the moon is 1080 miles. Use the formula for the radius r of a sphere given its surface area A,

$$r = \sqrt{\dfrac{A}{4\pi}}$$

to find the surface area of the moon. Round to the nearest square mile. (*Source:* National Space Science Data Center)

64. Police departments find it very useful to be able to approximate the speed of a car when they are given the distance that the car skidded before it came to a stop. If the road surface is wet concrete, the function $S(x) = \sqrt{10.5x}$ is used, where $S(x)$ is the speed of the car in miles per hour and x is the distance skidded in feet. Find how fast a car was moving if it skidded 280 feet on wet concrete.

65. The formula $v = \sqrt{2gh}$ gives the velocity v, in feet per second, of an object when it falls h feet accelerated by gravity g, in feet per second squared. If g is approximately 32 feet per second squared, find how far an object has fallen if its velocity is 80 feet per second.

66. Two tractors are pulling a tree stump from a field. If two forces A and B pull at right angles (90°) to each other, the size of the resulting force R is given by the formula $R = \sqrt{A^2 + B^2}$. If tractor A is exerting 600 pounds of force and the resulting force is 850 pounds, find how much force tractor B is exerting.

600 lb

In psychology, it has been suggested that the number S of nonsense syllables that a person can repeat consecutively depends on his or her IQ score I according to the equation $S = 2\sqrt{I} - 9$.

67. Use this relationship to estimate the IQ of a person who can repeat 11 nonsense syllables consecutively.

68. Use this relationship to estimate the IQ of a person who can repeat 15 nonsense syllables consecutively.

*The **period** of a pendulum is the time it takes for the pendulum to make one full back-and-forth swing. The period of a pendulum depends on the length of the pendulum. The formula for the period P, in seconds, is $P = 2\pi\sqrt{\dfrac{l}{32}}$, where l is the length of the pendulum in feet. Use this formula for Exercises 69 through 74.*

69. Find the period of a pendulum whose length is 2 feet. Give an exact answer and a two-decimal-place approximation.

2 feet

70. Klockit sells a 43-inch lyre pendulum. Find the period of this pendulum. Round your answer to 2 decimal places. (*Hint:* First convert inches to feet.)

71. Find the length of a pendulum whose period is 4 seconds. Round your answer to 2 decimal places.

72. Find the length of a pendulum whose period is 3 seconds. Round your answer to 2 decimal places.

73. Study the relationship between period and pendulum length in Exercises 69 through 72 and make a conjecture about this relationship.

74. Galileo experimented with pendulums. He supposedly made conjectures about pendulums of equal length with different bob weights. Try this experiment. Make two pendulums 3 feet long. Attach a heavy weight (lead) to one and a light weight (a cork) to the other. Pull both pendulums back the same angle measure and release. Make a conjecture from your observations.

If the three lengths of the sides of a triangle are known, Heron's formula can be used to find its area. If a, b, and c are the lengths of the three sides, Heron's formula for area is

$$A = \sqrt{s(s-a)(s-b)(s-c)}$$

where s is half the perimeter of the triangle, or $s = \dfrac{1}{2}(a+b+c)$.

Use this formula to find the area of each triangle. Give an exact answer and then a two-decimal-place approximation.

△ 75.   **△ 76.**

6 mi   10 mi   2 cm   3 cm
14 mi   3 cm

77. Describe when Heron's formula might be useful.

78. In your own words, explain why you think s in Heron's formula is called the *semiperimeter*.

The maximum distance $D(h)$ in kilometers that a person can see from a height h kilometers above the ground is given by the function $D(h) = 111.7\sqrt{h}$. Use this function for Exercises 79 and 80. Round your answers to two decimal places.

79. Find the height that would allow a person to see 80 kilometers.

80. Find the height that would allow a person to see 40 kilometers.

REVIEW AND PREVIEW

Use the vertical line test to determine whether each graph represents the graph of a function. See Section 3.6.

81.   **82.**

83.

84.

85.

86.

Simplify. See Section 7.7.

87. $\dfrac{\dfrac{x}{6}}{\dfrac{2x}{3} + \dfrac{1}{2}}$

88. $\dfrac{\dfrac{1}{y} + \dfrac{4}{5}}{-\dfrac{3}{20}}$

89. $\dfrac{\dfrac{z}{5} + \dfrac{1}{10}}{\dfrac{z}{20} - \dfrac{z}{5}}$

90. $\dfrac{\dfrac{1}{y} + \dfrac{1}{x}}{\dfrac{1}{y} - \dfrac{1}{x}}$

CONCEPT EXTENSIONS

Find the error in each solution and correct. See the second Concept Check in this section.

91.
$$\sqrt{5x - 1} + 4 = 7$$
$$(\sqrt{5x - 1} + 4)^2 = 7^2$$
$$5x - 1 + 16 = 49$$
$$5x = 34$$
$$x = \frac{34}{5}$$

92.
$$\sqrt{2x + 3} + 4 = 1$$
$$\sqrt{2x + 3} = 5$$
$$(\sqrt{2x + 3})^2 = 5^2$$
$$2x + 3 = 25$$
$$2x = 22$$
$$x = 11$$

93. Solve: $\sqrt{\sqrt{x + 3}} + \sqrt{x} = \sqrt{3}$

94. The cost $C(x)$ in dollars per day to operate a small delivery service is given by $C(x) = 80\sqrt[3]{x} + 500$, where x is the number of deliveries per day. In July, the manager decides that it is necessary to keep delivery costs below $1620.00. Find the greatest number of deliveries this company can make per day and still keep overhead below $1620.00.

95. Consider the equations $\sqrt{2x} = 4$ and $\sqrt[3]{2x} = 4$.
   a. Explain the difference in solving these equations.
   b. Explain the similarity in solving these equations.

96. Explain why proposed solutions of radical equations must be checked.

Example

For Exercises 97 through 100, see the example below.

Solve $(t^2 - 3t) - 2\sqrt{t^2 - 3t} = 0$.

Solution

Substitution can be used to make this problem somewhat simpler. Since $t^2 - 3t$ occurs more than once, let $x = t^2 - 3t$.

$$(t^2 - 3t) - 2\sqrt{t^2 - 3t} = 0$$
$$x - 2\sqrt{x} = 0$$
$$x = 2\sqrt{x}$$
$$x^2 = (2\sqrt{x})^2$$
$$x^2 = 4x$$
$$x^2 - 4x = 0$$
$$x(x - 4) = 0$$
$$x = 0 \quad \text{or} \quad x - 4 = 0$$
$$x = 4$$

Now we "undo" the substitution.
$x = 0$ Replace x with $t^2 - 3t$.
$$t^2 - 3t = 0$$
$$t(t - 3) = 0$$
$$t = 0 \quad \text{or} \quad t - 3 = 0$$
$$t = 3$$

$x = 4$ Replace x with $t^2 - 3t$.
$$t^2 - 3t = 4$$
$$t^2 - 3t - 4 = 0$$
$$(t - 4)(t + 1) = 0$$
$$t - 4 = 0 \quad \text{or} \quad t + 1 = 0$$
$$t = 4 \qquad\qquad t = -1$$

In this problem, we have four possible solutions: $0, 3, 4,$ and -1. All four solutions check in the original equation, so the solutions are $-1, 0, 3, 4$.

Solve. See the preceding example.

97. $3\sqrt{x^2 - 8x} = x^2 - 8x$

98. $\sqrt{(x^2 - x) + 7} = 2(x^2 - x) - 1$

99. $7 - (x^2 - 3x) = \sqrt{(x^2 - 3x)} + 5$

100. $x^2 + 6x = 4\sqrt{x^2 + 6x}$

10.7 Complex Numbers

OBJECTIVE

1   Writing Numbers in the Form bi

Our work with radical expressions has excluded expressions such as $\sqrt{-16}$ because $\sqrt{-16}$ is not a real number; there is no real number whose square is -16. In this section, we discuss a number system that includes roots of negative numbers. This number system is the **complex number system,** and it includes the set of real numbers as a subset. The complex number system allows us to solve equations such as $x^2 + 1 = 0$ that have no real number solutions. The set of complex numbers includes the **imaginary unit.**

> **Imaginary Unit**
>
> The imaginary unit, written i, is the number whose square is -1. That is,
> $$i^2 = -1 \quad \text{and} \quad i = \sqrt{-1}$$

To write the square root of a negative number in terms of i, use the property that if a is a positive number, then

$$\sqrt{-a} = \sqrt{-1} \cdot \sqrt{a}$$
$$= i \cdot \sqrt{a}$$

Using i, we can write $\sqrt{-16}$ as

$$\sqrt{-16} = \sqrt{-1 \cdot 16} = \sqrt{-1} \cdot \sqrt{16} = i \cdot 4, \text{ or } 4i$$

EXAMPLE 1   Write with i notation.

a. $\sqrt{-36}$ **b.** $\sqrt{-5}$ **c.** $-\sqrt{-20}$

Solution

a. $\sqrt{-36} = \sqrt{-1 \cdot 36} = \sqrt{-1} \cdot \sqrt{36} = i \cdot 6, \text{ or } 6i$

b. $\sqrt{-5} = \sqrt{-1(5)} = \sqrt{-1} \cdot \sqrt{5} = i\sqrt{5}.$

c. $-\sqrt{-20} = -\sqrt{-1 \cdot 20} = -\sqrt{-1} \cdot \sqrt{4 \cdot 5} = -i \cdot 2\sqrt{5} = -2i\sqrt{5}$

> ▶ Helpful Hint
>
> Since $\sqrt{5}i$ can easily be confused with $\sqrt{5i}$, we write $\sqrt{5}i$ as $i\sqrt{5}$.

PRACTICE

1   Write with i notation.

a. $\sqrt{-4}$ **b.** $\sqrt{-7}$ **c.** $-\sqrt{-18}$

The product rule for radicals does not necessarily hold true for imaginary numbers. *To multiply square roots of negative numbers, first we write each number in terms of the imaginary unit i.* For example, to multiply $\sqrt{-4}$ and $\sqrt{-9}$, we first write each number in the form bi.

$$\sqrt{-4}\sqrt{-9} = 2i(3i) = 6i^2 = 6(-1) = -6 \quad \text{Correct}$$

We will also use this method to simplify quotients of square roots of negative numbers. Why? The product rule does not work for this example. In other words,

$$\sqrt{-4} \cdot \sqrt{-9} = \sqrt{(-4)(-9)} = \sqrt{36} = 6 \quad \text{Incorrect}$$

EXAMPLE 2   Multiply or divide as indicated.

a. $\sqrt{-3}\cdot\sqrt{-5}$ **b.** $\sqrt{-36}\cdot\sqrt{-1}$ **c.** $\sqrt{8}\cdot\sqrt{-2}$ **d.** $\dfrac{\sqrt{-125}}{\sqrt{5}}$

Solution

a. $\sqrt{-3}\cdot\sqrt{-5} = i\sqrt{3}\,(i\sqrt{5}) = i^2\sqrt{15} = -1\sqrt{15} = -\sqrt{15}$

b. $\sqrt{-36}\cdot\sqrt{-1} = 6i(i) = 6i^2 = 6(-1) = -6$

c. $\sqrt{8}\cdot\sqrt{-2} = 2\sqrt{2}\,(i\sqrt{2}) = 2i(\sqrt{2}\sqrt{2}) = 2i(2) = 4i$

d. $\dfrac{\sqrt{-125}}{\sqrt{5}} = \dfrac{i\sqrt{125}}{\sqrt{5}} = i\sqrt{25} = 5i$

PRACTICE
2   Multiply or divide as indicated.

a. $\sqrt{-5}\cdot\sqrt{-6}$ **b.** $\sqrt{-9}\cdot\sqrt{-1}$ **c.** $\sqrt{125}\cdot\sqrt{-5}$ **d.** $\dfrac{\sqrt{-27}}{\sqrt{3}}$

Now that we have practiced working with the imaginary unit, we define complex numbers.

> **Complex Numbers**
>
> A **complex number** is a number that can be written in the form $a + bi$, where a and b are real numbers.

Notice that the set of real numbers is a subset of the complex numbers since any real number can be written in the form of a complex number. For example,

$$16 = 16 + 0i$$

In general, a complex number $a + bi$ is a real number if $b = 0$. Also, a complex number is called a **pure imaginary number** or an imaginary number if $a = 0$ and $b \neq 0$. For example,

$$3i = 0 + 3i \quad \text{and} \quad i\sqrt{7} = 0 + i\sqrt{7}$$

are pure imaginary numbers.

The following diagram shows the relationship between complex numbers and their subsets.

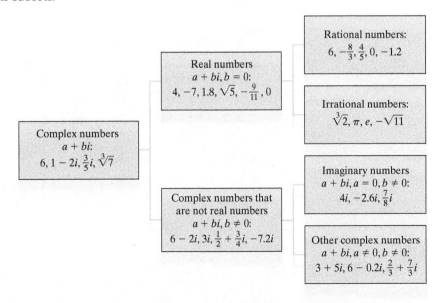

> ✓CONCEPT CHECK
> True or false? Every complex number is also a real number.

OBJECTIVE

2 Adding or Subtracting Complex Numbers

Two complex numbers $a + bi$ and $c + di$ are equal if and only if $a = c$ and $b = d$. Complex numbers can be added or subtracted by adding or subtracting their real parts and then adding or subtracting their imaginary parts.

Sum or Difference of Complex Numbers

If $a + bi$ and $c + di$ are complex numbers, then their sum is

$$(a + bi) + (c + di) = (a + c) + (b + d)i$$

Their difference is

$$(a + bi) - (c + di) = a + bi - c - di = (a - c) + (b - d)i$$

EXAMPLE 3 Add or subtract the complex numbers. Write the sum or difference in the form $a + bi$.

a. $(2 + 3i) + (-3 + 2i)$ **b.** $5i - (1 - i)$ **c.** $(-3 - 7i) - (-6)$

Solution

a. $(2 + 3i) + (-3 + 2i) = (2 - 3) + (3 + 2)i = -1 + 5i$

b. $5i - (1 - i) = 5i - 1 + i$
$$= -1 + (5 + 1)i$$
$$= -1 + 6i$$

c. $(-3 - 7i) - (-6) = -3 - 7i + 6$
$$= (-3 + 6) - 7i$$
$$= 3 - 7i$$ □

PRACTICE

3   Add or subtract the complex numbers. Write the sum or difference in the form $a + bi$.

a. $(3 - 5i) + (-4 + i)$ **b.** $4i - (3 - i)$ **c.** $(-5 - 2i) - (-8)$

OBJECTIVE

3 Multiplying Complex Numbers

To multiply two complex numbers of the form $a + bi$, we multiply as though they are binomials. Then we use the relationship $i^2 = -1$ to simplify.

EXAMPLE 4 Multiply the complex numbers. Write the product in the form $a + bi$.

a. $-7i \cdot 3i$ **b.** $3i(2 - i)$ **c.** $(2 - 5i)(4 + i)$

d. $(2 - i)^2$ **e.** $(7 + 3i)(7 - 3i)$

Solution

a. $-7i \cdot 3i = -21i^2$
$$= -21(-1)$$ Replace i^2 with -1.
$$= 21 + 0i$$

b. $3i(2 - i) = 3i \cdot 2 - 3i \cdot i$ Use the distributive property.

$\qquad = 6i - 3i^2$ Multiply.

$\qquad = 6i - 3(-1)$ Replace i^2 with -1.

$\qquad = 6i + 3$

$\qquad = 3 + 6i$

Use the FOIL order below. (First, Outer, Inner, Last)

c. $(2 - 5i)(4 + i) = 2(4) + 2(i) - 5i(4) - 5i(i)$

$\qquad\qquad\qquad\quad$ F$\qquad$O$\qquad$I$\qquad$L

$\qquad\qquad = 8 + 2i - 20i - 5i^2$

$\qquad\qquad = 8 - 18i - 5(-1)$ $\qquad\qquad\qquad i^2 = -1$

$\qquad\qquad = 8 - 18i + 5$

$\qquad\qquad = 13 - 18i$

d. $(2 - i)^2 = (2 - i)(2 - i)$

$\qquad\qquad = 2(2) - 2(i) - 2(i) + i^2$

$\qquad\qquad = 4 - 4i + (-1)$ $\qquad\qquad i^2 = -1$

$\qquad\qquad = 3 - 4i$

e. $(7 + 3i)(7 - 3i) = 7(7) - 7(3i) + 3i(7) - 3i(3i)$

$\qquad\qquad\qquad\quad = 49 - 21i + 21i - 9i^2$

$\qquad\qquad\qquad\quad = 49 - 9(-1)$ $\qquad\qquad\qquad i^2 = -1$

$\qquad\qquad\qquad\quad = 49 + 9$

$\qquad\qquad\qquad\quad = 58 + 0i$

PRACTICE

4   Multiply the complex numbers. Write the product in the form $a + bi$.

a. $-4i \cdot 5i$ $\qquad\qquad$ **b.** $5i(2 + i)$ $\qquad\qquad$ **c.** $(2 + 3i)(6 - i)$

d. $(3 - i)^2$ $\qquad\qquad$ **e.** $(9 + 2i)(9 - 2i)$

Notice that if you add, subtract, or multiply two complex numbers, just like real numbers, the result is a complex number.

OBJECTIVE

4   Dividing Complex Numbers

From Example 4e, notice that the product of $7 + 3i$ and $7 - 3i$ is a real number. These two complex numbers are called **complex conjugates** of one another. In general, we have the following definition.

Complex Conjugates

The complex numbers $(a + bi)$ and $(a - bi)$ are called **complex conjugates** of each other, and

$$(a + bi)(a - bi) = a^2 + b^2.$$

To see that the product of a complex number $a + bi$ and its conjugate $a - bi$ is the real number $a^2 + b^2$, we multiply.

$$(a + bi)(a - bi) = a^2 - abi + abi - b^2i^2$$

$$= a^2 - b^2(-1)$$

$$= a^2 + b^2$$

We use complex conjugates to divide by a complex number.

EXAMPLE 5 Divide. Write in the form $a + bi$.

a. $\dfrac{2 + i}{1 - i}$ **b.** $\dfrac{7}{3i}$

Solution

a. Multiply the numerator and denominator by the complex conjugate of $1 - i$ to eliminate the imaginary number in the denominator.

$$
\begin{aligned}
\frac{2 + i}{1 - i} &= \frac{(2 + i)(1 + i)}{(1 - i)(1 + i)} \\[4pt]
&= \frac{2(1) + 2(i) + 1(i) + i^2}{1^2 - i^2} \\[4pt]
&= \frac{2 + 3i - 1}{1 + 1} \qquad \text{Here. } i^2 = -1. \\[4pt]
&= \frac{1 + 3i}{2} \quad \text{or} \quad \frac{1}{2} + \frac{3}{2}i
\end{aligned}
$$

b. Multiply the numerator and denominator by the conjugate of $3i$. Note that $3i = 0 + 3i$, so its conjugate is $0 - 3i$ or $-3i$.

$$
\frac{7}{3i} = \frac{7(-3i)}{(3i)(-3i)} = \frac{-21i}{-9i^2} = \frac{-21i}{-9(-1)} = \frac{-21i}{9} = \frac{-7i}{3} \quad \text{or} \quad 0 - \frac{7}{3}i
$$

PRACTICE
5   Divide. Write in the form $a + bi$.

a. $\dfrac{4 - i}{3 + i}$ **b.** $\dfrac{5}{2i}$

> ▶ **Helpful Hint**
>
> Recall that division can be checked by multiplication.
>
> To check that $\dfrac{2 + i}{1 - i} = \dfrac{1}{2} + \dfrac{3}{2}i$, in Example 5a, multiply $\left(\dfrac{1}{2} + \dfrac{3}{2}i\right)(1 - i)$ to verify that the product is $2 + i$.

OBJECTIVE
5   **Finding Powers of i** ▶

We can use the fact that $i^2 = -1$ to find higher powers of i. To find i^3, we rewrite it as the product of i^2 and i.

$$
\begin{aligned}
i^3 &= i^2 \cdot i = (-1)i = -i \\
i^4 &= i^2 \cdot i^2 = (-1) \cdot (-1) = 1
\end{aligned}
$$

We continue this process and use the fact that $i^4 = 1$ and $i^2 = -1$ to simplify i^5 and i^6.

$$
\begin{aligned}
i^5 &= i^4 \cdot i = 1 \cdot i = i \\
i^6 &= i^4 \cdot i^2 = 1 \cdot (-1) = -1
\end{aligned}
$$

If we continue finding powers of i, we generate the following pattern. Notice that the values i, -1, $-i$, and 1 repeat as i is raised to higher and higher powers.

$i^1 = i$	$i^5 = i$	$i^9 = i$
$i^2 = -1$	$i^6 = -1$	$i^{10} = -1$
$i^3 = -i$	$i^7 = -i$	$i^{11} = -i$
$i^4 = 1$	$i^8 = 1$	$i^{12} = 1$

This pattern allows us to find other powers of i. To do so, we will use the fact that $i^4 = 1$ and rewrite a power of i in terms of i^4. For example,

$$i^{22} = i^{20} \cdot i^2 = (i^4)^5 \cdot i^2 = 1^5 \cdot (-1) = 1 \cdot (-1) = -1.$$

EXAMPLE 6   Find the following powers of i.

a. i^7 **b.** i^{20} **c.** i^{46} **d.** i^{-12}

Solution

a. $i^7 = i^4 \cdot i^3 = 1(-i) = -i$

b. $i^{20} = (i^4)^5 = 1^5 = 1$

c. $i^{46} = i^{44} \cdot i^2 = (i^4)^{11} \cdot i^2 = 1^{11}(-1) = -1$

d. $i^{-12} = \dfrac{1}{i^{12}} = \dfrac{1}{(i^4)^3} = \dfrac{1}{(1)^3} = \dfrac{1}{1} = 1$

PRACTICE
6   Find the following powers of i.

a. i^9 **b.** i^{16} **c.** i^{34} **d.** i^{-24}

Vocabulary, Readiness & Video Check

Use the choices below to fill in each blank. Not all choices will be used.

-1	$\sqrt{-1}$	real	imaginary unit
1	$\sqrt{1}$	complex	pure imaginary

1. A _____ number is one that can be written in the form $a + bi$, where a and b are real numbers.

2. In the complex number system, i denotes the _____.

3. $i^2 =$ _____

4. $i =$ _____

5. A complex number, $a + bi$, is a _____ number if $b = 0$.

6. A complex number, $a + bi$, is a _____ number if $a = 0$ and $b \neq 0$.

Martin-Gay Interactive Videos

See Video 10.7

Watch the section lecture video and answer the following questions.

OBJECTIVE
1

7. From ▭ Example 4, with what rule must you be especially careful when working with imaginary numbers and why?

OBJECTIVE
2

8. In ▭ Examples 5 and 6, what is the process of adding and subtracting complex numbers compared to? What important reminder is given about i?

OBJECTIVE
3

9. In ▭ Examples 7 and 8, what part of the definition of the imaginary unit i may be used during the multiplication of complex numbers to help simplify products?

OBJECTIVE
4

10. In ▭ Example 9, using complex conjugates to divide complex numbers is compared to what process?

OBJECTIVE
5

11. From the lecture before ▭ Example 10, what are the first four powers of i whose values keep repeating?

10.7 **Exercise Set** MyMathLab®

Simplify. See Example 1.

1. $\sqrt{-81}$

2. $\sqrt{-49}$

3. $\sqrt{-7}$

4. $\sqrt{-3}$

5. $-\sqrt{16}$

6. $-\sqrt{4}$

7. $\sqrt{-64}$

8. $\sqrt{-100}$

Write in terms of i. See Example 1.

9. $\sqrt{-24}$

10. $\sqrt{-32}$

11. $-\sqrt{-36}$

12. $-\sqrt{-121}$

13. $8\sqrt{-63}$

14. $4\sqrt{-20}$

15. $-\sqrt{54}$

16. $\sqrt{-63}$

Multiply or divide. See Example 2.

17. $\sqrt{-2} \cdot \sqrt{-7}$

18. $\sqrt{-11} \cdot \sqrt{-3}$

19. $\sqrt{-5} \cdot \sqrt{-10}$

20. $\sqrt{-2} \cdot \sqrt{-6}$

21. $\sqrt{16} \cdot \sqrt{-1}$

22. $\sqrt{3} \cdot \sqrt{-27}$

23. $\dfrac{\sqrt{-9}}{\sqrt{3}}$

24. $\dfrac{\sqrt{49}}{\sqrt{-10}}$

25. $\dfrac{\sqrt{-80}}{\sqrt{-10}}$

26. $\dfrac{\sqrt{-40}}{\sqrt{-8}}$

Add or subtract. Write the sum or difference in the form $a + bi$. See Example 3.

27. $(4 - 7i) + (2 + 3i)$

28. $(2 - 4i) - (2 - i)$

29. $(6 + 5i) - (8 - i)$

30. $(8 - 3i) + (-8 + 3i)$

31. $6 - (8 + 4i)$

32. $(9 - 4i) - 9$

Multiply. Write the product in the form $a + bi$. See Example 4.

33. $-10i \cdot -4i$

34. $-2i \cdot -11i$

35. $6i(2 - 3i)$

36. $5i(4 - 7i)$

37. $(\sqrt{3} + 2i)(\sqrt{3} - 2i)$

38. $(\sqrt{5} - 5i)(\sqrt{5} + 5i)$

39. $(4 - 2i)^2$

40. $(6 - 3i)^2$

Write each quotient in the form $a + bi$. See Example 5.

41. $\dfrac{4}{i}$

42. $\dfrac{5}{6i}$

43. $\dfrac{7}{4 + 3i}$

44. $\dfrac{9}{1 - 2i}$

45. $\dfrac{3 + 5i}{1 + i}$

46. $\dfrac{6 + 2i}{4 - 3i}$

47. $\dfrac{5 - i}{3 - 2i}$

48. $\dfrac{6 - i}{2 + i}$

MIXED PRACTICE

Perform each indicated operation. Write the result in the form $a + bi$.

49. $(7i)(-9i)$

50. $(-6i)(-4i)$

51. $(6 - 3i) - (4 - 2i)$

52. $(-2 - 4i) - (6 - 8i)$

53. $-3i(-1 + 9i)$

54. $-5i(-2 + i)$

55. $\dfrac{4 - 5i}{2i}$

56. $\dfrac{6 + 8i}{3i}$

57. $(4 + i)(5 + 2i)$

58. $(3 + i)(2 + 4i)$

59. $(6 - 2i)(3 + i)$

60. $(2 - 4i)(2 - i)$

61. $(8 - 3i) + (2 + 3i)$

62. $(7 + 4i) + (4 - 4i)$

63. $(1 - i)(1 + i)$

64. $(6 + 2i)(6 - 2i)$

65. $\dfrac{16 + 15i}{-3i}$

66. $\dfrac{2 - 3i}{-7i}$

67. $(9 + 8i)^2$

68. $(4 - 7i)^2$

69. $\dfrac{2}{3 + i}$

70. $\dfrac{5}{3 - 2i}$

71. $(5 - 6i) - 4i$

72. $(6 - 2i) + 7i$

73. $\dfrac{2 - 3i}{2 + i}$

74. $\dfrac{6 + 5i}{6 - 5i}$

75. $(2 + 4i) + (6 - 5i)$

76. $(5 - 3i) + (7 - 8i)$

77. $(\sqrt{6} + i)(\sqrt{6} - i)$

78. $(\sqrt{14} - 4i)(\sqrt{14} + 4i)$

79. $4(2 - i)^2$

80. $9(2 - i)^2$

Find each power of i. See Example 6.

81. i^8

82. i^{10}

83. i^{21}

84. i^{15}

85. i^{11}

86. i^{40}

87. i^{-6}

88. i^{-9}

89. $(2i)^6$

90. $(5i)^4$

91. $(-3i)^5$

92. $(-2i)^7$

REVIEW AND PREVIEW

Recall that the sum of the measures of the angles of a triangle is $180°$. Find the unknown angle in each triangle.

93.

94.

Use synthetic division to divide the following. See Section 5.7.

95. $(x^3 - 6x^2 + 3x - 4) \div (x - 1)$

96. $(5x^4 - 3x^2 + 2) \div (x + 2)$

Thirty people were recently polled about the average monthly balance in their checking accounts. The results of this poll are shown in the following histogram. Use this graph to answer Exercises 97 through 102. See Section 3.1.

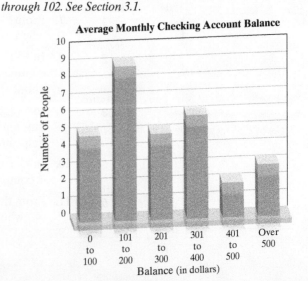

97. How many people polled reported an average checking balance of $201 to $300?

98. How many people polled reported an average checking balance of $0 to $100?

99. How many people polled reported an average checking balance of $200 or less?

100. How many people polled reported an average checking balance of $301 or more?

101. What percent of people polled reported an average checking balance of $201 to $300? Round to the nearest tenth of a percent.

102. What percent of people polled reported an average checking balance of $0 to $100? Round to the nearest tenth of a percent.

CONCEPT EXTENSIONS

Write in the form a + bi.

103. $i^3 - i^4$

104. $i^8 - i^7$

105. $i^6 + i^8$

106. $i^4 + i^{12}$

107. $2 + \sqrt{-9}$

108. $5 - \sqrt{-16}$

109. $\dfrac{6 + \sqrt{-18}}{3}$

110. $\dfrac{4 - \sqrt{-8}}{2}$

111. $\dfrac{5 - \sqrt{-75}}{10}$

112. $\dfrac{7 + \sqrt{-98}}{14}$

113. Describe how to find the conjugate of a complex number.

114. Explain why the product of a complex number and its complex conjugate is a real number.

Simplify.

115. $\left(8 - \sqrt{-3}\right) - \left(2 + \sqrt{-12}\right)$

116. $\left(8 - \sqrt{-4}\right) - \left(2 + \sqrt{-16}\right)$

117. Determine whether $2i$ is a solution of $x^2 + 4 = 0$.

118. Determine whether $-1 + i$ is a solution of $x^2 + 2x = -2$.

Man has always desired to reach the stars, and some buildings seem to be trying to do just that. As populations expand and land becomes scarcer, ever taller and more spectacular buildings are being constructed. As of 2010, the tallest building in the world was the Burj Khalifa, in Dubai. In Exercise 80, Section 11.1, you will explore the height of the Burj Khalifa. (*Source:* Council on Tall Buildings and Urban Habitat, *Fast Company*)

An important part of the study of algebra is learning to model and solve problems. Often, the model of a problem is a quadratic equation or a function containing a second-degree polynomial. In this chapter, we continue the work begun in Chapter 6, when we solved polynomial equations in one variable by factoring. Two additional methods of solving quadratic equations are analyzed as well as methods of solving nonlinear inequalities in one variable.

Snapshot of Selected Tall Structures (with completion dates)

Source: Council on Tall Buildings and Urban Habitat, (*Fast Company*)

11.1 Solving Quadratic Equations by Completing the Square

OBJECTIVES

1 Use the Square Root Property to Solve Quadratic Equations.

2 Solve Quadratic Equations by Completing the Square.

3 Use Quadratic Equations to Solve Problems.

OBJECTIVE

1   Using the Square Root Property

In Chapter 6, we solved quadratic equations by factoring. Recall that a **quadratic,** or **second-degree, equation** is an equation that can be written in the form $ax^2 + bx + c = 0$, where a, b, and c are real numbers and a is not 0. To solve a quadratic equation such as $x^2 = 9$ by factoring, we use the zero factor theorem. To use the zero factor theorem, the equation must first be written in standard form, $ax^2 + bx + c = 0$.

$$x^2 = 9$$
$$x^2 - 9 = 0 \qquad \text{Subtract 9 from both sides.}$$
$$(x + 3)(x - 3) = 0 \qquad \text{Factor.}$$
$$x + 3 = 0 \quad \text{or} \quad x - 3 = 0 \quad \text{Set each factor equal to 0.}$$
$$x = -3 \qquad\qquad x = 3 \quad \text{Solve.}$$

The solution set is $\{-3, 3\}$, the positive and negative square roots of 9. Not all quadratic equations can be solved by factoring, so we need to explore other methods. Notice that the solutions of the equation $x^2 = 9$ are two numbers whose square is 9.

$$3^2 = 9 \qquad \text{and} \qquad (-3)^2 = 9$$

Thus, we can solve the equation $x^2 = 9$ by taking the square root of both sides. Be sure to include both $\sqrt{9}$ and $-\sqrt{9}$ as solutions since both $\sqrt{9}$ and $-\sqrt{9}$ are numbers whose square is 9.

$$x^2 = 9$$
$$\sqrt{x^2} = \pm\sqrt{9} \quad \text{The notation } \pm\sqrt{9} \text{ (read as "plus or minus } \sqrt{9}\text{")}$$
$$x = \pm 3 \qquad \text{indicates the pair of numbers } +\sqrt{9} \text{ and } -\sqrt{9}.$$

This illustrates the square root property.

Square Root Property

If b is a real number and if $a^2 = b$, then $a = \pm\sqrt{b}$.

▶ Helpful Hint

The notation ± 3, for example, is read as "plus or minus 3." It is a shorthand notation for the pair of numbers $+3$ and -3.

EXAMPLE 1   Use the square root property to solve $x^2 = 50$.

Solution
$$x^2 = 50$$
$$x = \pm\sqrt{50} \quad \text{Use the square root property.}$$
$$x = \pm 5\sqrt{2} \quad \text{Simplify the radical.}$$

Check: Let $x = 5\sqrt{2}$.   Let $x = -5\sqrt{2}$.

$$x^2 = 50 \qquad\qquad\qquad x^2 = 50$$
$$(5\sqrt{2})^2 \stackrel{?}{=} 50 \qquad\qquad (-5\sqrt{2})^2 \stackrel{?}{=} 50$$
$$25 \cdot 2 \stackrel{?}{=} 50 \qquad\qquad\quad 25 \cdot 2 \stackrel{?}{=} 50$$
$$50 = 50 \quad \text{True} \qquad\qquad 50 = 50 \quad \text{True}$$

The solutions are $5\sqrt{2}$ and $-5\sqrt{2}$, or the solution set is $\{-5\sqrt{2}, 5\sqrt{2}\}$.   □

PRACTICE

1   Use the square root property to solve $x^2 = 32$.

EXAMPLE 2   Use the square root property to solve $2x^2 - 14 = 0$.

Solution   First we get the squared variable alone on one side of the equation.

$$2x^2 - 14 = 0$$
$$2x^2 = 14 \qquad \text{Add 14 to both sides.}$$
$$x^2 = 7 \qquad \text{Divide both sides by 2.}$$
$$x = \pm\sqrt{7} \qquad \text{Use the square root property.}$$

Check to see that the solutions are $\sqrt{7}$ and $-\sqrt{7}$, or the solution set is $\{-\sqrt{7}, \sqrt{7}\}$. □

PRACTICE
2   Use the square root property to solve $5x^2 - 50 = 0$.

EXAMPLE 3   Use the square root property to solve $(x + 1)^2 = 12$.

Solution

$$(x + 1)^2 = 12$$
$$x + 1 = \pm\sqrt{12} \qquad \text{Use the square root property.}$$
$$x + 1 = \pm2\sqrt{3} \qquad \text{Simplify the radical.}$$
$$x = -1 \pm 2\sqrt{3} \qquad \text{Subtract 1 from both sides.}$$

> ▶ **Helpful Hint**
> Don't forget that $-1 \pm 2\sqrt{3}$, for example, means $-1 + 2\sqrt{3}$ and $-1 - 2\sqrt{3}$. In other words, the equation in Example 3 has two solutions.

Check: Below is a check for $-1 + 2\sqrt{3}$. The check for $-1 - 2\sqrt{3}$ is almost the same and is left for you to do on your own.

$$(x + 1)^2 = 12$$
$$(-1 + 2\sqrt{3} + 1)^2 \overset{?}{=} 12$$
$$(2\sqrt{3})^2 \overset{?}{=} 12$$
$$4 \cdot 3 \overset{?}{=} 12$$
$$12 = 12 \quad \text{True}$$

The solutions are $-1 + 2\sqrt{3}$ and $-1 - 2\sqrt{3}$. □

PRACTICE
3   Use the square root property to solve $(x + 3)^2 = 20$.

EXAMPLE 4   Use the square root property to solve $(2x - 5)^2 = -16$.

Solution

$$(2x - 5)^2 = -16$$
$$2x - 5 = \pm\sqrt{-16} \qquad \text{Use the square root property.}$$
$$2x - 5 = \pm4i \qquad \text{Simplify the radical.}$$
$$2x = 5 \pm 4i \qquad \text{Add 5 to both sides.}$$
$$x = \frac{5 \pm 4i}{2} \qquad \text{Divide both sides by 2.}$$

The solutions are $\dfrac{5 + 4i}{2}$ and $\dfrac{5 - 4i}{2}$, or in standard form $a + bi$ for complex numbers, $\dfrac{5}{2} + 2i$ and $\dfrac{5}{2} - 2i$. □

PRACTICE
4   Use the square root property to solve $(5x - 2)^2 = -9$.

✓CONCEPT CHECK
How do you know just by looking that $(x - 2)^2 = -4$ has complex but not real solutions?

OBJECTIVE
2   Solving by Completing the Square

Notice from Examples 3 and 4 that, if we write a quadratic equation so that one side is the square of a binomial, we can solve by using the square root property. To write the square of a binomial, we write perfect square trinomials. Recall that a perfect square trinomial is a trinomial that can be factored into two identical binomial factors.

Perfect Square Trinomials	**Factored Form**
$x^2 + 8x + 16$	$(x + 4)^2$
$x^2 - 6x + 9$	$(x - 3)^2$
$x^2 + 3x + \dfrac{9}{4}$	$\left(x + \dfrac{3}{2}\right)^2$

Notice that for each perfect square trinomial in x, **the constant term of the trinomial is the square of half the coefficient of the x-term.** For example,

$$x^2 + 8x + 16 \qquad x^2 - 6x + 9$$

$$\frac{1}{2}(8) = 4 \text{ and } 4^2 = 16 \qquad \frac{1}{2}(-6) = -3 \text{ and } (-3)^2 = 9$$

The process of writing a quadratic equation so that one side is a perfect square trinomial is called **completing the square.**

EXAMPLE 5   Solve $p^2 + 2p = 4$ by completing the square.

Solution   First, add the square of half the coefficient of p to both sides so that the resulting trinomial will be a perfect square trinomial. The coefficient of p is 2.

$$\frac{1}{2}(2) = 1 \quad \text{and} \quad 1^2 = 1$$

Add 1 to both sides of the original equation.

$$p^2 + 2p = 4$$
$$p^2 + 2p + 1 = 4 + 1 \quad \text{Add 1 to both sides.}$$
$$(p + 1)^2 = 5 \quad \text{Factor the trinomial; simplify the right side.}$$

We may now use the square root property and solve for p.

$$p + 1 = \pm\sqrt{5} \quad \text{Use the square root property.}$$
$$p = -1 \pm \sqrt{5} \quad \text{Subtract 1 from both sides.}$$

Notice that there are two solutions: $-1 + \sqrt{5}$ and $-1 - \sqrt{5}$.   □

PRACTICE
5   Solve $b^2 + 4b = 3$ by completing the square.

EXAMPLE 6   Solve $m^2 - 7m - 1 = 0$ for m by completing the square.

Solution   First, add 1 to both sides of the equation so that the left side has no constant term.

$$m^2 - 7m - 1 = 0$$
$$m^2 - 7m = 1$$

Now find the constant term that makes the left side a perfect square trinomial by squaring half the coefficient of m. Add this constant to both sides of the equation.

$$\frac{1}{2}(-7) = -\frac{7}{2} \quad \text{and} \quad \left(-\frac{7}{2}\right)^2 = \frac{49}{4}$$

$$m^2 - 7m + \frac{49}{4} = 1 + \frac{49}{4} \qquad \text{Add } \frac{49}{4} \text{ to both sides of the equation.}$$

$$\left(m - \frac{7}{2}\right)^2 = \frac{53}{4} \qquad \text{Factor the perfect square trinomial and simplify the right side.}$$

$$m - \frac{7}{2} = \pm\sqrt{\frac{53}{4}} \qquad \text{Apply the square root property.}$$

$$m = \frac{7}{2} \pm \frac{\sqrt{53}}{2} \qquad \text{Add } \frac{7}{2} \text{ to both sides and simplify } \sqrt{\frac{53}{4}}.$$

$$m = \frac{7 \pm \sqrt{53}}{2} \qquad \text{Simplify.}$$

The solutions are $\dfrac{7 + \sqrt{53}}{2}$ and $\dfrac{7 - \sqrt{53}}{2}$.

PRACTICE
6   Solve $p^2 - 3p + 1 = 0$ by completing the square.

The following steps may be used to solve a quadratic equation such as $ax^2 + bx + c = 0$ by completing the square. This method may be used whether or not the polynomial $ax^2 + bx + c$ is factorable.

Solving a Quadratic Equation in x by Completing the Square

Step 1. If the coefficient of x^2 is 1, go to Step 2. Otherwise, divide both sides of the equation by the coefficient of x^2.

Step 2. Isolate all variable terms on one side of the equation.

Step 3. Complete the square for the resulting binomial by adding the square of half of the coefficient of x to both sides of the equation.

Step 4. Factor the resulting perfect square trinomial and write it as the square of a binomial.

Step 5. Use the square root property to solve for x.

EXAMPLE 7   Solve: $2x^2 - 8x + 3 = 0$.

Solution   Our procedure for finding the constant term to complete the square works only if the coefficient of the squared variable term is 1. Therefore, to solve this equation, the first step is to divide both sides by 2, the coefficient of x^2.

$$2x^2 - 8x + 3 = 0$$

Step 1. $x^2 - 4x + \dfrac{3}{2} = 0 \qquad \text{Divide both sides by 2.}$

Step 2. $\qquad x^2 - 4x = -\dfrac{3}{2} \qquad \text{Subtract } \frac{3}{2} \text{ from both sides.}$

Next find the square of half of -4.

$$\frac{1}{2}(-4) = -2 \quad \text{and} \quad (-2)^2 = 4$$

Add 4 to both sides of the equation to complete the square.

Step 3. $x^2 - 4x + 4 = -\dfrac{3}{2} + 4$

(Continued on next page)

Step 4. $(x - 2)^2 = \dfrac{5}{2}$ Factor the perfect square and simplify the right side.

Step 5. $x - 2 = \pm\sqrt{\dfrac{5}{2}}$ Apply the square root property.

$x - 2 = \pm\dfrac{\sqrt{10}}{2}$ Rationalize the denominator.

$x = 2 \pm \dfrac{\sqrt{10}}{2}$ Add 2 to both sides.

$= \dfrac{4}{2} \pm \dfrac{\sqrt{10}}{2}$ Find a common denominator.

$= \dfrac{4 \pm \sqrt{10}}{2}$ Simplify.

The solutions are $\dfrac{4 + \sqrt{10}}{2}$ and $\dfrac{4 - \sqrt{10}}{2}$.

PRACTICE
7   Solve: $3x^2 - 12x + 1 = 0$.

EXAMPLE 8   Solve $3x^2 - 9x + 8 = 0$ by completing the square.

Solution $3x^2 - 9x + 8 = 0$

Step 1. $x^2 - 3x + \dfrac{8}{3} = 0$ Divide both sides of the equation by 3.

Step 2. $x^2 - 3x = -\dfrac{8}{3}$ Subtract $\dfrac{8}{3}$ from both sides.

Since $\dfrac{1}{2}(-3) = -\dfrac{3}{2}$ and $\left(-\dfrac{3}{2}\right)^2 = \dfrac{9}{4}$, we add $\dfrac{9}{4}$ to both sides of the equation.

Step 3. $x^2 - 3x + \dfrac{9}{4} = \underbrace{-\dfrac{8}{3} + \dfrac{9}{4}}$

Step 4. $\left(x - \dfrac{3}{2}\right)^2 = -\dfrac{5}{12}$ Factor the perfect square trinomial.

Step 5. $x - \dfrac{3}{2} = \pm\sqrt{-\dfrac{5}{12}}$ Apply the square root property.

$x - \dfrac{3}{2} = \pm\dfrac{i\sqrt{5}}{2\sqrt{3}}$ Simplify the radical.

$x - \dfrac{3}{2} = \pm\dfrac{i\sqrt{15}}{6}$ Rationalize the denominator.

$x = \dfrac{3}{2} \pm \dfrac{i\sqrt{15}}{6}$ Add $\dfrac{3}{2}$ to both sides.

$= \dfrac{9}{6} \pm \dfrac{i\sqrt{15}}{6}$ Find a common denominator.

$= \dfrac{9 \pm i\sqrt{15}}{6}$ Simplify.

The solutions are $\dfrac{9 + i\sqrt{15}}{6}$ and $\dfrac{9 - i\sqrt{15}}{6}$, or in $a + bi$ form, $\dfrac{3}{2} + \dfrac{\sqrt{15}}{6}i$ and $\dfrac{3}{2} - \dfrac{\sqrt{15}}{6}i$.

PRACTICE
8   Solve $2x^2 - 5x + 7 = 0$ by completing the square.

OBJECTIVE

3   Solving Problems Modeled by Quadratic Equations

Recall the **simple interest** formula $I = Prt$, where I is the interest earned, P is the principal, r is the rate of interest, and t is time in years. If $100 is invested at a simple interest rate of 5% annually, at the end of 3 years the total interest I earned is

$$I = P \cdot r \cdot t$$

or

$$I = 100 \cdot 0.05 \cdot 3 = \$15$$

and the new principal is

$$\$100 + \$15 = \$115$$

Most of the time, the interest computed on money borrowed or money deposited is **compound interest.** Compound interest, unlike simple interest, is computed on original principal *and* on interest already earned. To see the difference between simple interest and compound interest, suppose that $100 is invested at a rate of 5% compounded annually. To find the total amount of money at the end of 3 years, we calculate as follows.

$$I = P \cdot r \cdot t$$

First year:	Interest $= \$100 \cdot 0.05 \cdot 1 = \$5.00$
	New principal $= \$100.00 + \$5.00 = \$105.00$
Second year:	Interest $= \$105.00 \cdot 0.05 \cdot 1 = \$5.25$
	New principal $= \$105.00 + \$5.25 = \$110.25$
Third year:	Interest $= \$110.25 \cdot 0.05 \cdot 1 \approx \$5.51$
	New principal $= \$110.25 + \$5.51 = \$115.76$

At the end of the third year, the total compound interest earned is $115.76, whereas the total simple interest earned is $15.

It is tedious to calculate compound interest as we did above, so we use a compound interest formula. The formula for calculating the total amount of money when interest is compounded annually is

$$A = P(1 + r)^t$$

where P is the original investment, r is the interest rate per compounding period, and t is the number of periods. For example, the amount of money A at the end of 3 years if $100 is invested at 5% compounded annually is

$$A = \$100(1 + 0.05)^3 \approx \$100(1.1576) = \$115.76$$

as we previously calculated.

EXAMPLE 9   **Finding Interest Rates**

Use the formula $A = P(1 + r)^t$ to find the interest rate r if $2000 compounded annually grows to $2420 in 2 years.

Solution

1. **UNDERSTAND** the problem. Since the $2000 is compounded annually, we use the compound interest formula. For this example, make sure that you understand the formula for compounding interest annually.

2. **TRANSLATE.** We substitute the given values into the formula.

$$A = P(1 + r)^t$$

$$2420 = 2000(1 + r)^2 \qquad \text{Let } A = 2420, P = 2000, \text{ and } t = 2.$$

(Continued on next page)

3. SOLVE. Solve the equation for r.

$$2420 = 2000(1 + r)^2$$

$$\frac{2420}{2000} = (1 + r)^2 \qquad \text{Divide both sides by 2000.}$$

$$\frac{121}{100} = (1 + r)^2 \qquad \text{Simplify the fraction.}$$

$$\pm\sqrt{\frac{121}{100}} = 1 + r \qquad \text{Use the square root property.}$$

$$\pm\frac{11}{10} = 1 + r \qquad \text{Simplify.}$$

$$-1 \pm \frac{11}{10} = r$$

$$-\frac{10}{10} \pm \frac{11}{10} = r$$

$$\frac{1}{10} = r \quad \text{or} \quad -\frac{21}{10} = r$$

4. INTERPRET. The rate cannot be negative, so we reject $-\frac{21}{10}$.

Check: $\frac{1}{10} = 0.10 = 10\%$ per year. If we invest \$2000 at 10% compounded annually, in 2 years the amount in the account would be $2000(1 + 0.10)^2 = 2420$ dollars, the desired amount.

State: The interest rate is 10% compounded annually.

PRACTICE

9   Use the formula from Example 9 to find the interest rate r if \$5000 compounded annually grows to \$5618 in 2 years.

Graphing Calculator Explorations

In Section 6.6, we showed how we can use a grapher to approximate real number solutions of a quadratic equation written in standard form. We can also use a grapher to solve a quadratic equation when it is not written in standard form. For example, to solve $(x + 1)^2 = 12$, the quadratic equation in Example 3, we graph the following on the same set of axes. Use Xmin $= -10$, Xmax $= 10$, Ymin $= -13$, and Ymax $= 13$.

$$Y_1 = (x + 1)^2 \quad \text{and} \quad Y_2 = 12$$

Use the Intersect feature or the Zoom and Trace features to locate the points of intersection of the graphs. (See your manuals for specific instructions.) The x-values of these points are the solutions of $(x + 1)^2 = 12$. The solutions, rounded to two decimal places, are 2.46 and -4.46.

Check to see that these numbers are approximations of the exact solutions $-1 \pm 2\sqrt{3}$.

Use a graphing calculator to solve each quadratic equation. Round all solutions to the nearest hundredth.

1. $x(x - 5) = 8$ **2.** $x(x + 2) = 5$

3. $x^2 + 0.5x = 0.3x + 1$ **4.** $x^2 - 2.6x = -2.2x + 3$

5. Use a graphing calculator and solve $(2x - 5)^2 = -16$, Example 4 in this section, using the window

$$Xmin = -20$$
$$Xmax = 20$$
$$Xscl = 1$$
$$Ymin = -20$$
$$Ymax = 20$$
$$Yscl = 1$$

Explain the results. Compare your results with the solution found in Example 4.

6. What are the advantages and disadvantages of using a graphing calculator to solve quadratic equations?

Vocabulary, Readiness & Video Check

Use the choices below to fill in each blank. Not all choices will be used.

binomial	$\sqrt{b}$	$\pm\sqrt{b}$	b^2	9	25	completing the square
quadratic	$-\sqrt{b}$	$\dfrac{b}{2}$	$\left(\dfrac{b}{2}\right)^2$	3	5	

1. By the square root property, if b is a real number, and $a^2 = b$, then $a = $ _____.

2. A _____ equation can be written in the form $ax^2 + bx + c = 0, a \neq 0$.

3. The process of writing a quadratic equation so that one side is a perfect square trinomial is called _____.

4. A perfect square trinomial is one that can be factored as a _____ squared.

5. To solve $x^2 + 6x = 10$ by completing the square, add _____ to both sides.

6. To solve $x^2 + bx = c$ by completing the square, add _____ to both sides.

Martin-Gay Interactive Videos

See Video 11.1

Watch the section lecture video and answer the following questions.

OBJECTIVE 1

7. From Examples 2 and 3, explain a step you can perform so that you may easily apply the square root property to $2x^2 = 16$. Explain why you perform this step.

OBJECTIVE 2

8. In Example 5, why is the equation first divided through by 3?

OBJECTIVE 3

9. In Example 6, why is the negative solution not considered?

11.1 Exercise Set   MyMathLab®

Use the square root property to solve each equation. These equations have real number solutions. See Examples 1 through 3.

1. $x^2 = 16$

2. $x^2 = 49$

3. $x^2 - 7 = 0$

4. $x^2 - 11 = 0$

5. $x^2 = 18$

6. $y^2 = 20$

7. $3z^2 - 30 = 0$

8. $2x^2 - 4 = 0$

9. $(x + 5)^2 = 9$

10. $(y - 3)^2 = 4$

11. $(z - 6)^2 = 18$

12. $(y + 4)^2 = 27$

13. $(2x - 3)^2 = 8$

14. $(4x + 9)^2 = 6$

Use the square root property to solve each equation. See Examples 1 through 4.

15. $x^2 + 9 = 0$

16. $x^2 + 4 = 0$

17. $x^2 - 6 = 0$

18. $y^2 - 10 = 0$

19. $2z^2 + 16 = 0$

20. $3p^2 + 36 = 0$

21. $(3x - 1)^2 = -16$

22. $(4y + 2)^2 = -25$

23. $(z + 7)^2 = 5$

24. $(x + 10)^2 = 11$

25. $(x + 3)^2 + 8 = 0$

26. $(y - 4)^2 + 18 = 0$

Add the proper constant to each binomial so that the resulting trinomial is a perfect square trinomial. Then factor the trinomial.

27. $x^2 + 16x + $ _____

28. $y^2 + 2y + $ _____

29. $z^2 - 12z + $ _____

30. $x^2 - 8x + $ _____

31. $p^2 + 9p + $ _____

32. $n^2 + 5n + $ _____

33. $x^2 + x + $ _____

34. $y^2 - y + $ _____

MIXED PRACTICE

Solve each equation by completing the square. These equations have real number solutions. See Examples 5 through 7.

35. $x^2 + 8x = -15$

36. $y^2 + 6y = -8$

37. $x^2 + 6x + 2 = 0$

38. $x^2 - 2x - 2 = 0$

39. $x^2 + x - 1 = 0$

40. $x^2 + 3x - 2 = 0$

41. $x^2 + 2x - 5 = 0$

42. $x^2 - 6x + 3 = 0$

43. $y^2 + y - 7 = 0$

44. $x^2 - 7x - 1 = 0$

45. $3p^2 - 12p + 2 = 0$

46. $2x^2 + 14x - 1 = 0$

47. $4y^2 - 2 = 12y$

48. $6x^2 - 3 = 6x$

49. $2x^2 + 7x = 4$

50. $3x^2 - 4x = 4$

51. $x^2 + 8x + 1 = 0$

52. $x^2 - 10x + 2 = 0$

53. $3y^2 + 6y - 4 = 0$

54. $2y^2 + 12y + 3 = 0$

55. $2x^2 - 3x - 5 = 0$ **56.** $5x^2 + 3x - 2 = 0$

Solve each equation by completing the square. See Examples 5 through 8.

57. $y^2 + 2y + 2 = 0$

58. $x^2 + 4x + 6 = 0$

59. $y^2 + 6y - 8 = 0$

60. $y^2 + 10y - 26 = 0$

61. $2a^2 + 8a = -12$

62. $3x^2 + 12x = -14$

63. $5x^2 + 15x - 1 = 0$

64. $16y^2 + 16y - 1 = 0$

65. $2x^2 - x + 6 = 0$

66. $4x^2 - 2x + 5 = 0$

67. $x^2 + 10x + 28 = 0$

68. $y^2 + 8y + 18 = 0$

69. $z^2 + 3z - 4 = 0$

70. $y^2 + y - 2 = 0$

71. $2x^2 - 4x = -3$

72. $9x^2 - 36x = -40$

73. $3x^2 + 3x = 5$

74. $10y^2 - 30y = 2$

Use the formula $A = P(1 + r)^t$ to solve Exercises 75 through 78. See Example 9.

75. Find the rate r at which $3000 compounded annually grows to $4320 in 2 years.

76. Find the rate r at which $800 compounded annually grows to $882 in 2 years.

77. Find the rate at which $15,000 compounded annually grows to $16,224 in 2 years.

78. Find the rate at which $2000 compounded annually grows to $2880 in 2 years.

Neglecting air resistance, the distance $s(t)$ in feet traveled by a freely falling object is given by the function $s(t) = 16t^2$, where t is time in seconds. Use this formula to solve Exercises 79 through 82. Round answers to two decimal places.

79. The Petronas Towers in Kuala Lumpur, completed in 1998, are the tallest buildings in Malaysia. Each tower is 1483 feet tall. How long would it take an object to fall to the ground from the top of one of the towers? (*Source:* Council on Tall Buildings and Urban Habitat, Lehigh University)

80. The Burj Khalifa, the tallest building in the world, was completed in 2010 in Dubai. It is estimated to be 2717 feet tall. How long would it take an object to fall to the ground from the top of the building? (*Source:* Council on Tall Buildings and Urban Habitat)

81. The Rogun Dam in Tajikistan (part of the former USSR that borders Afghanistan) is the tallest dam in the world at 1100 feet. How long would it take an object to fall from the top to the base of the dam? (*Source:* U.S. Committee on Large Dams of the International Commission on Large Dams)

82. The Hoover Dam, located on the Colorado River on the border of Nevada and Arizona near Las Vegas, is 725 feet tall. How long would it take an object to fall from the top to the base of the dam? (*Source:* U.S. Committee on Large Dams of the International Commission on Large Dams)

Solve.

△ **83.** The area of a square room is 225 square feet. Find the dimensions of the room.

△ **84.** The area of a circle is 36π square inches. Find the radius of the circle.

△ **85.** An isosceles right triangle has legs of equal length. If the hypotenuse is 20 centimeters long, find the length of each leg.

△ **86.** The top of a square coffee table has a diagonal that measures 30 inches. Find the length of each side of the top of the coffee table.

REVIEW AND PREVIEW

Simplify each expression. See Section 10.1

87. $\dfrac{1}{2} - \sqrt{\dfrac{9}{4}}$

88. $\dfrac{9}{10} - \sqrt{\dfrac{49}{100}}$

Simplify each expression. See Section 10.5.

89. $\dfrac{6 + 4\sqrt{5}}{2}$

90. $\dfrac{10 - 20\sqrt{3}}{2}$

91. $\dfrac{3 - 9\sqrt{2}}{6}$

92. $\dfrac{12 - 8\sqrt{7}}{16}$

Evaluate $\sqrt{b^2 - 4ac}$ for each set of values. See Section 10.3.

93. $a = 2, b = 4, c = -1$ **94.** $a = 1, b = 6, c = 2$

95. $a = 3, b = -1, c = -2$ **96.** $a = 1, b = -3, c = -1$

CONCEPT EXTENSIONS

Without solving, determine whether the solutions of each equation are real numbers or complex but not real numbers. See the Concept Check in this section.

97. $(x + 1)^2 = -1$

98. $(y - 5)^2 = -9$

99. $3z^2 = 10$

100. $4x^2 = 17$

101. $(2y - 5)^2 + 7 = 3$

102. $(3m + 2)^2 + 4 = 1$

Find two possible missing terms so that each is a perfect square trinomial.

103. $x^2 + \ \_\_\_ + 16$ **104.** $y^2 + \ \_\_\_ + 9$

105. $z^2 + \ \_\_\_ + \dfrac{25}{4}$ **106.** $x^2 + \ \_\_\_ + \dfrac{1}{4}$

✎ **107.** In your own words, explain how to calculate the number that will complete the square on an expression such as $x^2 - 5x$.

✎ **108.** In your own words, what is the difference between simple interest and compound interest?

✎ **109.** If you are depositing money in an account that pays 4%, would you prefer the interest to be simple or compound? Explain your answer.

✎ **110.** If you are borrowing money at a rate of 10%, would you prefer the interest to be simple or compound? Explain your answer.

A common equation used in business is a demand equation. It expresses the relationship between the unit price of some commodity and the quantity demanded. For Exercises 111 and 112, p represents the unit price and x represents the quantity demanded in thousands.

111. A manufacturing company has found that the demand equation for a certain type of scissors is given by the equation $p = -x^2 + 47$. Find the demand for the scissors if the price is $11 per pair.

112. Acme, Inc., sells desk lamps and has found that the demand equation for a certain style of desk lamp is given by the equation $p = -x^2 + 15$. Find the demand for the desk lamp if the price is $7 per lamp.

11.2 Solving Quadratic Equations by the Quadratic Formula

OBJECTIVES

1 Solve Quadratic Equations by Using the Quadratic Formula.

2 Determine the Number and Type of Solutions of a Quadratic Equation by Using the Discriminant.

3 Solve Problems Modeled by Quadratic Equations.

OBJECTIVE

1 Solving Quadratic Equations by Using the Quadratic Formula

Any quadratic equation can be solved by completing the square. Since the same sequence of steps is repeated each time we complete the square, let's complete the square for a general quadratic equation, $ax^2 + bx + c = 0, a \neq 0$. By doing so, we find a pattern for the solutions of a quadratic equation known as the **quadratic formula.**

Recall that to complete the square for an equation such as $ax^2 + bx + c = 0$, we first divide both sides by the coefficient of x^2.

$$ax^2 + bx + c = 0$$

$$x^2 + \frac{b}{a}x + \frac{c}{a} = 0 \qquad \text{Divide both sides by } a, \text{ the coefficient of } x^2.$$

$$x^2 + \frac{b}{a}x = -\frac{c}{a} \qquad \text{Subtract the constant } \frac{c}{a} \text{ from both sides.}$$

Next, find the square of half $\frac{b}{a}$, the coefficient of x.

$$\frac{1}{2}\left(\frac{b}{a}\right) = \frac{b}{2a} \quad \text{and} \quad \left(\frac{b}{2a}\right)^2 = \frac{b^2}{4a^2}$$

Add this result to both sides of the equation.

$$x^2 + \frac{b}{a}x + \frac{b^2}{4a^2} = -\frac{c}{a} + \frac{b^2}{4a^2} \qquad \text{Add } \frac{b^2}{4a^2} \text{ to both sides.}$$

$$x^2 + \frac{b}{a}x + \frac{b^2}{4a^2} = \frac{-c \cdot 4a}{a \cdot 4a} + \frac{b^2}{4a^2} \qquad \text{Find a common denominator on the right side.}$$

$$x^2 + \frac{b}{a}x + \frac{b^2}{4a^2} = \frac{b^2 - 4ac}{4a^2} \qquad \text{Simplify the right side.}$$

$$\left(x + \frac{b}{2a}\right)^2 = \frac{b^2 - 4ac}{4a^2} \qquad \text{Factor the perfect square trinomial on the left side.}$$

$$x + \frac{b}{2a} = \pm\sqrt{\frac{b^2 - 4ac}{4a^2}} \qquad \text{Apply the square root property.}$$

$$x + \frac{b}{2a} = \pm\frac{\sqrt{b^2 - 4ac}}{2a} \qquad \text{Simplify the radical.}$$

$$x = -\frac{b}{2a} \pm \frac{\sqrt{b^2 - 4ac}}{2a} \qquad \text{Subtract } \frac{b}{2a} \text{ from both sides.}$$

$$x = \frac{-b \pm \sqrt{b^2 - 4ac}}{2a} \qquad \text{Simplify.}$$

This equation identifies the solutions of the general quadratic equation in standard form and is called the quadratic formula. It can be used to solve any equation written in standard form $ax^2 + bx + c = 0$ as long as a is not 0.

Quadratic Formula

A quadratic equation written in the form $ax^2 + bx + c = 0$ has the solutions

$$x = \frac{-b \pm \sqrt{b^2 - 4ac}}{2a}$$

EXAMPLE 1   Solve $3x^2 + 16x + 5 = 0$ for x.

Solution   This equation is in standard form, so $a = 3$, $b = 16$, and $c = 5$. Substitute these values into the quadratic formula.

$$x = \frac{-b \pm \sqrt{b^2 - 4ac}}{2a} \qquad \text{Quadratic formula}$$

$$= \frac{-16 \pm \sqrt{16^2 - 4(3)(5)}}{2 \cdot 3} \qquad \text{Use } a = 3, b = 16, \text{ and } c = 5.$$

$$= \frac{-16 \pm \sqrt{256 - 60}}{6}$$

$$= \frac{-16 \pm \sqrt{196}}{6} = \frac{-16 \pm 14}{6}$$

$$x = \frac{-16 + 14}{6} = -\frac{1}{3} \quad \text{or} \quad x = \frac{-16 - 14}{6} = -\frac{30}{6} = -5$$

The solutions are $-\dfrac{1}{3}$ and -5, or the solution set is $\left\{ -\dfrac{1}{3}, -5 \right\}$.

PRACTICE
1   Solve $3x^2 - 5x - 2 = 0$ for x.

> ▶ **Helpful Hint**
>
> To replace a, b, and c correctly in the quadratic formula, write the quadratic equation in standard form $ax^2 + bx + c = 0$.

EXAMPLE 2   Solve: $2x^2 - 4x = 3$.

Solution   First write the equation in standard form by subtracting 3 from both sides.

$$2x^2 - 4x - 3 = 0$$

Now $a = 2$, $b = -4$, and $c = -3$. Substitute these values into the quadratic formula.

$$x = \frac{-b \pm \sqrt{b^2 - 4ac}}{2a}$$

$$= \frac{-(-4) \pm \sqrt{(-4)^2 - 4(2)(-3)}}{2 \cdot 2}$$

$$= \frac{4 \pm \sqrt{16 + 24}}{4}$$

$$= \frac{4 \pm \sqrt{40}}{4} = \frac{4 \pm 2\sqrt{10}}{4}$$

$$= \frac{2(2 \pm \sqrt{10})}{2 \cdot 2} = \frac{2 \pm \sqrt{10}}{2}$$

The solutions are $\dfrac{2 + \sqrt{10}}{2}$ and $\dfrac{2 - \sqrt{10}}{2}$, or the solution set is $\left\{ \dfrac{2 - \sqrt{10}}{2}, \dfrac{2 + \sqrt{10}}{2} \right\}$.

PRACTICE
2   Solve: $3x^2 - 8x = 2$.

> ▶ **Helpful Hint**
>
> To simplify the expression $\dfrac{4 \pm 2\sqrt{10}}{4}$ in the preceding example, note that 2 is factored out of both terms of the numerator *before* simplifying.
>
> $$\frac{4 \pm 2\sqrt{10}}{4} = \frac{2(2 \pm \sqrt{10})}{2 \cdot 2} = \frac{2 \pm \sqrt{10}}{2}$$

EXAMPLE 3 Solve: $\dfrac{1}{4}m^2 - m + \dfrac{1}{2} = 0$.

Solution We could use the quadratic formula with $a = \dfrac{1}{4}$, $b = -1$, and $c = \dfrac{1}{2}$. Instead, we find a simpler, equivalent standard form equation whose coefficients are not fractions.

Multiply both sides of the equation by the LCD 4 to clear fractions.

$$4\left(\frac{1}{4}m^2 - m + \frac{1}{2}\right) = 4 \cdot 0$$

$$m^2 - 4m + 2 = 0 \quad \text{Simplify.}$$

Substitute $a = 1$, $b = -4$, and $c = 2$ into the quadratic formula and simplify.

$$m = \frac{-(-4) \pm \sqrt{(-4)^2 - 4(1)(2)}}{2 \cdot 1} = \frac{4 \pm \sqrt{16 - 8}}{2}$$

$$= \frac{4 \pm \sqrt{8}}{2} = \frac{4 \pm 2\sqrt{2}}{2} = \frac{2(2 \pm \sqrt{2})}{2}$$

$$= 2 \pm \sqrt{2}$$

The solutions are $2 + \sqrt{2}$ and $2 - \sqrt{2}$.

PRACTICE
3 Solve: $\dfrac{1}{8}x^2 - \dfrac{1}{4}x - 2 = 0$.

EXAMPLE 4 Solve: $x = -3x^2 - 3$.

Solution The equation in standard form is $3x^2 + x + 3 = 0$. Thus, let $a = 3, b = 1$, and $c = 3$ in the quadratic formula.

$$x = \frac{-1 \pm \sqrt{1^2 - 4(3)(3)}}{2 \cdot 3} = \frac{-1 \pm \sqrt{1 - 36}}{6} = \frac{-1 \pm \sqrt{-35}}{6} = \frac{-1 \pm i\sqrt{35}}{6}$$

The solutions are $\dfrac{-1 + i\sqrt{35}}{6}$ and $\dfrac{-1 - i\sqrt{35}}{6}$, or in the form $a + bi$, $-\dfrac{1}{6} + \dfrac{\sqrt{35}}{6}i$ and $-\dfrac{1}{6} - \dfrac{\sqrt{35}}{6}i$.

PRACTICE
4 Solve: $x = -2x^2 - 2$.

Answers to Concept Checks:
a
Write the equation in standard form.

In Example 1, the equation $3x^2 + 16x + 5 = 0$ had 2 real roots, $-\dfrac{1}{3}$ and -5. In Example 4, the equation $3x^2 + x + 3 = 0$ (written in standard form) had no real roots. How do their related graphs compare? Recall that the x-intercepts of

$f(x) = 3x^2 + 16x + 5$ occur where $f(x) = 0$ or where $3x^2 + 16x + 5 = 0$. Since this equation has 2 real roots, the graph has 2 x-intercepts. Similarly, since the equation $3x^2 + x + 3 = 0$ has no real roots, the graph of $f(x) = 3x^2 + x + 3$ has no x-intercepts.

 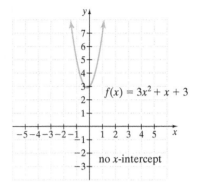

OBJECTIVE

2 Using the Discriminant

In the quadratic formula, $x = \dfrac{-b \pm \sqrt{b^2 - 4ac}}{2a}$, the radicand $b^2 - 4ac$ is called the **discriminant** because, by knowing its value, we can **discriminate** among the possible number and type of solutions of a quadratic equation. Possible values of the discriminant and their meanings are summarized next.

Discriminant

The following table corresponds the discriminant $b^2 - 4ac$ of a quadratic equation of the form $ax^2 + bx + c = 0$ with the number and type of solutions of the equation.

$b^2 - 4ac$	*Number and Type of Solutions*
Positive	Two real solutions
Zero	One real solution
Negative	Two complex but not real solutions

EXAMPLE 5 Use the discriminant to determine the number and type of solutions of each quadratic equation.

a. $x^2 + 2x + 1 = 0$ **b.** $3x^2 + 2 = 0$ **c.** $2x^2 - 7x - 4 = 0$

Solution

a. In $x^2 + 2x + 1 = 0$, $a = 1$, $b = 2$, and $c = 1$. Thus,

$$b^2 - 4ac = 2^2 - 4(1)(1) = 0$$

Since $b^2 - 4ac = 0$, this quadratic equation has one real solution.

b. In this equation, $a = 3$, $b = 0$, $c = 2$. Then $b^2 - 4ac = 0 - 4(3)(2) = -24$. Since $b^2 - 4ac$ is negative, the quadratic equation has two complex but not real solutions.

c. In this equation, $a = 2$, $b = -7$, and $c = -4$. Then

$$b^2 - 4ac = (-7)^2 - 4(2)(-4) = 81$$

Since $b^2 - 4ac$ is positive, the quadratic equation has two real solutions.   ☐

PRACTICE

5 Use the discriminant to determine the number and type of solutions of each quadratic equation.

a. $x^2 - 6x + 9 = 0$ **b.** $x^2 - 3x - 1 = 0$ **c.** $7x^2 + 11 = 0$

The discriminant helps us determine the number and type of solutions of a quadratic equation, $ax^2 + bx + c = 0$. Recall that the solutions of this equation are the same as the x-intercepts of its related graph $f(x) = ax^2 + bx + c$. This means that the discriminant of $ax^2 + bx + c = 0$ also tells us the number of x-intercepts for the graph of $f(x) = ax^2 + bx + c$ or, equivalently, $y = ax^2 + bx + c$.

Graph of $f(x) = ax^2 + bx + c$ or $y = ax^2 + bx + c$

| $b^2 - 4ac > 0$, | $b^2 - 4ac = 0$, | $b^2 - 4ac < 0$, |
| $f(x)$ has two x-intercepts | $f(x)$ has one x-intercept | $f(x)$ has no x-intercepts |

OBJECTIVE

3 **Solving Problems Modeled by Quadratic Equations**

The quadratic formula is useful in solving problems that are modeled by quadratic equations.

△ **EXAMPLE 6** **Calculating Distance Saved**

At a local university, students often leave the sidewalk and cut across the lawn to save walking distance. Given the diagram below of a favorite place to cut across the lawn, approximate how many feet of walking distance a student saves by cutting across the lawn instead of walking on the sidewalk.

Solution

1. UNDERSTAND. Read and reread the problem. In the diagram, notice that a triangle is formed. Since the corner of the block forms a right angle, we use the Pythagorean theorem for right triangles. You may want to review this theorem.

2. TRANSLATE. By the Pythagorean theorem, we have

$$\text{In words: } (\text{leg})^2 + (\text{leg})^2 = (\text{hypotenuse})^2$$
$$\text{Translate: } x^2 + (x + 20)^2 = 50^2$$

3. SOLVE. Use the quadratic formula to solve.

$$x^2 + x^2 + 40x + 400 = 2500 \quad \text{Square } (x + 20) \text{ and } 50.$$
$$2x^2 + 40x - 2100 = 0 \quad \text{Set the equation equal to 0.}$$
$$x^2 + 20x - 1050 = 0 \quad \text{Divide by 2.}$$

Here, $a = 1, b = 20, c = -1050$. By the quadratic formula,

$$x = \frac{-20 \pm \sqrt{20^2 - 4(1)(-1050)}}{2 \cdot 1}$$

$$= \frac{-20 \pm \sqrt{400 + 4200}}{2} = \frac{-20 \pm \sqrt{4600}}{2}$$

$$= \frac{-20 \pm \sqrt{100 \cdot 46}}{2} = \frac{-20 \pm 10\sqrt{46}}{2}$$

$$= -10 \pm 5\sqrt{46} \quad \text{Simplify.}$$

4. INTERPRET

Check: Your calculations in the quadratic formula. The length of a side of a triangle can't be negative, so we reject $-10 - 5\sqrt{46}$. Since $-10 + 5\sqrt{46} \approx 24$ feet, the walking distance along the sidewalk is

$$x + (x + 20) \approx 24 + (24 + 20) = 68 \text{ feet.}$$

State: A student saves about $68 - 50$ or 18 feet of walking distance by cutting across the lawn.   □

PRACTICE

6   Given the diagram, approximate to the nearest foot how many feet of walking distance a person can save by cutting across the lawn instead of walking on the sidewalk.

EXAMPLE 7   **Calculating Landing Time**

An object is thrown upward from the top of a 200-foot cliff with a velocity of 12 feet per second. The height h in feet of the object after t seconds is

$$h = -16t^2 + 12t + 200$$

How long after the object is thrown will it strike the ground? Round to the nearest tenth of a second.

Solution

1. UNDERSTAND. Read and reread the problem.

2. TRANSLATE. Since we want to know when the object strikes the ground, we want to know when the height $h = 0$, or

$$0 = -16t^2 + 12t + 200$$

3. SOLVE. First we divide both sides of the equation by -4.

$$0 = 4t^2 - 3t - 50 \quad \text{Divide both sides by } -4.$$

Here, $a = 4, b = -3$, and $c = -50$. By the quadratic formula,

$$t = \frac{-(-3) \pm \sqrt{(-3)^2 - 4(4)(-50)}}{2 \cdot 4}$$

$$= \frac{3 \pm \sqrt{9 + 800}}{8}$$

$$= \frac{3 \pm \sqrt{809}}{8}$$

(Continued on next page)

4. INTERPRET.

Check: We check our calculations from the quadratic formula. Since the time won't be negative, we reject the proposed solution

$$\frac{3 - \sqrt{809}}{8}.$$

State: The time it takes for the object to strike the ground is exactly

$$\frac{3 + \sqrt{809}}{8} \text{ seconds} \approx 3.9 \text{ seconds}.$$

PRACTICE

7 A toy rocket is shot upward from the top of a building, 45 feet high, with an initial velocity of 20 feet per second. The height h in feet of the rocket after t seconds is

$$h = -16t^2 + 20t + 45$$

How long after the rocket is launched will it strike the ground? Round to the nearest tenth of a second.

Vocabulary, Readiness & Video Check

Fill in each blank.

1. The quadratic formula is _____.

2. For $2x^2 + x + 1 = 0$, if $a = 2$, then $b =$ _____ and $c =$ _____.

3. For $5x^2 - 5x - 7 = 0$, if $a = 5$, then $b =$ _____ and $c =$ _____.

4. For $7x^2 - 4 = 0$, if $a = 7$, then $b =$ _____ and $c =$ _____.

5. For $x^2 + 9 = 0$, if $c = 9$, then $a =$ _____ and $b =$ _____.

6. The correct simplified form of $\dfrac{5 \pm 10\sqrt{2}}{5}$ is _____.

    a. $1 \pm 10\sqrt{2}$ **b.** $2\sqrt{2}$ **c.** $1 \pm 2\sqrt{2}$ **d.** $\pm 5\sqrt{2}$

Martin-Gay Interactive Videos

See Video 11.2

Watch the section lecture video and answer the following questions.

OBJECTIVE 1

7. Based on ⊞ Examples 1–3, answer the following.
    a. Must a quadratic equation be written in standard form in order to use the quadratic formula? Why or why not?
    b. Must fractions be cleared from an equation before using the quadratic formula? Why or why not?

OBJECTIVE 2

8. Based on ⊞ Example 4 and the lecture before, complete the following statements. The discriminant is the _____ in the quadratic formula and can be used to find the number and type of solutions of a quadratic equation without _____ the equation. To use the discriminant, the quadratic equation needs to be written in _____ form.

OBJECTIVE 3

9. In ⊞ Example 5, the value of x is found, which is then used to find the dimensions of the triangle. Yet all this work still does solve the problem. Explain.

11.2 Exercise Set MyMathLab®

Use the quadratic formula to solve each equation. These equations have real number solutions only. See Examples 1 through 3.

1. $m^2 + 5m - 6 = 0$

2. $p^2 + 11p - 12 = 0$

3. $2y = 5y^2 - 3$

4. $5x^2 - 3 = 14x$

5. $x^2 - 6x + 9 = 0$

6. $y^2 + 10y + 25 = 0$

7. $x^2 + 7x + 4 = 0$

8. $y^2 + 5y + 3 = 0$

9. $8m^2 - 2m = 7$

10. $11n^2 - 9n = 1$

11. $3m^2 - 7m = 3$

12. $x^2 - 13 = 5x$

13. $\frac{1}{2}x^2 - x - 1 = 0$

14. $\frac{1}{6}x^2 + x + \frac{1}{3} = 0$

15. $\frac{2}{5}y^2 + \frac{1}{5}y = \frac{3}{5}$

16. $\frac{1}{8}x^2 + x = \frac{5}{2}$

17. $\frac{1}{3}y^2 = y + \frac{1}{6}$

18. $\frac{1}{2}y^2 = y + \frac{1}{2}$

19. $x^2 + 5x = -2$

20. $y^2 - 8 = 4y$

21. $(m + 2)(2m - 6) = 5(m - 1) - 12$

22. $7p(p - 2) + 2(p + 4) = 3$

MIXED PRACTICE

Use the quadratic formula to solve each equation. These equations have real solutions and complex but not real solutions. See Examples 1 through 4.

23. $x^2 + 6x + 13 = 0$

24. $x^2 + 2x + 2 = 0$

25. $(x + 5)(x - 1) = 2$

26. $x(x + 6) = 2$

27. $6 = -4x^2 + 3x$

28. $2 = -9x^2 - x$

29. $\frac{x^2}{3} - x = \frac{5}{3}$

30. $\frac{x^2}{2} - 3 = -\frac{9}{2}x$

31. $10y^2 + 10y + 3 = 0$

32. $3y^2 + 6y + 5 = 0$

33. $x(6x + 2) = 3$

34. $x(7x + 1) = 2$

35. $\frac{2}{5}y^2 + \frac{1}{5}y + \frac{3}{5} = 0$

36. $\frac{1}{8}x^2 + x + \frac{5}{2} = 0$

37. $\frac{1}{2}y^2 = y - \frac{1}{2}$

38. $\frac{2}{3}x^2 - \frac{20}{3}x = -\frac{100}{6}$

39. $(n - 2)^2 = 2n$

40. $\left(p - \frac{1}{2}\right)^2 = \frac{p}{2}$

Use the discriminant to determine the number and types of solutions of each equation. See Example 5.

41. $x^2 - 5 = 0$

42. $x^2 - 7 = 0$

43. $4x^2 + 12x = -9$

44. $9x^2 + 1 = 6x$

45. $3x = -2x^2 + 7$

46. $3x^2 = 5 - 7x$

47. $6 = 4x - 5x^2$

48. $8x = 3 - 9x^2$

49. $9x - 2x^2 + 5 = 0$

50. $5 - 4x + 12x^2 = 0$

Solve. See Examples 7 and 8.

51. Nancy, Thelma, and John Varner live on a corner lot. Often, neighborhood children cut across their lot to save walking distance. Given the diagram below, approximate to the nearest foot how many feet of walking distance is saved by cutting across their property instead of walking around the lot.

△ **52.** Given the diagram below, approximate to the nearest foot how many feet of walking distance a person saves by cutting across the lawn instead of walking on the sidewalk.

△ **53.** The hypotenuse of an isosceles right triangle is 2 centimeters longer than either of its legs. Find the exact length of each side. (*Hint:* An isosceles right triangle is a right triangle whose legs are the same length.)

△ **54.** The hypotenuse of an isosceles right triangle is one meter longer than either of its legs. Find the length of each side.

△ **55.** Bailey's rectangular dog pen for his Irish setter must have an area of 400 square feet. Also, the length must be 10 feet longer than the width. Find the dimensions of the pen.

△ **56.** An entry in the Peach Festival Poster Contest must be rectangular and have an area of 1200 square inches. Furthermore, its length must be 20 inches longer than its width. Find the dimensions each entry must have.

△ **57.** A holding pen for cattle must be square and have a diagonal length of 100 meters.

 a. Find the length of a side of the pen.

 b. Find the area of the pen.

△ **58.** A rectangle is three times longer than it is wide. It has a diagonal of length 50 centimeters.

 a. Find the dimensions of the rectangle.

 b. Find the perimeter of the rectangle.

△ **59.** The heaviest reported door in the world is the 708.6 ton radiation shield door in the National Institute for Fusion Science at Toki, Japan. If the height of the door is 1.1 feet longer than its width, and its front area (neglecting depth) is 1439.9 square feet, find its width and height [Interesting note: The door is 6.6 feet thick.] (*Source: Guinness World Records*)

△ **60.** Christi and Robbie Wegmann are constructing a rectangular stained glass window whose length is 7.3 inches longer than its width. If the area of the window is 569.9 square inches, find its width and length.

△ **61.** The base of a triangle is four more than twice its height. If the area of the triangle is 42 square centimeters, find its base and height.

 62. If a point *B* divides a line segment such that the smaller portion is to the larger portion as the larger is to the whole, the whole is the length of the *golden ratio*.

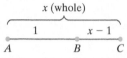

The golden ratio was thought by the Greeks to be the most pleasing to the eye, and many of their buildings contained numerous examples of the golden ratio. The value of the golden ratio is the positive solution of

$$\begin{matrix}(\text{smaller}) \\ (\text{larger})\end{matrix} \quad \frac{x-1}{1} = \frac{1}{x} \quad \begin{matrix}(\text{larger}) \\ (\text{whole})\end{matrix}$$

Find this value.

The Wollomombi Falls in Australia have a height of 1100 feet. A pebble is thrown upward from the top of the falls with an initial velocity of 20 feet per second. The height of the pebble h after t seconds is given by the equation $h = -16t^2 + 20t + 1100$. Use this equation for Exercises 63 and 64.

 63. How long after the pebble is thrown will it hit the ground? Round to the nearest tenth of a second.

 64. How long after the pebble is thrown will it be 550 feet from the ground? Round to the nearest tenth of a second.

A ball is thrown downward from the top of a 180-foot building with an initial velocity of 20 feet per second. The height of the ball h after t seconds is given by the equation $h = -16t^2 - 20t + 180$. Use this equation to answer Exercises 65 and 66.

 65. How long after the ball is thrown will it strike the ground? Round the result to the nearest tenth of a second.

66. How long after the ball is thrown will it be 50 feet from the ground? Round the result to the nearest tenth of a second.

REVIEW AND PREVIEW

Solve each equation. See Sections 7.5 and 10.6.

67. $\sqrt{5x - 2} = 3$

68. $\sqrt{y + 2} + 7 = 12$

69. $\dfrac{1}{x} + \dfrac{2}{5} = \dfrac{7}{x}$

70. $\dfrac{10}{z} = \dfrac{5}{z} - \dfrac{1}{3}$

Factor. See Sections 6.3 through 6.5.

71. $x^4 + x^2 - 20$

72. $2y^4 + 11y^2 - 6$

73. $z^4 - 13z^2 + 36$

74. $x^4 - 1$

CONCEPT EXTENSIONS

For each quadratic equation, choose the correct substitution for a, b, and c in the standard form $ax^2 + bx + c = 0$.

75. $x^2 = -10$

  a. $a = 1, b = 0, c = -10$

  b. $a = 1, b = 0, c = 10$

  c. $a = 0, b = 1, c = -10$

  d. $a = 1, b = 1, c = 10$

76. $x^2 + 5 = -x$

  a. $a = 1, b = 5, c = -1$

  b. $a = 1, b = -1, c = 5$

  c. $a = 1, b = 5, c = 1$

  d. $a = 1, b = 1, c = 5$

77. Solve Exercise 1 by factoring. Explain the result.

78. Solve Exercise 2 by factoring. Explain the result.

Use the quadratic formula and a calculator to approximate each solution to the nearest tenth.

79. $2x^2 - 6x + 3 = 0$

80. $3.6x^2 + 1.8x - 4.3 = 0$

The accompanying graph shows the daily low temperatures for one week in New Orleans, Louisiana.

81. Between which days of the week was there the greatest decrease in the low temperature?

82. Between which days of the week was there the greatest increase in the low temperature?

83. Which day of the week had the lowest low temperature?

84. Use the graph to estimate the low temperature on Thursday.

Notice that the shape of the temperature graph is similar to the curve drawn. In fact, this graph can be modeled by the quadratic function $f(x) = 3x^2 - 18x + 56$, where $f(x)$ is the temperature in degrees Fahrenheit and x is the number of days from Sunday. (This graph is shown in blue.) Use this function to answer Exercises 85 and 86.

85. Use the quadratic function given to approximate the temperature on Thursday. Does your answer agree with the graph?

86. Use the function given and the quadratic formula to find when the temperature was $35°$ F. [*Hint:* Let $f(x) = 35$ and solve for *x*.] Round your answer to one decimal place and interpret your result. Does your answer agree with the graph?

87. The number of college students in the United States can be modeled by the quadratic function $f(x) = 22x^2 + 274x + 15,628$, where $f(x)$ is the number of college students in thousands of students, and x is the number of years after 2000. (*Source:* Based on data from the U.S. Department of Education)

  a. Find the number of college students in the United States in 2010.

  b. If the trend described by this model continues, find the year after 2000 in which the population of American college students reaches 24,500 students.

88. The projected number of Wi-Fi-enabled cell phones in the United States can be modeled by the quadratic function $c(x) = -0.4x^2 + 21x + 35$, where $c(x)$ is the projected number of Wi-Fi-enabled cell phones in millions and x is the number of years after 2009. Round to the nearest million. (*Source:* Techcrunchies.com)

  a. Find the number of Wi-Fi-enabled cell phones in the United States in 2010.

  b. Find the estimated number of Wi-Fi-enabled cell phones in the United States in 2012.

  c. If the trend described by this model continues, find the year in which the projected number of Wi-Fi-enabled cell phones in the United States reaches 150 million.

89. The average total daily supply y of motor gasoline (in thousands of barrels per day) in the United States for the period 2000–2008 can be approximated by the equation $y = -10x^2 + 193x + 8464$, where x is the number of years after 2000. (*Source:* Based on data from the Energy Information Administration)

  a. Find the average total daily supply of motor gasoline in 2004.

  b. According to this model, in what year, from 2000 to 2008, was the average total daily supply of gasoline 9325 thousand barrels per day?

  c. According to this model, in what year, from 2009 on, will the average total supply of gasoline be 9325 thousand barrels per day?

90. The relationship between body weight and the Recommended Dietary Allowance (RDA) for vitamin A in children up to age 10 is modeled by the quadratic equation $y = 0.149x^2 - 4.475x + 406.478$, where y is the RDA for vitamin A in micrograms for a child whose weight is x pounds. (*Source:* Based on data from the Food and Nutrition Board, National Academy of Sciences–Institute of Medicine, 1989)

   a. Determine the vitamin A requirements of a child who weighs 35 pounds.

   b. What is the weight of a child whose RDA of vitamin A is 600 micrograms? Round your answer to the nearest pound.

The solutions of the quadratic equation $ax^2 + bx + c = 0$ are
$$\frac{-b + \sqrt{b^2 - 4ac}}{2a} \text{ and } \frac{-b - \sqrt{b^2 - 4ac}}{2a}.$$

91. Show that the sum of these solutions is $\dfrac{-b}{a}$.

92. Show that the product of these solutions is $\dfrac{c}{a}$.

Use the quadratic formula to solve each quadratic equation.

93. $3x^2 - \sqrt{12}x + 1 = 0$
   (*Hint: $a = 3, b = -\sqrt{12}, c = 1$*)

94. $5x^2 + \sqrt{20}x + 1 = 0$

95. $x^2 + \sqrt{2}x + 1 = 0$

96. $x^2 - \sqrt{2}x + 1 = 0$

97. $2x^2 - \sqrt{3}x - 1 = 0$

98. $7x^2 + \sqrt{7}x - 2 = 0$

99. Use a graphing calculator to solve Exercises 63 and 65.

100. Use a graphing calculator to solve Exercises 64 and 66.

Recall that the discriminant also tells us the number of x-intercepts of the related function.

101. Check the results of Exercise 49 by graphing $y = 9x - 2x^2 + 5$.

102. Check the results of Exercise 50 by graphing $y = 5 - 4x + 12x^2$.

11.3   Solving Equations by Using Quadratic Methods

OBJECTIVES

1 Solve Various Equations That Are Quadratic in Form.

2 Solve Problems That Lead to Quadratic Equations.

OBJECTIVE

1   **Solving Equations That Are Quadratic in Form**

In this section, we discuss various types of equations that can be solved in part by using the methods for solving quadratic equations.

   Once each equation is simplified, you may want to use these steps when deciding which method to use to solve the quadratic equation.

Solving a Quadratic Equation

Step 1. If the equation is in the form $(ax + b)^2 = c$, use the square root property and solve. If not, go to Step 2.

Step 2. Write the equation in standard form: $ax^2 + bx + c = 0$.

Step 3. Try to solve the equation by the factoring method. If not possible, go to Step 4.

Step 4. Solve the equation by the quadratic formula.

   The first example is a radical equation that becomes a quadratic equation once we square both sides.

EXAMPLE 1   Solve: $x - \sqrt{x} - 6 = 0$.

Solution   Recall that to solve a radical equation, first get the radical alone on one side of the equation. Then square both sides.

$$x - 6 = \sqrt{x} \qquad \text{Add } \sqrt{x} \text{ to both sides.}$$
$$(x - 6)^2 = \left(\sqrt{x}\right)^2 \qquad \text{Square both sides.}$$
$$x^2 - 12x + 36 = x$$
$$x^2 - 13x + 36 = 0 \qquad \text{Set the equation equal to 0.}$$
$$(x - 9)(x - 4) = 0$$
$$x - 9 = 0 \quad \text{or} \quad x - 4 = 0$$
$$x = 9 \qquad\qquad x = 4$$

Check:

<table>
<tr><td>Let $x = 9$</td><td>Let $x = 4$</td></tr>
<tr><td>$x - \sqrt{x} - 6 = 0$</td><td>$x - \sqrt{x} - 6 = 0$</td></tr>
<tr><td>$9 - \sqrt{9} - 6 \stackrel{?}{=} 0$</td><td>$4 - \sqrt{4} - 6 \stackrel{?}{=} 0$</td></tr>
<tr><td>$9 - 3 - 6 \stackrel{?}{=} 0$</td><td>$4 - 2 - 6 \stackrel{?}{=} 0$</td></tr>
<tr><td>$0 = 0$ True</td><td>$-4 = 0$ False</td></tr>
</table>

The solution is 9 or the solution set is {9}.

PRACTICE
1 Solve: $x - \sqrt{x + 1} - 5 = 0$.

EXAMPLE 2 Solve: $\dfrac{3x}{x - 2} - \dfrac{x + 1}{x} = \dfrac{6}{x(x - 2)}$.

Solution In this equation, x cannot be either 2 or 0 because these values cause denominators to equal zero. To solve for x, we first multiply both sides of the equation by $x(x - 2)$ to clear the fractions. By the distributive property, this means that we multiply each term by $x(x - 2)$.

$$x(x - 2)\left(\dfrac{3x}{x - 2}\right) - x(x - 2)\left(\dfrac{x + 1}{x}\right) = x(x - 2)\left[\dfrac{6}{x(x - 2)}\right]$$

$$3x^2 - (x - 2)(x + 1) = 6 \quad \text{Simplify.}$$
$$3x^2 - (x^2 - x - 2) = 6 \quad \text{Multiply.}$$
$$3x^2 - x^2 + x + 2 = 6$$
$$2x^2 + x - 4 = 0 \quad \text{Simplify.}$$

This equation cannot be factored using integers, so we solve by the quadratic formula.

$$x = \dfrac{-1 \pm \sqrt{1^2 - 4(2)(-4)}}{2 \cdot 2} \quad \text{Use } a = 2, b = 1, \text{ and } c = -4 \text{ in the quadratic formula.}$$
$$= \dfrac{-1 \pm \sqrt{1 + 32}}{4} \quad \text{Simplify.}$$
$$= \dfrac{-1 \pm \sqrt{33}}{4}$$

Neither proposed solution will make the denominators 0.

The solutions are $\dfrac{-1 + \sqrt{33}}{4}$ and $\dfrac{-1 - \sqrt{33}}{4}$ or the solution set is $\left\{\dfrac{-1 + \sqrt{33}}{4}, \dfrac{-1 - \sqrt{33}}{4}\right\}$.

PRACTICE
2 Solve: $\dfrac{5x}{x + 1} - \dfrac{x + 4}{x} = \dfrac{3}{x(x + 1)}$.

EXAMPLE 3 Solve: $p^4 - 3p^2 - 4 = 0$.

Solution First we factor the trinomial.

$$p^4 - 3p^2 - 4 = 0$$
$$(p^2 - 4)(p^2 + 1) = 0 \quad \text{Factor.}$$
$$(p - 2)(p + 2)(p^2 + 1) = 0 \quad \text{Factor further.}$$
$$p - 2 = 0 \quad \text{or} \quad p + 2 = 0 \quad \text{or} \quad p^2 + 1 = 0 \quad \text{Set each factor equal}$$
$$p = 2 \qquad\qquad p = -2 \qquad\qquad p^2 = -1 \quad \text{to 0 and solve.}$$
$$p = \pm\sqrt{-1} = \pm i$$

(Continued on next page)

The solutions are $2, -2, i$ and $-i$. □

3 Solve: $p^4 - 7p^2 - 144 = 0$.

▷ Helpful Hint

Example 3 can be solved using substitution also. Think of $p^4 - 3p^2 - 4 = 0$ as

$$(p^2)^2 - 3p^2 - 4 = 0 \quad \text{Then let } x = p^2 \text{ and solve and substitute back.}$$
$$\text{The solutions will be the same.}$$
$$x^2 - 3x - 4 = 0$$

✓CONCEPT CHECK

  a. True or false? The maximum number of solutions that a quadratic equation can have is 2.
  b. True or false? The maximum number of solutions that an equation in quadratic form can have is 2.

EXAMPLE 4 Solve: $(x - 3)^2 - 3(x - 3) - 4 = 0$.

Solution Notice that the quantity $(x - 3)$ is repeated in this equation. Sometimes it is helpful to substitute a variable (in this case other than x) for the repeated quantity. We will let $y = x - 3$. Then

$$(x - 3)^2 - 3(x - 3) - 4 = 0$$

becomes

$$y^2 - 3y - 4 = 0 \quad \text{Let } x - 3 = y.$$
$$(y - 4)(y + 1) = 0 \quad \text{Factor.}$$

To solve, we use the zero factor property.

$$y - 4 = 0 \quad \text{or} \quad y + 1 = 0 \quad \text{Set each factor equal to 0.}$$
$$y = 4 \qquad\qquad y = -1 \quad \text{Solve.}$$

▷ Helpful Hint

When using substitution, don't forget to substitute back to the original variable.

To find values of x, we substitute back. That is, we substitute $x - 3$ for y.

$$x - 3 = 4 \quad \text{or} \quad x - 3 = -1$$
$$x = 7 \qquad\qquad x = 2$$

Both 2 and 7 check. The solutions are 2 and 7. □

PRACTICE

4 Solve: $(x + 2)^2 - 2(x + 2) - 3 = 0$.

EXAMPLE 5 Solve: $x^{2/3} - 5x^{1/3} + 6 = 0$.

Solution The key to solving this equation is recognizing that $x^{2/3} = (x^{1/3})^2$. We replace $x^{1/3}$ with m so that

$$(x^{1/3})^2 - 5x^{1/3} + 6 = 0$$

becomes

$$m^2 - 5m + 6 = 0$$

Now we solve by factoring.

$$m^2 - 5m + 6 = 0$$
$$(m - 3)(m - 2) = 0 \qquad \text{Factor.}$$
$$m - 3 = 0 \quad \text{or} \quad m - 2 = 0 \quad \text{Set each factor equal to 0.}$$
$$m = 3 \qquad\qquad m = 2$$

Since $m = x^{1/3}$, we have

$$x^{1/3} = 3 \qquad \text{or} \qquad x^{1/3} = 2$$
$$x = 3^3 = 27 \quad \text{or} \qquad x = 2^3 = 8$$

Both 8 and 27 check. The solutions are 8 and 27.

PRACTICE
> **5**   Solve: $x^{2/3} - 5x^{1/3} + 4 = 0$.

OBJECTIVE

2   Solving Problems That Lead to Quadratic Equations

The next example is a work problem. This problem is modeled by a rational equation that simplifies to a quadratic equation.

EXAMPLE 6   **Finding Work Time**

Together, an experienced word processor and an apprentice word processor can create a word document in 6 hours. Alone, the experienced word processor can create the document 2 hours faster than the apprentice word processor can. Find the time in which each person can create the word document alone.

Solution

1. **UNDERSTAND.** Read and reread the problem. The key idea here is the relationship between the *time* (hours) it takes to complete the job and the *part of the job* completed in one unit of time (hour). For example, because they can complete the job together in 6 hours, the *part of the job* they can complete in 1 hour is $\frac{1}{6}$.

   Let

   > $x =$ the *time* in hours it takes the apprentice word processor to complete the job alone

   > $x - 2 =$ the *time* in hours it takes the experienced word processor to complete the job alone

   We can summarize in a chart the information discussed

	Total Hours to Complete Job	*Part of Job Completed in 1 Hour*
Apprentice Word Processor	x	$\dfrac{1}{x}$
Experienced Word Processor	$x - 2$	$\dfrac{1}{x-2}$
Together	6	$\dfrac{1}{6}$

2. **TRANSLATE.**

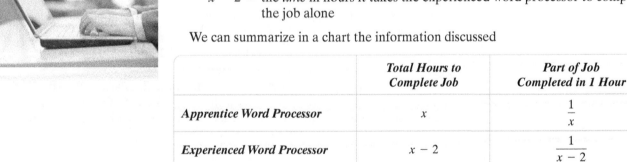

In words:	part of job completed by apprentice word processor in 1 hour	added to	part of job completed by experienced word processor in 1 hour	is equal to	part of job completed together in 1 hour
	↓	↓	↓	↓	↓
Translate:	$\dfrac{1}{x}$	$+$	$\dfrac{1}{x-2}$	$=$	$\dfrac{1}{6}$

(Continued on next page)

3. SOLVE.

$$\frac{1}{x} + \frac{1}{x-2} = \frac{1}{6}$$

$$6x(x-2)\left(\frac{1}{x} + \frac{1}{x-2}\right) = 6x(x-2)\cdot\frac{1}{6} \qquad \text{Multiply both sides by the LCD } 6x(x-2).$$

$$6x(x-2)\cdot\frac{1}{x} + 6x(x-2)\cdot\frac{1}{x-2} = 6x(x-2)\cdot\frac{1}{6} \qquad \text{Use the distributive property.}$$

$$6(x-2) + 6x = x(x-2)$$

$$6x - 12 + 6x = x^2 - 2x$$

$$0 = x^2 - 14x + 12$$

Now we can substitute $a = 1$, $b = -14$, and $c = 12$ into the quadratic formula and simplify.

$$x = \frac{-(-14) \pm \sqrt{(-14)^2 - 4(1)(12)}}{2\cdot 1} = \frac{14 \pm \sqrt{148}^{*}}{2}$$

Using a calculator or a square root table, we see that $\sqrt{148} \approx 12.2$ rounded to one decimal place. Thus,

$$x \approx \frac{14 \pm 12.2}{2}$$

$$x \approx \frac{14 + 12.2}{2} = 13.1 \quad \text{or} \quad x \approx \frac{14 - 12.2}{2} = 0.9$$

4. INTERPRET.

Check: If the apprentice word processor completes the job alone in 0.9 hours, the experienced word processor completes the job alone in $x - 2 = 0.9 - 2 = -1.1$ hours. Since this is not possible, we reject the solution of 0.9. The approximate solution thus is 13.1 hours.

State: The apprentice word processor can complete the job alone in approximately 13.1 hours, and the experienced word processor can complete the job alone in approximately

$$x - 2 = 13.1 - 2 = 11.1 \text{ hours.} \qquad \square$$

PRACTICE

6   Together, Katy and Steve can groom all the dogs at the Barkin' Doggie Day Care in 4 hours. Alone, Katy can groom the dogs 1 hour faster than Steve can groom the dogs alone. Find the time in which each of them can groom the dogs alone.

EXAMPLE 7   **Finding Driving Speeds**

Beach and Fargo are about 400 miles apart. A salesperson travels from Fargo to Beach one day at a certain speed. She returns to Fargo the next day and drives 10 mph faster. Her total travel time was $14\frac{2}{3}$ hours. Find her speed to Beach and the return speed to Fargo.

(*This expression can be simplified further, but this will suffice because we are approximating.)

Solution

1. UNDERSTAND. Read and reread the problem. Let

$$x = \text{the speed to Beach, so}$$

$$x + 10 = \text{the return speed to Fargo.}$$

Then organize the given information in a table.

> ▶ **Helpful Hint**
>
> Since $d = rt$, $t = \dfrac{d}{r}$. The time column was completed using $\dfrac{d}{r}$.

	distance	=	rate	·	time	
To Beach	400		x		$\dfrac{400}{x}$	← distance ← rate
Return to Fargo	400		$x + 10$		$\dfrac{400}{x + 10}$	← distance ← rate

2. TRANSLATE.

In words:
| time to Beach | + | return time to Fargo | = | $14\dfrac{2}{3}$ hours |

Translate:

$$\frac{400}{x} + \frac{400}{x + 10} = \frac{44}{3}$$

3. SOLVE.

$$\frac{400}{x} + \frac{400}{x + 10} = \frac{44}{3}$$

$$\frac{100}{x} + \frac{100}{x + 10} = \frac{11}{3} \qquad \text{Divide both sides by 4.}$$

$$3x(x + 10)\left(\frac{100}{x} + \frac{100}{x + 10}\right) = 3x(x + 10) \cdot \frac{11}{3} \qquad \text{Multiply both sides by the LCD } 3x(x + 10).$$

$$3x(x + 10) \cdot \frac{100}{x} + 3x(x + 10) \cdot \frac{100}{x + 10} = 3x(x + 10) \cdot \frac{11}{3} \qquad \text{Use the distributive property.}$$

$$3(x + 10) \cdot 100 + 3x \cdot 100 = x(x + 10) \cdot 11$$

$$300x + 3000 + 300x = 11x^2 + 110x$$

$$0 = 11x^2 - 490x - 3000 \qquad \text{Set equation equal to 0.}$$

$$0 = (11x + 60)(x - 50) \qquad \text{Factor.}$$

$$11x + 60 = 0 \quad \text{or} \quad x - 50 = 0 \qquad \text{Set each factor equal to 0.}$$

$$x = -\frac{60}{11} \text{ or } -5\frac{5}{11}; \quad x = 50$$

4. INTERPRET.

Check: The speed is not negative, so it's not $-5\dfrac{5}{11}$. The number 50 does check.

State: The speed to Beach was 50 mph, and her return speed to Fargo was 60 mph. ☐

PRACTICE

7   The 36-km S-shaped Hangzhou Bay Bridge is the longest cross-sea bridge in the world, linking Ningbo and Shanghai, China. A merchant drives over the bridge one morning from Ningbo to Shanghai in very heavy traffic and returns home that night driving 50 km per hour faster. The total travel time was 1.3 hours. Find the speed to Shanghai and the return speed to Ningbo.

Vocabulary, Readiness & Video Check

Martin-Gay Interactive Videos

Watch the section lecture video and answer the following questions.

OBJECTIVE
1

1. From Examples 1 and 2, what's the main thing to remember when using a substitution in order to solve an equation by quadratic methods?

OBJECTIVE
2

2. In Example 4, the translated equation is actually a rational equation. Explain how we end up solving it using quadratic methods.

See Video 11.3

11.3 Exercise Set

Solve. See Example 1.

1. $2x = \sqrt{10 + 3x}$

2. $3x = \sqrt{8x + 1}$

3. $x - 2\sqrt{x} = 8$

4. $x - \sqrt{2x} = 4$

5. $\sqrt{9x} = x + 2$

6. $\sqrt{16x} = x + 3$

Solve. See Example 2.

7. $\dfrac{2}{x} + \dfrac{3}{x - 1} = 1$

8. $\dfrac{6}{x^2} = \dfrac{3}{x + 1}$

9. $\dfrac{3}{x} + \dfrac{4}{x + 2} = 2$

10. $\dfrac{5}{x - 2} + \dfrac{4}{x + 2} = 1$

11. $\dfrac{7}{x^2 - 5x + 6} = \dfrac{2x}{x - 3} - \dfrac{x}{x - 2}$

12. $\dfrac{11}{2x^2 + x - 15} = \dfrac{5}{2x - 5} - \dfrac{x}{x + 3}$

Solve. See Example 3.

13. $p^4 - 16 = 0$

14. $x^4 + 2x^2 - 3 = 0$

15. $4x^4 + 11x^2 = 3$

16. $z^4 = 81$

17. $z^4 - 13z^2 + 36 = 0$

18. $9x^4 + 5x^2 - 4 = 0$

Solve. See Examples 4 and 5.

19. $x^{2/3} - 3x^{1/3} - 10 = 0$

20. $x^{2/3} + 2x^{1/3} + 1 = 0$

21. $(5n + 1)^2 + 2(5n + 1) - 3 = 0$

22. $(m - 6)^2 + 5(m - 6) + 4 = 0$

23. $2x^{2/3} - 5x^{1/3} = 3$

24. $3x^{2/3} + 11x^{1/3} = 4$

25. $1 + \dfrac{2}{3t - 2} = \dfrac{8}{(3t - 2)^2}$

26. $2 - \dfrac{7}{x + 6} = \dfrac{15}{(x + 6)^2}$

27. $20x^{2/3} - 6x^{1/3} - 2 = 0$

28. $4x^{2/3} + 16x^{1/3} = -15$

MIXED PRACTICE

Solve. See Examples 1 through 5.

29. $a^4 - 5a^2 + 6 = 0$

30. $x^4 - 12x^2 + 11 = 0$

31. $\dfrac{2x}{x - 2} + \dfrac{x}{x + 3} = -\dfrac{5}{x + 3}$

32. $\dfrac{5}{x - 3} + \dfrac{x}{x + 3} = \dfrac{19}{x^2 - 9}$

33. $(p + 2)^2 = 9(p + 2) - 20$

34. $2(4m - 3)^2 - 9(4m - 3) = 5$

35. $2x = \sqrt{11x + 3}$

36. $4x = \sqrt{2x + 3}$

37. $x^{2/3} - 8x^{1/3} + 15 = 0$

38. $x^{2/3} - 2x^{1/3} - 8 = 0$

39. $y^3 + 9y - y^2 - 9 = 0$

40. $x^3 + x - 3x^2 - 3 = 0$

41. $2x^{2/3} + 3x^{1/3} - 2 = 0$

42. $6x^{2/3} - 25x^{1/3} - 25 = 0$

43. $x^{-2} - x^{-1} - 6 = 0$

44. $y^{-2} - 8y^{-1} + 7 = 0$

45. $x - \sqrt{x} = 2$

46. $x - \sqrt{3x} = 6$

47. $\dfrac{x}{x-1} + \dfrac{1}{x+1} = \dfrac{2}{x^2-1}$

48. $\dfrac{x}{x-5} + \dfrac{5}{x+5} = -\dfrac{1}{x^2-25}$

49. $p^4 - p^2 - 20 = 0$

50. $x^4 - 10x^2 + 9 = 0$

51. $(x+3)(x^2 - 3x + 9) = 0$

52. $(x-6)(x^2 + 6x + 36) = 0$

53. $1 = \dfrac{4}{x-7} + \dfrac{5}{(x-7)^2}$

54. $3 + \dfrac{1}{2p+4} = \dfrac{10}{(2p+4)^2}$

55. $27y^4 + 15y^2 = 2$

56. $8z^4 + 14z^2 = -5$

57. $x - \sqrt{19 - 2x} - 2 = 0$

58. $x - \sqrt{17 - 4x} - 3 = 0$

Solve. For Exercises 59 and 60, the solutions have been started for you. See Examples 6 and 7.

59. Roma Sherry drove 330 miles from her hometown to Tucson. During her return trip, she was able to increase her speed by 11 miles per hour. If her return trip took 1 hour less time, find her original speed and her speed returning home.

Start the solution:

1. UNDERSTAND the problem. Reread it as many times as needed. Let

$$x = \text{original speed}$$
$$x + 11 = \text{return-trip speed}$$

Organize the information in a table.

	distance	=	rate	·	time	
To Tucson	330		x		$\dfrac{330}{x}$	← distance ← rate
Return trip	330		___		$\dfrac{330}{\underline{\quad}}$	← distance ← rate

2. TRANSLATE into an equation. (Fill in the blanks below.)

Time to Tucson	equals	Return trip time	plus	1 hour
↓	↓	↓	↓	↓
___	=	___	+	1

Finish with:

3. SOLVE and 4. INTERPRET

60. A salesperson drove to Portland, a distance of 300 miles. During the last 80 miles of his trip, heavy rainfall forced him to decrease his speed by 15 miles per hour. If his total driving time was 6 hours, find his original speed and his speed during the rainfall.

Start the solution:

1. UNDERSTAND the problem. Reread it as many times as needed. Let

$$x = \text{original speed}$$
$$x - 15 = \text{rainfall speed}$$

Organize the information in a table.

	distance	=	rate	·	time	
First part of trip	$300 - 80$, or 220		x		$\dfrac{220}{x}$	← distance ← rate
Heavy rainfall part of trip	80		$x - 15$		$\dfrac{80}{\underline{\quad}}$	← distance ← rate

2. TRANSLATE into an equation. (Fill in the blanks below.)

Time during first part of trip	plus	Time during heavy rainfall	equals	6 hr
↓	↓	↓	↓	↓
___	+	___	=	6

Finish with:

3. SOLVE and 4. INTERPRET

61. A jogger ran 3 miles, decreased her speed by 1 mile per hour, and then ran another 4 miles. If her total time jogging was $1\dfrac{3}{5}$ hours, find her speed for each part of her run.

62. Mark Keaton's workout consists of jogging for 3 miles and then riding his bike for 5 miles at a speed 4 miles per hour faster than he jogs. If his total workout time is 1 hour, find his jogging speed and his biking speed.

63. A Chinese restaurant in Mandeville, Louisiana, has a large goldfish pond around the restaurant. Suppose that an inlet pipe and a hose together can fill the pond in 8 hours. The inlet pipe alone can complete the job in one hour less time than the hose alone. Find the time that the hose can complete the job alone and the time that the inlet pipe can complete the job alone. Round each to the nearest tenth of an hour.

64. A water tank on a farm in Flatonia, Texas, can be filled with a large inlet pipe and a small inlet pipe in 3 hours. The large inlet pipe alone can fill the tank in 2 hours less time than the small inlet pipe alone. Find the time to the nearest tenth of an hour each pipe can fill the tank alone.

65. Bill Shaughnessy and his son Billy can clean the house together in 4 hours. When the son works alone, it takes him an hour longer to clean than it takes his dad alone. Find how long to the nearest tenth of an hour it takes the son to clean alone.

66. Together, Noodles and Freckles eat a 50-pound bag of dog food in 30 days. Noodles by himself eats a 50-pound bag in 2 weeks less time than Freckles does by himself. How many days to the nearest whole day would a 50-pound bag of dog food last Freckles?

67. The product of a number and 4 less than the number is 96. Find the number.

68. A whole number increased by its square is two more than twice itself. Find the number.

△ **69.** Suppose that an open box is to be made from a square sheet of cardboard by cutting out squares from each corner as shown and then folding along the dotted lines. If the box is to have a volume of 300 cubic inches, find the original dimensions of the sheet of cardboard.

  a. The ? in the drawing above will be the length (and the width) of the box as shown. Represent this length in terms of x.
  b. Use the formula for volume of a box, $V = l \cdot w \cdot h$, to write an equation in x.
  c. Solve the equation for x and give the dimensions of the sheet of cardboard. Check your solution.

△ **70.** Suppose that an open box is to be made from a square sheet of cardboard by cutting out squares from each corner as shown and then folding along the dotted lines. If the box is to have a volume of 128 cubic inches, find the original dimensions of the sheet of cardboard.

  a. The ? in the drawing above will be the length (and the width) of the box as shown. Represent this length in terms of x.
  b. Use the formula for volume of a box, $V = l \cdot w \cdot h$, to write an equation in x.
  c. Solve the equation for x and give the dimensions of the sheet of cardboard. Check your solution.

△ **71.** A sprinkler that sprays water in a circular pattern is to be used to water a square garden. If the area of the garden is 920 square feet, find the smallest whole number *radius* that the sprinkler can be adjusted to so that the entire garden is watered.

△ **72.** Suppose that a square field has an area of 6270 square feet. See Exercise 71 and find a new sprinkler radius.

REVIEW AND PREVIEW

Solve each inequality. See Section 2.8.

73. $\dfrac{5x}{3} + 2 \leq 7$

74. $\dfrac{2x}{3} + \dfrac{1}{6} \geq 2$

75. $\dfrac{y-1}{15} > -\dfrac{2}{5}$

76. $\dfrac{z-2}{12} < \dfrac{1}{4}$

Find the domain and range of each graphed relation. Decide which relations are also functions. See Section 3.6.

77.

78.

79.

80.

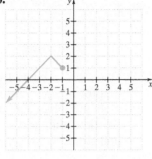

86. $y^3 - 216 = 0$

87. Write a polynomial equation that has three solutions: 2, 5, and −7.

88. Write a polynomial equation that has three solutions: 0, $2i$, and $-2i$.

89. During the seventh stage of the 2010 Paris–Nice bicycle race, Thomas Voeckler posted the fastest average speed, but Alberto Contador won the race. The seventh stage was 119 kilometers long. Voeckler's average speed was 0.0034 meters per second faster than Contador's. Traveling at these average speeds, Contador took 3 seconds longer than Voeckler to complete the race stage. (*Source:* Based on data from cyclingnews.com)

   a. Find Thomas Voeckler's average speed during the seventh stage of the 2010 Paris–Nice cycle race. Round to three decimal places.

   b. Find Alberto Contador's average speed during the seventh stage of the 2010 Paris–Nice cycle race. Round to three decimal places.

   c. Convert Voeckler's average speed to miles per hour. Round to three decimal places.

90. Use a graphing calculator to solve Exercise 29. Compare the solution with the solution from Exercise 29. Explain any differences.

CONCEPT EXTENSIONS

Solve.

81. $5y^3 + 45y - 5y^2 - 45 = 0$

82. $10x^3 + 10x - 30x^2 - 30 = 0$

83. $3x^{-2} - 3x^{-1} - 18 = 0$

84. $2y^{-2} - 16y^{-1} + 14 = 0$

85. $2x^3 = -54$

Sections 11.1–11.3

Use the square root property to solve each equation.

1. $x^2 - 10 = 0$

2. $x^2 - 14 = 0$

3. $(x - 1)^2 = 8$

4. $(x + 5)^2 = 12$

Solve each equation by completing the square.

5. $x^2 + 2x - 12 = 0$

6. $x^2 - 12x + 11 = 0$

7. $3x^2 + 3x = 5$

8. $16y^2 + 16y = 1$

Use the quadratic formula to solve each equation

9. $2x^2 - 4x + 1 = 0$

10. $\dfrac{1}{2}x^2 + 3x + 2 = 0$

11. $x^2 + 4x = -7$

12. $x^2 + x = -3$

Solve each equation. Use a method of your choice.

13. $x^2 + 3x + 6 = 0$

14. $2x^2 + 18 = 0$

15. $x^2 + 17x = 0$

16. $4x^2 - 2x - 3 = 0$

17. $(x - 2)^2 = 27$

18. $\dfrac{1}{2}x^2 - 2x + \dfrac{1}{2} = 0$

19. $3x^2 + 2x = 8$

20. $2x^2 = -5x - 1$

21. $x(x - 2) = 5$

22. $x^2 - 31 = 0$

23. $5x^2 - 55 = 0$

24. $5x^2 + 55 = 0$

25. $x(x + 5) = 66$

26. $5x^2 + 6x - 2 = 0$

27. $2x^2 + 3x = 1$

28. $x - \sqrt{13 - 3x} - 3 = 0$

29. $\dfrac{5x}{x - 2} - \dfrac{x + 1}{x} = \dfrac{3}{x(x - 2)}$

△ **30.** The diagonal of a square room measures 20 feet. Find the exact length of a side of the room. Then approximate the length to the nearest tenth of a foot.

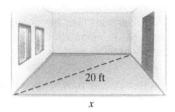

31. Together, Jack and Lucy Hoag can prepare a crawfish boil for a large party in 4 hours. Lucy alone can complete the job in 2 hours less time than Jack alone. Find the time that each person can prepare the crawfish boil alone. Round each time to the nearest tenth of an hour.

32. Diane Gray exercises at Total Body Gym. On the treadmill, she runs 5 miles, then increases her speed by 1 mile per hour and runs an additional 2 miles. If her total time on the treadmill is $1\dfrac{1}{3}$ hours, find her speed during each part of her run.

11.4 Nonlinear Inequalities in One Variable

OBJECTIVES

1 Solve Polynomial Inequalities of Degree 2 or Greater.

2 Solve Inequalities That Contain Rational Expressions with Variables in the Denominator.

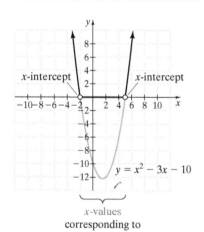

x-intercept

x-intercept

$y = x^2 - 3x - 10$

x-values corresponding to *negative* y-values

OBJECTIVE

1   Solving Polynomial Inequalities

Just as we can solve linear inequalities in one variable, so can we also solve quadratic inequalities in one variable. A **quadratic inequality** is an inequality that can be written so that one side is a quadratic expression and the other side is 0. Here are examples of quadratic inequalities in one variable. Each is written in **standard form.**

$$x^2 - 10x + 7 \leq 0 \qquad 3x^2 + 2x - 6 > 0$$
$$2x^2 + 9x - 2 < 0 \qquad x^2 - 3x + 11 \geq 0$$

A solution of a quadratic inequality in one variable is a value of the variable that makes the inequality a true statement.

The value of an expression such as $x^2 - 3x - 10$ will sometimes be positive, sometimes negative, and sometimes 0, depending on the value substituted for x. To solve the inequality $x^2 - 3x - 10 < 0$, we are looking for all values of x that make the expression $x^2 - 3x - 10$ less than 0, or negative. To understand how we find these values, we'll study the graph of the quadratic function $y = x^2 - 3x - 10$.

Notice that the x-values for which y is positive are separated from the x-values for which y is negative by the x-intercepts. (Recall that the x-intercepts correspond to values of x for which $y = 0$.) Thus, the solution set of $x^2 - 3x - 10 < 0$ consists of all real numbers from -2 to 5 or, in interval notation, $(-2, 5)$.

It is not necessary to graph $y = x^2 - 3x - 10$ to solve the related inequality $x^2 - 3x - 10 < 0$. Instead, we can draw a number line representing the x-axis and keep the following in mind: *A region on the number line for which the value of $x^2 - 3x - 10$ is positive is separated from a region on the number line for which the value of $x^2 - 3x - 10$ is negative by a value for which the expression is 0.*

Let's find these values for which the expression is 0 by solving the related equation:

$$x^2 - 3x - 10 = 0$$
$$(x - 5)(x + 2) = 0 \qquad \text{Factor.}$$
$$x - 5 = 0 \quad \text{or} \quad x + 2 = 0 \qquad \text{Set each factor equal to 0.}$$
$$x = 5 \qquad\qquad x = -2 \qquad \text{Solve.}$$

These two numbers, -2 and 5, divide the number line into three regions. We will call the regions A, B, and C. These regions are important because, if the value of $x^2 - 3x - 10$ is negative when a number from a region is substituted for x, then $x^2 - 3x - 10$ is negative when any number in that region is substituted for x. The same is true if the value of $x^2 - 3x - 10$ is positive for a particular value of x in a region.

To see whether the inequality $x^2 - 3x - 10 < 0$ is true or false in each region, we choose a test point from each region and substitute its value for x in the inequality $x^2 - 3x - 10 < 0$. If the resulting inequality is true, the region containing the test point is a solution region.

Region	Test Point Value	$(x - 5)(x + 2) < 0$	Result
A	-3	$(-8)(-1) < 0$	False
B	0	$(-5)(2) < 0$	True
C	6	$(1)(8) < 0$	False

The values in region B satisfy the inequality. The numbers -2 and 5 are not included in the solution set since the inequality symbol is $<$. The solution set is $(-2, 5)$, and its graph is shown.

EXAMPLE 1 Solve: $(x + 3)(x - 3) > 0$.

Solution First we solve the related equation, $(x + 3)(x - 3) = 0$.

$$(x + 3)(x - 3) = 0$$
$$x + 3 = 0 \quad \text{or} \quad x - 3 = 0$$
$$x = -3 \qquad\qquad x = 3$$

The two numbers -3 and 3 separate the number line into three regions, A, B, and C.

Now we substitute the value of a test point from each region. If the test value satisfies the inequality, every value in the region containing the test value is a solution.

Region	Test Point Value	$(x + 3)(x - 3) > 0$	Result
A	-4	$(-1)(-7) > 0$	True
B	0	$(3)(-3) > 0$	False
C	4	$(7)(1) > 0$	True

The points in regions A and C satisfy the inequality. The numbers -3 and 3 are not included in the solution since the inequality symbol is $>$. The solution set is $(-\infty, -3) \cup (3, \infty)$, and its graph is shown.

PRACTICE
1 Solve: $(x - 4)(x + 3) > 0$.

The following steps may be used to solve a polynomial inequality.

Solving a Polynomial Inequality

Step 1. Write the inequality in standard form and then solve the related equation.

Step 2. Separate the number line into regions with the solutions from Step 1.

Step 3. For each region, choose a test point and determine whether its value satisfies the *original inequality*.

Step 4. The solution set includes the regions whose test point value is a solution. If the inequality symbol is $\leq$ or $\geq$, the values from Step 1 are solutions; if $<$ or $>$, they are not.

✓CONCEPT CHECK

When choosing a test point in Step 3, why would the solutions from Step 1 not make good choices for test points?

EXAMPLE 2 Solve: $x^2 - 4x \leq 0$.

Solution First we solve the related equation, $x^2 - 4x = 0$.

$$x^2 - 4x = 0$$
$$x(x - 4) = 0$$
$$x = 0 \quad \text{or} \quad x = 4$$

The numbers 0 and 4 separate the number line into three regions, A, B, and C.

We check a test value in each region in the original inequality. Values in region B satisfy the inequality. The numbers 0 and 4 are included in the solution since the inequality symbol is $\leq$. The solution set is $[0, 4]$, and its graph is shown.

PRACTICE
2 Solve: $x^2 - 8x \leq 0$.

EXAMPLE 3 Solve: $(x + 2)(x - 1)(x - 5) \leq 0$.

Solution First we solve $(x + 2)(x - 1)(x - 5) = 0$. By inspection, we see that the solutions are -2, 1, and 5. They separate the number line into four regions, A, B, C, and D. Next we check test points from each region.

Region	Test Point Value	$(x + 2)(x - 1)(x - 5) \leq 0$	Result
A	-3	$(-1)(-4)(-8) \leq 0$	True
B	0	$(2)(-1)(-5) \leq 0$	False
C	2	$(4)(1)(-3) \leq 0$	True
D	6	$(8)(5)(1) \leq 0$	False

Answer to Concept Check:
The solutions found in Step 1 have a value of 0 in the original inequality.

The solution set is $(-\infty, -2] \cup [1, 5]$, and its graph is shown. We include the numbers -2, 1, and 5 because the inequality symbol is $\le$.

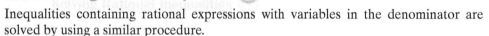

PRACTICE
3 Solve: $(x + 3)(x - 2)(x + 1) \le 0$.

OBJECTIVE
2 Solving Rational Inequalities

Inequalities containing rational expressions with variables in the denominator are solved by using a similar procedure.

EXAMPLE 4 Solve: $\dfrac{x + 2}{x - 3} \le 0$.

Solution First we find all values that make the denominator equal to 0. To do this, we solve $x - 3 = 0$ and find that $x = 3$.

Next, we solve the related equation $\dfrac{x + 2}{x - 3} = 0$.

$$\frac{x + 2}{x - 3} = 0$$

$$x + 2 = 0 \qquad \text{Multiply both sides by the LCD, } x - 3.$$

$$x = -2$$

Now we place these numbers on a number line and proceed as before, checking test point values in the original inequality.

Choose -3 from region A.

$$\frac{x + 2}{x - 3} \le 0$$

$$\frac{-3 + 2}{-3 - 3} \le 0$$

$$\frac{-1}{-6} \le 0$$

$$\frac{1}{6} \le 0 \quad \text{False}$$

Choose 0 from region B.

$$\frac{x + 2}{x - 3} \le 0$$

$$\frac{0 + 2}{0 - 3} \le 0$$

$$-\frac{2}{3} \le 0 \quad \text{True}$$

Choose 4 from region C.

$$\frac{x + 2}{x - 3} \le 0$$

$$\frac{4 + 2}{4 - 3} \le 0$$

$$6 \le 0 \quad \text{False}$$

The solution set is $[-2, 3)$. This interval includes -2 because -2 satisfies the original inequality. This interval does not include 3 because 3 would make the denominator 0.

PRACTICE
4 Solve: $\dfrac{x - 5}{x + 4} \le 0$.

The following steps may be used to solve a rational inequality with variables in the denominator.

> **Solving a Rational Inequality**
>
> **Step 1.** Solve for values that make all denominators 0.
>
> **Step 2.** Solve the related equation.
>
> **Step 3.** Separate the number line into regions with the solutions from Steps 1 and 2.
>
> **Step 4.** For each region, choose a test point and determine whether its value satisfies the *original inequality*.
>
> **Step 5.** The solution set includes the regions whose test point value is a solution. Check whether to include values from Step 2. Be sure *not* to include values that make any denominator 0.

EXAMPLE 5 Solve: $\dfrac{5}{x+1} < -2$.

Solution First we find values for x that make the denominator equal to 0.

$$x + 1 = 0$$
$$x = -1$$

Next we solve $\dfrac{5}{x+1} = -2$.

$$(x+1) \cdot \frac{5}{x+1} = (x+1) \cdot -2 \quad \text{Multiply both sides by the LCD, } x + 1.$$
$$5 = -2x - 2 \quad \text{Simplify.}$$
$$7 = -2x$$
$$-\frac{7}{2} = x$$

We use these two solutions to divide a number line into three regions and choose test points. Only a test point value from region B satisfies the *original inequality*. The solution set is $\left(-\dfrac{7}{2}, -1\right)$, and its graph is shown.

PRACTICE
5 Solve: $\dfrac{7}{x+3} < 5$.

Vocabulary, Readiness & Video Check

Write the graphed solution set in interval notation.

1.

2.

3.

4.

5.

6.

Martin-Gay Interactive Videos

See Video 11.4

Watch the section lecture video and answer the following questions.

OBJECTIVE
1

7. From Examples 1–3, how does solving a related equation help you solve a polynomial inequality? Are the solutions to the related equation ever solutions to the inequality?

OBJECTIVE
2

8. In Example 4, one of the values that separates the number line into regions is 4. The inequality is ≥, so why isn't 4 included in the solution set?

11.4 Exercise Set   MyMathLab®

Solve each polynomial inequality. Write the solution set in interval notation. See Examples 1 through 3.

1. $(x + 1)(x + 5) > 0$

2. $(x + 1)(x + 5) \leq 0$

3. $(x - 3)(x + 4) \leq 0$

4. $(x + 4)(x - 1) > 0$

5. $x^2 - 7x + 10 \leq 0$

6. $x^2 + 8x + 15 \geq 0$

7. $3x^2 + 16x < -5$

8. $2x^2 - 5x < 7$

9. $(x - 6)(x - 4)(x - 2) > 0$

10. $(x - 6)(x - 4)(x - 2) \leq 0$

11. $x(x - 1)(x + 4) \leq 0$

12. $x(x - 6)(x + 2) > 0$

13. $(x^2 - 9)(x^2 - 4) > 0$

14. $(x^2 - 16)(x^2 - 1) \leq 0$

Solve each inequality. Write the solution set in interval notation. See Example 4.

15. $\dfrac{x + 7}{x - 2} < 0$

16. $\dfrac{x - 5}{x - 6} > 0$

17. $\dfrac{5}{x + 1} > 0$

18. $\dfrac{3}{y - 5} < 0$

19. $\dfrac{x + 1}{x - 4} \geq 0$

20. $\dfrac{x + 1}{x - 4} \leq 0$

Solve each inequality. Write the solution set in interval notation. See Example 5.

21. $\dfrac{3}{x - 2} < 4$

22. $\dfrac{-2}{y + 3} > 2$

23. $\dfrac{x^2 + 6}{5x} \geq 1$

24. $\dfrac{y^2 + 15}{8y} \leq 1$

25. $\dfrac{x + 2}{x - 3} < 1$

26. $\dfrac{x - 1}{x + 4} > 2$

MIXED PRACTICE

Solve each inequality. Write the solution set in interval notation.

27. $(2x - 3)(4x + 5) \leq 0$

28. $(6x + 7)(7x - 12) > 0$

29. $x^2 > x$

30. $x^2 < 25$

31. $(2x - 8)(x + 4)(x - 6) \leq 0$

32. $(3x - 12)(x + 5)(2x - 3) \geq 0$

33. $6x^2 - 5x \geq 6$

34. $12x^2 + 11x \leq 15$

35. $4x^3 + 16x^2 - 9x - 36 > 0$

36. $x^3 + 2x^2 - 4x - 8 < 0$

37. $x^4 - 26x^2 + 25 \geq 0$

38. $16x^4 - 40x^2 + 9 \leq 0$

39. $(2x - 7)(3x + 5) > 0$

40. $(4x - 9)(2x + 5) < 0$

41. $\dfrac{x}{x - 10} < 0$

42. $\dfrac{x + 10}{x - 10} > 0$

43. $\dfrac{x - 5}{x + 4} \geq 0$

44. $\dfrac{x - 3}{x + 2} \leq 0$

45. $\dfrac{x(x + 6)}{(x - 7)(x + 1)} \geq 0$

46. $\dfrac{(x - 2)(x + 2)}{(x + 1)(x - 4)} \leq 0$

47. $\dfrac{-1}{x - 1} > -1$

48. $\dfrac{4}{y + 2} < -2$

49. $\dfrac{x}{x + 4} \leq 2$

50. $\dfrac{4x}{x - 3} \geq 5$

51. $\dfrac{z}{z - 5} \geq 2z$

52. $\dfrac{p}{p + 4} \leq 3p$

53. $\dfrac{(x + 1)^2}{5x} > 0$

54. $\dfrac{(2x - 3)^2}{x} < 0$

REVIEW AND PREVIEW

Recall that the graph of $f(x) + K$ is the same as the graph of $f(x)$ shifted K units upward if $K > 0$ and $|K|$ units downward if $K < 0$. Use the graph of $f(x) = |x|$ below to sketch the graph of each function. See Section 8.3.

55. $g(x) = |x| + 2$

56. $H(x) = |x| - 2$

57. $f(x) = |x| - 1$

58. $h(x) = |x| + 5$

Use the graph of $f(x) = x^2$ below to sketch the graph of each function.

59. $F(x) = x^2 - 3$

60. $h(x) = x^2 - 4$

61. $H(x) = x^2 + 1$

62. $g(x) = x^2 + 3$

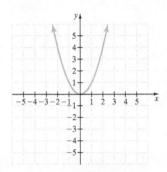

CONCEPT EXTENSIONS

63. Explain why $\dfrac{x + 2}{x - 3} > 0$ and $(x + 2)(x - 3) > 0$ have the same solutions.

64. Explain why $\dfrac{x + 2}{x - 3} \geq 0$ and $(x + 2)(x - 3) \geq 0$ do not have the same solutions.

Find all numbers that satisfy each of the following.

65. A number minus its reciprocal is less than zero. Find the numbers.

66. Twice a number added to its reciprocal is nonnegative. Find the numbers.

67. The total profit function $P(x)$ for a company producing x thousand units is given by

$$P(x) = -2x^2 + 26x - 44$$

Find the values of x for which the company makes a profit. [*Hint:* The company makes a profit when $P(x) > 0$.]

68. A projectile is fired straight up from the ground with an initial velocity of 80 feet per second. Its height $s(t)$ in feet at any time t is given by the function

$$s(t) = -16t^2 + 80t$$

Find the interval of time for which the height of the projectile is greater than 96 feet.

Use a graphing calculator to check each exercise.

69. Exercise 37

70. Exercise 38

71. Exercise 39

72. Exercise 40

11.5 Quadratic Functions and Their Graphs

OBJECTIVES

1 Graph Quadratic Functions of the Form $f(x) = x^2 + k$.

2 Graph Quadratic Functions of the Form $f(x) = (x - h)^2$.

3 Graph Quadratic Functions of the Form $f(x) = (x - h)^2 + k$.

4 Graph Quadratic Functions of the Form $f(x) = ax^2$.

5 Graph Quadratic Functions of the Form $f(x) = a(x - h)^2 + k$.

OBJECTIVE

1 Graphing $f(x) = x^2 + k$

We first graphed the quadratic equation $y = x^2$ in Section 8.2. In Sections 8.2 and 8.3, we learned that this graph defines a function, and we wrote $y = x^2$ as $f(x) = x^2$. In these sections, we discovered that the graph of a quadratic function is a parabola opening upward or downward. In this section, we continue our study of quadratic functions and their graphs. (Much of the contents of this section is a review of shifting and reflecting techniques from Section 8.3, but specific to quadratic functions.)

First, let's recall the definition of a quadratic function.

Quadratic Function

A quadratic function is a function that can be written in the form $f(x) = ax^2 + bx + c$, where a, b, and c are real numbers and $a \neq 0$.

Notice that equations of the form $y = ax^2 + bx + c$, where $a \neq 0$, define quadratic functions, since y is a function of x or $y = f(x)$.

Recall that if $a > 0$, the parabola opens upward and if $a < 0$, the parabola opens downward. Also, the vertex of a parabola is the lowest point if the parabola opens upward and the highest point if the parabola opens downward. The axis of symmetry is the vertical line that passes through the vertex.

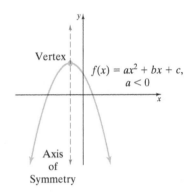

EXAMPLE 1 Graph $f(x) = x^2$ and $g(x) = x^2 + 6$ on the same set of axes.

Solution First we construct a table of values for $f(x)$ and plot the points. Notice that for each x-value, the corresponding value of $g(x)$ must be 6 more than the corresponding value of $f(x)$ since $f(x) = x^2$ and $g(x) = x^2 + 6$. In other words, the graph of $g(x) = x^2 + 6$ is the same as the graph of $f(x) = x^2$ shifted upward 6 units. The axis of symmetry for both graphs is the y-axis.

x	$f(x) = x^2$	$g(x) = x^2 + 6$
-2	4	10
-1	1	7
0	0	6
1	1	7
2	4	10

Each y-value is increased by 6.

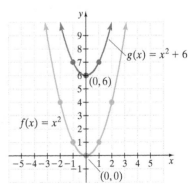

PRACTICE

1 Graph $f(x) = x^2$ and $g(x) = x^2 - 4$ on the same set of axes.

In general, we have the following properties.

Graphing the Parabola Defined by $f(x) = x^2 + k$

If k is positive, the graph of $f(x) = x^2 + k$ is the graph of $y = x^2$ shifted upward k units.
If k is negative, the graph of $f(x) = x^2 + k$ is the graph of $y = x^2$ shifted downward $|k|$ units.
The vertex is $(0, k)$, and the axis of symmetry is the y-axis.

EXAMPLE 2   Graph each function.

a. $F(x) = x^2 + 2$
b. $g(x) = x^2 - 3$

Solution

a. $F(x) = x^2 + 2$

The graph of $F(x) = x^2 + 2$ is obtained by shifting the graph of $y = x^2$ upward 2 units.

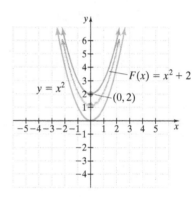

b. $g(x) = x^2 - 3$

The graph of $g(x) = x^2 - 3$ is obtained by shifting the graph of $y = x^2$ downward 3 units.

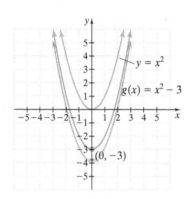

PRACTICE

2   Graph each function.

a. $f(x) = x^2 - 5$
b. $g(x) = x^2 + 3$

OBJECTIVE

2   Graphing $f(x) = (x - h)^2$

Now we will graph functions of the form $f(x) = (x - h)^2$.

EXAMPLE 3 Graph $f(x) = x^2$ and $g(x) = (x - 2)^2$ on the same set of axes.

Solution By plotting points, we see that for each x-value, the corresponding value of $g(x)$ is the same as the value of $f(x)$ when the x-value is increased by 2. Thus, the graph of $g(x) = (x - 2)^2$ is the graph of $f(x) = x^2$ shifted to the right 2 units. The axis of symmetry for the graph of $g(x) = (x - 2)^2$ is also shifted 2 units to the right and is the line $x = 2$.

x	$f(x) = x^2$	x	$g(x) = (x - 2)^2$
-2	4	0	4
-1	1	1	1
0	0	2	0
1	1	3	1
2	4	4	4

Each x-value increased by 2 corresponds to same y-value.

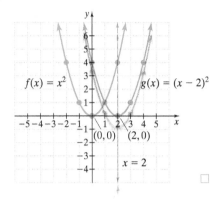

PRACTICE

3 Graph $f(x) = x^2$ and $g(x) = (x + 6)^2$ on the same set of axes.

In general, we have the following properties.

Graphing the Parabola Defined by $f(x) = (x - h)^2$

If h is positive, the graph of $f(x) = (x - h)^2$ is the graph of $y = x^2$ shifted to the right h units.
If h is negative, the graph of $f(x) = (x - h)^2$ is the graph of $y = x^2$ shifted to the left $|h|$ units.
The vertex is $(h, 0)$, and the axis of symmetry is the vertical line $x = h$.

EXAMPLE 4 Graph each function.

a. $G(x) = (x - 3)^2$ **b.** $F(x) = (x + 1)^2$

Solution

a. The graph of $G(x) = (x - 3)^2$ is obtained by shifting the graph of $y = x^2$ to the right 3 units. The graph of $G(x)$ is below on the left.

b. The equation $F(x) = (x + 1)^2$ can be written as $F(x) = [x - (-1)]^2$. The graph of $F(x) = [x - (-1)]^2$ is obtained by shifting the graph of $y = x^2$ to the left 1 unit. The graph of $F(x)$ is below on the right.

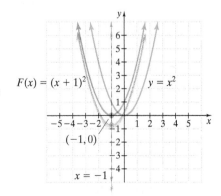

(Continued on next page)

PRACTICE

4   Graph each function.

a. $G(x) = (x + 4)^2$ **b.** $H(x) = (x - 7)^2$

OBJECTIVE

3   Graphing $f(x) = (x - h)^2 + k$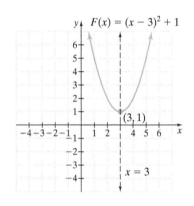

As we will see in graphing functions of the form $f(x) = (x - h)^2 + k$, it is possible to combine vertical and horizontal shifts.

> **Graphing the Parabola Defined by $f(x) = (x - h)^2 + k$**
>
> The parabola has the same shape as $y = x^2$.
> The vertex is (h, k), and the axis of symmetry is the vertical line $x = h$.

EXAMPLE 5   Graph $F(x) = (x - 3)^2 + 1$.

Solution   The graph of $F(x) = (x - 3)^2 + 1$ is the graph of $y = x^2$ shifted 3 units to the right and 1 unit up. The vertex is then $(3, 1)$, and the axis of symmetry is $x = 3$. A few ordered pair solutions are plotted to aid in graphing.

x	$F(x) = (x - 3)^2 + 1$
1	5
2	2
4	2
5	5

PRACTICE

5   Graph $f(x) = (x + 2)^2 + 2$.

OBJECTIVE

4   Graphing $f(x) = ax^2$

Next, we discover the change in the shape of the graph when the coefficient of x^2 is not 1.

EXAMPLE 6   Graph $f(x) = x^2$, $g(x) = 3x^2$, and $h(x) = \dfrac{1}{2}x^2$ on the same set of axes.

Solution   Comparing the tables of values, we see that for each x-value, the corresponding value of $g(x)$ is triple the corresponding value of $f(x)$. Similarly, the value of $h(x)$ is half the value of $f(x)$.

x	$f(x) = x^2$
-2	4
-1	1
0	0
1	1
2	4

x	$g(x) = 3x^2$
-2	12
-1	3
0	0
1	3
2	12

x	$h(x) = \dfrac{1}{2}x^2$
-2	2
-1	$\dfrac{1}{2}$
0	0
1	$\dfrac{1}{2}$
2	2

Graphing Calculator Explorations

Use a graphing calculator to graph the first function of each pair that follows. Then use its graph to predict the graph of the second function. Check your prediction by graphing both on the same set of axes.

1. $F(x) = \sqrt{x}; G(x) = \sqrt{x} + 1$

2. $g(x) = x^3; H(x) = x^3 - 2$

3. $H(x) = |x|; f(x) = |x - 5|$

4. $h(x) = x^3 + 2; g(x) = (x - 3)^3 + 2$

5. $f(x) = |x + 4|; F(x) = |x + 4| + 3$

6. $G(x) = \sqrt{x} - 2; g(x) = \sqrt{x - 4} - 2$

Vocabulary, Readiness & Video Check

Use the choices below to fill in each blank. Some choices will be used more than once.

upward   highest   parabola   downward   lowest   quadratic

1. A(n) _____ function is one that can be written in the form $f(x) = ax^2 + bx + c, a \neq 0$.

2. The graph of a quadratic function is a(n) _____ opening _____ or _____ .

3. If $a > 0$, the graph of the quadratic function opens _____ .

4. If $a < 0$, the graph of the quadratic function opens _____ .

5. The vertex of a parabola is the _____ point if $a > 0$.

6. The vertex of a parabola is the _____ point if $a < 0$.

State the vertex of the graph of each quadratic function.

7. $f(x) = x^2$ **8.** $f(x) = -5x^2$ **9.** $g(x) = (x - 2)^2$ **10.** $g(x) = (x + 5)^2$

11. $f(x) = 2x^2 + 3$ **12.** $h(x) = x^2 - 1$ **13.** $g(x) = (x + 1)^2 + 5$ **14.** $h(x) = (x - 10)^2 - 7$

Martin-Gay Interactive Videos

See Video 11.5

Watch the section lecture video and answer the following questions.

OBJECTIVE 1

15. From Examples 1 and 2 and the lecture before, how do graphs of the form $f(x) = x^2 + k$ differ from $y = x^2$? Consider the location of the vertex $(0, k)$ on these graphs of the form $f(x) = x^2 + k$—by what other name do we call this point on a graph?

OBJECTIVE 2

16. From Example 3 and the lecture before, how do graphs of the form $f(x) = (x - h)^2$ differ from $y = x^2$? Consider the location of the vertex $(h, 0)$ on these graphs of the form $f(x) = (x - h)^2$—by what other name do we call this point on a graph?

OBJECTIVE 3

17. From Example 4 and the lecture before, what general information does the equation $f(x) = (x - h)^2 + k$ tell us about its graph?

OBJECTIVE 4

18. From the lecture before Example 5, besides the direction a parabola opens, what other graphing information can the value of a tell us?

OBJECTIVE 5

19. In Examples 6 and 7, what four properties of the graph did we learn from the equation that helped us locate and draw the general shape of the parabola?

11.5 Exercise Set MyMathLab®

MIXED PRACTICE

Sketch the graph of each quadratic function. Label the vertex and sketch and label the axis of symmetry. See Examples 1 through 5.

1. $f(x) = x^2 - 1$
2. $g(x) = x^2 + 3$
3. $h(x) = x^2 + 5$
4. $h(x) = x^2 - 4$
5. $g(x) = x^2 + 7$
6. $f(x) = x^2 - 2$
7. $f(x) = (x - 5)^2$
8. $g(x) = (x + 5)^2$
9. $h(x) = (x + 2)^2$
10. $H(x) = (x - 1)^2$
11. $G(x) = (x + 3)^2$
12. $f(x) = (x - 6)^2$
13. $f(x) = (x - 2)^2 + 5$
14. $g(x) = (x - 6)^2 + 1$
15. $h(x) = (x + 1)^2 + 4$
16. $G(x) = (x + 3)^2 + 3$
17. $g(x) = (x + 2)^2 - 5$
18. $h(x) = (x + 4)^2 - 6$

Sketch the graph of each quadratic function. Label the vertex, and sketch and label the axis of symmetry. See Examples 6 and 7.

19. $H(x) = 2x^2$
20. $f(x) = 5x^2$
21. $h(x) = \frac{1}{3}x^2$
22. $f(x) = -\frac{1}{4}x^2$
23. $g(x) = -x^2$
24. $g(x) = -3x^2$

Sketch the graph of each quadratic function. Label the vertex and sketch and label the axis of symmetry. See Example 8.

25. $f(x) = 2(x - 1)^2 + 3$
26. $g(x) = 4(x - 4)^2 + 2$
27. $h(x) = -3(x + 3)^2 + 1$
28. $f(x) = -(x - 2)^2 - 6$
29. $H(x) = \frac{1}{2}(x - 6)^2 - 3$
30. $G(x) = \frac{1}{5}(x + 4)^2 + 3$

MIXED PRACTICE

Sketch the graph of each quadratic function. Label the vertex and sketch and label the axis of symmetry.

31. $f(x) = -(x - 2)^2$
32. $g(x) = -(x + 6)^2$
33. $F(x) = -x^2 + 4$
34. $H(x) = -x^2 + 10$
35. $F(x) = 2x^2 - 5$
36. $g(x) = \frac{1}{2}x^2 - 2$
37. $h(x) = (x - 6)^2 + 4$
38. $f(x) = (x - 5)^2 + 2$
39. $F(x) = \left(x + \frac{1}{2}\right)^2 - 2$
40. $H(x) = \left(x + \frac{1}{2}\right)^2 - 3$
41. $F(x) = \frac{3}{2}(x + 7)^2 + 1$
42. $g(x) = -\frac{3}{2}(x - 1)^2 - 5$
43. $f(x) = \frac{1}{4}x^2 - 9$
44. $H(x) = \frac{3}{4}x^2 - 2$
45. $G(x) = 5\left(x + \frac{1}{2}\right)^2$
46. $F(x) = 3\left(x - \frac{3}{2}\right)^2$
47. $h(x) = -(x - 1)^2 - 1$
48. $f(x) = -3(x + 2)^2 + 2$
49. $g(x) = \sqrt{3}(x + 5)^2 + \frac{3}{4}$
50. $G(x) = \sqrt{5}(x - 7)^2 - \frac{1}{2}$

51. $h(x) = 10(x + 4)^2 - 6$
52. $h(x) = 8(x + 1)^2 + 9$
53. $f(x) = -2(x - 4)^2 + 5$
54. $G(x) = -4(x + 9)^2 - 1$

REVIEW AND PREVIEW

Add the proper constant to each binomial so that the resulting trinomial is a perfect square trinomial. See Section 11.1.

55. $x^2 + 8x$
56. $y^2 + 4y$
57. $z^2 - 16z$
58. $x^2 - 10x$
59. $y^2 + y$
60. $z^2 - 3z$

Solve by completing the square. See Section 11.1.

61. $x^2 + 4x = 12$
62. $y^2 + 6y = -5$
63. $z^2 + 10z - 1 = 0$
64. $x^2 + 14x + 20 = 0$
65. $z^2 - 8z = 2$
66. $y^2 - 10y = 3$

CONCEPT EXTENSIONS

Solve. See the Concept Check in this section.

67. Which description of $f(x) = -213(x - 0.1)^2 + 3.6$ is correct?

Graph Opens	Vertex
a. upward	$(0.1, 3.6)$
b. upward	$(-213, 3.6)$
c. downward	$(0.1, 3.6)$
d. downward	$(-0.1, 3.6)$

68. Which description of $f(x) = 5\left(x + \frac{1}{2}\right)^2 + \frac{1}{2}$ is correct?

Graph Opens	Vertex
a. upward	$\left(\frac{1}{2}, \frac{1}{2}\right)$
b. upward	$\left(-\frac{1}{2}, \frac{1}{2}\right)$
c. downward	$\left(\frac{1}{2}, -\frac{1}{2}\right)$
d. downward	$\left(-\frac{1}{2}, -\frac{1}{2}\right)$

Write the equation of the parabola that has the same shape as $f(x) = 5x^2$ but with the following vertex.

69. $(2, 3)$
70. $(1, 6)$
71. $(-3, 6)$
72. $(4, -1)$

The shifting properties covered in this section apply to the graphs of all functions. Given the graph of $y = f(x)$ below, sketch the graph of each of the following.

73. $y = f(x) + 1$

74. $y = f(x) - 2$

75. $y = f(x - 3)$

76. $y = f(x + 3)$

77. $y = f(x + 2) + 2$

78. $y = f(x - 1) + 1$

79. The quadratic function $f(x) = 2158x^2 - 10{,}339x + 6731$ approximates the number of text messages sent in the United States each month between 2000 and 2008, where x is the number of years past 2000 and $f(x)$ is the number of text messages sent in the U.S. each month in millions. (*Source:* cellsigns)

  a. Use this function to find the number of text messages sent in the U.S. each month in 2010.

  b. Use this function to predict the number of text messages sent in the U.S. each month in 2014.

80. Use the function in Exercise 79.

  a. Use this function to predict the number of text messages sent in the U.S. each month in 2018.

  b. Look up the current number of cell phone subscribers in the U.S.

  c. Based on your answers for parts **a.** and **b.**, discuss some possible limitations of using this quadratic function to predict data.

11.6   Further Graphing of Quadratic Functions

OBJECTIVES

1 Write Quadratic Functions in the Form $y = a(x - h)^2 + k$.

2 Derive a Formula for Finding the Vertex of a Parabola.

3 Find the Minimum or Maximum Value of a Quadratic Function.

OBJECTIVE

1   **Writing Quadratic Functions in the Form** $y = a(x - h)^2 + k$

We know that the graph of a quadratic function is a parabola. If a quadratic function is written in the form

$$f(x) = a(x - h)^2 + k$$

we can easily find the vertex (h, k) and graph the parabola. To write a quadratic function in this form, complete the square. (See Section 11.1 for a review of completing the square.)

EXAMPLE 1   Graph $f(x) = x^2 - 4x - 12$. Find the vertex and any intercepts.

Solution   The graph of this quadratic function is a parabola. To find the vertex of the parabola, we will write the function in the form $y = (x - h)^2 + k$. To do this, we complete the square on the binomial $x^2 - 4x$. To simplify our work, we let $f(x) = y$.

$$y = x^2 - 4x - 12 \quad \text{Let } f(x) = y.$$
$$y + 12 = x^2 - 4x \qquad \text{Add 12 to both sides to get the } x\text{-variable terms alone.}$$

Now we add the square of half of -4 to both sides.

$$\frac{1}{2}(-4) = -2 \quad \text{and} \quad (-2)^2 = 4$$

$$y + 12 + 4 = x^2 - 4x + 4 \qquad \text{Add 4 to both sides.}$$
$$y + 16 = (x - 2)^2 \qquad \text{Factor the trinomial.}$$
$$y = (x - 2)^2 - 16 \quad \text{Subtract 16 from both sides.}$$
$$f(x) = (x - 2)^2 - 16 \quad \text{Replace } y \text{ with } f(x).$$

From this equation, we can see that the vertex of the parabola is $(2, -16)$, a point in quadrant IV, and the axis of symmetry is the line $x = 2$.

Notice that $a = 1$. Since $a > 0$, the parabola opens upward. This parabola opening upward with vertex $(2, -16)$ will have two x-intercepts and one y-intercept. (See the Helpful Hint after this example.)

(Continued on next page)

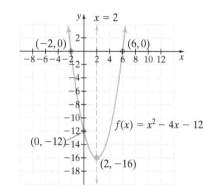

x-intercepts: let y or $f(x) = 0$

$$f(x) = x^2 - 4x - 12$$
$$0 = x^2 - 4x - 12$$
$$0 = (x - 6)(x + 2)$$
$$0 = x - 6 \quad \text{or} \quad 0 = x + 2$$
$$6 = x \qquad\qquad -2 = x$$

y-intercept: let $x = 0$

$$f(x) = x^2 - 4x - 12$$
$$f(0) = 0^2 - 4 \cdot 0 - 12$$
$$= -12$$

The two x-intercepts are $(6, 0)$ and $(-2, 0)$. The y-intercept is $(0, -12)$. The sketch of $f(x) = x^2 - 4x - 12$ is shown.

Notice that the axis of symmetry is always halfway between the x-intercepts. For this example, halfway between -2 and 6 is $\dfrac{-2 + 6}{2} = 2$, and the axis of symmetry is $x = 2$.

PRACTICE
1 Graph $g(x) = x^2 - 2x - 3$. Find the vertex and any intercepts.

▶ Helpful Hint

Parabola Opens Upward
Vertex in I or II: no x-intercept
Vertex in III or IV: 2 x-intercepts

Parabola Opens Downward
Vertex in I or II: 2 x-intercepts
Vertex in III or IV: no x-intercept.

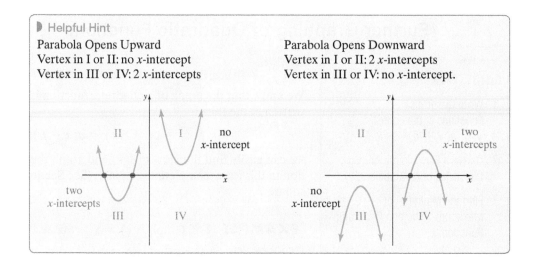

EXAMPLE 2 Graph $f(x) = 3x^2 + 3x + 1$. Find the vertex and any intercepts.

Solution Replace $f(x)$ with y and complete the square on x to write the equation in the form $y = a(x - h)^2 + k$.

$$y = 3x^2 + 3x + 1 \qquad \text{Replace } f(x) \text{ with } y.$$
$$y - 1 = 3x^2 + 3x \qquad \text{Isolate } x\text{-variable terms.}$$

Factor 3 from the terms $3x^2 + 3x$ so that the coefficient of x^2 is 1.

$$y - 1 = 3(x^2 + x) \qquad \text{Factor out 3.}$$

The coefficient of x in the parentheses above is 1. Then $\dfrac{1}{2}(1) = \dfrac{1}{2}$ and $\left(\dfrac{1}{2}\right)^2 = \dfrac{1}{4}$.

Since we are adding $\dfrac{1}{4}$ inside the parentheses, we are really adding $3\left(\dfrac{1}{4}\right)$, so we *must* add $3\left(\dfrac{1}{4}\right)$ to the left side.

$$y - 1 + 3\left(\frac{1}{4}\right) = 3\left(x^2 + x + \frac{1}{4}\right)$$

$$y - \frac{1}{4} = 3\left(x + \frac{1}{2}\right)^2 \qquad \text{Simplify the left side and factor the right side.}$$

$$y = 3\left(x + \frac{1}{2}\right)^2 + \frac{1}{4} \qquad \text{Add } \frac{1}{4} \text{ to both sides.}$$

$$f(x) = 3\left(x + \frac{1}{2}\right)^2 + \frac{1}{4} \qquad \text{Replace } y \text{ with } f(x).$$

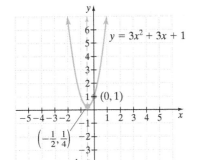

Then $a = 3, h = -\frac{1}{2}$, and $k = \frac{1}{4}$. This means that the parabola opens upward with vertex $\left(-\frac{1}{2}, \frac{1}{4}\right)$ and that the axis of symmetry is the line $x = -\frac{1}{2}$.

To find the y-intercept, let $x = 0$. Then

$$f(0) = 3(0)^2 + 3(0) + 1 = 1$$

Thus the y-intercept is $(0, 1)$.

This parabola has no x-intercepts since the vertex is in the second quadrant and the parabola opens upward. Use the vertex, axis of symmetry, and y-intercept to sketch the parabola.   ☐

PRACTICE

2   Graph $g(x) = 4x^2 + 4x + 3$. Find the vertex and any intercepts.

EXAMPLE 3   Graph $f(x) = -x^2 - 2x + 3$. Find the vertex and any intercepts.

Solution   We write $f(x)$ in the form $a(x - h)^2 + k$ by completing the square. First we replace $f(x)$ with y.

$$f(x) = -x^2 - 2x + 3$$

$$y = -x^2 - 2x + 3$$

$$y - 3 = -x^2 - 2x \qquad \text{Subtract 3 from both sides to get the } x\text{-variable terms alone.}$$

$$y - 3 = -1(x^2 + 2x) \qquad \text{Factor } -1 \text{ from the terms } -x^2 - 2x.$$

The coefficient of x is 2. Then $\frac{1}{2}(2) = 1$ and $1^2 = 1$. We add 1 to the right side inside the parentheses and add $-1(1)$ to the left side.

$$y - 3 - 1(1) = -1(x^2 + 2x + 1)$$

$$y - 4 = -1(x + 1)^2 \qquad \text{Simplify the left side and factor the right side.}$$

$$y = -1(x + 1)^2 + 4 \qquad \text{Add 4 to both sides.}$$

$$f(x) = -1(x + 1)^2 + 4 \qquad \text{Replace } y \text{ with } f(x).$$

▶ **Helpful Hint**
This can be written as
$f(x) = -1[x - (-1)]^2 + 4$.
Notice that the vertex is $(-1, 4)$.

Since $a = -1$, the parabola opens downward with vertex $(-1, 4)$ and axis of symmetry $x = -1$.

To find the y-intercept, we let $x = 0$ and solve for y. Then

$$f(0) = -0^2 - 2(0) + 3 = 3$$

Thus, $(0, 3)$ is the y-intercept.

To find the x-intercepts, we let y or $f(x) = 0$ and solve for x.

$$f(x) = -x^2 - 2x + 3$$

$$0 = -x^2 - 2x + 3 \qquad \text{Let } f(x) = 0.$$

(Continued on next page)

$$f(x) = -x^2 - 2x + 3$$

$$x = -1$$

Now we divide both sides by -1 so that the coefficient of x^2 is 1.

$$\frac{0}{-1} = \frac{-x^2}{-1} - \frac{2x}{-1} + \frac{3}{-1} \qquad \text{Divide both sides by } -1.$$

$$0 = x^2 + 2x - 3 \qquad \text{Simplify.}$$

$$0 = (x + 3)(x - 1) \qquad \text{Factor.}$$

$$x + 3 = 0 \quad \text{or} \quad x - 1 = 0 \qquad \text{Set each factor equal to 0.}$$

$$x = -3 \qquad\qquad x = 1 \qquad \text{Solve.}$$

The x-intercepts are $(-3, 0)$ and $(1, 0)$. Use these points to sketch the parabola.

PRACTICE

3   Graph $g(x) = -x^2 + 5x + 6$. Find the vertex and any intercepts.

OBJECTIVE

2   Deriving a Formula for Finding the Vertex

There is also a formula that may be used to find the vertex of a parabola. Now that we have practiced completing the square, we will show that the x-coordinate of the vertex of the graph of $f(x)$ or $y = ax^2 + bx + c$ can be found by the formula $x = \dfrac{-b}{2a}$. To do so, we complete the square on x and write the equation in the form $y = a(x - h)^2 + k$.

First, isolate the x-variable terms by subtracting c from both sides.

$$y = ax^2 + bx + c$$

$$y - c = ax^2 + bx$$

Next, factor a from the terms $ax^2 + bx$.

$$y - c = a\left(x^2 + \frac{b}{a}x\right)$$

Next, add the square of half of $\dfrac{b}{a}$, or $\left(\dfrac{b}{2a}\right)^2 = \dfrac{b^2}{4a^2}$, to the right side inside the paren-theses. Because of the factor a, what we really added was $a\left(\dfrac{b^2}{4a^2}\right)$, and this must be added to the left side.

$$y - c + a\left(\frac{b^2}{4a^2}\right) = a\left(x^2 + \frac{b}{a}x + \frac{b^2}{4a^2}\right)$$

$$y - c + \frac{b^2}{4a} = a\left(x + \frac{b}{2a}\right)^2 \qquad \text{Simplify the left side and factor the right side.}$$

$$y = a\left(x + \frac{b}{2a}\right)^2 + c - \frac{b^2}{4a} \qquad \text{Add } c \text{ to both sides and subtract } \frac{b^2}{4a} \text{ from both sides.}$$

Compare this form with $f(x)$ or $y = a(x - h)^2 + k$ and see that h is $\dfrac{-b}{2a}$, which means that the x-coordinate of the vertex of the graph of $f(x) = ax^2 + bx + c$ is $\dfrac{-b}{2a}$.

Vertex Formula

The graph of $f(x) = ax^2 + bx + c$, when $a \neq 0$, is a parabola with vertex

$$\left(\frac{-b}{2a}, f\left(\frac{-b}{2a}\right)\right)$$

Let's use this formula to find the vertex of the parabola we graphed in Example 1.

EXAMPLE 4   Find the vertex of the graph of $f(x) = x^2 - 4x - 12$.

Solution   In the quadratic function $f(x) = x^2 - 4x - 12$, notice that $a = 1, b = -4$, and $c = -12$. Then

$$\frac{-b}{2a} = \frac{-(-4)}{2(1)} = 2$$

The x-value of the vertex is 2. To find the corresponding $f(x)$ or y-value, find $f(2)$. Then

$$f(2) = 2^2 - 4(2) - 12 = 4 - 8 - 12 = -16$$

The vertex is $(2, -16)$. These results agree with our findings in Example 1.   □

PRACTICE

4   Find the vertex of the graph of $g(x) = x^2 - 2x - 3$.

OBJECTIVE

3   **Finding Minimum and Maximum Values**

The vertex of a parabola gives us some important information about its corresponding quadratic function. The quadratic function whose graph is a parabola that opens upward has a minimum value, and the quadratic function whose graph is a parabola that opens downward has a maximum value. The $f(x)$ or y-value of the vertex is the minimum or maximum value of the function.

✓**CONCEPT CHECK**
Without making any calculations, tell whether the graph of $f(x) = 7 - x - 0.3x^2$ has a maximum value or a minimum value. Explain your reasoning.

EXAMPLE 5   **Finding Maximum Height**

A rock is thrown upward from the ground. Its height in feet above ground after t seconds is given by the function $f(t) = -16t^2 + 20t$. Find the maximum height of the rock and the number of seconds it took for the rock to reach its maximum height.

Solution

1. UNDERSTAND. The maximum height of the rock is the largest value of $f(t)$. Since the function $f(t) = -16t^2 + 20t$ is a quadratic function, its graph is a parabola. It opens downward since $-16 < 0$. Thus, the maximum value of $f(t)$ is the $f(t)$ or y-value of the vertex of its graph.

Answer to Concept Check:
$f(x)$ has a maximum value since it opens downward.

(Continued on next page)

2. TRANSLATE. To find the vertex (h, k), notice that for $f(t) = -16t^2 + 20t$, $a = -16, b = 20$, and $c = 0$. We will use these values and the vertex formula

$$\left(\frac{-b}{2a}, f\left(\frac{-b}{2a}\right)\right)$$

3. SOLVE.

$$h = \frac{-b}{2a} = \frac{-20}{-32} = \frac{5}{8}$$

$$f\left(\frac{5}{8}\right) = -16\left(\frac{5}{8}\right)^2 + 20\left(\frac{5}{8}\right)$$

$$= -16\left(\frac{25}{64}\right) + \frac{25}{2}$$

$$= -\frac{25}{4} + \frac{50}{4} = \frac{25}{4}$$

4. INTERPRET. The graph of $f(t)$ is a parabola opening downward with vertex $\left(\frac{5}{8}, \frac{25}{4}\right)$. This means that the rock's maximum height is $\frac{25}{4}$ feet, or $6\frac{1}{4}$ feet, which was reached in $\frac{5}{8}$ second. ☐

PRACTICE

5   A ball is tossed upward from the ground. Its height in feet above ground after t seconds is given by the function $h(t) = -16t^2 + 24t$. Find the maximum height of the ball and the number of seconds it took for the ball to reach the maximum height. ■

Vocabulary, Readiness & Video Check

Fill in each blank.

1. If a quadratic function is in the form $f(x) = a(x - h)^2 + k$, the vertex of its graph is _____.

2. The graph of $f(x) = ax^2 + bx + c, a \neq 0$, is a parabola whose vertex has x-value _____.

Martin-Gay Interactive Videos

See Video 11.6

Watch the section lecture video and answer the following questions.

OBJECTIVE
1   **3.** From ▣ Example 1, how does writing a quadratic function in the form $f(x) = a(x - h)^2 + k$ help us graph the function? What procedure can we use to write a quadratic function in this form?

OBJECTIVE
2   **4.** From ▣ Example 2, how can locating the vertex and knowing whether the parabola opens upward or downward potentially help save unnecessary work? Explain.

OBJECTIVE
3   **5.** From ▣ Example 4, when an application involving a quadratic function asks for the maximum or minimum, what part of a parabola should we find?

11.6   Exercise Set   MyMathLab®

Fill in each blank.

	Parabola Opens	Vertex Location	Number of x-intercept(s)	Number of y-intercept(s)
1.	up	Q I		
2.	up	Q III		
3.	down	Q II		
4.	down	Q IV		
5.	up	x-axis		
6.	down	x-axis		
7.		Q III	0	
8.		Q I	2	
9.		Q IV	2	
10.		Q II	0	

Find the vertex of the graph of each quadratic function. See Examples 1 through 4.

11. $f(x) = x^2 + 8x + 7$

12. $f(x) = x^2 + 6x + 5$

13. $f(x) = -x^2 + 10x + 5$

14. $f(x) = -x^2 - 8x + 2$

15. $f(x) = 5x^2 - 10x + 3$

16. $f(x) = -3x^2 + 6x + 4$

17. $f(x) = -x^2 + x + 1$

18. $f(x) = x^2 - 9x + 8$

Match each function with its graph. See Examples 1 through 4.

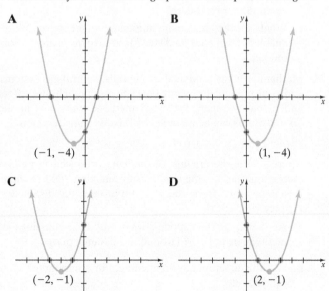

A   (−1, −4)

B   (1, −4)

C   (−2, −1)

D   (2, −1)

19. $f(x) = x^2 - 4x + 3$

20. $f(x) = x^2 + 2x - 3$

21. $f(x) = x^2 - 2x - 3$

22. $f(x) = x^2 + 4x + 3$

MIXED PRACTICE

Find the vertex of the graph of each quadratic function. Determine whether the graph opens upward or downward, find any intercepts, and sketch the graph. See Examples 1 through 4.

23. $f(x) = x^2 + 4x - 5$ **24.** $f(x) = x^2 + 2x - 3$

25. $f(x) = -x^2 + 2x - 1$ **26.** $f(x) = -x^2 + 4x - 4$

27. $f(x) = x^2 - 4$ **28.** $f(x) = x^2 - 1$

29. $f(x) = 4x^2 + 4x - 3$ **30.** $f(x) = 2x^2 - x - 3$

31. $f(x) = \dfrac{1}{2}x^2 + 4x + \dfrac{15}{2}$ **32.** $f(x) = \dfrac{1}{5}x^2 + 2x + \dfrac{9}{5}$

33. $f(x) = x^2 - 6x + 5$ **34.** $f(x) = x^2 - 4x + 3$

35. $f(x) = x^2 - 4x + 5$ **36.** $f(x) = x^2 - 6x + 11$

37. $f(x) = 2x^2 + 4x + 5$ **38.** $f(x) = 3x^2 + 12x + 16$

39. $f(x) = -2x^2 + 12x$ **40.** $f(x) = -4x^2 + 8x$

41. $f(x) = x^2 + 1$ **42.** $f(x) = x^2 + 4$

43. $f(x) = x^2 - 2x - 15$ **44.** $f(x) = x^2 - x - 12$

45. $f(x) = -5x^2 + 5x$ **46.** $f(x) = 3x^2 - 12x$

47. $f(x) = -x^2 + 2x - 12$ **48.** $f(x) = -x^2 + 8x - 17$

49. $f(x) = 3x^2 - 12x + 15$ **50.** $f(x) = 2x^2 - 8x + 11$

51. $f(x) = x^2 + x - 6$ **52.** $f(x) = x^2 + 3x - 18$

53. $f(x) = -2x^2 - 3x + 35$ **54.** $f(x) = 3x^2 - 13x - 10$

Solve. See Example 5.

55. If a projectile is fired straight upward from the ground with an initial speed of 96 feet per second, then its height h in feet after t seconds is given by the equation

$$h(t) = -16t^2 + 96t$$

Find the maximum height of the projectile.

56. If Rheam Gaspar throws a ball upward with an initial speed of 32 feet per second, then its height h in feet after t seconds is given by the equation

$$h(t) = -16t^2 + 32t$$

Find the maximum height of the ball.

57. The cost C in dollars of manufacturing x bicycles at Holladay's Production Plant is given by the function

$$C(x) = 2x^2 - 800x + 92,000.$$

a. Find the number of bicycles that must be manufactured to minimize the cost.

b. Find the minimum cost.

58. The Utah Ski Club sells calendars to raise money. The profit P, in cents, from selling x calendars is given by the equation $P(x) = 360x - x^2$.

a. Find how many calendars must be sold to maximize profit.

b. Find the maximum profit.

59. Find two numbers whose sum is 60 and whose product is as large as possible. [*Hint:* Let x and $60 - x$ be the two positive numbers. Their product can be described by the function $f(x) = x(60 - x)$.]

60. Find two numbers whose sum is 11 and whose product is as large as possible. (Use the hint for Exercise 59.)

61. Find two numbers whose difference is 10 and whose product is as small as possible. (Use the hint for Exercise 59.)

62. Find two numbers whose difference is 8 and whose product is as small as possible.

△ **63.** The length and width of a rectangle must have a sum of 40. Find the dimensions of the rectangle that will have the maximum area. (Use the hint for Exercise 59.)

△ **64.** The length and width of a rectangle must have a sum of 50. Find the dimensions of the rectangle that will have maximum area.

REVIEW AND PREVIEW

Sketch the graph of each function. See Section 11.5.

65. $f(x) = x^2 + 2$ **66.** $f(x) = (x - 3)^2$

67. $g(x) = x + 2$ **68.** $h(x) = x - 3$

69. $f(x) = (x + 5)^2 + 2$ **70.** $f(x) = 2(x - 3)^2 + 2$

71. $f(x) = 3(x - 4)^2 + 1$ **72.** $f(x) = (x + 1)^2 + 4$

73. $f(x) = -(x - 4)^2 + \frac{3}{2}$ **74.** $f(x) = -2(x + 7)^2 + \frac{1}{2}$

CONCEPT EXTENSIONS

Without calculating, tell whether each graph has a minimum value or a maximum value. See the Concept Check in the section.

75. $f(x) = 2x^2 - 5$

76. $g(x) = -7x^2 + x + 1$

77. $f(x) = 3 - \frac{1}{2}x^2$

78. $G(x) = 3 - \frac{1}{2}x + 0.8x^2$

Find the vertex of the graph of each quadratic function. Determine whether the graph opens upward or downward, find the y-intercept, approximate the x-intercepts to one decimal place, and sketch the graph.

79. $f(x) = x^2 + 10x + 15$ **80.** $f(x) = x^2 - 6x + 4$

81. $f(x) = 3x^2 - 6x + 7$ **82.** $f(x) = 2x^2 + 4x - 1$

Find the maximum or minimum value of each function. Approximate to two decimal places.

83. $f(x) = 2.3x^2 - 6.1x + 3.2$

84. $f(x) = 7.6x^2 + 9.8x - 2.1$

85. $f(x) = -1.9x^2 + 5.6x - 2.7$

86. $f(x) = -5.2x^2 - 3.8x + 5.1$

87. The projected number of Wi-Fi-enabled cell phones in the United States can be modeled by the quadratic function $c(x) = -0.4x^2 + 21x + 35$, where $c(x)$ is the projected number of Wi-Fi-enabled cell phones in millions and x is the number of years after 2009. (*Source:* Techcrunchies.com)

a. Will this function have a maximum or a minimum? How can you tell?

b. According to this model, in what year will the number of Wi-Fi-enabled cell phones in the United States be at its maximum or minimum?

c. What is the maximum/minimum number of Wi-Fi-enabled cell phones predicted? Round to the nearest whole million.

88. Methane is a gas produced by landfills, natural gas systems, and coal mining that contributes to the greenhouse effect and global warming. Projected methane emissions in the United States can be modeled by the quadratic function

$$f(x) = -0.072x^2 + 1.93x + 173.9$$

where $f(x)$ is the amount of methane produced in million metric tons and x is the number of years after 2000. (*Source:* Based on data from the U.S. Environmental Protection Agency, 2000–2020)

a. According to this model, what will U.S. emissions of methane be in 2018? (Round to 2 decimal places.)

b. Will this function have a maximum or a minimum? How can you tell?

c. In what year will methane emissions in the United States be at their maximum/minimum? Round to the nearest whole year.

d. What is the level of methane emissions for that year? (Use your rounded answer from part (c).) (Round this answer to 2 decimal places.)

Use a graphing calculator to check each exercise.

89. Exercise 37

90. Exercise 38

91. Exercise 47

92. Exercise 48

CHAPTER 12

Exponential and Logarithmic Functions

In this chapter, we discuss two closely related functions: exponential and logarithmic functions. These functions are vital to applications in economics, finance, engineering, the sciences, education, and other fields. Models of tumor growth and learning curves are two examples of the uses of exponential and logarithmic functions.

A compact fluorescent lamp (or light) (CFL) is a type of fluorescent light that is quickly gaining popularity for many reasons. Compared to an incandescent bulb, CFLs use less power and last between 8 and 15 times as long. Although a CFL has a higher price, the savings per bulb are substantial (possibly $30 per life of bulb). Many CFLs are now manufactured to replace an incandescent bulb and can fit into existing fixtures. It should be noted that since CFLs are a type of fluorescent light, they do contain a small amount of mercury.

Although we have no direct applications in this chapter, it should be noted that the light output of a CFL decays exponentially. By the end of their lives, they produce 70–80% of their original output, with the fastest losses occurring soon after the light is first used. Also, it should be noted that the response of the human eye to light is logarithmic.

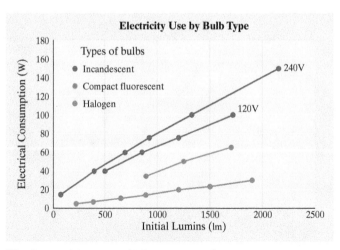

(*Note:* Lower points correspond to lower energy use.)

12.1 The Algebra of Functions; Composite Functions

OBJECTIVE

1 Adding, Subtracting, Multiplying, and Dividing Functions

As we have seen in earlier chapters, it is possible to add, subtract, multiply, and divide functions. Although we have not stated it as such, the sums, differences, products, and quotients of functions are themselves functions. For example, if $f(x) = 3x$ and $g(x) = x + 1$, their product, $f(x) \cdot g(x) = 3x(x + 1) = 3x^2 + 3x$, is a new function. We can use the notation $(f \cdot g)(x)$ to denote this new function. Finding the sum, difference, product, and quotient of functions to generate new functions is called the **algebra of functions.**

Algebra of Functions

Let f and g be functions. New functions from f and g are defined as follows.

Sum $(f + g)(x) = f(x) + g(x)$

Difference $(f - g)(x) = f(x) - g(x)$

Product $(f \cdot g)(x) = f(x) \cdot g(x)$

Quotient $\left(\dfrac{f}{g}\right)(x) = \dfrac{f(x)}{g(x)}, \quad g(x) \neq 0$

EXAMPLE 1 If $f(x) = x - 1$ and $g(x) = 2x - 3$, find

a. $(f + g)(x)$ **b.** $(f - g)(x)$ **c.** $(f \cdot g)(x)$ **d.** $\left(\dfrac{f}{g}\right)(x)$

Solution Use the algebra of functions and replace $f(x)$ by $x - 1$ and $g(x)$ by $2x - 3$. Then we simplify.

a. $(f + g)(x) = f(x) + g(x)$
$= (x - 1) + (2x - 3) = 3x - 4$

b. $(f - g)(x) = f(x) - g(x)$
$= (x - 1) - (2x - 3)$
$= x - 1 - 2x + 3$
$= -x + 2$

c. $(f \cdot g)(x) = f(x) \cdot g(x)$
$= (x - 1)(2x - 3)$
$= 2x^2 - 5x + 3$

d. $\left(\dfrac{f}{g}\right)(x) = \dfrac{f(x)}{g(x)} = \dfrac{x - 1}{2x - 3}$, where $x \neq \dfrac{3}{2}$

PRACTICE

1 If $f(x) = x + 2$ and $g(x) = 3x + 5$, find

a. $(f + g)(x)$ **b.** $(f - g)(x)$ **c.** $(f \cdot g)(x)$ **d.** $\left(\dfrac{f}{g}\right)(x)$

There is an interesting but not surprising relationship between the graphs of functions and the graphs of their sum, difference, product, and quotient. For example, the graph of $(f + g)(x)$ can be found by adding the graph of $f(x)$ to the graph of $g(x)$. We add two graphs by adding y-values of corresponding x-values.

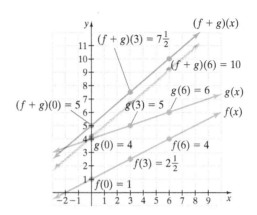

2 Constructing Composite Functions

Another way to combine functions is called **function composition.** To understand this new way of combining functions, study the diagrams below. The right diagram shows an illustration by tables, and the left diagram is the same illustration but by thermometers. In both illustrations, we show degrees Celsius $f(x)$ as a function of degrees Fahrenheit x, then Kelvins $g(x)$ as a function of degrees Celsius x. (The Kelvin scale is a temperature scale devised by Lord Kelvin in 1848.) The first function we will call f, and the second function we will call g.

Table Illustration

x = Degrees Fahrenheit (Input)	−13	32	68	212
$f(x)$ = Degrees Celsius (Output)	−25	0	20	100

x = Degrees Celsius (Input)	−25	0	20	100
$g(x)$ = Kelvins (Output)	248.15	273.15	293.15	373.15

Suppose that we want a function that shows a direct conversion from degrees Fahrenheit to Kelvins. In other words, suppose that a function is needed that shows Kelvins as a function of degrees Fahrenheit. This can easily be done because the output of the first function $f(x)$ is the same as the input of the second function. If we use $g(f(x))$ to represent this, then we get the diagrams below.

x = Degrees Fahrenheit (Input)	−13	32	68	212
$g(f(x))$ = Kelvins (Output)	248.15	273.15	293.15	373.15

For example $g(f(-13)) = 248.15$, and so on.

Since the output of the first function is used as the input of the second function, we write the new function as $g(f(x))$. The new function is formed from the composition of the other two functions. The mathematical symbol for this composition is $(g \circ f)(x)$. Thus, $(g \circ f)(x) = g(f(x))$.

It is possible to find an equation for the composition of the two functions f and g. In other words, we can find a function that converts degrees Fahrenheit directly to Kelvins. The function $f(x) = \dfrac{5}{9}(x - 32)$ converts degrees Fahrenheit to degrees Celsius, and the function $g(x) = x + 273.15$ converts degrees Celsius to Kelvins. Thus,

$$(g \circ f)(x) = g(f(x)) = g\left(\frac{5}{9}(x - 32)\right) = \frac{5}{9}(x - 32) + 273.15$$

In general, the notation $g(f(x))$ means "g composed with f" and can be written as $(g \circ f)(x)$. Also $f(g(x))$, or $(f \circ g)(x)$, means "f composed with g."

Composition of Functions

The composition of functions f and g is

$$(f \circ g)(x) = f(g(x))$$

▶ Helpful Hint

$(f \circ g)(x)$ does not mean the same as $(f \cdot g)(x)$.

$$(f \circ g)(x) = f(g(x)) \text{ while } (f \cdot g)(x) = f(x) \cdot g(x)$$

↑ Composition of functions   ↑ Multiplication of functions

EXAMPLE 2   If $f(x) = x^2$ and $g(x) = x + 3$, find each composition.

a. $(f \circ g)(2)$ and $(g \circ f)(2)$ **b.** $(f \circ g)(x)$ and $(g \circ f)(x)$

Solution

a. $(f \circ g)(2) = f(g(2))$

$\qquad\qquad = f(5)$ Replace $g(2)$ with 5. [Since $g(x) = x + 3$, then

$\qquad\qquad = 5^2 = 25$ $g(2) = 2 + 3 = 5$.]

$\quad (g \circ f)(2) = g(f(2))$

$\qquad\qquad = g(4)$ Since $f(x) = x^2$, then $f(2) = 2^2 = 4$.

$\qquad\qquad = 4 + 3 = 7$

b. $(f \circ g)(x) = f(g(x))$

$\qquad\qquad = f(x + 3)$ Replace $g(x)$ with $x + 3$.

$\qquad\qquad = (x + 3)^2$ $f(x + 3) = (x + 3)^2$

$\qquad\qquad = x^2 + 6x + 9$ Square $(x + 3)$.

$\quad (g \circ f)(x) = g(f(x))$

$\qquad\qquad = g(x^2)$ Replace $f(x)$ with x^2.

$\qquad\qquad = x^2 + 3$ $g(x^2) = x^2 + 3$

PRACTICE

2   If $f(x) = x^2 + 1$ and $g(x) = 3x - 5$, find

a. $(f \circ g)(4)$ **b.** $(f \circ g)(x)$

$\quad (g \circ f)(4)$ $\quad (g \circ f)(x)$

EXAMPLE 3   If $f(x) = |x|$ and $g(x) = x - 2$, find each composition.

a. $(f \circ g)(x)$ **b.** $(g \circ f)(x)$

Solution

a. $(f \circ g)(x) = f(g(x)) = f(x - 2) = |x - 2|$

b. $(g \circ f)(x) = g(f(x)) = g(|x|) = |x| - 2$

▶ Helpful Hint

In Examples 2 and 3, notice that $(g \circ f)(x) \neq (f \circ g)(x)$.   In general, $(g \circ f)(x)$ *may* or *may not* equal $(f \circ g)(x)$.

PRACTICE

3   If $f(x) = x^2 + 5$ and $g(x) = x + 3$, find each composition.

a. $(f \circ g)(x)$ **b.** $(g \circ f)(x)$

EXAMPLE 4 If $f(x) = 5x, g(x) = x - 2$, and $h(x) = \sqrt{x}$, write each function as a composition using two of the given functions.

a. $F(x) = \sqrt{x - 2}$ **b.** $G(x) = 5x - 2$

Solution

a. Notice the order in which the function F operates on an input value x. First, 2 is subtracted from x. This is the function $g(x) = x - 2$. Then the square root *of that result* is taken. The square root function is $h(x) = \sqrt{x}$. This means that $F = h \circ g$. To check, we find $h \circ g$.

$$F(x) = (h \circ g)(x) = h(g(x)) = h(x - 2) = \sqrt{x - 2}$$

b. Notice the order in which the function G operates on an input value x. First, x is multiplied by 5, and then 2 is subtracted from the result. This means that $G = g \circ f$. To check, we find $g \circ f$.

$$G(x) = (g \circ f)(x) = g(f(x)) = g(5x) = 5x - 2$$

PRACTICE

4 If $f(x) = 3x, g(x) = x - 4$, and $h(x) = |x|$, write each function as a composition using two of the given functions.

a. $F(x) = |x - 4|$ **b.** $G(x) = 3x - 4$

Graphing Calculator Explorations

$Y_3 = \frac{1}{3}x^2 + \frac{1}{2}x + 6$ $Y_2 = \frac{1}{3}x^2 + 4$

$Y_1 = \frac{1}{2}x + 2$

If $f(x) = \frac{1}{2}x + 2$ and $g(x) = \frac{1}{3}x^2 + 4$, then

$$(f + g)(x) = f(x) + g(x)$$

$$= \left(\frac{1}{2}x + 2\right) + \left(\frac{1}{3}x^2 + 4\right)$$

$$= \frac{1}{3}x^2 + \frac{1}{2}x + 6.$$

To visualize this addition of functions with a graphing calculator, graph

$$Y_1 = \frac{1}{2}x + 2, \qquad Y_2 = \frac{1}{3}x^2 + 4, \qquad Y_3 = \frac{1}{3}x^2 + \frac{1}{2}x + 6$$

Use a TABLE feature to verify that for a given x value, $Y_1 + Y_2 = Y_3$. For example, verify that when $x = 0$, $Y_1 = 2$, $Y_2 = 4$, and $Y_3 = 2 + 4 = 6$.

Vocabulary, Readiness & Video Check

Match each function with its definition.

1. $(f \circ g)(x)$ **4.** $(g \circ f)(x)$ **A.** $g(f(x))$ **D.** $\dfrac{f(x)}{g(x)}, g(x) \neq 0$

2. $(f \cdot g)(x)$ **5.** $\left(\dfrac{f}{g}\right)(x)$ **B.** $f(x) + g(x)$ **E.** $f(x) \cdot g(x)$

3. $(f - g)(x)$ **6.** $(f + g)(x)$ **C.** $f(g(x))$ **F.** $f(x) - g(x)$

Martin-Gay Interactive Videos

See Video 12.1

Watch the section lecture video and answer the following questions.

OBJECTIVE 1

7. From Example 1 and the lecture before, we know that $(f + g)(x) = f(x) + g(x)$. Use this fact to explain two ways you can find $(f + g)(2)$.

OBJECTIVE 2

8. From Example 3, given two functions $f(x)$ and $g(x)$, can $f(g(x))$ ever equal $g(f(x))$?

12.1 Exercise Set   MyMathLab®

For the functions f and g, find **a.** $(f + g)(x)$, **b.** $(f - g)(x)$, **c.** $(f \cdot g)(x)$, *and* **d.** $\left(\dfrac{f}{g}\right)(x)$. *See Example 1.*

1. $f(x) = x - 7, g(x) = 2x + 1$

2. $f(x) = x + 4, g(x) = 5x - 2$

3. $f(x) = x^2 + 1, g(x) = 5x$

4. $f(x) = x^2 - 2, g(x) = 3x$

5. $f(x) = \sqrt[3]{x}, g(x) = x + 5$

6. $f(x) = \sqrt[3]{x}, g(x) = x - 3$

7. $f(x) = -3x, g(x) = 5x^2$

8. $f(x) = 4x^3, g(x) = -6x$

If $f(x) = x^2 - 6x + 2, g(x) = -2x$, and $h(x) = \sqrt{x}$, find each composition. See Example 2.

9. $(f \circ g)(2)$

10. $(h \circ f)(-2)$

11. $(g \circ f)(-1)$

12. $(f \circ h)(1)$

13. $(g \circ h)(0)$

14. $(h \circ g)(0)$

Find $(f \circ g)(x)$ and $(g \circ f)(x)$. See Examples 2 and 3.

15. $f(x) = x^2 + 1, g(x) = 5x$

16. $f(x) = x - 3, g(x) = x^2$

17. $f(x) = 2x - 3, g(x) = x + 7$

18. $f(x) = x + 10, g(x) = 3x + 1$

19. $f(x) = x^3 + x - 2, g(x) = -2x$

20. $f(x) = -4x, g(x) = x^3 + x^2 - 6$

21. $f(x) = |x|; g(x) = 10x - 3$

22. $f(x) = |x|; g(x) = 14x - 8$

23. $f(x) = \sqrt{x}, g(x) = -5x + 2$

24. $f(x) = 7x - 1, g(x) = \sqrt[3]{x}$

If $f(x) = 3x, g(x) = \sqrt{x}$, and $h(x) = x^2 + 2$, write each function as a composition using two of the given functions. See Example 4.

25. $H(x) = \sqrt{x^2 + 2}$

26. $G(x) = \sqrt{3x}$

27. $F(x) = 9x^2 + 2$

28. $H(x) = 3x^2 + 6$

29. $G(x) = 3\sqrt{x}$

30. $F(x) = x + 2$

Find $f(x)$ and $g(x)$ so that the given function $h(x) = (f \circ g)(x)$.

31. $h(x) = (x + 2)^2$

32. $h(x) = |x - 1|$

33. $h(x) = \sqrt{x + 5} + 2$

34. $h(x) = (3x + 4)^2 + 3$

35. $h(x) = \dfrac{1}{2x - 3}$

36. $h(x) = \dfrac{1}{x + 10}$

REVIEW AND PREVIEW

Solve each equation for y. See Section 2.5.

37. $x = y + 2$

38. $x = y - 5$

39. $x = 3y$

40. $x = -6y$

41. $x = -2y - 7$

42. $x = 4y + 7$

CONCEPT EXTENSIONS

Given that $f(-1) = 4$ $g(-1) = -4$

$\qquad\qquad f(0) = 5$ $\quad g(0) = -3$

$\qquad\qquad f(2) = 7$ $\quad g(2) = -1$

$\qquad\qquad f(7) = 1$ $\quad g(7) = 4$

find each function value.

43. $(f + g)(2)$

44. $(f - g)(7)$

45. $(f \circ g)(2)$

46. $(g \circ f)(2)$

47. $(f \cdot g)(7)$

48. $(f \cdot g)(0)$

49. $\left(\dfrac{f}{g}\right)(-1)$

50. $\left(\dfrac{g}{f}\right)(-1)$

51. If you are given $f(x)$ and $g(x)$, explain in your own words how to find $(f \circ g)(x)$ and then how to find $(g \circ f)(x)$.

52. Given $f(x)$ and $g(x)$, describe in your own words the difference between $(f \circ g)(x)$ and $(f \cdot g)(x)$.

Solve.

53. Business people are concerned with cost functions, revenue functions, and profit functions. Recall that the profit $P(x)$ obtained from x units of a product is equal to the revenue $R(x)$ from selling the x units minus the cost $C(x)$ of manufacturing the x units. Write an equation expressing this relationship among $C(x)$, $R(x)$, and $P(x)$.

54. Suppose the revenue $R(x)$ for x units of a product can be described by $R(x) = 25x$, and the cost $C(x)$ can be described by $C(x) = 50 + x^2 + 4x$. Find the profit $P(x)$ for x units. (See Exercise 53.)

12.2 Inverse Functions

OBJECTIVES

1 Determine Whether a Function Is a One-to-One Function.

2 Use the Horizontal Line Test to Decide Whether a Function Is a One-to-One Function.

3 Find the Inverse of a Function.

4 Find the Equation of the Inverse of a Function.

5 Graph Functions and Their Inverses.

6 Determine Whether Two Functions Are Inverses of Each Other.

OBJECTIVE

1 Determining Whether a Function Is One-to-One

In the next three sections, we begin a study of two new functions: exponential and logarithmic functions. As we learn more about these functions, we will discover that they share a special relation to each other: They are inverses of each other.

Before we study these functions, we need to learn about inverses. We begin by defining one-to-one functions.

Study the following table.

Degrees Fahrenheit (Input)	-31	-13	32	68	149	212
Degrees Celsius (Output)	-35	-25	0	20	65	100

Recall that since each degrees Fahrenheit (input) corresponds to exactly one degrees Celsius (output), this pairing of inputs and outputs does describe a function. Also notice that each output corresponds to exactly one input. This type of function is given a special name—a one-to-one function.

Does the set $f = \{(0, 1), (2, 2), (-3, 5), (7, 6)\}$ describe a one-to-one function? It is a function since each x-value corresponds to a unique y-value. For this particular function f, each y-value also corresponds to a unique x-value. Thus, this function is also a **one-to-one function.**

> **One-to-One Function**
>
> For a **one-to-one function,** each x-value (input) corresponds to only one y-value (output), and each y-value (output) corresponds to only one x-value (input).

EXAMPLE 1 Determine whether each function described is one-to-one.

a. $f = \{(6,2),(5,4),(-1,0),(7,3)\}$

b. $g = \{(3,9),(-4,2),(-3,9),(0,0)\}$

c. $h = \{(1,1),(2,2),(10,10),(-5,-5)\}$

d.

Mineral (Input)	Talc	Gypsum	Diamond	Topaz	Stibnite
Hardness on the Mohs Scale (Output)	1	2	10	8	2

e.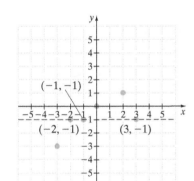

f.

Cities	Percent of Cell Phone Subscribers Who Text
El Paso (highest) ⟶	57
Buffalo ⟶	47
Austin ⟶	49
Tulsa ⟶	
Charleston ⟶	36
Detroit ⟶	45

Solution

a. f is one-to-one since each y-value corresponds to only one x-value.

b. g is not one-to-one because the y-value 9 in $(3, 9)$ and $(-3, 9)$ corresponds to different x-values.

c. h is a one-to-one function since each y-value corresponds to only one x-value.

d. This table does not describe a one-to-one function since the output 2 corresponds to two inputs, gypsum and stibnite.

e. This graph does not describe a one-to-one function since the y-value -1 corresponds to three x-values, -2, -1, and 3. (See the graph to the left.)

f. The mapping is not one-to-one since 49% corresponds to Austin and Tulsa. □

PRACTICE

1 Determine whether each function described is one-to-one.

a. $f = \{(4,-3),(3,-4),(2,7),(5,0)\}$

b. $g = \{(8,4),(-2,0),(6,4),(2,6)\}$

c. $h = \{(2,4),(1,3),(4,6),(-2,4)\}$

d.

Year	1950	1963	1968	1975	1997	2008
Federal Minimum Wage	$0.75	$1.25	$1.60	$2.10	$5.15	$6.55

e.

f.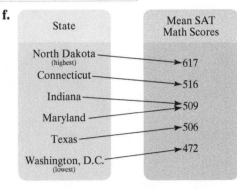

State	Mean SAT Math Scores
North Dakota (highest)	⟶ 617
Connecticut	⟶ 516
Indiana	⟶ 509
Maryland	⟶ 506
Texas	⟶ 472
Washington, D.C. (lowest)	

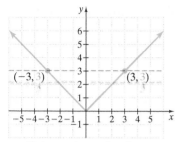

Not a one-to-one function.

OBJECTIVE
2   Using the Horizontal Line Test

Recall that we recognize the graph of a function when it passes the vertical line test. Since every *x*-value of the function corresponds to exactly one *y*-value, each vertical line intersects the function's graph at most once. The graph shown (left), for instance, is the graph of a function.

Is this function a *one-to-one* function? The answer is no. To see why not, notice that the *y*-value of the ordered pair $(-3, 3)$, for example, is the same as the *y*-value of the ordered pair $(3, 3)$. In other words, the *y*-value 3 corresponds to two *x*-values, -3 and 3. This function is therefore not one-to-one.

To test whether a graph is the graph of a one-to-one function, apply the vertical line test to see if it is a function and then apply a similar **horizontal line test** to see if it is a one-to-one function.

Horizontal Line Test

If every horizontal line intersects the graph of a function at most once, then the function is a one-to-one function.

EXAMPLE 2   Determine whether each graph is the graph of a one-to-one function.

a.

b.

c.

d.

e.

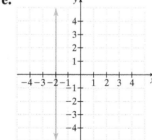

Solution   Graphs **a, b, c,** and **d** all pass the vertical line test, so only these graphs are graphs of functions. But, of these, only **b** and **c** pass the horizontal line test, so only **b** and **c** are graphs of one-to-one functions.

PRACTICE

2   Determine whether each graph is the graph of a one-to-one function.

a.

b.

c.

d.

e.

f

Input:
degrees
Fahrenheit

Output:
degrees
Celsius

212   100

68   20

32   0

−13   −25

f^{-1}

> **Helpful Hint**
> All linear equations are one-to-one func-
> tions except those whose graphs are hori-
> zontal or vertical lines. A vertical line does
> not pass the vertical line test and hence is
> not the graph of a function. A horizontal
> line is the graph of a function but does not
> pass the horizontal line test and hence is
> not the graph of a one-to-one function.

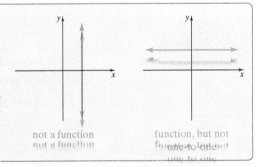

not a function   function, but not
                         one-to-one

OBJECTIVE

3   Finding the Inverse of a Function

One-to-one functions are special in that their graphs pass both the vertical and horizontal
line tests. They are special, too, in another sense: For each one-to-one function, we can
find its **inverse function** by switching the coordinates of the ordered pairs of the function,
or the inputs and the outputs. For example, the inverse of the one-to-one function

Degrees Fahrenheit (Input)	−31	−13	32	68	149	212
Degrees Celsius (Output)	−35	−25	0	20	65	100

is the function

Degrees Celsius (Input)	−35	−25	0	20	65	100
Degrees Fahrenheit (Output)	−31	−13	32	68	149	212

Notice that the ordered pair $(-31, -35)$ of the function, for example, becomes the ordered pair $(-35, -31)$ of its inverse.

Also, the inverse of the one-to-one function $f = \{(2, -3), (5, 10), (9, 1)\}$ is $\{(-3, 2), (10, 5), (1, 9)\}$. For a function f, we use the notation f^{-1}, read "f inverse," to denote its inverse function. Notice that since the coordinates of each ordered pair have been switched, the domain (set of inputs) of f is the range (set of outputs) of f^{-1}, and the range of f is the domain of f^{-1}.

Inverse Function

The inverse of a one-to-one function f is the one-to-one function f^{-1} that consists of the set of all ordered pairs (y, x) where (x, y) belongs to f.

▶ Helpful Hint

If a function is not one-to-one, it does not have an inverse function.

EXAMPLE 3 Find the inverse of the one-to-one function.

$$f = \{(0, 1), (-2, 7), (3, -6), (4, 4)\}$$

Solution $f^{-1} = \{(1, 0), (7, -2), (-6, 3), (4, 4)\}$

↑ ↑ ↑ ↑ Switch coordinates of each ordered pair. □

PRACTICE

3 Find the inverse of the one-to-one function.

$$f = \{(3, 4), (-2, 0), (2, 8), (6, 6)\}$$

▶ Helpful Hint

The symbol f^{-1} is the single symbol that denotes the inverse of the function f.

It is read as "f inverse." This symbol *does not mean* $\dfrac{1}{f}$.

✓**CONCEPT CHECK**

Suppose that f is a one-to-one function and that $f(1) = 5$.

a. Write the corresponding ordered pair.

b. Write one point that we know must belong to the inverse function f^{-1}.

OBJECTIVE

4 Finding the Equation of the Inverse of a Function

If a one-to-one function f is defined as a set of ordered pairs, we can find f^{-1} by interchanging the x- and y-coordinates of the ordered pairs. If a one-to-one function f is given in the form of an equation, we can find f^{-1} by using a similar procedure.

Answer to Concept Check:
a. $(1, 5)$, **b.** $(5, 1)$

Finding the Inverse of a One-to-One Function f(x)

Step 1.   Replace $f(x)$ with y.

Step 2.   Interchange x and y.

Step 3.   Solve the equation for y.

Step 4.   Replace y with the notation $f^{-1}(x)$.

EXAMPLE 4   Find an equation of the inverse of $f(x) = x + 3$.

Solution $f(x) = x + 3$

Step 1. $y = x + 3$ Replace $f(x)$ with y.

Step 2. $x = y + 3$ Interchange x and y.

Step 3. $x - 3 = y$ Solve for y.

Step 4. $f^{-1}(x) = x - 3$ Replace y with $f^{-1}(x)$.

The inverse of $f(x) = x + 3$ is $f^{-1}(x) = x - 3$. Notice that, for example,

$$f(1) = 1 + 3 = 4 \quad \text{and} \quad f^{-1}(4) = 4 - 3 = 1$$

Ordered pair: $(1, 4)$ Ordered pair: $(4, 1)$

The coordinates are switched, as expected.

PRACTICE
4   Find the equation of the inverse of $f(x) = 6 - x$.

EXAMPLE 5   Find the equation of the inverse of $f(x) = 3x - 5$. Graph f and f^{-1} on the same set of axes.

Solution $f(x) = 3x - 5$

Step 1. $y = 3x - 5$ Replace $f(x)$ with y.

Step 2. $x = 3y - 5$ Interchange x and y.

Step 3. $3y = x + 5$ Solve for y.

$$y = \frac{x + 5}{3}$$

Step 4. $f^{-1}(x) = \dfrac{x + 5}{3}$ Replace y with $f^{-1}(x)$.

Now we graph $f(x)$ and $f^{-1}(x)$ on the same set of axes. Both $f(x) = 3x - 5$ and $f^{-1}(x) = \dfrac{x + 5}{3}$ are linear functions, so each graph is a line.

$f(x) = 3x - 5$	
x	$y = f(x)$
1	-2
0	-5
$\dfrac{5}{3}$	0

$f^{-1}(x) = \dfrac{x + 5}{3}$	
x	$y = f^{-1}(x)$
-2	1
-5	0
0	$\dfrac{5}{3}$

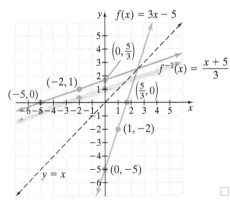

(Continued on next page)

PRACTICE
5 Find the equation of the inverse of $f(x) = 5x + 2$. Graph f and f^{-1} on the same set of axes.

OBJECTIVE
5 Graphing Inverse Functions

Notice that the graphs of f and f^{-1} in Example 5 are mirror images of each other, and the "mirror" is the dashed line $y = x$. This is true for every function and its inverse. For this reason, we say that *the graphs of f and f^{-1} are symmetric about the line $y = x$.*

To see why this happens, study the graph of a few ordered pairs and their switched coordinates in the diagram below.

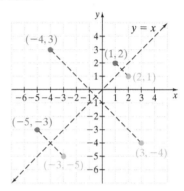

EXAMPLE 6 Graph the inverse of each function.

Solution The function is graphed in blue and the inverse is graphed in red.

a.

b.

PRACTICE
6 Graph the inverse of each function.

a.

b.

OBJECTIVE

6   Determining Whether Functions Are Inverses of Each Other

Notice in the table of values in Example 5 that $f(0) = -5$ and $f^{-1}(-5) = 0$, as expected. Also, for example, $f(1) = -2$ and $f^{-1}(-2) = 1$. In words, we say that for some input x, the function f^{-1} takes the output of x, called $f(x)$, back to x.

$$x \to f(x) \quad \text{and} \quad f^{-1}(f(x)) \to x$$

$$f(0) = -5 \quad \text{and} \quad f^{-1}(-5) = 0$$
$$f(1) = -2 \quad \text{and} \quad f^{-1}(-2) = 1$$

In general,

> If f is a one-to-one function, then the inverse of f is the function f^{-1} such that
> $$(f^{-1} \circ f)(x) = x \quad \text{and} \quad (f \circ f^{-1})(x) = x$$

EXAMPLE 7   Show that if $f(x) = 3x + 2$, then $f^{-1}(x) = \dfrac{x - 2}{3}$.

Solution   See that $(f^{-1} \circ f)(x) = x$ and $(f \circ f^{-1})(x) = x$.

$$
\begin{aligned}
(f^{-1} \circ f)(x) &= f^{-1}(f(x)) \\
&= f^{-1}(3x + 2) \qquad \text{Replace } f(x) \text{ with } 3x + 2. \\
&= \frac{3x + 2 - 2}{3} \\
&= \frac{3x}{3} \\
&= x
\end{aligned}
$$

$$
\begin{aligned}
(f \circ f^{-1})(x) &= f(f^{-1}(x)) \\
&= f\left(\frac{x - 2}{3}\right) \qquad \text{Replace } f^{-1}(x) \text{ with } \frac{x - 2}{3}. \\
&= 3\left(\frac{x - 2}{3}\right) + 2 \\
&= x - 2 + 2 \\
&= x
\end{aligned}
$$

PRACTICE

7   Show that if $f(x) = 4x - 1$, then $f^{-1}(x) = \dfrac{x + 1}{4}$.

Graphing Calculator Explorations

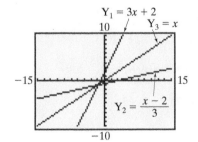

A graphing calculator can be used to visualize the results of Example 7. Recall that the graph of a function f and its inverse f^{-1} are mirror images of each other across the line $y = x$. To see this for the function from Example 7, use a square window and graph

the given function: $Y_1 = 3x + 2$

its inverse: $Y_2 = \dfrac{x - 2}{3}$

and the line: $Y_3 = x$

See Exercises 67–70 in Exercise Set 12.2.

Vocabulary, Readiness & Video Check

Use the choices below to fill in each blank. Some choices will not be used, and some will be used more than once.

vertical	$(3, 7)$	$(11, 2)$	$y = x$	x	true
horizontal	$(7, 3)$	$(2, 11)$	$\dfrac{1}{f}$	the inverse of f	false

1. If $f(2) = 11$, the corresponding ordered pair is _____.
2. If $(7, 3)$ is an ordered pair solution of $f(x)$, and $f(x)$ has an inverse, then an ordered pair solution of $f^{-1}(x)$ is _____.
3. The symbol f^{-1} means _____.
4. True or false: The function notation $f^{-1}(x)$ means $\dfrac{1}{f(x)}$. _____
5. To tell whether a graph is the graph of a function, use the _____ line test.
6. To tell whether the graph of a function is also a one-to-one function, use the _____ line test.
7. The graphs of f and f^{-1} are symmetric about the line _____.
8. Two functions are inverses of each other if $(f \circ f^{-1})(x) =$ _____ and $(f^{-1} \circ f)(x) =$ _____.

Martin-Gay Interactive Videos

See Video 12.2

Watch the section lecture video and answer the following questions.

OBJECTIVE 1
9. From ▦ Example 1 and the definition before, what makes a one-to-one function different from other types of functions?

OBJECTIVE 2
10. From ▦ Examples 2 and 3, if a graph passes the horizontal line test, but not the vertical line test, is it a one-to-one function? Explain.

OBJECTIVE 3
11. From ▦ Example 4 and the lecture before, if you find the inverse of a one-to-one function, is this inverse function also a one-to-one function? How do you know?

OBJECTIVE 4
12. From ▦ Examples 5 and 6, explain why the interchanging of x and y when finding an inverse equation makes sense given the definition of an inverse function.

OBJECTIVE 5
13. From ▦ Example 7, if you have the equation or graph of a one-to-one function, how can you graph its inverse without finding the inverse's equation?

OBJECTIVE 6
14. Based on ▦ Example 8 and the lecture before, what's wrong with the following statement? "If f is a one-to-one function, you can prove that f and f^{-1} are inverses of each other by showing that $f(f^{-1}(x)) = f^{-1}(f(x))$."

12.2 Exercise Set

MyMathLab®

Determine whether each function is a one-to-one function. If it is one-to-one, list the inverse function by switching coordinates, or inputs and outputs. See Examples 1 and 3.

1. $f = \{(-1, -1), (1, 1), (0, 2), (2, 0)\}$

2. $g = \{(8, 6), (9, 6), (3, 4), (-4, 4)\}$

3. $h = \{(10, 10)\}$

4. $r = \{(1, 2), (3, 4), (5, 6), (6, 7)\}$

⊙ 5. $f = \{(11, 12), (4, 3), (3, 4), (6, 6)\}$

6. $g = \{(0, 3), (3, 7), (6, 7), (-2, -2)\}$

7.

Month of 2009 (Input)	July	August	September	October	November	December
Unemployment Rate in Percent (Output)	9.4	9.7	9.8	10.1	10.0	10.0

(*Source:* U.S. Bureau of Labor Statistics)

8.

State (Input)	Texas	Massachusetts	Nevada	Idaho	Wisconsin
Number of Two-Year Colleges (Output)	70	22	3	3	31

(*Source:* University of Texas at Austin)

9.

State (Input)	California	Alaska	Indiana	Louisiana	New Mexico	Ohio
Rank in Population (Output)	1	47	16	25	36	7

(*Source:* U.S. Bureau of the Census)

△ **10.**

Shape (Input)	Triangle	Pentagon	Quadrilateral	Hexagon	Decagon
Number of Sides (Output)	3	5	4	6	10

Given the one-to-one function $f(x) = x^3 + 2$, find the following. [Hint: You do not need to find the equation for $f^{-1}(x)$.]

11. a. $f(1)$
   b. $f^{-1}(3)$

12. a. $f(0)$
   b. $f^{-1}(2)$

13. a. $f(-1)$
   b. $f^{-1}(1)$

14. a. $f(-2)$
   b. $f^{-1}(-6)$

Determine whether the graph of each function is the graph of a one-to-one function. See Example 2.

15.

16.

17.

18.

19.

20.

21.

22.

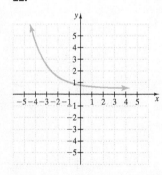

MIXED PRACTICE

Each of the following functions is one-to-one. Find the inverse of each function and graph the function and its inverse on the same set of axes. See Examples 4 and 5.

23. $f(x) = x + 4$

24. $f(x) = x - 5$

25. $f(x) = 2x - 3$

26. $f(x) = 4x + 9$

27. $f(x) = \frac{1}{2}x - 1$

28. $f(x) = -\frac{1}{2}x + 2$

29. $f(x) = x^3$

30. $f(x) = x^3 - 1$

Find the inverse of each one-to-one function. See Examples 4 and 5.

31. $f(x) = 5x + 2$

32. $f(x) = 6x - 1$

33. $f(x) = \frac{x - 2}{5}$

34. $f(x) = \frac{x - 3}{2}$

35. $f(x) = \sqrt[3]{x}$

36. $f(x) = \sqrt[3]{x + 1}$

▶ **37.** $f(x) = \frac{5}{3x + 1}$

38. $f(x) = \frac{7}{2x + 4}$

39. $f(x) = (x + 2)^3$

40. $f(x) = (x - 5)^3$

Graph the inverse of each function on the same set of axes. See Example 6.

41.

42.

43.

44.

45.

46.

Solve. See Example 7.

▶ **47.** If $f(x) = 2x + 1$, show that $f^{-1}(x) = \frac{x - 1}{2}$.

48. If $f(x) = 3x - 10$, show that $f^{-1}(x) = \frac{x + 10}{3}$.

49. If $f(x) = x^3 + 6$, show that $f^{-1}(x) = \sqrt[3]{x - 6}$.

50. If $f(x) = x^3 - 5$, show that $f^{-1}(x) = \sqrt[3]{x + 5}$.

REVIEW AND PREVIEW

Evaluate each of the following. See Section 10.2.

51. $25^{1/2}$

52. $49^{1/2}$

53. $16^{3/4}$

54. $27^{2/3}$

55. $9^{-3/2}$

56. $81^{-3/4}$

If $f(x) = 3^x$, find the following. In Exercises 59 and 60, give an exact answer and a two-decimal-place approximation. See Sections 5.1, 8.2, and 10.2.

57. $f(2)$

58. $f(0)$

59. $f\left(\frac{1}{2}\right)$

60. $f\left(\frac{2}{3}\right)$

CONCEPT EXTENSIONS

Solve. See the Concept Check in this section.

61. Suppose that f is a one-to-one function and that $f(2) = 9$.

   a. Write the corresponding ordered pair.

   b. Name one ordered pair that we know is a solution of the inverse of f, or f^{-1}.

62. Suppose that F is a one-to-one function and that $F\left(\frac{1}{2}\right) = -0.7$.

   a. Write the corresponding ordered pair.

   b. Name one ordered pair that we know is a solution of the inverse of F, or F^{-1}.

For Exercises 63 and 64,

a. *Write the ordered pairs for $f(x)$ whose points are highlighted. (Include the points whose coordinates are given.)*

b. *Write the corresponding ordered pairs for the inverse of f, f^{-1}.*

c. *Graph the ordered pairs for f^{-1} found in part **b**.*

d. *Graph $f^{-1}(x)$ by drawing a smooth curve through the plotted points.*

63.

64.

65. If you are given the graph of a function, describe how you can tell from the graph whether a function has an inverse.

66. Describe the appearance of the graphs of a function and its inverse.

 Find the inverse of each given one-to-one function. Then use a graphing calculator to graph the function and its inverse on a square window.

67. $f(x) = 3x + 1$

68. $f(x) = -2x - 6$

69. $f(x) = \sqrt[3]{x + 1}$

70. $f(x) = x^3 - 3$

12.3 Exponential Functions

OBJECTIVES

1 Graph Exponential Functions.

2 Solve Equations of the Form $b^x = b^y$.

3 Solve Problems Modeled by Exponential Equations.

OBJECTIVE

1   Graphing Exponential Functions

In earlier chapters, we gave meaning to exponential expressions such as 2^x, where x is a rational number. For example,

$$2^3 = 2 \cdot 2 \cdot 2 \qquad \text{Three factors; each factor is 2}$$
$$2^{3/2} = (2^{1/2})^3 = \sqrt{2} \cdot \sqrt{2} \cdot \sqrt{2} \quad \text{Three factors; each factor is } \sqrt{2}$$

When x is an irrational number (for example, $\sqrt{3}$), what meaning can we give to $2^{\sqrt{3}}$?

It is beyond the scope of this book to give precise meaning to 2^x if x is irrational. We can confirm your intuition and say that $2^{\sqrt{3}}$ is a real number and, since $1 < \sqrt{3} < 2$, $2^1 < 2^{\sqrt{3}} < 2^2$. We can also use a calculator and approximate $2^{\sqrt{3}}$: $2^{\sqrt{3}} \approx 3.321997$. In fact, as long as the base b is positive, b^x is a real number for all real numbers x. Finally, the rules of exponents apply whether x is rational or irrational as long as b is positive. In this section, we are interested in functions of the form $f(x) = b^x$, where $b > 0$. A function of this form is called an **exponential function.**

> **Exponential Function**
>
> A function of the form
>
> $$f(x) = b^x$$
>
> is called an **exponential function** if $b > 0$, b is not 1, and x is a real number.

Next, we practice graphing exponential functions.

EXAMPLE 1   Graph the exponential functions defined by $f(x) = 2^x$ and $g(x) = 3^x$ on the same set of axes.

Solution   Graph each function by plotting points. Set up a table of values for each of the two functions.

(Continued on next page)

If each set of points is plotted and connected with a smooth curve, the following graphs result.

$f(x) = 2^x$	x	0	1	2	3	-1	-2
	$f(x)$	1	2	4	8	$\dfrac{1}{2}$	$\dfrac{1}{4}$

$g(x) = 3^x$	x	0	1	2	3	-1	-2
	$g(x)$	1	3	9	27	$\dfrac{1}{3}$	$\dfrac{1}{9}$

PRACTICE

1 Graph the exponential functions defined by $f(x) = 2^x$ and $g(x) = 7^x$ on the same set of axes.

A number of things should be noted about the two graphs of exponential functions in Example 1. First, the graphs show that $f(x) = 2^x$ and $g(x) = 3^x$ are one-to-one functions since each graph passes the vertical and horizontal line tests. The y-intercept of each graph is $(0, 1)$, but neither graph has an x-intercept. From the graph, we can also see that the domain of each function is all real numbers and that the range is $(0, \infty)$. We can also see that as x-values are increasing, y-values are increasing also.

EXAMPLE 2 Graph the exponential functions $y = \left(\dfrac{1}{2}\right)^x$ and $y = \left(\dfrac{1}{3}\right)^x$ on the same set of axes.

Solution As before, plot points and connect them with a smooth curve.

$y = \left(\dfrac{1}{2}\right)^x$	x	0	1	2	3	-1	-2
	y	1	$\dfrac{1}{2}$	$\dfrac{1}{4}$	$\dfrac{1}{8}$	2	4

$y = \left(\dfrac{1}{3}\right)^x$	x	0	1	2	3	-1	-2
	y	1	$\dfrac{1}{3}$	$\dfrac{1}{9}$	$\dfrac{1}{27}$	3	9

PRACTICE

2 Graph the exponential functions $f(x) = \left(\dfrac{1}{3}\right)^x$ and $g(x) = \left(\dfrac{1}{5}\right)^x$ on the same set of axes.

Each function in Example 2 again is a one-to-one function. The y-intercept of both is $(0, 1)$. The domain is the set of all real numbers, and the range is $(0, \infty)$.

Notice the difference between the graphs of Example 1 and the graphs of Example 2. An exponential function is always increasing if the base is greater than 1.

When the base is between 0 and 1, the graph is always decreasing. The figures on the next page summarize these characteristics of exponential functions.

$$f(x) = b^x, \quad b > 0, \quad b \neq 1$$

- one-to-one function
- y-intercept $(0, 1)$
- no x-intercept

- domain: $(-\infty, \infty)$
- range: $(0, \infty)$

EXAMPLE 3   Graph the exponential function $f(x) = 3^{x+2}$.

Solution   As before, we find and plot a few ordered pair solutions. Then we connect the points with a smooth curve.

$f(x) = 3^{x+2}$	
x	$f(x)$
0	9
−1	3
−2	1
−3	$\frac{1}{3}$
−4	$\frac{1}{9}$

PRACTICE
3   Graph the exponential function $f(x) = 2^{x-3}$.

✓CONCEPT CHECK
Which functions are exponential functions?

a. $f(x) = x^3$ **b.** $g(x) = \left(\dfrac{2}{3}\right)^x$ **c.** $h(x) = 5^{x-2}$ **d.** $w(x) = (2x)^2$

OBJECTIVE
2   **Solving Equations of the Form $b^x = b^y$** ▶

We have seen that an exponential function $y = b^x$ is a one-to-one function. Another way of stating this fact is a property that we can use to solve exponential equations.

Uniqueness of b^x

Let $b > 0$ and $b \neq 1$. Then $b^x = b^y$ is equivalent to $x = y$.

Thus, one way to solve an exponential equation depends on whether it's possible to write each side of the equation with the same base; that is, $b^x = b^y$. We solve by this method first.

Answer to Concept Check:
b, c

EXAMPLE 4 Solve each equation for x.

a. $2^x = 16$ **b.** $9^x = 27$ **c.** $4^{x+3} = 8^x$

Solution

a. We write 16 as a power of 2 and then use the uniqueness of b^x to solve.

$$2^x = 16$$
$$2^x = 2^4$$

Since the bases are the same and are nonnegative, by the uniqueness of b^x, we then have that the exponents are equal. Thus,

$$x = 4$$

The solution is 4, or the solution set is $\{4\}$.

b. Notice that both 9 and 27 are powers of 3.

$$9^x = 27$$
$$(3^2)^x = 3^3 \qquad \text{Write 9 and 27 as powers of 3.}$$
$$3^{2x} = 3^3$$
$$2x = 3 \qquad \text{Apply the uniqueness of } b^x.$$
$$x = \frac{3}{2} \qquad \text{Divide by 2.}$$

To check, replace x with $\frac{3}{2}$ in the original expression, $9^x = 27$. The solution is $\frac{3}{2}$.

c. Write both 4 and 8 as powers of 2.

$$4^{x+3} = 8^x$$
$$(2^2)^{x+3} = (2^3)^x$$
$$2^{2x+6} = 2^{3x}$$
$$2x + 6 = 3x \qquad \text{Apply the uniqueness of } b^x.$$
$$6 = x \qquad \text{Subtract } 2x \text{ from both sides.}$$

The solution is 6.   □

PRACTICE

4   Solve each equation for x.

a. $3^x = 9$ **b.** $8^x = 16$ **c.** $125^x = 25^{x-2}$

There is one major problem with the preceding technique. Often the two sides of an equation cannot easily be written as powers of a common base. We explore how to solve an equation such as $4 = 3^x$ with the help of **logarithms** later.

OBJECTIVE

3   Solving Problems Modeled by Exponential Equations

The bar graph on the next page shows the increase in the number of cellular phone users. Notice that the graph of the exponential function $y = 136.76(1.107)^x$ approximates the heights of the bars. This is just one example of how the world abounds with patterns that can be modeled by exponential functions. To make these applications realistic, we use numbers that warrant a calculator.

Cellular Phone Users

$$y = 136.76(1.107)^x$$
where $x = 0$ corresponds to 2002, $x = 1$ corresponds to 2003, and so on

Source: CTIA — The Wireless Association

Another application of an exponential function has to do with interest rates on loans. The exponential function defined by $A = P\left(1 + \dfrac{r}{n}\right)^{nt}$ models the dollars A accrued (or owed) after P dollars are invested (or loaned) at an annual rate of interest r compounded n times each year for t years. This function is known as the compound interest formula.

EXAMPLE 5 Using the Compound Interest Formula

Find the amount owed at the end of 5 years if $1600 is loaned at a rate of 9% compounded monthly.

Solution We use the formula $A = P\left(1 + \dfrac{r}{n}\right)^{nt}$, with the following values.

$P = \$1600$ (the amount of the loan)
$r = 9\% = 0.09$ (the annual rate of interest)
$n = 12$ (the number of times interest is compounded each year)
$t = 5$ (the duration of the loan, in years)

$$A = P\left(1 + \frac{r}{n}\right)^{nt} \qquad \text{Compound interest formula}$$

$$= 1600\left(1 + \frac{0.09}{12}\right)^{12(5)} \qquad \text{Substitute known values.}$$

$$= 1600(1.0075)^{60}$$

To approximate A, use the $\boxed{y^x}$ or $\boxed{\wedge}$ key on your calculator.

$$\boxed{2505.0896}$$

Thus, the amount A owed is approximately $2505.09.

PRACTICE

5 Find the amount owed at the end of 4 years if $3000 is loaned at a rate of 7% compounded semiannually (twice a year).

EXAMPLE 6 **Estimating Percent of Radioactive Material**

As a result of a nuclear accident, radioactive debris was carried through the atmosphere. One immediate concern was the impact that the debris had on the milk supply. The percent y of radioactive material in raw milk after t days is estimated by $y = 100(2.7)^{-0.1t}$. Estimate the expected percent of radioactive material in the milk after 30 days.

Solution Replace t with 30 in the given equation.

$$y = 100(2.7)^{-0.1t}$$
$$= 100(2.7)^{-0.1(30)} \quad \text{Let } t = 30.$$
$$= 100(2.7)^{-3}$$

To approximate the percent y, the following keystrokes may be used on a scientific calculator.

The display should read

$$\boxed{5.0805263}$$

Thus, approximately 5% of the radioactive material still remained in the milk supply after 30 days. □

PRACTICE

6 The percent p of light that passes through n successive sheets of a particular glass is given approximately by the function $p(n) = 100(2.7)^{-0.05n}$. Estimate the expected percent of light that will pass through the following numbers of sheets of glass. Round each to the nearest hundredth of a percent.

a. 2 sheets of glass   **b.** 10 sheets of glass

Graphing Calculator Explorations

We can use a graphing calculator and its TRACE feature to solve Example 6 graphically.

To estimate the expected percent of radioactive material in the milk after 30 days, enter $Y_1 = 100(2.7)^{-0.1x}$. (The variable t in Example 6 is changed to x here to accommodate our work better on the graphing calculator.) The graph does not appear on a standard viewing window, so we need to determine an appropriate viewing window. Because it doesn't make sense to look at radioactivity *before* the nuclear accident, we use Xmin = 0. We are interested in finding the percent of radioactive material in the milk when $x = 30$, so we choose Xmax = 35 to leave enough space to see the graph at $x = 30$. Because the values of y are percents, it seems appropriate that $0 \le y \le 100$. (We also use Xscl = 1 and Yscl = 10.) Now we graph the function.

We can use the TRACE feature to obtain an approximation of the expected percent of radioactive material in the milk when $x = 30$. (A TABLE feature may also be used to approximate the percent.) To obtain a better approximation, let's use the ZOOM feature several times to zoom in near $x = 30$.

The percent of radioactive material in the milk 30 days after the nuclear accident was 5.08%, accurate to two decimal places.

Use a graphing calculator to find each percent. Approximate your solutions so that they are accurate to two decimal places.

1. Estimate the expected percent of radioactive material in the milk 2 days after the nuclear accident.

2. Estimate the expected percent of radioactive material in the milk 10 days after the nuclear accident.

3. Estimate the expected percent of radioactive material in the milk 15 days after the nuclear accident.

4. Estimate the expected percent of radioactive material in the milk 25 days after the nuclear accident.

Vocabulary, Readiness & Video Check

Use the choices to fill in each blank.

1. A function such as $f(x) = 2^x$ is a(n) _____ function.
   A. linear   **B.** quadratic   **C.** exponential

2. If $7^x = 7^y$, then _____ .
   A. $x = 7^y$ **B.** $x = y$ **C.** $y = 7^x$ **D.** $7 = 7^y$

Answer the questions about the graph of $y = 2^x$, shown to the right.

3. Is this a function? _____

4. Is this a one-to-one function? _____

5. Is there an x-intercept? _____ If so, name the coordinates. _____

6. Is there a y-intercept? _____ If so, name the coordinates. _____

7. The domain of this function, in interval notation, is _____ .

8. The range of this function, in interval notation, is _____ .

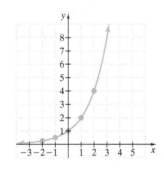

Martin-Gay Interactive Videos

Watch the section lecture video and answer the following questions.

OBJECTIVE 1
9. From the lecture before Example 1, what's the main difference between a polynomial function and an exponential function?

OBJECTIVE 2
10. From Examples 2 and 3, you can only apply the uniqueness of b^x to solve an exponential equation if you're able to do what?

OBJECTIVE 3
11. For Example 4, write the equation and find how much uranium will remain after 101 days. Round your answer to the nearest tenth.

See Video 12.3

12.3 Exercise Set   MyMathLab®

Graph each exponential function. See Examples 1 through 3.

1. $y = 5^x$

2. $y = 4^x$

3. $y = 2^x + 1$

4. $y = 3^x - 1$

5. $y = \left(\dfrac{1}{4}\right)^x$

6. $y = \left(\dfrac{1}{5}\right)^x$

7. $y = \left(\dfrac{1}{2}\right)^x - 2$

8. $y = \left(\dfrac{1}{3}\right)^x + 2$

9. $y = -2^x$

10. $y = -3^x$

11. $y = -\left(\dfrac{1}{4}\right)^x$

12. $y = -\left(\dfrac{1}{5}\right)^x$

13. $f(x) = 2^{x+1}$

14. $f(x) = 3^{x-1}$

15. $f(x) = 4^{x-2}$

16. $f(x) = 2^{x+3}$

Match each exponential equation with its graph below. See Examples 1 through 3.

17. $f(x) = \left(\dfrac{1}{2}\right)^x$

18. $f(x) = \left(\dfrac{1}{4}\right)^x$

19. $f(x) = 2^x$

20. $f(x) = 3^x$

A. / B.

C. / D.

Solve each equation for x. See Example 4.

21. $3^x = 27$

22. $6^x = 36$

23. $16^x = 8$

24. $64^x = 16$

25. $32^{2x-3} = 2$

26. $9^{2x+1} = 81$

27. $\dfrac{1}{4} = 2^{3x}$

28. $\dfrac{1}{27} = 3^{2x}$

29. $5^x = 625$

30. $2^x = 64$

31. $4^x = 8$

32. $32^x = 4$

33. $27^{x+1} = 9$

34. $125^{x-2} = 25$

35. $81^{x-1} = 27^{2x}$

36. $4^{3x-7} = 32^{2x}$

Solve. Unless otherwise indicated, round results to one decimal place. See Example 6.

37. One type of uranium has a radioactive decay rate of 0.4% per day. If 30 pounds of this uranium is available today, how much will still remain after 50 days? Use $y = 30(0.996)^x$ and let x be 50.

38. The nuclear waste from an atomic energy plant decays at a rate of 3% each century. If 150 pounds of nuclear waste is disposed of, how much of it will still remain after 10 centuries? Use $y = 150(0.97)^x$, and let x be 10.

39. Cheese production in the United States is currently growing at a rate of 3% per year. The equation $y = 8.6(1.03)^x$ models the cheese production in the United States from 2003 to 2009. In this equation, y is the amount of cheese produced, in billions of pounds, and x represents the number of years after 2003. Round answers to the nearest tenth of a billion. (*Source:* National Agricultural Statistics Service)

a. Estimate the total cheese production in the United States in 2007.

b. Assuming this equation continues to be valid in the future, use the equation to predict the total amount of cheese produced in the United States in 2015.

40. Retail revenue from shopping on the Internet is currently growing at rate of 26% per year. In 2003, a total of $39 billion in revenue was collected through Internet retail sales. Answer the following questions using $y = 39(1.26)^t$, where y is Internet revenues in billions of dollars and t is the number of years after 2003. Round answers to the nearest tenth of a billion dollars. (*Source:* U.S. Bureau of the Census)

a. According to the model, what level of retail revenues from Internet shopping was expected in 2005?

b. If the given model continues to be valid, predict the level of Internet shopping revenues in 2015.

41. The equation $y = 140,242(1.083)^x$ models the number of American college students who studied abroad each year from 2000 through 2009. In the equation, y is the number of American students studying abroad, and x represents the number of years after 2000. Round answers to the nearest whole. (*Source:* Based on data from Institute of International Education, Open Doors)

a. Estimate the number of American students studying abroad in 2004.

b. Assuming this equation continues to be valid in the future, use this equation to predict the number of American students studying abroad in 2015.

42. Carbon dioxide (CO_2) is a greenhouse gas that contributes to global warming. Partially due to the combustion of fossil fuel, the amount of CO_2 in Earth's atmosphere has been increasing by 0.5% annually over the past century. In 2000, the concentration of CO_2 in the atmosphere was 369.4 parts per million by volume. To make the following predictions, use $y = 369.4(1.005)^t$ where y is the concentration of CO_2 in parts per million by volume and t is the number of years after 2000. (*Sources:* Based on data from the United Nations Environment Programme and the Carbon Dioxide Information Analysis Center)

a. Predict the concentration of CO_2 in the atmosphere in the year 2015.

b. Predict the concentration of CO_2 in the atmosphere in the year 2030.

The equation $y = 136.76(1.107)^x$ gives the number of cellular phone users y (in millions) in the United States for the years 2002 through 2010. In this equation, $x = 0$ corresponds to 2002, $x = 1$ corresponds to 2003, and so on. Use this model to solve Exercises 43 and 44. Round answers to the nearest tenth of a million.

43. Estimate the number of cell phone users in the year 2012.

44. Predict the number of cell phone users in 2014.

45. An unusually wet spring has caused the size of the Cape Cod mosquito population to increase by 8% each day. If an estimated 200,000 mosquitoes are on Cape Cod on May 12, find how many mosquitoes will inhabit the Cape on May 25. Use $y = 200{,}000(1.08)^x$ where x is number of days since May 12. Round to the nearest thousand.

46. The atmospheric pressure p, in pascals, on a weather balloon decreases with increasing height. This pressure, measured in millimeters of mercury, is related to the number of kilometers h above sea level by the function $p(h) = 760(2.7)^{-0.145h}$. Round to the nearest tenth of a pascal.
   a. Find the atmospheric pressure at a height of 1 kilometer.
   b. Find the atmospheric pressure at a height of 10 kilometers.

Solve. Use $A = P\left(1 + \dfrac{r}{n}\right)^{nt}$. Round answers to two decimal places. See Example 5.

47. Find the amount Erica owes at the end of 3 years if $6000 is loaned to her at a rate of 8% compounded monthly.

48. Find the amount owed at the end of 5 years if $3000 is loaned at a rate of 10% compounded quarterly.

49. Find the total amount Janina has in a college savings account if $2000 was invested and earned 6% compounded semiannually for 12 years.

50. Find the amount accrued if $500 is invested and earns 7% compounded monthly for 4 years.

REVIEW AND PREVIEW

Solve each equation. See Sections 2.3 and 6.6.

51. $5x - 2 = 18$ **52.** $3x - 7 = 11$

53. $3x - 4 = 3(x + 1)$ **54.** $2 - 6x = 6(1 - x)$

55. $x^2 + 6 = 5x$ **56.** $18 = 11x - x^2$

By inspection, find the value for x that makes each statement true. See Section 5.1.

57. $2^x = 8$ **58.** $3^x = 9$

59. $5^x = \dfrac{1}{5}$ **60.** $4^x = 1$

CONCEPT EXTENSIONS

Is the given function an exponential function? See the Concept Check in this section.

61. $f(x) = 1.5x^2$ **62.** $g(x) = 3^x$

63. $h(x) = \left(\dfrac{1}{2}x\right)^2$ **64.** $F(x) = 0.4^{x+1}$

Match each exponential function with its graph.

65. $f(x) = 2^{-x}$ **66.** $f(x) = \left(\dfrac{1}{2}\right)^{-x}$

67. $f(x) = 4^{-x}$ **68.** $f(x) = \left(\dfrac{1}{3}\right)^{-x}$

69. Explain why the graph of an exponential function $y = b^x$ contains the point $(1, b)$.

70. Explain why an exponential function $y = b^x$ has a y-intercept of $(0, 1)$.

Graph.

71. $y = |3^x|$ **72.** $y = \left|\left(\dfrac{1}{3}\right)^x\right|$

73. $y = 3^{|x|}$ **74.** $y = \left(\dfrac{1}{3}\right)^{|x|}$

75. Graph $y = 2^x$ and $y = \left(\dfrac{1}{2}\right)^{-x}$ on the same set of axes. Describe what you see and why.

76. Graph $y = 2^x$ and $x = 2^y$ on the same set of axes. Describe what you see.

Use a graphing calculator to solve. Estimate your results to two decimal places.

77. Verify the results of Exercise 37.

78. Verify the results of Exercise 38.

79. From Exercise 37, estimate the number of pounds of uranium that will be available after 100 days.

80. From Exercise 37, estimate the number of pounds of uranium that will be available after 120 days.

12.5 Logarithmic Functions

OBJECTIVES

1 Write Exponential Equations with Logarithmic Notation and Write Logarithmic Equations with Exponential Notation.

2 Solve Logarithmic Equations by Using Exponential Notation.

3 Identify and Graph Logarithmic Functions.

OBJECTIVE

1 Using Logarithmic Notation

Since the exponential function $f(x) = 2^x$ is a one-to-one function, it has an inverse. We can create a table of values for f^{-1} by switching the coordinates in the accompanying table of values for $f(x) = 2^x$.

x	$y = f(x)$
-3	$\frac{1}{8}$
-2	$\frac{1}{4}$
-1	$\frac{1}{2}$
0	1
1	2
2	4
3	8

x	$y = f^{-1}(x)$
$\frac{1}{8}$	-3
$\frac{1}{4}$	-2
$\frac{1}{2}$	-1
1	0
2	1
4	2
8	3

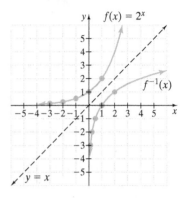

The graphs of $f(x)$ and its inverse are shown on the previous page. Notice that the graphs of f and f^{-1} are symmetric about the line $y = x$, as expected.

Now we would like to be able to write an equation for f^{-1}. To do so, we follow the steps for finding an inverse.

$$f(x) = 2^x$$

Step 1. Replace $f(x)$ by y. $y = 2^x$

Step 2. Interchange x and y. $x = 2^y$

Step 3. Solve for y.

At this point, we are stuck. To solve this equation for y, a new notation, the **logarithmic notation,** is needed.

The symbol $\log_b x$ means "the power to which b is raised to produce a result of x." In other words,

$$\log_b x = y \quad \text{means} \quad b^y = x$$

We say that $\log_b x$ is "the logarithm of x to the base b" or "the log of x to the base b."

Logarithmic Definition

If $b > 0$ and $b \neq 1$, then

$$y = \log_b x \text{ means } x = b^y$$

for every $x > 0$ and every real number y.

> **Helpful Hint**
>
> Notice that a *logarithm* is an *exponent*. In other words, $\log_3 9$ is the *power* that we raise 3 in order to get 9.

Before returning to the function $x = 2^y$ and solving it for y in terms of x, let's practice using the new notation $\log_b x$.

It is important to be able to write exponential equations from logarithmic notation and vice versa. The following table shows examples of both forms.

Logarithmic Equation	Corresponding Exponential Equation
$\log_3 9 = 2$	$3^2 = 9$
$\log_6 1 = 0$	$6^0 = 1$
$\log_2 8 = 3$	$2^3 = 8$
$\log_4 \dfrac{1}{16} = -2$	$4^{-2} = \dfrac{1}{16}$
$\log_8 2 = \dfrac{1}{3}$	$8^{1/3} = 2$

EXAMPLE 1   Write each as an exponential equation.

a. $\log_5 25 = 2$ **b.** $\log_6 \dfrac{1}{6} = -1$ **c.** $\log_2 \sqrt{2} = \dfrac{1}{2}$ **d.** $\log_7 x = 5$

Solution

a. $\log_5 25 = 2$ means $5^2 = 25$

b. $\log_6 \dfrac{1}{6} = -1$ means $6^{-1} = \dfrac{1}{6}$

c. $\log_2 \sqrt{2} = \dfrac{1}{2}$ means $2^{1/2} = \sqrt{2}$

d. $\log_7 x = 5$ means $7^5 = x$

(Continued on next page)

PRACTICE
1   Write each as an exponential equation.

a. $\log_3 81 = 4$ **b.** $\log_5 \dfrac{1}{5} = -1$ **c.** $\log_7 \sqrt{7} = \dfrac{1}{2}$ **d.** $\log_{13} y = 4$

EXAMPLE 2   Write each as a logarithmic equation.

a. $9^3 = 729$ **b.** $6^{-2} = \dfrac{1}{36}$ **c.** $5^{1/3} = \sqrt[3]{5}$ **d.** $\pi^4 = x$

Solution

a. $9^3 = 729$ means $\log_9 729 = 3$

b. $6^{-2} = \dfrac{1}{36}$ means $\log_6 \dfrac{1}{36} = -2$

c. $5^{1/3} = \sqrt[3]{5}$ means $\log_5 \sqrt[3]{5} = \dfrac{1}{3}$

d. $\pi^4 = x$ means $\log_\pi x = 4$

PRACTICE
2   Write each as a logarithmic equation.

a. $4^3 = 64$ **b.** $6^{1/3} = \sqrt[3]{6}$ **c.** $5^{-3} = \dfrac{1}{125}$ **d.** $\pi^7 = z$

EXAMPLE 3   Find the value of each logarithmic expression.

a. $\log_4 16$ **b.** $\log_{10} \dfrac{1}{10}$ **c.** $\log_9 3$

Solution

a. $\log_4 16 = 2$ because $4^2 = 16$

b. $\log_{10} \dfrac{1}{10} = -1$ because $10^{-1} = \dfrac{1}{10}$

c. $\log_9 3 = \dfrac{1}{2}$ because $9^{1/2} = \sqrt{9} = 3$

PRACTICE
3   Find the value of each logarithmic expression.

a. $\log_3 9$ **b.** $\log_2 \dfrac{1}{8}$ **c.** $\log_{49} 7$

▶ Helpful Hint

Another method for evaluating logarithms such as those in Example 3 is to set the expression equal to x and then write them in exponential form to find x. For example:

a. $\log_4 16 = x$ means $4^x = 16$. Since $4^2 = 16$, $x = 2$ or $\log_4 16 = 2$.

b. $\log_{10} \dfrac{1}{10} = x$ means $10^x = \dfrac{1}{10}$. Since $10^{-1} = \dfrac{1}{10}$, $x = -1$ or $\log_{10} \dfrac{1}{10} = -1$.

c. $\log_9 3 = x$ means $9^x = 3$. Since $9^{1/2} = 3$, $x = \dfrac{1}{2}$ or $\log_9 3 = \dfrac{1}{2}$.

OBJECTIVE

2   Solving Logarithmic Equations

The ability to interchange the logarithmic and exponential forms of a statement is often the key to solving logarithmic equations.

EXAMPLE 4   Solve each equation for x.

a. $\log_4 \dfrac{1}{4} = x$ **b.** $\log_5 x = 3$ **c.** $\log_x 25 = 2$ **d.** $\log_3 1 = x$ **e.** $\log_b 1 = x$

Solution

a. $\log_4 \dfrac{1}{4} = x$ means $4^x = \dfrac{1}{4}$. Solve $4^x = \dfrac{1}{4}$ for x.

$$4^x = \frac{1}{4}$$
$$4^x = 4^{-1}$$

Since the bases are the same, by the uniqueness of b^x, we have that

$$x = -1$$

The solution is -1 or the solution set is $\{-1\}$. To check, see that $\log_4 \dfrac{1}{4} = -1$, since $4^{-1} = \dfrac{1}{4}$.

b. $\log_5 x = 3$

$5^3 = x$ Write as an exponential equation.

$125 = x$

The solution is 125.

c. $\log_x 25 = 2$

$x^2 = 25$ Write as an exponential equation. Here $x > 0, x \neq 1$.

$x = 5$

Even though $(-5)^2 = 25$, the base b of a logarithm must be positive. The solution is 5.

d. $\log_3 1 = x$

$3^x = 1$ Write as an exponential equation.

$3^x = 3^0$ Write 1 as 3^0.

$x = 0$ Use the uniqueness of b^x.

The solution is 0.

e. $\log_b 1 = x$

$b^x = 1$ Write as an exponential equation. Here, $b > 0$ and $b \neq 1$.

$b^x = b^0$ Write 1 as b^0.

$x = 0$ Apply the uniqueness of b^x.

The solution is 0.   □

PRACTICE

4   Solve each equation for x.

a. $\log_5 \dfrac{1}{25} = x$ **b.** $\log_x 8 = 3$ **c.** $\log_6 x = 2$

d. $\log_{13} 1 = x$ **e.** $\log_h 1 = x$

In Example 4e, we proved an important property of logarithms. That is, $\log_b 1$ is always 0. This property as well as two important others are given next.

Properties of Logarithms

If b is a real number, $b > 0$, and $b \neq 1$, then

1. $\log_b 1 = 0$
2. $\log_b b^x = x$
3. $b^{\log_b x} = x$

To see that **2.** $\log_b b^x = x$, change the logarithmic form to exponential form. Then, $\log_b b^x = x$ means $b^x = b^x$. In exponential form, the statement is true, so in logarithmic form, the statement is also true.

To understand **3.** $b^{\log_b x} = x$, write this exponential equation as an equivalent logarithm.

EXAMPLE 5   Simplify.

a. $\log_3 3^2$ **b.** $\log_7 7^{-1}$ **c.** $5^{\log_5 3}$ **d.** $2^{\log_2 6}$

Solution

a. From Property 2, $\log_3 3^2 = 2$.
b. From Property 2, $\log_7 7^{-1} = -1$.
c. From Property 3, $5^{\log_5 3} = 3$.
d. From Property 3, $2^{\log_2 6} = 6$.

PRACTICE
5   Simplify.

a. $\log_5 5^4$ **b.** $\log_9 9^{-2}$ **c.** $6^{\log_6 5}$ **d.** $7^{\log_7 4}$

OBJECTIVE
3   **Graphing Logarithmic Functions** ▶

Let us now return to the function $f(x) = 2^x$ and write an equation for its inverse, $f^{-1}(x)$. Recall our earlier work.

$$f(x) = 2^x$$

Step 1. Replace $f(x)$ by y. $y = 2^x$

Step 2. Interchange x and y. $x = 2^y$

Having gained proficiency with the notation $\log_b x$, we can now complete the steps for writing the inverse equation by writing $x = 2^y$ as an equivalent logarithm.

Step 3. Solve for y. $y = \log_2 x$

Step 4. Replace y with $f^{-1}(x)$. $f^{-1}(x) = \log_2 x$

Thus, $f^{-1}(x) = \log_2 x$ defines a function that is the inverse function of the function $f(x) = 2^x$. The function $f^{-1}(x)$ or $y = \log_2 x$ is called a **logarithmic function.**

Logarithmic Function

If x is a positive real number, b is a constant positive real number, and b is not 1, then a **logarithmic function** is a function that can be defined by

$$f(x) = \log_b x$$

The domain of f is the set of positive real numbers, and the range of f is the set of real numbers.

✓CONCEPT CHECK

Let $f(x) = \log_3 x$ and $g(x) = 3^x$. These two functions are inverses of each other. Since $(2, 9)$ is an ordered pair solution of $g(x)$ or $g(2) = 9$, what ordered pair do we know to be a solution of $f(x)$? Also, find $f(9)$. Explain why.

We can explore logarithmic functions by graphing them.

EXAMPLE 6   Graph the logarithmic function $y = \log_2 x$.

Solution   First we write the equation with exponential notation as $2^y = x$. Then we find some ordered pair solutions that satisfy this equation. Finally, we plot the points and connect them with a smooth curve. The domain of this function is $(0, \infty)$, and the range is all real numbers.

Since $x = 2^y$ is solved for x, we choose y-values and compute corresponding x-values.

If $y = 0, x = 2^0 = 1$
If $y = 1, x = 2^1 = 2$
If $y = 2, x = 2^2 = 4$
If $y = -1, x = 2^{-1} = \dfrac{1}{2}$

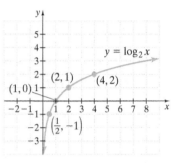

Notice that the x-intercept is $(1, 0)$ and there is no y-intercept.

PRACTICE

6   Graph the logarithmic function $y = \log_9 x$.

EXAMPLE 7   Graph the logarithmic function $f(x) = \log_{1/3} x$.

Solution   Replace $f(x)$ with y and write the result with exponential notation.

$$f(x) = \log_{1/3} x$$
$$y = \log_{1/3} x \quad \text{Replace } f(x) \text{ with } y.$$
$$\left(\frac{1}{3}\right)^y = x \quad \text{Write in exponential form.}$$

Now we can find ordered pair solutions that satisfy $\left(\frac{1}{3}\right)^y = x$, plot these points, and connect them with a smooth curve.

If $y = 0, x = \left(\dfrac{1}{3}\right)^0 = 1$

If $y = 1, x = \left(\dfrac{1}{3}\right)^1 = \dfrac{1}{3}$

If $y = -1, x = \left(\dfrac{1}{3}\right)^{-1} = 3$

If $y = -2, x = \left(\dfrac{1}{3}\right)^{-2} = 9$

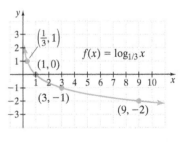

The domain of this function is $(0, \infty)$, and the range is the set of all real numbers. The x-intercept is $(1, 0)$ and there is no y-intercept.

PRACTICE

7   Graph the logarithmic function $y = \log_{1/4} x$.

Answer to Concept Check:
$(9, 2)$; $f(9) = 2$; answers may vary

The following figures summarize characteristics of logarithmic functions.

- one-to-one function
- x-intercept $(1, 0)$
- no y-intercept

- domain: $(0, \infty)$
- range: $(-\infty, \infty)$

Vocabulary, Readiness & Video Check

Use the choices to fill in each blank.

1. A function such as $y = \log_2 x$ is a(n) _____ function.

   A. linear   **B.** logarithmic   **C.** quadratic   **D.** exponential

2. If $y = \log_2 x$, then _____.

   A. $x = y$ **B.** $2^x = y$ **C.** $2^y = x$ **D.** $2y = x$

Answer the questions about the graph of $y = \log_2 x$, shown to the left.

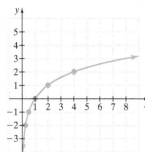

3. Is this a one-to-one function? _____

4. Is there an x-intercept? _____ If so, name the coordinates. _____

5. Is there a y-intercept? _____ If so, name the coordinates. _____

6. The domain of this function, in interval notation, is _____.

7. The range of this function, in interval notation, is _____.

Martin-Gay Interactive Videos

See Video 12.5

Watch the section lecture video and answer the following questions.

OBJECTIVE
1

8. Notice from the definition of a logarithm and from ⬜ Examples 1–4 that a logarithmic statement equals the power in the exponent statement, such as $b^y = x$. What conclusion can you make about logarithms and exponents?

OBJECTIVE
2

9. From ⬜ Examples 8 and 9, how do you solve a logarithmic equation?

OBJECTIVE
3

10. In ⬜ Example 12, why is it easier to choose values for y when finding ordered pairs for the graph?

12.5   Exercise Set   MyMathLab®

Write each as an exponential equation. See Example 1.

1. $\log_6 36 = 2$ **2.** $\log_2 32 = 5$

3. $\log_3 \dfrac{1}{27} = -3$ **4.** $\log_5 \dfrac{1}{25} = -2$

5. $\log_{10} 1000 = 3$ **6.** $\log_{10} 10 = 1$

7. $\log_9 x = 4$ **8.** $\log_8 y = 7$

9. $\log_\pi \dfrac{1}{\pi^2} = -2$ **10.** $\log_e \dfrac{1}{e} = -1$

11. $\log_7 \sqrt{7} = \dfrac{1}{2}$ **12.** $\log_{11} \sqrt[4]{11} = \dfrac{1}{4}$

13. $\log_{0.7} 0.343 = 3$ **14.** $\log_{1.2} 1.44 = 2$

15. $\log_3 \dfrac{1}{81} = -4$ **16.** $\log_{1/4} 16 = -2$

Write each as a logarithmic equation. See Example 2.

17. $2^4 = 16$ **18.** $5^3 = 125$

19. $10^2 = 100$ **20.** $10^4 = 10{,}000$

21. $\pi^3 = x$ **22.** $\pi^5 = y$

23. $10^{-1} = \dfrac{1}{10}$ **24.** $10^{-2} = \dfrac{1}{100}$

25. $4^{-2} = \dfrac{1}{16}$ **26.** $3^{-4} = \dfrac{1}{81}$

27. $5^{1/2} = \sqrt{5}$ **28.** $4^{1/3} = \sqrt[3]{4}$

Find the value of each logarithmic expression. See Examples 3 and 5.

29. $\log_2 8$ **30.** $\log_3 9$

31. $\log_3 \dfrac{1}{9}$ **32.** $\log_2 \dfrac{1}{32}$

33. $\log_{25} 5$ **34.** $\log_8 \dfrac{1}{2}$

35. $\log_{1/2} 2$ **36.** $\log_{2/3} \dfrac{4}{9}$

37. $\log_6 1$ **38.** $\log_9 9$

39. $\log_{10} 100$ **40.** $\log_{10} \dfrac{1}{10}$

41. $\log_3 81$ **42.** $\log_2 16$

43. $\log_4 \dfrac{1}{64}$ **44.** $\log_3 \dfrac{1}{9}$

Solve. See Example 4.

45. $\log_3 9 = x$ **46.** $\log_2 8 = x$

47. $\log_3 x = 4$ **48.** $\log_2 x = 3$

49. $\log_x 49 = 2$ **50.** $\log_x 8 = 3$

51. $\log_2 \dfrac{1}{8} = x$ **52.** $\log_3 \dfrac{1}{81} = x$

53. $\log_3 \dfrac{1}{27} = x$ **54.** $\log_5 \dfrac{1}{125} = x$

55. $\log_8 x = \dfrac{1}{3}$ **56.** $\log_9 x = \dfrac{1}{2}$

57. $\log_4 16 = x$ **58.** $\log_2 16 = x$

59. $\log_{3/4} x = 3$ **60.** $\log_{2/3} x = 2$

61. $\log_x 100 = 2$ **62.** $\log_x 27 = 3$

63. $\log_2 2^4 = x$ **64.** $\log_6 6^{-2} = x$

65. $3^{\log_3 5} = x$ **66.** $5^{\log_5 7} = x$

67. $\log_x \dfrac{1}{7} = \dfrac{1}{2}$ **68.** $\log_x 2 = -\dfrac{1}{3}$

Simplify. See Example 5.

69. $\log_5 5^3$ **70.** $\log_6 6^2$

71. $2^{\log_2 3}$ **72.** $7^{\log_7 4}$

73. $\log_9 9$ **74.** $\log_2 2$

75. $\log_8 (8)^{-1}$ **76.** $\log_{11} (11)^{-1}$

Graph each logarithmic function. Label any intercepts. See Examples 6 and 7.

77. $y = \log_3 x$ **78.** $y = \log_8 x$

79. $f(x) = \log_{1/4} x$ **80.** $f(x) = \log_{1/2} x$

81. $f(x) = \log_5 x$ **82.** $f(x) = \log_6 x$

83. $f(x) = \log_{1/6} x$ **84.** $f(x) = \log_{1/5} x$

REVIEW AND PREVIEW

Simplify each rational expression. See Section 7.1.

85. $\dfrac{x + 3}{3 + x}$ **86.** $\dfrac{x - 5}{5 - x}$

87. $\dfrac{x^2 - 8x + 16}{2x - 8}$ **88.** $\dfrac{x^2 - 3x - 10}{2 + x}$

Add or subtract as indicated. See Sections 7.3 and 7.4.

89. $\dfrac{2}{x} + \dfrac{3}{x^2}$ **90.** $\dfrac{5}{y + 1} - \dfrac{4}{y - 1}$

91. $\dfrac{3x}{x + 3} + \dfrac{9}{x + 3}$ **92.** $\dfrac{m^2}{m + 1} - \dfrac{1}{m + 1}$

CONCEPT EXTENSIONS

Solve. See the Concept Check in this section.

93. Let $f(x) = \log_5 x$. Then $g(x) = 5^x$ is the inverse of $f(x)$. The ordered pair $(2, 25)$ is a solution of the function $g(x)$.

   a. Write this solution using function notation.

   b. Write an ordered pair that we know to be a solution of $f(x)$.

   c. Use the answer to part b and write the solution using function notation.

94. Let $f(x) = \log_{0.3} x$. Then $g(x) = 0.3^x$ is the inverse of $f(x)$. The ordered pair $(3, 0.027)$ is a solution of the function $g(x)$.

   a. Write this solution using function notation.

   b. Write an ordered pair that we know to be a solution of $f(x)$.

   c. Use the answer to part b and write the solution using function notation.

95. Explain why negative numbers are not included as logarithmic bases.

96. Explain why 1 is not included as a logarithmic base.

Solve by first writing as an exponent.

97. $\log_7 (5x - 2) = 1$

98. $\log_3 (2x + 4) = 2$

99. Simplify: $\log_3(\log_5 125)$

100. Simplify: $\log_7(\log_4(\log_2 16))$

Graph each function and its inverse function on the same set of axes. Label any intercepts.

101. $y = 4^x; y = \log_4 x$

102. $y = 3^x; y = \log_3 x$

103. $y = \left(\dfrac{1}{3}\right)^x; y = \log_{1/3} x$

104. $y = \left(\dfrac{1}{2}\right)^x; y = \log_{1/2} x$

105. Explain why the graph of the function $y = \log_b x$ contains the point $(1, 0)$ no matter what b is.

106. $\log_3 10$ is between which two integers? Explain your answer.

107. The formula $\log_{10}(1 - k) = \dfrac{-0.3}{H}$ models the relationship between the half-life H of a radioactive material and its rate of decay k. Find the rate of decay of the iodine isotope I-131 if its half-life is 8 days. Round to four decimal places.

108. The formula $pH = -\log_{10}(H^+)$ provides the pH for a liquid, where H^+ stands for the concentration of hydronium ions. Find the pH of lemonade, whose concentration of hydronium ions is 0.0050 moles/liter. Round to the nearest tenth.

Appendix A

Operations on Decimals/Table of Percent, Decimal, and Fraction Equivalents

A.1 Operations on Decimals

To **add** or **subtract** decimals, write the numbers vertically with decimal points lined up. Add or subtract as with whole numbers and place the decimal point in the answer directly below the decimal points in the problem.

EXAMPLE 1   Add $5.87 + 23.279 + 0.003$.

Solution
$$
\begin{array}{r}
5.87 \\
23.279 \\
+\,0.003 \\
\hline
29.152
\end{array}
$$

EXAMPLE 2   Subtract $32.15 - 11.237$.

Solution

$$
\begin{array}{rccccc}
 & 3 & \overset{1}{2} . & \overset{11}{1} & \overset{4}{5} & \overset{10}{0} \\
- & 1 & 1 . & 2 & 3 & 7 \\
\hline
 & 2 & 0 . & 9 & 1 & 3
\end{array}
$$

To **multiply** decimals, multiply the numbers as if they were whole numbers. The decimal point in the product is placed so that the number of decimal places in the product is the same as the sum of the number of decimal places in the factors.

EXAMPLE 3   Multiply 0.072×3.5.

Solution
$$
\begin{array}{rl}
0.072 & \text{3 decimal places} \\
\times \quad 3.5 & \text{1 decimal place} \\
\hline
360 & \\
216 \quad\;\; & \\
\hline
0.2520 & \text{4 decimal places}
\end{array}
$$

To **divide** decimals, move the decimal point in the divisor to the right of the last digit. Move the decimal point in the dividend the same number of places that the decimal point in the divisor was moved. The decimal point in the quotient lies directly above the decimal point in the dividend.

EXAMPLE 4   Divide $9.46 \div 0.04$.

Solution
$$
\begin{array}{r}
236.5 \\
04.\overline{)946.0} \\
\underline{-8} \\
14 \\
\underline{-12} \\
26 \\
\underline{-24} \\
20 \\
\underline{-20}
\end{array}
$$

A Exercise Set

MyMathLab®

Perform the indicated operations.

1. 9.076 + 8.004

2. 6.3
× 0.05

3. 27.004
−14.2

4. 0.0036
7.12
32.502
+ 0.05

5. 107.92
+ 3.04

6. 7.2 ÷ 4

7. 10 − 7.6

8. 40 ÷ 0.25

9. 126.32 − 97.89

10. 3.62
7.11
12.36
4.15
+ 2.29

11. 3.25
× 70

12. 26.014
− 7.8

13. 8.1 ÷ 3

14. 1.2366
0.005
15.17
+ 0.97

15. 55.405 − 6.1711

16. 8.09 + 0.22

17. 60 ÷ 0.75

18. 20 − 12.29

19. 7.612 ÷ 100

20. 8.72
1.12
14.86
3.98
+ 1.99

21. 12.312 ÷ 2.7

22. 0.443 ÷ 100

23. 569.2
71.25
+ 8.01

24. 3.706 − 2.91

25. 768 − 0.17

26. 63 ÷ 0.28

27. 12 + 0.062

28. 0.42 + 18

29. 76 − 14.52

30. 1.1092 ÷ 0.47

31. 3.311 ÷ 0.43

32. 7.61 + 0.0004

33. 762.12
89.7
+ 11.55

34. 444 ÷ 0.6

35. 23.4 − 0.821

36. 3.7 + 5.6

37. 476.12 − 112.97

38. 19.872 ÷ 0.54

39. 0.007 + 7

40. 51.77
+ 3.6

A.2 Table of Percent, Decimal, and Fraction Equivalents

Percent, Decimal, and Fraction Equivalents

Percent	Decimal	Fraction
1%	0.01	$\frac{1}{100}$
5%	0.05	$\frac{1}{20}$
10%	0.1	$\frac{1}{10}$
12.5% or $12\frac{1}{2}$%	0.125	$\frac{1}{8}$
$16.\overline{6}$% or $16\frac{2}{3}$%	$0.1\overline{6}$	$\frac{1}{6}$
20%	0.2	$\frac{1}{5}$
25%	0.25	$\frac{1}{4}$
30%	0.3	$\frac{3}{10}$
$33.\overline{3}$% or $33\frac{1}{3}$%	$0.\overline{3}$	$\frac{1}{3}$
37.5% or $37\frac{1}{2}$%	0.375	$\frac{3}{8}$
40%	0.4	$\frac{2}{5}$
50%	0.5	$\frac{1}{2}$
60%	0.6	$\frac{3}{5}$
62.5% or $62\frac{1}{2}$%	0.625	$\frac{5}{8}$
$66.\overline{6}$% or $66\frac{2}{3}$%	$0.\overline{6}$	$\frac{2}{3}$
70%	0.7	$\frac{7}{10}$
75%	0.75	$\frac{3}{4}$
80%	0.8	$\frac{4}{5}$
$83.\overline{3}$% or $83\frac{1}{3}$%	$08.\overline{3}$	$\frac{5}{6}$
87.5% or $87\frac{1}{2}$%	0.875	$\frac{7}{8}$
90%	0.9	$\frac{9}{10}$
100%	1.0	1
110%	1.1	$1\frac{1}{10}$
125%	1.25	$1\frac{1}{4}$
$133.\overline{3}$% or $133\frac{1}{3}$%	$1.\overline{3}$	$1\frac{1}{3}$
150%	1.5	$1\frac{1}{2}$
$166.\overline{6}$% or $166\frac{2}{3}$%	$1.\overline{6}$	$1\frac{2}{3}$
175%	1.75	$1\frac{3}{4}$
200%	2.0	2

Appendix B

Review of Algebra Topics

Recall that equations model many real-life problems. For example, we can use a linear equation to calculate the increase in the number (in millions) of Wi-Fi-enabled cell phones.

Wi-Fi-enabled cell phones let you carry your Internet access with you. There are already several of these smart phones available, and this technology will continue to expand. Predicted numbers of Wi-Fi-enabled cell phones in the United States for various years are shown below.

To find the projected increase in the number of Wi-Fi-enabled cell phones in the United States from 2014 to 2015, for example, we can use the equation below.

In words:	Increase in cell phones	is	cell phones in 2015	minus	cell phones in 2014
Translate:	x	$=$	149	$-$	138

Since our variable x (increase in Wi-Fi-enabled cell phones) is by itself on one side of the equation, we can find the value of x by simplifying the right side.

$$x = 11$$

The projected increase in the number of Wi-Fi-enabled cell phones from 2014 to 2015 is 11 million.

The **equation** $x = 149 - 138$ is a linear equation in one variable. In this section, we review solving linear equations and quadratic equations that can be solved by factoring. We will learn other methods for solving quadratic equations in Chapter 11.

B.1 Equations (Linear and Quadratic Solved by Factoring)

OBJECTIVE

1 Solve linear and quadratic equations.

1 Solving Linear and Quadratic Equations

EXAMPLE 1   Solve: $2(x - 3) = 5x - 9$.

Solution   First, use the distributive property.

$$2(x - 3) = 5x - 9$$
$$2x - 6 = 5x - 9 \quad \text{Use the distributive property.}$$

Next, get variable terms on the same side of the equation by subtracting $5x$ from both sides.

$$2x - 6 - 5x = 5x - 9 - 5x \quad \text{Subtract } 5x \text{ from both sides.}$$
$$-3x - 6 = -9 \quad \text{Simplify.}$$
$$-3x - 6 + 6 = -9 + 6 \quad \text{Add 6 to both sides.}$$
$$-3x = -3 \quad \text{Simplify.}$$
$$\frac{-3x}{-3} = \frac{-3}{-3} \quad \text{Divide both sides by } -3.$$
$$x = 1$$

Let $x = 1$ in the original equation to see that 1 is the solution.

PRACTICE

1   Solve: $3(x - 5) = 6x - 3$.

Don't forget, if an equation contains fractions, you may want to first clear the equation of fractions by multiplying both sides of the equation by the *least common denominator* (LCD) of all fractions in the equation.

EXAMPLE 2   Solve for y: $\dfrac{y}{3} - \dfrac{y}{4} = \dfrac{1}{6}$.

Solution   First, clear the equation of fractions by multiplying both sides of the equation by 12, the LCD of denominators 3, 4, and 6.

$$\frac{y}{3} - \frac{y}{4} = \frac{1}{6}$$

$$12\left(\frac{y}{3} - \frac{y}{4}\right) = 12\left(\frac{1}{6}\right) \quad \text{Multiply both sides by the LCD 12.}$$

$$12\left(\frac{y}{3}\right) - 12\left(\frac{y}{4}\right) = 2 \quad \text{Apply the distributive property.}$$

$$4y - 3y = 2 \quad \text{Simplify.}$$

$$y = 2 \quad \text{Simplify.}$$

Check: To check, let $y = 2$ in the original equation.

$$\frac{y}{3} - \frac{y}{4} = \frac{1}{6} \quad \text{Original equation.}$$

$$\frac{2}{3} - \frac{2}{4} \stackrel{?}{=} \frac{1}{6} \quad \text{Let } y = 2.$$

$$\frac{8}{12} - \frac{6}{12} \stackrel{?}{=} \frac{1}{6} \qquad \text{Write fractions with the LCD.}$$

$$\frac{2}{12} \stackrel{?}{=} \frac{1}{6} \qquad \text{Subtract.}$$

$$\frac{1}{6} = \frac{1}{6} \qquad \text{Simplify.}$$

This is a true statement, so the solution is 2.

PRACTICE
2   Solve for y: $\dfrac{y}{2} - \dfrac{y}{5} = \dfrac{1}{4}$.

EXAMPLE 3   Solve: $3(x^2 + 4) + 5 = -6(x^2 + 2x) + 13$.

Solution   Rewrite the equation so that one side is 0.

$$3(x^2 + 4) + 5 = -6(x^2 + 2x) + 13$$
$$3x^2 + 12 + 5 = -6x^2 - 12x + 13 \qquad \text{Apply the distributive property.}$$
$$9x^2 + 12x + 4 = 0 \qquad \text{Rewrite the equation so that one side is 0.}$$
$$(3x + 2)(3x + 2) = 0 \qquad \text{Factor.}$$
$$3x + 2 = 0 \quad \text{or} \quad 3x + 2 = 0 \qquad \text{Set each factor equal to 0.}$$
$$3x = -2 \quad \text{or} \quad 3x = -2$$
$$x = -\frac{2}{3} \quad \text{or} \quad x = -\frac{2}{3} \qquad \text{Solve each equation.}$$

The solution is $-\dfrac{2}{3}$. Check by substituting $-\dfrac{2}{3}$ into the original equation.

PRACTICE
3   Solve: $8(x^2 + 3) + 4 = -8x(x + 3) + 19$.

EXAMPLE 4   Solve for x: $\dfrac{x + 5}{2} + \dfrac{1}{2} = 2x - \dfrac{x - 3}{8}$.

Solution   Multiply both sides of the equation by 8, the LCD of 2 and 8.

$$8\left(\frac{x + 5}{2} + \frac{1}{2}\right) = 8\left(2x - \frac{x - 3}{8}\right) \qquad \text{Multiply both sides by 8.}$$

$$8\left(\frac{x + 5}{2}\right) + 8 \cdot \frac{1}{2} = 8 \cdot 2x - 8\left(\frac{x - 3}{8}\right) \qquad \text{Apply the distributive property.}$$

$$4(x + 5) + 4 = 16x - (x - 3) \qquad \text{Simplify.}$$

$$4x + 20 + 4 = 16x - x + 3 \qquad \text{Use the distributive property to remove parentheses.}$$

$$4x + 24 = 15x + 3 \qquad \text{Combine like terms.}$$

$$-11x + 24 = 3 \qquad \text{Subtract 15x from both sides.}$$

$$-11x = -21 \qquad \text{Subtract 24 from both sides.}$$

$$\frac{-11x}{-11} = \frac{-21}{-11} \qquad \text{Divide both sides by } -11.$$

$$x = \frac{21}{11} \qquad \text{Simplify.}$$

> **Helpful Hint**
> When we multiply both sides of an equation by a number, the distributive property tells us that each term of the equation is multiplied by the number.

Check: To check, verify that replacing x with $\dfrac{21}{11}$ makes the original equation true. The solution is $\dfrac{21}{11}$.

PRACTICE
4   Solve for x: $x - \dfrac{x - 2}{12} = \dfrac{x + 3}{4} + \dfrac{1}{4}$.

EXAMPLE 5 Solve: $2x^2 = \dfrac{17}{3}x + 1$.

Solution

$$2x^2 = \frac{17}{3}x + 1$$

$$3(2x^2) = 3\left(\frac{17}{3}x + 1\right) \quad \text{Clear the equation of fractions.}$$

$$6x^2 = 17x + 3 \quad \text{Apply the distributive property.}$$

$$6x^2 - 17x - 3 = 0 \quad \text{Rewrite the equation in standard form.}$$

$$(6x + 1)(x - 3) = 0 \quad \text{Factor.}$$

$$6x + 1 = 0 \quad \text{or} \quad x - 3 = 0 \quad \text{Set each factor equal to zero.}$$

$$6x = -1$$

$$x = -\frac{1}{6} \quad \text{or} \quad x = 3 \quad \text{Solve each equation.}$$

The solutions are $-\dfrac{1}{6}$ and 3.

PRACTICE
5 Solve: $4x^2 = \dfrac{15}{2}x + 1$.

B.1 Exercise Set

MyMathLab®

MIXED PRACTICE

Solve each equation. See Examples 1 through 5.

1. $x^2 + 11x + 24 = 0$
2. $y^2 - 10y + 24 = 0$
3. $3x - 4 - 5x = x + 4 + x$
4. $13x - 15x + 8 = 4x + 2 - 24$
5. $12x^2 + 5x - 2 = 0$
6. $3y^2 - y - 14 = 0$
7. $z^2 + 9 = 10z$
8. $n^2 + n = 72$
9. $5(y + 4) = 4(y + 5)$
10. $6(y - 4) = 3(y - 8)$
11. $0.6x - 10 = 1.4x - 14$
12. $0.3x + 2.4 = 0.1x + 4$
13. $x(5x + 2) = 3$
14. $n(2n - 3) = 2$
15. $6x - 2(x - 3) = 4(x + 1) + 4$
16. $10x - 2(x + 4) = 8(x - 2) + 6$
17. $\dfrac{3}{8} + \dfrac{b}{3} = \dfrac{5}{12}$
18. $\dfrac{a}{2} + \dfrac{7}{4} = 5$
19. $x^2 - 6x = x(8 + x)$
20. $n(3 + n) = n^2 + 4n$
21. $\dfrac{z^2}{6} - \dfrac{z}{2} - 3 = 0$

22. $\dfrac{c^2}{20} - \dfrac{c}{4} + \dfrac{1}{5} = 0$
23. $-z + 3(2 + 4z) = 6(z + 1) + 5z$
24. $4(m - 6) - m = 8(m - 3) - 5m$
25. $\dfrac{x^2}{2} + \dfrac{x}{20} = \dfrac{1}{10}$
26. $\dfrac{y^2}{30} = \dfrac{y}{15} + \dfrac{1}{2}$
27. $\dfrac{4t^2}{5} = \dfrac{t}{5} + \dfrac{3}{10}$
28. $\dfrac{5x^2}{6} - \dfrac{7x}{2} + \dfrac{2}{3} = 0$
29. $\dfrac{3t + 1}{8} = \dfrac{5 + 2t}{7} + 2$
30. $4 - \dfrac{2z + 7}{9} = \dfrac{7 - z}{12}$
31. $\dfrac{m - 4}{3} - \dfrac{3m - 1}{5} = 1$
32. $\dfrac{n + 1}{8} - \dfrac{2 - n}{3} = \dfrac{5}{6}$
33. $3x^2 = -x$
34. $y^2 = -5y$
35. $x(x - 3) = x^2 + 5x + 7$
36. $z^2 - 4z + 10 = z(z - 5)$
37. $3(t - 8) + 2t = 7 + t$
38. $7c - 2(3c + 1) = 5(4 - 2c)$
39. $-3(x - 4) + x = 5(3 - x)$

40. $-4(a + 1) - 3a = -7(2a - 3)$

41. $(x - 1)(x + 4) = 24$

42. $(2x - 1)(x + 2) = -3$

43. $\dfrac{x^2}{4} - \dfrac{5}{2}x + 6 = 0$

44. $\dfrac{x^2}{18} + \dfrac{x}{2} + 1 = 0$

45. $y^2 + \dfrac{1}{4} = -y$

46. $\dfrac{x^2}{10} + \dfrac{5}{2} = x$

47. Which solution strategies are incorrect? Why?

  a. Solve $(y - 2)(y + 2) = 4$ by setting each factor equal to 4.

  b. Solve $(x + 1)(x + 3) = 0$ by setting each factor equal to 0.

  c. Solve $z^2 + 5z + 6 = 0$ by factoring $z^2 + 5z + 6$ and setting each factor equal to 0.

  d. Solve $x^2 + 6x + 8 = 10$ by factoring $x^2 + 6x + 8$ and setting each factor equal to 0.

48. Describe two ways a linear equation differs from a quadratic equation.

Find the value of K such that the equations are equivalent.

49. $3.2x + 4 = 5.4x - 7$
   $3.2x = 5.4x + K$

50. $-7.6y - 10 = -1.1y + 12$
   $-7.6y = -1.1y + K$

51. $\dfrac{x}{6} + 4 = \dfrac{x}{3}$
   $x + K = 2x$

52. $\dfrac{5x}{4} + \dfrac{1}{2} = \dfrac{x}{2}$
   $5x + K = 2x$

Solve and check.

53. $2.569x = -12.48534$

54. $-9.112y = -47.537304$

55. $2.86z - 8.1258 = -3.75$

56. $1.25x - 20.175 = -8.15$

B.2 | Problem Solving

OBJECTIVES

1 Write Algebraic Expressions That Can Be Simplified.

2 Apply the Steps for Problem Solving.

OBJECTIVE

1   Writing and Simplifying Algebraic Expressions

In order to prepare for problem solving, we practice writing algebraic expressions that can be simplified.

Our first example involves consecutive integers and perimeter. Recall that *consecutive integers* are integers that follow one another in order. Study the examples of consecutive, even, and odd integers and their representations.

Consecutive Integers:

Consecutive Even Integers:

Consecutive Odd Integers:

EXAMPLE 1   Write the following as algebraic expressions. Then simplify.

  a. The sum of three consecutive integers, if x is the first consecutive integer.

△ **b.** The perimeter of the triangle with sides of length x, $5x$, and $6x - 3$.

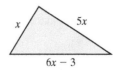

(Continued on next page)

Solution

a. Recall that if x is the first integer, then the next consecutive integer is 1 more, or $x + 1$, and the next consecutive integer is 1 more than $x + 1$, or $x + 2$.

In words:	first integer	plus	next consecutive integer	plus	next consecutive integer
	↓	↓	↓	↓	↓
Translate:	x	$+$	$(x + 1)$	$+$	$(x + 2)$

Then
$$x + (x + 1) + (x + 2) = x + x + 1 + x + 2$$
$$= 3x + 3 \quad \text{Simplify by combining like terms.}$$

b. The perimeter of a triangle is the sum of the lengths of the sides.

In words:	side	$+$	side	$+$	side
	↓		↓		↓
Translate:	x	$+$	$5x$	$+$	$(6x - 3)$

Then
$$x + 5x + (6x - 3) = x + 5x + 6x - 3$$
$$= 12x - 3 \quad \text{Simplify.} \qquad \square$$

PRACTICE

1   Write the following algebraic expressions. Then simplify.

a. The sum of three consecutive odd integers if x is the first consecutive odd integer

b. The perimeter of a trapezoid with bases x and $2x$ and sides of $x + 2$ and $2x - 3$

- ∎

EXAMPLE 2   **Writing Algebraic Expressions Representing Metropolitan Regions**

The most populous metropolitan region in the United States is New York City, although it is only the sixth most populous metropolis in the world. Tokyo is the most populous metropolitan region. Mexico City is the fifth most populous metropolis in the world. Mexico City's population is 0.03 million more than New York's, and Tokyo's is twice that of New York, decreased by 2.19 million. Write the sum of the populations of these three metropolitan regions as an algebraic expression. Let x be the population of New York (in millions). (*Source:* United Nations, Department of Economic and Social Affairs)

Solution:

$$\text{If } x = \text{ the population of New York (in millions), then}$$
$$x + 0.03 = \text{ the population of Mexico City (in millions) and}$$
$$2x - 2.19 = \text{ the population of Tokyo (in millions)}$$

In words:	population of New York		population of Mexico City		population of Tokyo
	↓		↓		↓
Translate:	x	$+$	$(x + 0.03)$	$+$	$(2x - 2.19)$

Then $x + (x + 0.03) + (2x - 2.19) = x + x + 2x + 0.03 - 2.19$
$$= 4x - 2.16 \quad \text{Combine like terms.}$$

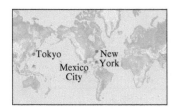

In Exercise 57, we will find the actual populations of these cities. $\square$

PRACTICE
2   The three busiest airports in Europe are in London, England; Paris, France; and Frankfurt, Germany. The airport in London has 12.9 million more arrivals and departures than the Frankfurt airport. The Paris airport has 5.2 million more arrivals and departures than the Frankfurt airport. Write the sum of the arrivals and departures from these three cities as a simplified algebraic expression. Let *x* be the number of arrivals and departures at the Frankfurt airport. (*Source:* Association of European Airlines)

OBJECTIVE
2   Applying Steps for Problem Solving

Our main purpose for studying algebra is to solve problems. The following problem-solving strategy will be used throughout this text and may also be used to solve real-life problems that occur outside the mathematics classroom.

General Strategy for Problem Solving

1. UNDERSTAND the problem. During this step, become comfortable with the problem. Some ways of doing this are to:

Read and reread the problem.

Propose a solution and check. Pay careful attention to how you check your proposed solution. This will help when writing an equation to model the problem.

Construct a drawing.

Choose a variable to represent the unknown. (Very important part)

2. TRANSLATE the problem into an equation.

3. SOLVE the equation.

4. INTERPRET the results: *Check* the proposed solution in the stated problem and *state* your conclusion.

Let's review this strategy by solving a problem involving unknown numbers.

EXAMPLE 3   **Finding Unknown Numbers**

Find three numbers such that the second number is 3 more than twice the first number, and the third number is four times the first number. The sum of the three numbers is 164.

Solution

> **▶ Helpful Hint**
>
> The purpose of guessing a solution is not to guess correctly but to gain confidence and to help understand the problem and how to model it.

1. UNDERSTAND the problem. First let's read and reread the problem and then propose a solution. For example, if the first number is 25, then the second number is 3 more than twice 25, or 53. The third number is four times 25, or 100. The sum of 25, 53, and 100 is 178, not the required sum, but we have gained some valuable information about the problem. First, we know that the first number is less than 25 since our guess led to a sum greater than the required sum. Also, we have gained some information as to how to model the problem.

   Next let's assign a variable and use this variable to represent any other unknown quantities. If we let

$$x = \text{the first number, then}$$

$$2x + 3 = \text{the second number}$$

3 more than
twice the first number

$$4x = \text{the third number}$$

(Continued on next page)

2. TRANSLATE the problem into an equation. To do so, we use the fact that the sum of the numbers is 164. First let's write this relationship in words and then translate to an equation.

In words:	first number	added to	second number	added to	third number	is	164
	↓	↓	↓	↓	↓	↓	↓
Translate:	x	+	$(2x + 3)$	+	$4x$	=	164

3. SOLVE the equation.

$$x + (2x + 3) + 4x = 164$$

$$x + 2x + 4x + 3 = 164 \quad \text{Remove parentheses.}$$

$$7x + 3 = 164 \quad \text{Combine like terms.}$$

$$7x = 161 \quad \text{Subtract 3 from both sides.}$$

$$x = 23 \quad \text{Divide both sides by 7.}$$

4. INTERPRET. Here, we *check* our work and *state* the solution. Recall that if the first number $x = 23$, then the second number $2x + 3 = 2 \cdot 23 + 3 = 49$ and the third number $4x = 4 \cdot 23 = 92$.

Check: Is the second number 3 more than twice the first number? Yes, since 3 more than twice 23 is $46 + 3$, or 49. Also, their sum, $23 + 49 + 92 = 164$, is the required sum.

State: The three numbers are 23, 49, and 92.   □

PRACTICE

3   Find three numbers such that the second number is 8 less than triple the first number, the third number is five times the first number, and the sum of the three numbers is 118.

Many of today's rates and statistics are given as percents. Interest rates, tax rates, nutrition labeling, and percent of households in a given category are just a few examples. Before we practice solving problems containing percents, let's briefly review the meaning of percent and how to find a percent of a number.

The word *percent* means "per hundred," and the symbol % denotes percent.

This means that 23% is 23 per hundred, or $\frac{23}{100}$. Also,

$$41\% = \frac{41}{100} = 0.41$$

To find a percent of a number, we multiply.

$$16\% \text{ of } 25 = 16\% \cdot 25 = 0.16 \cdot 25 = 4$$

Thus, 16% of 25 is 4.

Study the table below. It will help you become more familiar with finding percents.

Percent	*Meaning/Shortcut*	*Example*
50%	$\frac{1}{2}$ or half of a number	50% of 60 is 30.
25%	$\frac{1}{4}$ or a quarter of a number	25% of 60 is 15.
10%	0.1 or $\frac{1}{10}$ of a number (move the decimal point 1 place to the left)	10% of 60 is 6.0 or 6.
1%	0.01 or $\frac{1}{100}$ of a number (move the decimal point 2 places to the left)	1% of 60 is 0.60 or 0.6.
100%	1 or all of a number	100% of 60 is 60.
200%	2 or double a number	200% of 60 is 120.

✓CONCEPT CHECK
Suppose you are finding 112% of a number x. Which of the following is a correct description of the result? Explain.

a. The result is less than x.   **b.** The result is equal to x.   **c.** The result is greater than x.

Next, we solve a problem containing a percent.

EXAMPLE 4   **Finding the Original Price of a Computer**

Suppose that a computer store just announced an 8% decrease in the price of a particular computer model. If this computer sells for $2162 after the decrease, find the original price of this computer.

Solution

1. **UNDERSTAND.** Read and reread the problem. Recall that a percent decrease means a percent of the original price. Let's guess that the original price of the computer is $2500. The amount of decrease is then 8% of $2500, or $(0.08)(\$2500) = \$200$. This means that the new price of the computer is the original price minus the decrease, or $2500 − $200 = $2300. Our guess is incorrect, but we now have an idea of how to model this problem. In our model, we will let x = the original price of the computer.

2. **TRANSLATE.**

In words:	the original price of computer	minus	8% of the original price	is	the new price
	↓	↓	↓	↓	↓
Translate:	x	−	$0.08x$	=	2162

3. **SOLVE** the equation.

$$x - 0.08x = 2162$$
$$0.92x = 2162 \qquad \text{Combine like terms.}$$
$$x = \frac{2162}{0.92} = 2350 \qquad \text{Divide both sides by 0.92.}$$

4. **INTERPRET.**

Check: If the original price of the computer was $2350, the new price is
$$\$2350 - (0.08)(\$2350) = \$2350 - \$188$$
$$= \$2162 \qquad \text{The given new price}$$

State: The original price of the computer was $2350.

PRACTICE
4   At the end of the season, the cost of a snowboard was reduced by 40%. If the snowboard sells for $270 after the decrease, find the original price of the board.

Vocabulary & Readiness Check

Fill in each blank with $<$, $>$, or $=$. (Assume that the unknown number is a positive number.)

1. 130% of a number ____ the number.   **2.** 70% of a number ____ the number.

3. 100% of a number ____ the number.   **4.** 200% of a number ____ the number.

Complete the table. The first row has been completed for you.

	First Integer	All Described Integers
Three consecutive integers	18	18, 19, 20
5. Four consecutive integers	31	
6. Three consecutive odd integers	31	
7. Three consecutive even integers	18	
8. Four consecutive even integers	92	
9. Three consecutive integers	y	
10. Three consecutive even integers	z (z is even)	
11. Four consecutive integers	p	
12. Three consecutive odd integers	s (s is odd)	

B.2 Exercise Set MyMathLab®

Write the following as algebraic expressions. Then simplify. See Examples 1 and 2.

△ **1.** The perimeter of a square with side length y.

△ **2.** The perimeter of a rectangle with length x and width $x - 5$.

3. The sum of three consecutive integers if the first is z.

4. The sum of three consecutive odd integers if the first integer is z.

5. The total amount of money (in cents) in x nickels, $(x + 3)$ dimes, and $2x$ quarters. (*Hint:* The value of a nickel is 5 cents, the value of a dime is 10 cents, and the value of a quarter is 25 cents.)

6. The total amount of money (in cents) in y quarters, $7y$ dimes, and $(2y - 1)$ nickels. (Use the hint for Exercise 5.)

△ **7.** A piece of land along Bayou Liberty is to be fenced and subdivided as shown so that each rectangle has the same dimensions. Express the total amount of fencing needed as an algebraic expression in x.

8. A flooded piece of land near the Mississippi River in New Orleans is to be surveyed and divided into 4 rectangles of equal dimension. Express the total amount of fencing needed as an algebraic expression in x.

△ **9.** Write the perimeter of the floor plan shown as an algebraic expression in x.

10. Write the perimeter of the floor plan shown as an algebraic expression in x.

Solve. For Exercises 11 and 12, the solutions have been started for you. See Example 3.

11. Four times the difference of a number and 2 is the same as 2, increased by four times the number, plus twice the number. Find the number.

Start the solution:

1. UNDERSTAND the problem. Reread it as many times as needed.

2. TRANSLATE into an equation. (Fill in the blanks below.)

Four times	the difference of a number and 2	is the same as	2	increased by	four times the number	plus	twice the number
↓	↓	↓	↓	↓	↓	↓	↓
4 ·	(x − 2)	=	2	___	___	___	___

Finish with:

3. SOLVE and 4. INTERPRET

12. Twice the sum of a number and 3 is the same as five times the number, minus 1, minus four times the number. Find the number.

Start the solution:

1. UNDERSTAND the problem. Reread it as many times as needed.

2. TRANSLATE into an equation. (Fill in the blanks below.)

Twice	the sum of a number and 3	is the same as	five times the number	minus	1	minus	four times the number
↓	↓	↓	↓	↓	↓	↓	↓
2	(x + 3)	=	___	___	1	___	___

Finish with:

3. SOLVE and 4. INTERPRET

13. A second number is five times a first number. A third number is 100 more than the first number. If the sum of the three numbers is 415, find the numbers.

14. A second number is 6 less than a first number. A third number is twice the first number. If the sum of the three numbers is 306, find the numbers.

Solve. See Example 4.

15. The United States consists of 2271 million acres of land. Approximately 29% of this land is federally owned. Find the number of acres that are not federally owned. (*Source:* U.S. General Services Administration)

16. The state of Nevada contains the most federally owned acres of land in the United States. If 90% of the state's 70 million acres of land is federally owned, find the number of acres that are not federally owned. (*Source:* U.S. General Services Administration)

17. In 2010, 8476 earthquakes occurred in the United States. Of these, 91.4% were minor tremors with magnitudes of 3.9 or less on the Richter scale. How many minor earthquakes occurred in the United States in 2010? Round to the nearest whole. (*Source:* U.S. Geological Survey National Earthquake Information Center)

18. Of the 1543 tornadoes that occurred in the United States during 2010, 27.7% occurred during the month of June. How many tornadoes occurred in the United States during June 2010? Round to the nearest whole. (*Source:* Storm Prediction Center)

19. In a recent survey, 15% of online shoppers in the United States say that they prefer to do business only with large, well-known retailers. In a group of 1500 online shoppers, how many are willing to do business with any size retailers? (*Source:* Inc.com)

20. In 2010, the restaurant industry employed 9% of the U.S. workforce. If there are estimated to be 141 million Americans in the workforce, how many people are employed by the restaurant industry? Round to the nearest tenth. (*Source:* National Restaurant Association, U.S. Bureau of Labor Statistics)

The following graph is called a circle graph or a pie chart. The circle represents a whole, or in this case, 100%. This particular graph shows the number of minutes per day that people use email at work. Use this graph to answer Exercises 21 through 24.

Time Spent on Email at Work

Source: Pew Internet & American Life Project

21. What percent of email users at work spend less than 15 minutes on email per day?

22. Among email users at work, what is the most common time spent on email per day?

23. If it were estimated that a large company has 4633 employees, how many of these would you expect to be using email more than 3 hours per day?

24. If it were estimated that a medium-size company has 250 employees, how many of these would you expect to be using email between 2 and 3 hours per day?

MIXED PRACTICE

Use the diagrams to find the unknown measures of angles or lengths of sides. Recall that the sum of the angle measures of a triangle is 180°.

25.

26.

27.

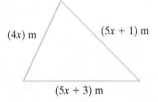

Perimeter is 102 meters.

28.

Perimeter is 75 centimeters.

29.

Perimeter is 99 inches.

30.

Perimeter is 324 feet.

Solve.

31. The sum of three consecutive integers is 228. Find the integers.

32. The sum of three consecutive odd integers is 327. Find the integers.

33. The ZIP codes of three Nevada locations—Fallon, Fernley, and Gardnerville Ranchos—are three consecutive even integers. If twice the first integer added to the third is 268,222, find each ZIP code.

34. During a recent year, the average SAT scores in math for the states of Alabama, Louisiana, and Michigan were 3 consecutive integers. If the sum of the first integer, second integer, and three times the third integer is 2637, find each score.

Many companies predict the growth or decline of various technologies. The following data is based on information from Techcrunchies, a technological information site. Notice that the first table is the predicted increase in the number of Wi-Fi-enabled cell phones (in millions), and the second is the predicted percent increase in the number of Wi-Fi-enabled cell phones in the United States.

35. Use the middle column in the table to find the predicted number of Wi-Fi-enabled cell phones for each year.

Year	Increase in Wi-Fi-Enabled Cell Phones	Predicted Number
2010	$2x - 21$	
2012	$\dfrac{5}{2}x + 2$	
2014	$3x + 24$	
Total	290 million	

36. Use the middle column in the table to find the predicted percent increase in the number of Wi-Fi-enabled cell phones for each year.

Year	Percent Increase in Wi-Fi-Enabled Cell Phones since 2009	Predicted Percent Increase
2010	x	
2011	$2x + 10$	
2012	$4x - 25$	
	300%	

Solve.

37. The occupations of biomedical engineers, skin care specialists, and physician assistants are among the 10 with the largest growth from 2008 to 2018. The number of physician assistant jobs will grow 7 thousand less than three times the number of biomedical engineer jobs. The number of skin care specialist jobs will grow 9 thousand more than half the number of biomedical engineer jobs. If the total growth of these three jobs is predicted to be 56 thousand, find the predicted growth of each job. (*Source:* U.S. Department of Labor, Bureau of Labor Statistics)

38. The occupations of farmer or rancher, file clerk, and telemarketer are among the 10 jobs with the largest decline from 2008 to 2018. The number of file clerk jobs is predicted to decline 11 thousand more than the number of telemarketer jobs. The number of farmer or rancher jobs is predicted to decline 3 thousand more than twice the number of telemarketer jobs. If the total decline of these three jobs is predicted to be 166 thousand, find the predicted decline of each job. (*Source:* U.S. Department of Labor, Bureau of Labor Statistics)

39. The B767-300ER aircraft has 88 more seats than the B737-200 aircraft. The F-100 has 32 fewer seats than the B737-200 aircraft. If their total number of seats is 413, find the number of seats for each aircraft. (*Source:* Air Transport Association of America)

40. Cowboy Stadium, home of the Dallas Cowboys of the NFL, seats approximately 9800 more fans than does Candlestick Park, home of the San Francisco 49ers. Soldier Field, home of the Chicago Bears, seats 8700 fewer fans than Candlestick Park. If the total seats in these three stadiums is 211,700, how many seats are in each of the three stadiums?

41. A new fax machine was recently purchased for an office in Hopedale for $464.40 including tax. If the tax rate in Hopedale is 8%, find the price of the fax machine before tax.

42. A premedical student at a local university was complaining that she had just paid $158.60 for her human anatomy book, including tax. Find the price of the book before taxes if the tax rate at this university is 9%.

43. The median compensation for a U.S. university president was $436,000 for the 2008–2009 academic year. Calculate the salary of a university president who received a 2.3% raise.

44. In 2009, the population of Brazil was 191.5 million. This represented a decrease in population of 3.7% from 2000. What was the population of Brazil in 2000? Round to the nearest tenth of a million. (*Source:* Population Reference Bureau)

45. In 2010, the population of Swaziland was 1,200,000 people. From 2010 to 2050, Swaziland's population is expected to increase by 50%. Find the expected population of Swaziland in 2050. (*Source:* Population Reference Bureau)

46. Dana, an auto parts supplier headquartered in Toledo, Ohio, recently announced it would be cutting 11,000 jobs worldwide. This is equivalent to 15% of Dana's workforce. Find the size of Dana's workforce prior to this round of job layoffs. Round to the nearest whole. (*Source:* Dana Corporation)

Recall that two angles are complements of each other if their sum is 90°. Two angles are supplements of each other if their sum is 180°. Find the measure of each angle.

47. One angle is three times its supplement increased by 20°. Find the measures of the two supplementary angles.

48. One angle is twice its complement increased by 30°. Find the measure of the two complementary angles.

Recall that the sum of the angle measures of a triangle is 180°.

49. Find the measures of the angles of a triangle if the measure of one angle is twice the measure of a second angle and the third angle measures 3 times the second angle decreased by 12.

50. Find the angles of an isoceles triangle whose two base angles are equal and whose third angle is 10° less than three times a base angle.

51. Two frames are needed with the same perimeter: one frame in the shape of a square and one in the shape of an equilateral triangle. Each side of the triangle is 6 centimeters longer than each side of the square. Find the dimensions of each frame. (An equilateral triangle has sides that are the same length.)

52. Two frames are needed with the same perimeter: one frame in the shape of a square and one in the shape of a regular pentagon. Each side of the square is 7 inches longer than each side of the pentagon. Find the dimensions of each frame. (A regular polygon has sides that are the same length.)

53. The sum of the first and third of three consecutive even integers is 156. Find the three even integers.

54. The sum of the second and fourth of four consecutive integers is 110. Find the four integers.

55. Daytona International Speedway in Florida has 37,000 more grandstand seats than twice the number of grandstand seats at Darlington Motor Raceway in South Carolina. Together, these two race tracks seat 220,000 NASCAR fans. How many seats does each race track have? (*Source:* NASCAR)

56. For the 2010–2011 National Hockey League season, the payroll for the San Jose Sharks was $5,986,667 more than that for the Montreal Canadiens. The total payroll for these two teams was $113,103,333. What were the payrolls for these two teams for the 2010–2011 NHL season?

57. The sum of the populations of the metropolitan regions of New York, Tokyo, and Mexico City is 75.56 million. Use this information and Example 2 in this section to find the population of each metropolitan region. (*Source:* United Nations Department of Economic and Social Affairs)

58. The airports in London, Paris, and Frankfurt have a total of 177.1 million annual arrivals and departures. Use this information and Practice 2 in this section to find the number from each airport.

59. Suppose the perimeter of the triangle in Example 1b in this section is 483 feet. Find the length of each side.

60. Suppose the perimeter of the trapezoid in Practice 1b in this section is 110 meters. Find the lengths of its sides and bases.

61. Incandescent, fluorescent, and halogen bulbs are lasting longer today than ever before. On average, the number of bulb hours for a fluorescent bulb is 25 times the number of bulb hours for a halogen bulb. The number of bulb hours for an incandescent bulb is 2500 less than the halogen bulb. If the total number of bulb hours for the three types of bulbs is 105,500, find the number of bulb hours for each type. (*Source: Popular Science* magazine)

62. Falkland Islands, Iceland, and Norway are the top three countries that have the greatest Internet penetration rate (percent of population) in the world. Falkland Islands has a 6.8 percent greater penetration rate than Iceland. Norway has a 2.3 percent less penetration rate than Iceland. If the sum of the penetration rates is 284.1, find the Internet penetration rate in each of these countries. (*Source*: Internet World Stats)

63. During the 2010 Major League Baseball season, the number of wins for the Milwaukee Brewers, Houston Astros, and Chicago Cubs was three consecutive integers. Of these three teams, the Milwaukee Brewers had the most wins. The Chicago Cubs had the least wins. The total number of wins by these three teams was 228. How many wins did each team have in the 2010 season?

64. In the 2010 Winter Olympics, Austria won more medals than the Russian Federation, which won more medals than South Korea. If the numbers of medals won by these three countries is three consecutive integers whose sum is 45, find the number of medals won by each. (*Source*: Vancouver 2010)

65. The three tallest hospitals in the world are Guy's Tower in London, Queen Mary Hospital in Hong Kong, and Galter Pavilion in Chicago. These buildings have a total height of 1320 feet. Guy's Tower is 67 feet taller than Galter Pavilion, and the Queen Mary Hospital is 47 feet taller than Galter Pavilion. Find the heights of the three hospitals.

66. The official manual for traffic signs is the *Manual on Uniform Traffic Control Devices* published by the Government Printing Office. The rectangular sign below has a length 12 inches more than twice its height. If the perimeter of the sign is 312 inches, find its dimensions.

B.3 Graphing

OBJECTIVES

1 Plot Ordered Pairs.

2 Graph Linear Equations.

OBJECTIVE

1 Plotting Ordered Pairs

Graphs are widely used today in newspapers, magazines, and all forms of newsletters. A few examples of graphs are shown here.

Percent of People Who Go to the Movies

Source: Motion Picture Association of America

Projected Growth of Wi-Fi-Enabled Cell Phones in U.S.

Source: Techcrunchies.com   * (projected)

To review how to read these graphs, we review their origin—the rectangular coordinate system. One way to locate points on a plane is by using a **rectangular coordinate system,** which is also called a **Cartesian coordinate system** after its inventor, René Descartes (1596–1650). The next diagram to the left shows the rectangular coordinate system. For further review of this system, see Section 3.1.

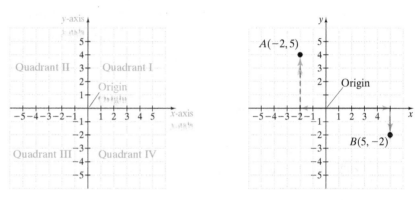

Recall that the location of point A in the figure above is described as 2 units to the left of the origin along the x-axis and 5 units upward parallel to the y-axis. Thus, we identify point A with the ordered pair $(-2, 5)$. Notice that the order of these numbers is *critical*. The x-value -2 is called the **x-coordinate** and is associated with the x-axis. The y-value 5 is called the **y-coordinate** and is associated with the y-axis. Compare the location of point A with the location of point B, which corresponds to the ordered pair $(5, -2)$.

Keep in mind that **each ordered pair corresponds to exactly one point in the real plane and that each point in the plane corresponds to exactly one ordered pair.** Thus, we may refer to the ordered pair (x, y) as the point (x, y).

EXAMPLE 1   Plot each ordered pair on a Cartesian coordinate system and name the quadrant or axis in which the point is located.

a. $(2, -1)$ **b.** $(0, 5)$ **c.** $(-3, 5)$

d. $(-2, 0)$ **e.** $\left(-\dfrac{1}{2}, -4\right)$ **f.** $(1.5, 1.5)$

Solution   The six points are graphed as shown on the next page.

a. $(2, -1)$ is in quadrant IV.   **b.** $(0, 5)$ is on the y-axis.

c. $(-3, 5)$ is in quadrant II.   **d.** $(-2, 0)$ is on the x-axis.

e. $\left(-\dfrac{1}{2}, -4\right)$ is in quadrant III.   **f.** $(1.5, 1.5)$ is in quadrant I.

(Continued on next page)

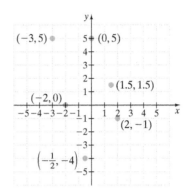

PRACTICE

1 Plot each ordered pair on a Cartesian coordinate system and name the quadrant or axis in which the point is located.

a. $(3, -4)$ **b.** $(0, -2)$ **c.** $(-2, 4)$ **d.** $(4, 0)$ **e.** $\left(-1\frac{1}{2}, -2\right)$ **f.** $(2.5, 3.5)$

Notice that the y-coordinate of any point on the x-axis is 0. For example, the point with coordinates $(-2, 0)$ lies on the x-axis. Also, the x-coordinate of any point on the y-axis is 0. For example, the point with coordinates $(0, 5)$ lies on the y-axis. These points that lie on the axes do not lie in any quadrants.

✓CONCEPT CHECK

Which of the following correctly describes the location of the point $(3, -6)$ in a rectangular coordinate system?

a. 3 units to the left of the y-axis and 6 units above the x-axis

b. 3 units above the x-axis and 6 units to the left of the y-axis

c. 3 units to the right of the y-axis and 6 units below the x-axis

d. 3 units below the x-axis and 6 units to the right of the y-axis

---

OBJECTIVE

2 Graphing Linear Equations

Recall that an equation such as $3x - y = 12$ is called a linear equation in two variables, and **the graph of every linear equation in two variables is a line.**

Linear Equation in Two Variables

A linear equation in two variables is an equation that can be written in the form

$$Ax + By = C$$

where A and B are not both 0. This form is called **standard form.**

Some examples of equations in standard form:

$$3x - y = 12$$
$$-2.1x + 5.6y = 0$$

▶ **Helpful Hint**

Remember: A linear equation is written in standard form when all of the variable terms are on one side of the equation and the constant is on the other side.

EXAMPLE 2 Graph the equation $y = -2x + 3$.

Solution This is a linear equation. (In standard form it is $2x + y = 3$.) Find three ordered pair solutions, and plot the ordered pairs. The line through the plotted points is the graph. Since the equation is solved for y, let's choose three x-values. We'll choose $0, 2$, and then -1 for x to find our three ordered pair solutions.

Let $x = 0$

$y = -2x + 3$
$y = -2 \cdot 0 + 3$
$y = 3$ Simplify.

Let $x = 2$

$y = -2x + 3$
$y = -2 \cdot 2 + 3$
$y = -1$ Simplify.

Let $x = -1$

$y = -2x + 3$
$y = -2(-1) + 3$
$y = 5$ Simplify.

The three ordered pairs $(0, 3)$, $(2, -1)$, and $(-1, 5)$ are listed in the table and the graph is shown.

x	y
0	3
2	-1
-1	5

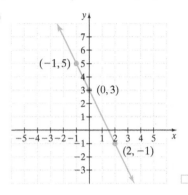

PRACTICE
2   Graph the equation $y = -3x - 2$.

Notice that the graph crosses the y-axis at the point $(0, 3)$. This point is called the **y-intercept.** (You may sometimes see just the number 3 called the y-intercept.) This graph also crosses the x-axis at the point $\left(\dfrac{3}{2}, 0\right)$. This point is called the **x-intercept.** (You may also see just the number $\dfrac{3}{2}$ called the x-intercept.)

Since every point on the y-axis has an x-value of 0, we can find the y-intercept of a graph by letting $x = 0$ and solving for y. Also, every point on the x-axis has a y-value of 0. To find the x-intercept, we let $y = 0$ and solve for x.

> **Finding x- and y-Intercepts**
>
> To find an x-intercept, let $y = 0$ and solve for x.
> To find a y-intercept, let $x = 0$ and solve for y.

EXAMPLE 3 Graph the linear equation $y = \dfrac{1}{3}x$.

Solution To graph, we find ordered pair solutions, plot the ordered pairs, and draw a line through the plotted points. We will choose x-values and substitute in the equation. To avoid fractions, we choose x-values that are multiples of 3. To find the y-intercept, we let $x = 0$.

> ▶ **Helpful Hint**
> Notice that by using multiples of 3 for x, we avoid fractions.

> ▶ **Helpful Hint**
> Since the equation $y = \dfrac{1}{3}x$ is solved for y, we choose x-values for finding points. This way, we simply need to evaluate an expression to find the y-value, as shown.

$$y = \frac{1}{3}x$$

If $x = 0$, then $y = \dfrac{1}{3}(0)$, or 0.

If $x = 6$, then $y = \dfrac{1}{3}(6)$, or 2.

If $x = -3$, then $y = \dfrac{1}{3}(-3)$, or -1.

x	y
0	0
6	2
-3	-1

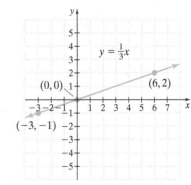

(Continued on next page)

This graph crosses the *x*-axis at $(0, 0)$ and the *y*-axis at $(0, 0)$. This means that the *x*-intercept is $(0, 0)$ and that the *y*-intercept is $(0, 0)$. ☐

PRACTICE
3 Graph the linear equation $y = -\dfrac{1}{2}x$.

B.3 Exercise Set

Determine the coordinates of each point on the graph.

1. Point *A*
2. Point *B*
3. Point *C*
4. Point *D*
5. Point *E*
6. Point *F*
7. Point *G*
8. Point *H*

Without graphing, visualize the location of each point. Then give its location by quadrant or x- or y-axis. See Example 1.

9. $(2, 3)$
10. $(0, 5)$
11. $(-2, 7)$
12. $(-3, 0)$
13. $(-1, -4)$
14. $(4, -2)$
15. $(0, -100)$
16. $(10, 30)$
17. $(-10, -30)$
18. $(0, 0)$
19. $(-87, 0)$
20. $(-42, 17)$

Given that x is a positive number and that y is a positive number, determine the quadrant or axis in which each point lies.

21. $(x, -y)$
22. $(-x, y)$
23. $(x, 0)$
24. $(0, -y)$
25. $(-x, -y)$
26. $(0, 0)$

Graph each linear equation. See Examples 2 and 3.

27. $y = -x - 2$
28. $y = -2x + 1$
29. $3x - 4y = 8$
30. $x - 9y = 3$
31. $y = \dfrac{1}{3}x$
32. $y = \dfrac{3}{2}x$
33. $y + 4 = 0$
34. $x = -1.5$

Recall that if $f(2) = 7$, for example, this corresponds to the ordered pair $(2, 7)$ on the graph of f. Use this information and the graphs of f and g below to answer Exercises 35 through 42.

 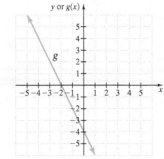

35. $f(4) =$
36. $f(0) =$
37. $g(0) =$
38. $g(-1) =$
39. Find all values for *x* such that $f(x) = 0$.
40. Find all values for *x* such that $g(x) = 0$.
41. If $(-1, -2)$ is a point on the graph of *g*, write this using function notation.
42. If $(-1, 2)$ is a point on the graph of *f*, write this using function notation.

B.4 Polynomials and Factoring

OBJECTIVE
1 Operations on Polynomials

OBJECTIVES

1 Review Operations on Polynomials.
2 Review Factoring Polynomials.

B.4 Exercise Set, Part 1

Perform each indicated operation.

1. $(-y^2 + 6y - 1) + (3y^2 - 4y - 10)$
2. $(5z^4 - 6z^2 + z + 1) - (7z^4 - 2z + 1)$
3. Subtract $(x - 5)$ from $(x^2 - 6x + 2)$.
4. $(2x^2 + 6x - 5) + (5x^2 - 10x)$
5. $(5x - 3)^2$
6. $(5x^2 - 14x - 3) \div (5x + 1)$

7. $(2x^4 - 3x^2 + 5x - 2) \div (x + 2)$

8. $(4x - 1)(x^2 - 3x - 2)$

2   Factoring Strategies

The key to proficiency in factoring polynomials is to practice until you are comfortable with each technique. A strategy for factoring polynomials completely is given next.

Factoring a Polynomial

Step 1. Are there any common factors? If so, factor out the greatest common factor.

Step 2. How many terms are in the polynomial?

   a. If there are *two* terms, decide if one of the following formulas may be applied:

   i. Difference of two squares: $a^2 - b^2 = (a - b)(a + b)$
   ii. Difference of two cubes: $a^3 - b^3 = (a - b)(a^2 + ab + b^2)$
   iii. Sum of two cubes: $a^3 + b^3 = (a + b)(a^2 - ab + b^2)$

   b. If there are *three* terms, try one of the following:

   i. Perfect square trinomial: $a^2 + 2ab + b^2 = (a + b)^2$
   $$a^2 - 2ab + b^2 = (a - b)^2$$

   ii. If not a perfect square trinomial, factor by using the methods presented in Sections 6.2 through 6.4.

   c. If there are *four* or more terms, try factoring by grouping.

Step 3. See whether any factors in the factored polynomial can be factored further.

A few examples are worked for you below.

EXAMPLE 1   Factor each polynomial completely.

a. $8a^2b - 4ab$ **b.** $36x^2 - 9$ **c.** $2x^2 - 5x - 7$
d. $5p^2 + 5 + qp^2 + q$ **e.** $9x^2 + 24x + 16$ **f.** $y^2 + 25$

Solution

a. Step 1. The terms have a common factor of $4ab$, which we factor out.

$$8a^2b - 4ab = 4ab(2a - 1)$$

    Step 2. There are two terms, but the binomial $2a - 1$ is not the difference of two squares or the sum or difference of two cubes.

    Step 3. The factor $2a - 1$ cannot be factored further.

b. Step 1. Factor out a common factor of 9.

$$36x^2 - 9 = 9(4x^2 - 1)$$

    Step 2. The factor $4x^2 - 1$ has two terms, and it is the difference of two squares.

$$9(4x^2 - 1) = 9(2x + 1)(2x - 1)$$

    Step 3. No factor with more than one term can be factored further.

c. Step 1. The terms of $2x^2 - 5x - 7$ contain no common factor other than 1 or -1.

    Step 2. There are three terms. The trinomial is not a perfect square, so we factor by methods from Section 6.3 or 6.4.

$$2x^2 - 5x - 7 = (2x - 7)(x + 1)$$

    Step 3. No factor with more than one term can be factored further.

(Continued on next page)

Appendix B content:

d. Step 1. There is no common factor of all terms of $5p^2 + 5 + qp^2 + q$.

Step 2. The polynomial has four terms, so try factoring by grouping.

$$5p^2 + 5 + qp^2 + q = (5p^2 + 5) + (qp^2 + q) \quad \text{Group the terms.}$$
$$= 5(p^2 + 1) + q(p^2 + 1)$$
$$= (p^2 + 1)(5 + q)$$

Step 3. No factor can be factored further.

e. Step 1. The terms of $9x^2 + 24x + 16$ contain no common factor other than 1 or -1.

Step 2. The trinomial $9x^2 + 24x + 16$ is a perfect square trinomial, and $9x^2 + 24x + 16 = (3x + 4)^2$.

Step 3. No factor can be factored further.

f. Step 1. There is no common factor of $y^2 + 25$ other than 1.

Step 2. This binomial is the sum of two squares and is prime.

Step 3. The binomial $y^2 + 25$ cannot be factored further.

PRACTICE

1 Factor each polynomial completely.

a. $12x^2y - 3xy$
b. $49x^2 - 4$
c. $5x^2 + 2x - 3$
d. $3x^2 + 6 + x^3 + 2x$
e. $4x^2 + 20x + 25$
f. $b^2 + 100$

EXAMPLE 2 Factor each polynomial completely.

a. $27a^3 - b^3$
b. $3n^2m^4 - 48m^6$
c. $2x^2 - 12x + 18 - 2z^2$
d. $8x^4y^2 + 125xy^2$
e. $(x - 5)^2 - 49y^2$

Solution

a. This binomial is the difference of two cubes.

$$27a^3 - b^3 = (3a)^3 - b^3$$
$$= (3a - b)[(3a)^2 + (3a)(b) + b^2]$$
$$= (3a - b)(9a^2 + 3ab + b^2)$$

b. $3n^2m^4 - 48m^6 = 3m^4(n^2 - 16m^2)$ Factor out the GCF $3m^4$.
$$= 3m^4(n + 4m)(n - 4m) \quad \text{Factor the difference of squares.}$$

c. $2x^2 - 12x + 18 - 2z^2 = 2(x^2 - 6x + 9 - z^2)$ The GCF is 2.
$$= 2[(x^2 - 6x + 9) - z^2] \quad \text{Group the first three terms together.}$$
$$= 2[(x - 3)^2 - z^2] \quad \text{Factor the perfect square trinomial.}$$
$$= 2[(x - 3) + z][(x - 3) - z] \quad \text{Factor the difference of squares.}$$
$$= 2(x - 3 + z)(x - 3 - z)$$

d. $8x^4y^2 + 125xy^2 = xy^2(8x^3 + 125)$ The GCF is xy^2.
$$= xy^2[(2x)^3 + 5^3]$$
$$= xy^2(2x + 5)[(2x)^2 - (2x)(5) + 5^2] \quad \text{Factor the sum of cubes.}$$
$$= xy^2(2x + 5)(4x^2 - 10x + 25)$$

e. This binomial is the difference of squares.

$$(x - 5)^2 - 49y^2 = (x - 5)^2 - (7y)^2$$
$$= [(x - 5) + 7y][(x - 5) - 7y]$$
$$= (x - 5 + 7y)(x - 5 - 7y)$$

PRACTICE

2   Factor each polynomial completely.

a. $64x^3 + y^3$

b. $7x^2y^2 - 63y^4$

c. $3x^2 + 12x + 12 - 3b^2$

d. $x^5y^4 + 27x^2y$

e. $(x + 7)^2 - 81y^2$

B.4   Exercise Set, Part 2

MyMathLab®

Factor completely.

9. $x^2 - 8x + 16 - y^2$

10. $12x^2 - 22x - 20$

11. $x^4 - x$

12. $(2x + 1)^2 - 3(2x + 1) + 2$

13. $14x^2y - 2xy$

14. $24ab^2 - 6ab$

15. $4x^2 - 16$

16. $9x^2 - 81$

17. $3x^2 - 8x - 11$

18. $5x^2 - 2x - 3$

19. $4x^2 + 8x - 12$

20. $6x^2 - 6x - 12$

21. $4x^2 + 36x + 81$

22. $25x^2 + 40x + 16$

23. $8x^3 + 125y^3$

24. $27x^3 - 64y^3$

25. $64x^2y^3 - 8x^2$

26. $27x^5y^4 - 216x^2y$

27. $(x + 5)^3 + y^3$

28. $(y - 1)^3 + 27x^3$

29. $(5a - 3)^2 - 6(5a - 3) + 9$

30. $(4r + 1)^2 + 8(4r + 1) + 16$

31. $7x^2 - 63x$

32. $20x^2 + 23x + 6$

33. $ab - 6a + 7b - 42$

34. $20x^2 - 220x + 600$

35. $x^4 - 1$

36. $15x^2 - 20x$

37. $10x^2 - 7x - 33$

38. $45m^3n^3 - 27m^2n^2$

39. $5a^3b^3 - 50a^3b$

40. $x^4 + x$

41. $16x^2 + 25$

42. $20x^3 + 20y^3$

43. $10x^3 - 210x^2 + 1100x$

44. $9y^2 - 42y + 49$

45. $64a^3b^4 - 27a^3b$

46. $y^4 - 16$

47. $2x^3 - 54$

48. $2sr + 10s - r - 5$

49. $3y^5 - 5y^4 + 6y - 10$

50. $64a^2 + b^2$

51. $100z^3 + 100$

52. $250x^4 - 16x$

53. $4b^2 - 36b + 81$

54. $2a^5 - a^4 + 6a - 3$

55. $(y - 6)^2 + 3(y - 6) + 2$

56. $(c + 2)^2 - 6(c + 2) + 5$

△ **57.** Express the area of the shaded region as a polynomial. Factor the polynomial completely.

B.5 Rational Expressions

OBJECTIVE

1 Perform Operations on Rational Expressions and Solve Equations Containing Rational Expressions.

OBJECTIVE

1 **Performing Operations on Rational Expressions and Solving Equations Containing Rational Expressions**

It is very important that you understand the difference between an expression and an equation containing rational expressions. An equation contains an equal sign; an expression does not.

Expression to be Simplified	Equation to be Solved

$$\frac{x}{2} + \frac{x}{6}$$

$$\frac{x}{2} + \frac{x}{6} = \frac{2}{3}$$

Write both rational expressions with the LCD, 6, as the denominator.

Multiply both sides by the LCD, 6.

$$\frac{x}{2} + \frac{x}{6} = \frac{x \cdot 3}{2 \cdot 3} + \frac{x}{6}$$

$$6\left(\frac{x}{2} + \frac{x}{6}\right) = 6\left(\frac{2}{3}\right)$$

$$= \frac{3x}{6} + \frac{x}{6}$$

$$3x + x = 4$$

$$= \frac{4x}{6} = \frac{2x}{3}$$

$$4x = 4$$

$$x = 1$$

Check to see that the solution is 1.

> **Helpful Hint**
> Remember: Equations can be cleared of fractions; expressions cannot.

EXAMPLE 1 Multiply. $\dfrac{x^3 - 1}{-3x + 3} \cdot \dfrac{15x^2}{x^2 + x + 1}$

Solution

$$\frac{x^3 - 1}{-3x + 3} \cdot \frac{15x^2}{x^2 + x + 1} = \frac{(x - 1)(x^2 + x + 1)}{-3(x - 1)} \cdot \frac{15x^2}{x^2 + x + 1} \quad \text{Factor.}$$

$$= \frac{(x - 1)(x^2 + x + 1) \cdot 3 \cdot 5x^2}{-1 \cdot 3(x - 1)(x^2 + x + 1)} \quad \text{Factor.}$$

$$= \frac{5x^2}{-1} = -5x^2 \quad \text{Simplest form} \quad \square$$

PRACTICE

1 Multiply.

a. $\dfrac{2 + 5n}{3n} \cdot \dfrac{6n + 3}{5n^2 - 3n - 2}$

b. $\dfrac{x^3 - 8}{-6x + 12} \cdot \dfrac{6x^2}{x^2 + 2x + 4}$

EXAMPLE 2 Divide. $\dfrac{8m^2}{3m^2 - 12} \div \dfrac{40}{2 - m}$

Solution

$$\frac{8m^2}{3m^2 - 12} \div \frac{40}{2 - m} = \frac{8m^2}{3m^2 - 12} \cdot \frac{2 - m}{40} \quad \text{Multiply by the reciprocal of the divisor.}$$

$$= \frac{8m^2(2 - m)}{3(m + 2)(m - 2) \cdot 40} \quad \text{Factor and multiply.}$$

$$= \frac{8 \, m^2 \cdot -1 \, (m - 2)}{3(m + 2) \, (m - 2) \cdot 8 \cdot 5} \quad \text{Write } (2 - m) \text{ as } -1(m - 2).$$

$$= -\frac{m^2}{15(m + 2)} \quad \text{Simplify.} \quad \square$$

PRACTICE
2   Divide.

a. $\dfrac{6y^3}{3y^2 - 27} \div \dfrac{42}{3 - y}$

b. $\dfrac{10x^2 + 23x - 5}{5x^2 - 51x + 10} \div \dfrac{2x^2 + 9x + 10}{7x^2 - 68x - 20}$

EXAMPLE 3   Perform the indicated operation.

$$\frac{3}{x + 2} + \frac{2x}{x - 2}$$

Solution   The LCD is the product of the two denominators: $(x + 2)(x - 2)$.

$$\frac{3}{x + 2} + \frac{2x}{x - 2} = \frac{3 \cdot (x - 2)}{(x + 2) \cdot (x - 2)} + \frac{2x \cdot (x + 2)}{(x - 2) \cdot (x + 2)} \quad \text{Write equivalent rational expressions.}$$

$$= \frac{3x - 6}{(x + 2)(x - 2)} + \frac{2x^2 + 4x}{(x + 2)(x - 2)} \quad \text{Multiply in the numerators.}$$

$$= \frac{3x - 6 + 2x^2 + 4x}{(x + 2)(x - 2)} \quad \text{Add the numerators.}$$

$$= \frac{2x^2 + 7x - 6}{(x + 2)(x - 2)} \quad \text{Simplify the numerator.} \quad \square$$

PRACTICE
3   Perform the indicated operation.

a. $\dfrac{4}{p^3 q} + \dfrac{3}{5p^4 q}$

b. $\dfrac{4}{y + 3} + \dfrac{5y}{y - 3}$

c. $\dfrac{3z - 18}{z - 5} - \dfrac{3}{5 - z}$

EXAMPLE 4   Solve: $\dfrac{2x}{x - 3} + \dfrac{6 - 2x}{x^2 - 9} = \dfrac{x}{x + 3}.$

Solution   We factor the second denominator to find that the LCD is $(x + 3)(x - 3)$. We multiply both sides of the equation by $(x + 3)(x - 3)$. By the distributive property, this is the same as multiplying each term by $(x + 3)(x - 3)$.

$$\frac{2x}{x - 3} + \frac{6 - 2x}{x^2 - 9} = \frac{x}{x + 3}$$

$$(x + 3)(x - 3) \cdot \frac{2x}{x - 3} + (x + 3)(x - 3) \cdot \frac{6 - 2x}{(x + 3)(x - 3)}$$

$$= (x + 3)(x - 3)\left(\frac{x}{x + 3}\right)$$

$$2x(x + 3) + (6 - 2x) = x(x - 3) \quad \text{Simplify.}$$

$$2x^2 + 6x + 6 - 2x = x^2 - 3x \quad \text{Use the distributive property.}$$

Next we solve this quadratic equation by the factoring method. To do so, we first write the equation so that one side is 0.

$$x^2 + 7x + 6 = 0$$

$$(x + 6)(x + 1) = 0 \quad \text{Factor.}$$

$$x = -6 \quad \text{or} \quad x = -1 \quad \text{Set each factor equal to 0.}$$

Neither -6 nor -1 makes any denominator 0, so they are both solutions. The solutions are -6 and -1. $\quad \square$

PRACTICE
4   Solve: $\dfrac{2}{x - 2} - \dfrac{5 + 2x}{x^2 - 4} = \dfrac{x}{x + 2}.$

B.5 Exercise Set MyMathLab®

Perform each indicated operation and simplify, or solve the equation for the variable.

1. $\dfrac{x}{2} = \dfrac{1}{8} + \dfrac{x}{4}$

2. $\dfrac{x}{4} = \dfrac{3}{2} + \dfrac{x}{10}$

3. $\dfrac{1}{8} + \dfrac{x}{4}$

4. $\dfrac{3}{2} + \dfrac{x}{10}$

5. $\dfrac{4}{x + 2} - \dfrac{2}{x - 1}$

6. $\dfrac{5}{x - 2} - \dfrac{10}{x + 4}$

7. $\dfrac{4}{x + 2} = \dfrac{2}{x - 1}$

8. $\dfrac{5}{x - 2} = \dfrac{10}{x + 4}$

9. $\dfrac{2}{x^2 - 4} = \dfrac{1}{x + 2} - \dfrac{3}{x - 2}$

10. $\dfrac{3}{x^2 - 25} = \dfrac{1}{x + 5} + \dfrac{2}{x - 5}$

11. $\dfrac{5}{x^2 - 3x} + \dfrac{4}{2x - 6}$

12. $\dfrac{5}{x^2 - 3x} \div \dfrac{4}{2x - 6}$

13. $\dfrac{x - 1}{x + 1} + \dfrac{x + 7}{x - 1} = \dfrac{4}{x^2 - 1}$

14. $\left(1 - \dfrac{y}{x}\right) \div \left(1 - \dfrac{x}{y}\right)$

15. $\dfrac{a^2 - 9}{a - 6} \cdot \dfrac{a^2 - 5a - 6}{a^2 - a - 6}$

16. $\dfrac{2}{a - 6} + \dfrac{3a}{a^2 - 5a - 6} - \dfrac{a}{5a + 5}$

17. $\dfrac{2x + 3}{3x - 2} = \dfrac{4x + 1}{6x + 1}$

18. $\dfrac{5x - 3}{2x} = \dfrac{10x + 3}{4x + 1}$

19. $\dfrac{a}{9a^2 - 1} + \dfrac{2}{6a - 2}$

20. $\dfrac{3}{4a - 8} - \dfrac{a + 2}{a^2 - 2a}$

21. $-\dfrac{3}{x^2} - \dfrac{1}{x} + 2 = 0$

22. $\dfrac{x}{2x + 6} + \dfrac{5}{x^2 - 9}$

23. $\dfrac{x - 8}{x^2 - x - 2} + \dfrac{2}{x - 2}$

24. $\dfrac{x - 8}{x^2 - x - 2} + \dfrac{2}{x - 2} = \dfrac{3}{x + 1}$

25. $\dfrac{3}{a} - 5 = \dfrac{7}{a} - 1$

26. $\dfrac{7}{3z - 9} + \dfrac{5}{z}$

Use $\dfrac{x}{5} - \dfrac{x}{4} = \dfrac{1}{10}$ *and* $\dfrac{x}{5} - \dfrac{x}{4} + \dfrac{1}{10}$ *for Exercises 27 and 28.*

27. a. Which one above is an expression?

   b. Describe the first step to simplify this expression.

   c. Simplify the expression.

28. a. Which one above is an equation?

   b. Describe the first step to solve this equation.

   c. Solve the equation.

For each exercise, choose the correct statement.* Each figure represents a real number, and no denominators are 0.

29. a. $\dfrac{\triangle + \square}{\triangle} = \square$ **b.** $\dfrac{\triangle + \square}{\triangle} = 1 + \dfrac{\square}{\triangle}$

   c. $\dfrac{\triangle + \square}{\triangle} = \dfrac{\square}{\triangle}$ **d.** $\dfrac{\triangle + \square}{\triangle} = 1 + \square$

   e. $\dfrac{\triangle + \square}{\triangle - \square} = -1$

*My thanks to Kelly Champagne for permission to use her Exercises for 29 through 33.

> ▶ Helpful Hint
>
> Remember: Equations can be cleared of fractions; expressions cannot.

30. **a.** $\dfrac{\triangle}{\square} + \dfrac{\square}{\triangle} = \dfrac{\triangle + \square}{\square + \triangle} = 1$

  b. $\dfrac{\triangle}{\square} + \dfrac{\square}{\triangle} = \dfrac{\triangle + \square}{\triangle\square}$

  c. $\dfrac{\triangle}{\square} + \dfrac{\square}{\triangle} = \triangle\triangle + \square\square$

  d. $\dfrac{\triangle}{\square} + \dfrac{\square}{\triangle} = \dfrac{\triangle\triangle + \square\square}{\square\triangle}$

  e. $\dfrac{\triangle}{\square} + \dfrac{\square}{\triangle} = \dfrac{\triangle\square}{\square\triangle} = 1$

31. **a.** $\dfrac{\triangle}{\square} \cdot \dfrac{\bigcirc}{\square} = \dfrac{\triangle\bigcirc}{\square}$ **b.** $\dfrac{\triangle}{\square} \cdot \dfrac{\bigcirc}{\square} = \triangle\bigcirc$

  c. $\dfrac{\triangle}{\square} \cdot \dfrac{\bigcirc}{\square} = \dfrac{\triangle + \bigcirc}{\square + \square}$ **d.** $\dfrac{\triangle}{\square} \cdot \dfrac{\bigcirc}{\square} = \dfrac{\triangle\bigcirc}{\square\square}$

32. **a.** $\dfrac{\triangle}{\square} \div \dfrac{\bigcirc}{\triangle} = \dfrac{\triangle\triangle}{\square\bigcirc}$ **b.** $\dfrac{\triangle}{\square} \div \dfrac{\bigcirc}{\triangle} = \dfrac{\bigcirc\square}{\triangle\triangle}$

  c. $\dfrac{\triangle}{\square} \div \dfrac{\bigcirc}{\triangle} = \dfrac{\bigcirc}{\square}$ **d.** $\dfrac{\triangle}{\square} \div \dfrac{\bigcirc}{\triangle} = \dfrac{\triangle + \triangle}{\square + \bigcirc}$

33. **a.** $\dfrac{\dfrac{\triangle + \square}{\bigcirc}}{\dfrac{\triangle}{\bigcirc}} = \square$ **b.** $\dfrac{\dfrac{\triangle + \square}{\bigcirc}}{\dfrac{\triangle}{\bigcirc}} = \dfrac{\triangle\triangle + \triangle\square}{\bigcirc\bigcirc}$

  c. $\dfrac{\dfrac{\triangle + \square}{\bigcirc}}{\dfrac{\triangle}{\bigcirc}} = 1 + \square$ **d.** $\dfrac{\dfrac{\triangle + \square}{\bigcirc}}{\dfrac{\triangle}{\bigcirc}} = \dfrac{\triangle + \square}{\triangle}$

Appendix C

An Introduction to Using a Graphing Utility

The Viewing Window and Interpreting Window Settings

In this appendix, we will use the term **graphing utility** to mean a graphing calculator or a computer software graphing package. All graphing utilities graph equations by plotting points on a screen. While plotting several points can be slow and sometimes tedious for us, a graphing utility can quickly and accurately plot hundreds of points. How does a graphing utility show plotted points? A computer or calculator screen is made up of a grid of small rectangular areas called **pixels.** If a pixel contains a point to be plotted, the pixel is turned "on"; otherwise, the pixel remains "off." The graph of an equation is then a collection of pixels turned "on." The graph of $y = 3x + 1$ from a graphing calculator is shown in Figure A-1. Notice the irregular shape of the line caused by the rectangular pixels.

Figure A-1

The portion of the coordinate plane shown on the screen in Figure A-1 is called the **viewing window** or the **viewing rectangle.** Notice the x-axis and the y-axis on the graph. While tick marks are shown on the axes, they are not labeled. This means that from this screen alone, we do not know how many units each tick mark represents. To see what each tick mark represents and the minimum and maximum values on the axes, check the window setting of the graphing utility. It defines the viewing window. The window of the graph of $y = 3x + 1$ shown in Figure A-1 has the following settings (Figure A-2):

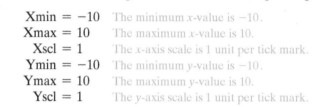

$$\text{Xmin} = -10 \quad \text{The minimum } x\text{-value is } -10.$$
$$\text{Xmax} = 10 \quad \text{The maximum } x\text{-value is } 10.$$
$$\text{Xscl} = 1 \quad \text{The } x\text{-axis scale is 1 unit per tick mark.}$$
$$\text{Ymin} = -10 \quad \text{The minimum } y\text{-value is } -10.$$
$$\text{Ymax} = 10 \quad \text{The maximum } y\text{-value is 10.}$$
$$\text{Yscl} = 1 \quad \text{The } y\text{-axis scale is 1 unit per tick mark.}$$

Figure A-2

By knowing the scale, we can find the minimum and the maximum values on the axes simply by counting tick marks. For example, if both the Xscl (x-axis scale) and the Yscl (y-axis scale) are 1 unit per tick mark on the graph in Figure A-3, we can count the tick marks and find that the minimum x-value is -10 and the maximum x-value is 10. Also, the minimum y-value is -10 and the maximum y-value is 10. If the Xscl changes to 2 units per tick mark (shown in Figure A-4), by counting tick marks, we see that the minimum x-value is now -20 and the maximum x-value is now 20.

Figure A-3

Figure A-4

Figure A-5

It is also true that if we know the Xmin and the Xmax values, we can calculate the Xscl by the displayed axes. For example, the Xscl of the graph in Figure A-5 must be 3 units per tick mark for the maximum and minimum x-values to be as shown. Also, the Yscl of that graph must be 2 units per tick mark for the maximum and minimum y-values to be as shown.

We will call the viewing window in Figure A-3 a *standard* viewing window or rectangle. Although a standard viewing window is sufficient for much of this text, special care must be taken to ensure that all key features of a graph are shown. Figures A-6, A-7, and A-8 show the graph of $y = x^2 + 11x - 1$ on three different viewing windows. Note that certain viewing windows for this equation are misleading.

Figure A-6

Figure A-7

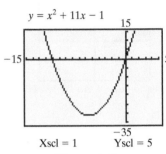

Figure A-8

How do we ensure that all distinguishing features of the graph of an equation are shown? It helps to know about the equation that is being graphed. For example, the equation $y = x^2 + 11x - 1$ is not a linear equation and its graph is not a line. This equation is a quadratic equation and, therefore, its graph is a parabola. By knowing this information, we know that the graph shown in Figure A-6, although correct, is misleading. Of the three viewing rectangles shown, the graph in Figure A-8 is best because it shows more of the distinguishing features of the parabola. Properties of equations needed for graphing will be studied in this text.

The Viewing Window and Interpreting Window Settings Exercise Set

In Exercises 1–4, determine whether all ordered pairs listed will lie within a standard viewing rectangle.

1. $(-9, 0), (5, 8), (1, -8)$

2. $(4, 7), (0, 0), (-8, 9)$

3. $(-11, 0), (2, 2), (7, -5)$

4. $(3, 5), (-3, -5), (15, 0)$

In Exercises 5–10, choose an Xmin, Xmax, Ymin, and Ymax so that all ordered pairs listed will lie within the viewing rectangle.

5. $(-90, 0), (55, 80), (0, -80)$

6. $(4, 70), (20, 20), (-18, 90)$

7. $(-11, 0), (2, 2), (7, -5)$

8. $(3, 5), (-3, -5), (15, 0)$

9. $(200, 200), (50, -50), (70, -50)$

10. $(40, 800), (-30, 500), (15, 0)$

Write the window setting for each viewing window shown. Use the following format:

11.

12.

13.

14.

15.

16.

19.
Xscl = 5, Yscl = 10

20.
Xscl = 100, Yscl = 200

17.
Xscl = 1, Yscl = 3

18.
Xscl = 10, Yscl = 2

Graphing Equations and Square Viewing Window

In general, the following steps may be used to graph an equation on a standard viewing window.

Graphing an Equation in *X* and *Y* with a Graphing Utility on a Standard Viewing Window

Step 1: Solve the equation for y.

Step 2: Using your graphing utility, enter the equation in the form
$Y = expression\ involving\ x$.

Step 3: Activate the graphing utility.

Special care must be taken when entering the *expression involving x* in Step 2. You must be sure that the graphing utility you are using interprets the expression as you want it to. For example, let's graph $3y = 4x$. To do so,

Step 1: Solve the equation for y.

$$3y = 4x$$
$$\frac{3y}{3} = \frac{4x}{3}$$
$$y = \frac{4}{3}x$$

Step 2: Using your graphing utility, enter the expression $\frac{4}{3}x$ after the $Y =$ prompt.

In order for your graphing utility to correctly interpret the expression, you may need to enter $(4/3)x$ or $(4 \div 3)x$.

Step 3: Activate the graphing utility. The graph should appear as in Figure A-9.

Distinguishing features of the graph of a line include showing all the intercepts of the line. For example, the window of the graph of the line in Figure A-10 does not show both intercepts of the line, but the window of the graph of the same line in Figure A-11 does show both intercepts. Notice the notation below each graph. This is a shorthand notation of the range setting of the graph. This notation means [Xmin, Xmax] by [Ymin, Ymax].

Figure A-9

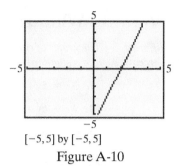

[-5, 5] by [-5, 5]

Figure A-10

[-4, 8] by [-8, 5]

Figure A-11

On a standard viewing window, the tick marks on the *y*-axis are closer together than the tick marks on the *x*-axis. This happens because the viewing window is a rectangle, and so 10 equally spaced tick marks on the positive *y*-axis will be closer together than 10 equally spaced tick marks on the positive *x*-axis. This causes the appearance of graphs to be distorted.

For example, notice the different appearances of the same line graphed using different viewing windows. The line in Figure A-12 is distorted because the tick marks along the *x*-axis are farther apart than the tick marks along the *y*-axis. The graph of the same line in Figure A-13 is not distorted because the viewing rectangle has been selected so that there is equal spacing between tick marks on both axes.

Figure A-12

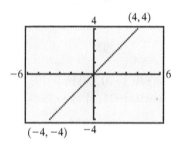

Figure A-13

We say that the line in Figure A-13 is graphed on a *square* setting. Some graphing utilities have a built-in program that, if activated, will automatically provide a square setting. A square setting is especially helpful when we are graphing perpendicular lines, circles, or when a true geometric perspective is desired. Some examples of square screens are shown in Figures A-14 and A-15.

Figure A-14

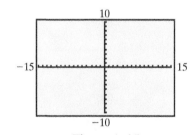

Figure A-15

Other features of a graphing utility such as Trace, Zoom, Intersect, and Table are discussed in appropriate Graphing Calculator Explorations in this text.

Graphing Equations and Square Viewing Window Exercise Set

Graph each linear equation in two variables using the two different range settings given. Determine which setting shows all intercepts of a line.

1. $y = 2x + 12$
Setting A: $[-10, 10]$ by $[-10, 10]$
Setting B: $[-10, 10]$ by $[-10, 15]$

2. $y = -3x + 25$
Setting A: $[-5, 5]$ by $[-30, 10]$
Setting B: $[-10, 10]$ by $[-10, 30]$

3. $y = -x - 41$
Setting A: $[-50, 10]$ by $[-10, 10]$
Setting B: $[-50, 10]$ by $[-50, 15]$

4. $y = 6x - 18$
Setting A: $[-10, 10]$ by $[-20, 10]$
Setting B: $[-10, 10]$ by $[-10, 10]$

5. $y = \dfrac{1}{2}x - 15$
Setting B: $[-10, 10]$ by $[-20, 10]$
Setting B: $[-10, 35]$ by $[-20, 15]$

6. $y = -\dfrac{2}{3}x - \dfrac{29}{3}$
Setting A: $[-10, 10]$ by $[-10, 10]$
Setting B: $[-15, 5]$ by $[-15, 5]$

The graph of each equation is a line. Use a graphing utility and a standard viewing window to graph each equation.

7. $3x = 5y$ **8.** $7y = -3x$ **9.** $9x - 5y = 30$

10. $4x + 6y = 20$ **11.** $y = -7$ **12.** $y = 2$

13. $x + 10y = -5$ **14.** $x - 5y = 9$

Graph the following equations using the square setting given. Some keystrokes that may be helpful are given.

15. $y = \sqrt{x}$ $[-12, 12]$ by $[-8, 8]$
Suggested keystrokes: $\sqrt{\ } x$

16. $y = \sqrt{2x}$ $[-12, 12]$ by $[-8, 8]$
Suggested keystrokes: $\sqrt{\ } (2x)$

17. $y = x^2 + 2x + 1$ $[-15, 15]$ by $[-10, 10]$
Suggested keystrokes: $x\char`^2 + 2x + 1$

18. $y = x^2 - 5$ $[-15, 15]$ by $[-10, 10]$
Suggested keystrokes: $x\char`^2 - 5$

19. $y = |x|$ $[-9, 9]$ by $[-6, 6]$
Suggested keystrokes: $ABS\,(x)$

20. $y = |x - 2|$ $[-9, 9]$ by $[-6, 6]$
Suggested keystrokes: $ABS\,(x - 2)$

Graph each line. Use a standard viewing window; then, if necessary, change the viewing window so that all intercepts of each line show.

21. $x + 2y = 30$ **22.** $1.5x - 3.7y = 40.3$

Appendix D

Solving Systems of Equations by Matrices

By now, you may have noticed that the solution of a system of equations depends on the coefficients of the equations in the system and not on the variables. In this section, we introduce solving a system of equations by a **matrix.**

OBJECTIVE

1   Using Matrices to Solve a System of Two Equations

A matrix (plural: **matrices**) is a rectangular array of numbers. The following are examples of matrices.

$$\begin{bmatrix} 1 & 0 \\ 0 & 1 \end{bmatrix} \quad \begin{bmatrix} 2 & 1 & 3 & -1 \\ 0 & -1 & 4 & 5 \\ -6 & 2 & 1 & 0 \end{bmatrix} \quad \begin{bmatrix} a & b & c \\ d & e & f \end{bmatrix}$$

The numbers aligned horizontally in a matrix are in the same **row.** The numbers aligned vertically are in the same **column.**

row 1 → $\begin{bmatrix} 2 & 1 & 0 \\ -1 & 6 & 2 \end{bmatrix}$
row 2 →

column 1
column 2
column 3

This matrix has 2 rows and 3 columns. It is called a 2 × 3 (read "two by three") matrix.

To see the relationship between systems of equations and matrices, study the example below.

> **Helpful Hint**
>
> Before writing the corresponding matrix associated with a system of equations, make sure that the equations are written in standard form.

System of Equations (in standard form)	Corresponding Matrix

$$\begin{cases} 2x - 3y = 6 & \text{Equation 1} \\ x + y = 0 & \text{Equation 2} \end{cases} \qquad \begin{bmatrix} 2 & -3 & 6 \\ 1 & 1 & 0 \end{bmatrix} \begin{matrix} \text{Row 1} \\ \text{Row 2} \end{matrix}$$

Notice that the rows of the matrix correspond to the equations in the system. The coefficients of each variable are placed to the left of a vertical dashed line. The constants are placed to the right. Each of the numbers in the matrix is called an **element.**

The method of solving systems by matrices is to write this matrix as an equivalent matrix from which we easily identify the solution. Two matrices are equivalent if they represent systems that have the same solution set. The following **row operations** can be performed on matrices, and the result is an equivalent matrix.

> **Helpful Hint**
>
> Notice that these *row* operations are the same operations that we can perform on *equations* in a system.

Elementary Row Operations

1. Any two rows in a matrix may be interchanged.
2. The elements of any row may be multiplied (or divided) by the same nonzero number.
3. The elements of any row may be multiplied (or divided) by a nonzero number and added to their corresponding elements in any other row.

To solve a system of two equations in x and y by matrices, write the corresponding matrix associated with the system. Then use elementary row operations to write equivalent matrices until you have a matrix of the form

$$\begin{bmatrix} 1 & a & | & b \\ 0 & 1 & | & c \end{bmatrix},$$

where a, b, and c are constants. Why? If a matrix associated with a system of equations is in this form, we can easily solve for x and y. For example,

Matrix   **System of Equations**

$$\begin{bmatrix} 1 & 2 & | & -3 \\ 0 & 1 & | & 5 \end{bmatrix} \text{ corresponds to } \begin{cases} 1x + 2y = -3 \\ 0x + 1y = 5 \end{cases} \text{ or } \begin{cases} x + 2y = -3 \\ y = 5 \end{cases}$$

In the second equation, we have $y = 5$. Substituting this in the first equation, we have $x + 2(5) = -3$ or $x = -13$. The solution of the system is the ordered pair $(-13, 5)$.

EXAMPLE 1   Use matrices to solve the system.

$$\begin{cases} x + 3y = 5 \\ 2x - y = -4 \end{cases}$$

Solution   The corresponding matrix is $\begin{bmatrix} 1 & 3 & | & 5 \\ 2 & -1 & | & -4 \end{bmatrix}$. We use elementary row operations to write an equivalent matrix that looks like $\begin{bmatrix} 1 & a & | & b \\ 0 & 1 & | & c \end{bmatrix}$.

For the matrix given, the element in the first row, first column is already 1, as desired. Next we write an equivalent matrix with a 0 below the 1. To do this, we multiply row 1 by -2 and add to row 2. *We will change only row 2.*

$$\begin{bmatrix} 1 & 3 & | & 5 \\ -2(1) + 2 & -2(3) + (-1) & | & -2(5) + (-4) \end{bmatrix} \text{ simplifies to } \begin{bmatrix} 1 & 3 & | & 5 \\ 0 & -7 & | & -14 \end{bmatrix}$$

row 1   row 2   row 1   row 2   row 1   row 2
element element element element element element

Now we change the -7 to a 1 by use of an elementary row operation. We divide row 2 by -7, then

$$\begin{bmatrix} 1 & 3 & | & 5 \\ \frac{0}{-7} & \frac{-7}{-7} & | & \frac{-14}{-7} \end{bmatrix} \text{ simplifies to } \begin{bmatrix} 1 & 3 & | & 5 \\ 0 & 1 & | & 2 \end{bmatrix}$$

This last matrix corresponds to the system

$$\begin{cases} x + 3y = 5 \\ y = 2 \end{cases}$$

To find x, we let $y = 2$ in the first equation, $x + 3y = 5$.

$$x + 3y = 5 \quad \text{First equation}$$
$$x + 3(2) = 5 \quad \text{Let } y = 2.$$
$$x = -1$$

The ordered pair solution is $(-1, 2)$. Check to see that this ordered pair satisfies both equations.   □

PRACTICE

1   Use matrices to solve the system.

$$\begin{cases} x + 4y = -2 \\ 3x - y = 7 \end{cases}$$

EXAMPLE 2   Use matrices to solve the system.

$$\begin{cases} 2x - y = 3 \\ 4x - 2y = 5 \end{cases}$$

Solution   The corresponding matrix is $\begin{bmatrix} 2 & -1 & | & 3 \\ 4 & -2 & | & 5 \end{bmatrix}$. To get 1 in the row 1, column 1 position, we divide the elements of row 1 by 2.

$$\begin{bmatrix} \frac{2}{2} & -\frac{1}{2} & | & \frac{3}{2} \\ 4 & -2 & | & 5 \end{bmatrix} \quad \text{simplifies to} \quad \begin{bmatrix} 1 & -\frac{1}{2} & | & \frac{3}{2} \\ 4 & -2 & | & 5 \end{bmatrix}$$

To get 0 under the 1, we multiply the elements of row 1 by -4 and add the new elements to the elements of row 2.

$$\begin{bmatrix} 1 & -\frac{1}{2} & | & \frac{3}{2} \\ -4(1)+4 & -4\left(-\frac{1}{2}\right)-2 & | & -4\left(\frac{3}{2}\right)+5 \end{bmatrix} \quad \text{simplifies to} \quad \begin{bmatrix} 1 & -\frac{1}{2} & | & \frac{3}{2} \\ 0 & 0 & | & -1 \end{bmatrix}$$

The corresponding system is $\begin{cases} x - \frac{1}{2}y = \frac{3}{2} \\ 0 = -1 \end{cases}$. The equation $0 = -1$ is false for all y or x values; hence, the system is inconsistent and has no solution. The solution set is $\{\ \}$ or $\varnothing$.

PRACTICE
2   Use matrices to solve the system.

$$\begin{cases} x - 3y = 3 \\ -2x + 6y = 4 \end{cases}$$

✔**CONCEPT CHECK**
Consider the system

$$\begin{cases} 2x - 3y = 8 \\ x + 5y = -3 \end{cases}$$

What is wrong with its corresponding matrix shown below?

$$\begin{bmatrix} 2 & -3 & | & 8 \\ 0 & 5 & | & -3 \end{bmatrix}$$

OBJECTIVE
2   Using Matrices to Solve a System of Three Equations

To solve a system of three equations in three variables using matrices, we will write the corresponding matrix in the form

$$\begin{bmatrix} 1 & a & b & | & d \\ 0 & 1 & c & | & e \\ 0 & 0 & 1 & | & f \end{bmatrix}$$

Answer to Concept Check:
matrix should be $\begin{bmatrix} 2 & -3 & | & 8 \\ 1 & 5 & | & -3 \end{bmatrix}$

EXAMPLE 3   Use matrices to solve the system.

$$\begin{cases} x + 2y + z = 2 \\ -2x - y + 2z = 5 \\ x + 3y - 2z = -8 \end{cases}$$

Solution   The corresponding matrix is $\begin{bmatrix} 1 & 2 & 1 & \vdots & 2 \\ -2 & -1 & 2 & \vdots & 5 \\ 1 & 3 & -2 & \vdots & -8 \end{bmatrix}$. Our goal is to write

an equivalent matrix with 1's along the diagonal (see the numbers in red) and 0's below the 1's. The element in row 1, column 1 is already 1. Next we get 0's for each element in the rest of column 1. To do this, first we multiply the elements of row 1 by 2 and add the new elements to row 2. Also, we multiply the elements of row 1 by −1 and add the new elements to the elements of row 3. We *do not change row 1*. Then

$$\begin{bmatrix} 1 & 2 & 1 & \vdots & 2 \\ 2(1)-2 & 2(2)-1 & 2(1)+2 & \vdots & 2(2)+5 \\ -1(1)+1 & -1(2)+3 & -1(1)-2 & \vdots & -1(2)-8 \end{bmatrix} \text{ simplifies to } \begin{bmatrix} 1 & 2 & 1 & \vdots & 2 \\ 0 & 3 & 4 & \vdots & 9 \\ 0 & 1 & -3 & \vdots & -10 \end{bmatrix}$$

We continue down the diagonal and use elementary row operations to get 1 where the element 3 is now. To do this, we interchange rows 2 and 3.

$$\begin{bmatrix} 1 & 2 & 1 & \vdots & 2 \\ 0 & 3 & 4 & \vdots & 9 \\ 0 & 1 & -3 & \vdots & -10 \end{bmatrix} \text{ is equivalent to } \begin{bmatrix} 1 & 2 & 1 & \vdots & 2 \\ 0 & 1 & -3 & \vdots & -10 \\ 0 & 3 & 4 & \vdots & 9 \end{bmatrix}$$

Next we want the new row 3, column 2 element to be 0. We multiply the elements of row 2 by −3 and add the result to the elements of row 3.

$$\begin{bmatrix} 1 & 2 & 1 & \vdots & 2 \\ 0 & 1 & -3 & \vdots & -10 \\ -3(0)+0 & -3(1)+3 & -3(-3)+4 & \vdots & -3(-10)+9 \end{bmatrix} \text{ simplifies to }$$

$$\begin{bmatrix} 1 & 2 & 1 & \vdots & 2 \\ 0 & 1 & -3 & \vdots & -10 \\ 0 & 0 & 13 & \vdots & 39 \end{bmatrix}$$

Finally, we divide the elements of row 3 by 13 so that the final diagonal element is 1.

$$\begin{bmatrix} 1 & 2 & 1 & \vdots & 2 \\ 0 & 1 & -3 & \vdots & -10 \\ \frac{0}{13} & \frac{0}{13} & \frac{13}{13} & \vdots & \frac{39}{13} \end{bmatrix} \text{ simplifies to } \begin{bmatrix} 1 & 2 & 1 & \vdots & 2 \\ 0 & 1 & -3 & \vdots & -10 \\ 0 & 0 & 1 & \vdots & 3 \end{bmatrix}$$

This matrix corresponds to the system

$$\begin{cases} x + 2y + z = 2 \\ y - 3z = -10 \\ z = 3 \end{cases}$$

We identify the z-coordinate of the solution as 3. Next, we replace z with 3 in the second equation and solve for y.

$$y - 3z = -10 \quad \text{Second equation}$$
$$y - 3(3) = -10 \quad \text{Let } z = 3.$$
$$y = -1$$

To find x, we let $z = 3$ and $y = -1$ in the first equation.

$$x + 2y + z = 2 \quad \text{First equation}$$
$$x + 2(-1) + 3 = 2 \quad \text{Let } z = 3 \text{ and } y = -1.$$
$$x = 1$$

The ordered triple solution is $(1, -1, 3)$. Check to see that it satisfies all three equations in the original system.   □

PRACTICE

3   Use matrices to solve the system.

$$\begin{cases} x + 3y - z = 0 \\ 2x + y + 3z = 5 \\ -x - 2y + 4z = 7 \end{cases}$$

D Exercise Set   MyMathLab®

Solve each system of linear equations using matrices. See Example 1.

1. $\begin{cases} x + y = 1 \\ x - 2y = 4 \end{cases}$

2. $\begin{cases} 2x - y = 8 \\ x + 3y = 11 \end{cases}$

3. $\begin{cases} x + 3y = 2 \\ x + 2y = 0 \end{cases}$

4. $\begin{cases} 4x - y = 5 \\ 3x + 3y = 0 \end{cases}$

Solve each system of linear equations using matrices. See Example 2.

5. $\begin{cases} x - 2y = 4 \\ 2x - 4y = 4 \end{cases}$

6. $\begin{cases} -x + 3y = 6 \\ 3x - 9y = 9 \end{cases}$

7. $\begin{cases} 3x - 3y = 9 \\ 2x - 2y = 6 \end{cases}$

8. $\begin{cases} 9x - 3y = 6 \\ -18x + 6y = -12 \end{cases}$

Solve each system of linear equations using matrices. See Example 3.

9. $\begin{cases} x + y = 3 \\ 2y = 10 \\ 3x + 2y - 4z = 12 \end{cases}$

10. $\begin{cases} 5x = 5 \\ 2x + y = 4 \\ 3x + y - 5z = -15 \end{cases}$

11. $\begin{cases} 2y - z = -7 \\ x + 4y + z = -4 \\ 5x - y + 2z = 13 \end{cases}$

12. $\begin{cases} 4y + 3z = -2 \\ 5x - 4y = 1 \\ -5x + 4y + z = -3 \end{cases}$

MIXED PRACTICE

Solve each system of linear equations using matrices. See Examples 1 through 3.

13. $\begin{cases} x - 4 = 0 \\ x + y = 1 \end{cases}$

14. $\begin{cases} 3y = 6 \\ x + y = 7 \end{cases}$

15. $\begin{cases} x + y + z = 2 \\ 2x - z = 5 \\ 3y + z = 2 \end{cases}$

16. $\begin{cases} x + 2y + z = 5 \\ x - y - z = 3 \\ y + z = 2 \end{cases}$

17. $\begin{cases} 5x - 2y = 27 \\ -3x + 5y = 18 \end{cases}$

18. $\begin{cases} 4x - y = 9 \\ 2x + 3y = -27 \end{cases}$

19. $\begin{cases} 4x - 7y = 7 \\ 12x - 21y = 24 \end{cases}$

20. $\begin{cases} 2x - 5y = 12 \\ -4x + 10y = 20 \end{cases}$

21. $\begin{cases} 4x - y + 2z = 5 \\ 2y + z = 4 \\ 4x + y + 3z = 10 \end{cases}$

22. $\begin{cases} 5y - 7z = 14 \\ 2x + y + 4z = 10 \\ 2x + 6y - 3z = 30 \end{cases}$

23. $\begin{cases} 4x + y + z = 3 \\ -x + y - 2z = -11 \\ x + 2y + 2z = -1 \end{cases}$

24. $\begin{cases} x + y + z = 9 \\ 3x - y + z = -1 \\ -2x + 2y - 3z = -2 \end{cases}$

CONCEPT EXTENSIONS

Solve. See the Concept Check in this section.

25. For the system $\begin{cases} x + z = 7 \\ y + 2z = -6, \text{ which is the correct} \\ 3x - y = 0 \end{cases}$

corresponding matrix?

a. $\begin{bmatrix} 1 & 1 & \vdots & 7 \\ 1 & 2 & \vdots & -6 \\ 3 & -1 & \vdots & 0 \end{bmatrix}$

b. $\begin{bmatrix} 1 & 0 & 1 & \vdots & 7 \\ 1 & 2 & 0 & \vdots & -6 \\ 3 & -1 & 0 & \vdots & 0 \end{bmatrix}$

c. $\begin{bmatrix} 1 & 0 & 1 & \vdots & 7 \\ 0 & 1 & 2 & \vdots & -6 \\ 3 & -1 & 0 & \vdots & 0 \end{bmatrix}$

Appendix E

Solving Systems of Equations by Determinants

OBJECTIVES

1 Define and Evaluate a 2 × 2 Determinant.

2 Use Cramer's Rule to Solve a System of Two Linear Equations in Two Variables.

3 Define and Evaluate a 3 × 3 Determinant.

4 Use Cramer's Rule to Solve a System of Three Linear Equations in Three Variables.

We have solved systems of two linear equations in two variables in four different ways: graphically, by substitution, by elimination, and by matrices. Now we analyze another method, called **Cramer's rule.**

OBJECTIVE

1   Evaluating 2 × 2 Determinants

Recall that a matrix is a rectangular array of numbers. If a matrix has the same number of rows and columns, it is called a **square matrix.** Examples of square matrices are

$$\begin{bmatrix} 1 & 6 \\ 5 & 2 \end{bmatrix} \qquad \begin{bmatrix} 2 & 4 & 1 \\ 0 & 5 & 2 \\ 3 & 6 & 9 \end{bmatrix}$$

A **determinant** is a real number associated with a square matrix. The determinant of a square matrix is denoted by placing vertical bars about the array of numbers. Thus,

The determinant of the square matrix $\begin{bmatrix} 1 & 6 \\ 5 & 2 \end{bmatrix}$ is $\begin{vmatrix} 1 & 6 \\ 5 & 2 \end{vmatrix}$.

The determinant of the square matrix $\begin{bmatrix} 2 & 4 & 1 \\ 0 & 5 & 2 \\ 3 & 6 & 9 \end{bmatrix}$ is $\begin{vmatrix} 2 & 4 & 1 \\ 0 & 5 & 2 \\ 3 & 6 & 9 \end{vmatrix}$.

We define the determinant of a 2 × 2 matrix first. (Recall that 2 × 2 is read "two by two." It means that the matrix has 2 rows and 2 columns.)

Determinant of a 2 × 2 Matrix

$$\begin{vmatrix} a & b \\ c & d \end{vmatrix} = ad - bc$$

EXAMPLE 1   Evaluate each determinant

a. $\begin{vmatrix} -1 & 2 \\ 3 & -4 \end{vmatrix}$ **b.** $\begin{vmatrix} 2 & 0 \\ 7 & -5 \end{vmatrix}$

Solution   First we identify the values of $a, b, c,$ and d. Then we perform the evaluation.

a. Here $a = -1, b = 2, c = 3,$ and $d = -4.$

$$\begin{vmatrix} -1 & 2 \\ 3 & -4 \end{vmatrix} = ad - bc = (-1)(-4) - (2)(3) = -2$$

b. In this example, $a = 2, b = 0, c = 7,$ and $d = -5.$

$$\begin{vmatrix} 2 & 0 \\ 7 & -5 \end{vmatrix} = ad - bc = 2(-5) - (0)(7) = -10$$

2   Using Cramer's Rule to Solve a System of Two Linear Equations

To develop Cramer's rule, we solve the system $\begin{cases} ax + by = h \\ cx + dy = k \end{cases}$ using elimination. First, we eliminate y by multiplying both sides of the first equation by d and both sides of the second equation by $-b$ so that the coefficients of y are opposites. The result is that

$$\begin{cases} d(ax + by) = d \cdot h \\ -b(cx + dy) = -b \cdot k \end{cases} \quad \text{simplifies to} \quad \begin{cases} adx + bdy = hd \\ -bcx - bdy = -kb \end{cases}$$

We now add the two equations and solve for x.

$$
\begin{aligned}
adx + bdy &= hd \\
-bcx - bdy &= -kb \\
\hline
adx - bcx &= hd - kb \quad \text{Add the equations.} \\
(ad - bc)x &= hd - kb \\
x &= \frac{hd - kb}{ad - bc} \quad \text{Solve for } x.
\end{aligned}
$$

When we replace x with $\dfrac{hd - kb}{ad - bc}$ in the equation $ax + by = h$ and solve for y, we find that $y = \dfrac{ak - ch}{ad - bc}$.

Notice that the numerator of the value of x is the determinant of

$$\begin{vmatrix} h & b \\ k & d \end{vmatrix} = hd - kb$$

Also, the numerator of the value of y is the determinant of

$$\begin{vmatrix} a & h \\ c & k \end{vmatrix} = ak - hc$$

Finally, the denominators of the values of x and y are the same and are the determinant of

$$\begin{vmatrix} a & b \\ c & d \end{vmatrix} = ad - bc$$

This means that the values of x and y can be written in determinant notation:

$$x = \frac{\begin{vmatrix} h & b \\ k & d \end{vmatrix}}{\begin{vmatrix} a & b \\ c & d \end{vmatrix}} \quad \text{and} \quad y = \frac{\begin{vmatrix} a & h \\ c & k \end{vmatrix}}{\begin{vmatrix} a & b \\ c & d \end{vmatrix}}$$

For convenience, we label the determinants D, D_x, and D_y.

$$
\underbrace{\begin{vmatrix} a & b \\ c & d \end{vmatrix}}_{} = D \qquad \begin{vmatrix} h & b \\ k & d \end{vmatrix} = D_x \qquad \begin{vmatrix} a & h \\ c & k \end{vmatrix} = D_y
$$

x-coefficients

y-coefficients

x-column replaced by constants

y-column replaced by constants

These determinant formulas for the coordinates of the solution of a system are known as **Cramer's rule.**

Cramer's Rule for Two Linear Equations in Two Variables

The solution of the system $\begin{cases} ax + by = h \\ cx + dy = k \end{cases}$ is given by

$$x = \frac{\begin{vmatrix} h & b \\ k & d \end{vmatrix}}{\begin{vmatrix} a & b \\ c & d \end{vmatrix}} = \frac{D_x}{D} \qquad y = \frac{\begin{vmatrix} a & h \\ c & k \end{vmatrix}}{\begin{vmatrix} a & b \\ c & d \end{vmatrix}} = \frac{D_y}{D}$$

as long as $D = ad - bc$ is not 0.

When $D = 0$, the system is either inconsistent or the equations are dependent. When this happens, we need to use another method to see which is the case.

EXAMPLE 2   Use Cramer's rule to solve the system

$$\begin{cases} 3x + 4y = -7 \\ x - 2y = -9 \end{cases}$$

Solution   First we find D, D_x, and D_y.

$$\begin{array}{ccc} a & b & h \\ \downarrow & \downarrow & \downarrow \end{array}$$

$$\begin{cases} 3x + 4y = -7 \\ x - 2y = -9 \end{cases}$$

$$\begin{array}{ccc} \uparrow & \uparrow & \uparrow \\ c & d & k \end{array}$$

$$D = \begin{vmatrix} a & b \\ c & d \end{vmatrix} = \begin{vmatrix} 3 & 4 \\ 1 & -2 \end{vmatrix} = 3(-2) - 4(1) = -10$$

$$D_x = \begin{vmatrix} h & b \\ k & d \end{vmatrix} = \begin{vmatrix} -7 & 4 \\ -9 & -2 \end{vmatrix} = (-7)(-2) - 4(-9) = 50$$

$$D_y = \begin{vmatrix} a & h \\ c & k \end{vmatrix} = \begin{vmatrix} 3 & -7 \\ 1 & -9 \end{vmatrix} = 3(-9) - (-7)(1) = -20$$

Then $x = \dfrac{D_x}{D} = \dfrac{50}{-10} = -5$ and $y = \dfrac{D_y}{D} = \dfrac{-20}{-10} = 2$.

The ordered pair solution is $(-5, 2)$.
As always, check the solution in both original equations. $\square$

EXAMPLE 3   Use Cramer's rule to solve the system

$$\begin{cases} 5x + y = 5 \\ -7x - 2y = -7 \end{cases}$$

Solution   First we find D, D_x, and D_y.

$$D = \begin{vmatrix} 5 & 1 \\ -7 & -2 \end{vmatrix} = 5(-2) - (-7)(1) = -3$$

$$D_x = \begin{vmatrix} 5 & 1 \\ -7 & -2 \end{vmatrix} = 5(-2) - (-7)(1) = -3$$

$$D_y = \begin{vmatrix} 5 & 5 \\ -7 & -7 \end{vmatrix} = 5(-7) - 5(-7) = 0$$

Then

$$x = \frac{D_x}{D} = \frac{-3}{-3} = 1 \qquad y = \frac{D_y}{D} = \frac{0}{-3} = 0$$

The ordered pair solution is $(1, 0)$.

OBJECTIVE

3   Evaluating 3×3 Determinants

A 3×3 determinant can be used to solve a system of three equations in three variables. The determinant of a 3×3 matrix, however, is considerably more complex than a 2×2 one.

Determinant of a 3 × 3 Matrix

$$\begin{vmatrix} a_1 & b_1 & c_1 \\ a_2 & b_2 & c_2 \\ a_3 & b_3 & c_3 \end{vmatrix} = a_1 \cdot \begin{vmatrix} b_2 & c_2 \\ b_3 & c_3 \end{vmatrix} - a_2 \cdot \begin{vmatrix} b_1 & c_1 \\ b_3 & c_3 \end{vmatrix} + a_3 \cdot \begin{vmatrix} b_1 & c_1 \\ b_2 & c_2 \end{vmatrix}$$

Notice that the determinant of a 3×3 matrix is related to the determinants of three 2×2 matrices. Each determinant of these 2×2 matrices is called a **minor,** and every element of a 3×3 matrix has a minor associated with it. For example, the minor of c_2 is the determinant of the 2×2 matrix found by deleting the row and column containing c_2.

$$\begin{array}{ccc} a_1 & b_1 & c_1 \\ a_2 & b_2 & c_2 \\ a_3 & b_3 & c_3 \end{array} \qquad \text{The minor of } c_2 \text{ is } \begin{vmatrix} a_1 & b_1 \\ a_3 & b_3 \end{vmatrix}$$

Also, the minor of element a_1 is the determinant of the 2×2 matrix that has no row or column containing a_1.

$$\begin{array}{ccc} a_1 & b_1 & c_1 \\ a_2 & b_2 & c_2 \\ a_3 & b_3 & c_3 \end{array} \qquad \text{The minor of } a_1 \text{ is } \begin{vmatrix} b_2 & c_2 \\ b_3 & c_3 \end{vmatrix}$$

So the determinant of a 3×3 matrix can be written as

$$a_1 \cdot (\text{minor of } a_1) - a_2 \cdot (\text{minor of } a_2) + a_3 \cdot (\text{minor of } a_3)$$

Finding the determinant by using minors of elements in the first column is called **expanding** by the minors of the first column. *The value of a determinant can be found by expanding by the minors of any row or column.* The following **array of signs** is helpful in determining whether to add or subtract the product of an element and its minor.

$$\begin{array}{ccc} + & - & + \\ - & + & - \\ + & - & + \end{array}$$

If an element is in a position marked $+$, we add. If marked $-$, we subtract.

EXAMPLE 4 Evaluate by expanding by the minors of the given row or column.

$$\begin{vmatrix} 0 & 5 & 1 \\ 1 & 3 & -1 \\ -2 & 2 & 4 \end{vmatrix}$$

a. First column **b.** Second row

Solution

a. The elements of the first column are $0, 1$, and -2. The first column of the array of signs is $+, -, +$.

$$\begin{vmatrix} 0 & 5 & 1 \\ 1 & 3 & -1 \\ -2 & 2 & 4 \end{vmatrix} = 0 \cdot \begin{vmatrix} 3 & -1 \\ 2 & 4 \end{vmatrix} - 1 \cdot \begin{vmatrix} 5 & 1 \\ 2 & 4 \end{vmatrix} + (-2) \cdot \begin{vmatrix} 5 & 1 \\ 3 & -1 \end{vmatrix}$$
$$= 0(12 - (-2)) - 1(20 - 2) + (-2)(-5 - 3)$$
$$= 0 - 18 + 16 = -2$$

b. The elements of the second row are $1, 3$, and -1. This time, the signs begin with $-$ and again alternate.

$$\begin{vmatrix} 0 & 5 & 1 \\ 1 & 3 & -1 \\ -2 & 2 & 4 \end{vmatrix} = -1 \cdot \begin{vmatrix} 5 & 1 \\ 2 & 4 \end{vmatrix} + 3 \cdot \begin{vmatrix} 0 & 1 \\ -2 & 4 \end{vmatrix} - (-1) \cdot \begin{vmatrix} 0 & 5 \\ -2 & 2 \end{vmatrix}$$
$$= -1(20 - 2) + 3(0 - (-2)) - (-1)(0 - (-10))$$
$$= -18 + 6 + 10 = -2$$

Notice that the determinant of the 3×3 matrix is the same regardless of the row or column you select to expand by. □

✓CONCEPT CHECK

Why would expanding by minors of the second row be a good choice for the determinant $\begin{vmatrix} 3 & 4 & -2 \\ 5 & 0 & 0 \\ 6 & -3 & 7 \end{vmatrix}$?

OBJECTIVE

4 **Using Cramer's Rule to Solve a System of Three Linear Equations**

A system of three equations in three variables may be solved with Cramer's rule also. Using the elimination process to solve a system with unknown constants as coefficients leads to the following.

Cramer's Rule for Three Equations in Three Variables

The solution of the system $\begin{cases} a_1x + b_1y + c_1z = k_1 \\ a_2x + b_2y + c_2z = k_2 \\ a_3x + b_3y + c_3z = k_3 \end{cases}$ is given by

$$x = \frac{D_x}{D} \qquad y = \frac{D_y}{D} \qquad \text{and} \qquad z = \frac{D_z}{D}$$

where

$$D = \begin{vmatrix} a_1 & b_1 & c_1 \\ a_2 & b_2 & c_2 \\ a_3 & b_3 & c_3 \end{vmatrix} \qquad D_x = \begin{vmatrix} k_1 & b_1 & c_1 \\ k_2 & b_2 & c_2 \\ k_3 & b_3 & c_3 \end{vmatrix}$$

$$D_y = \begin{vmatrix} a_1 & k_1 & c_1 \\ a_2 & k_2 & c_2 \\ a_3 & k_3 & c_3 \end{vmatrix} \qquad D_z = \begin{vmatrix} a_1 & b_1 & k_1 \\ a_2 & b_2 & k_2 \\ a_3 & b_3 & k_3 \end{vmatrix}$$

as long as D is not 0.

Answer to Concept Check:
Two elements of the second row are 0, which makes calculations easier.

EXAMPLE 5   Use Cramer's rule to solve the system

$$\begin{cases} x - 2y + z = 4 \\ 3x + y - 2z = 3 \\ 5x + 5y + 3z = -8 \end{cases}$$

Solution   First we find D, D_x, D_y, and D_z. Beginning with D, we expand by the minors of the first column.

$$D = \begin{vmatrix} 1 & -2 & 1 \\ 3 & 1 & -2 \\ 5 & 5 & 3 \end{vmatrix} = 1 \cdot \begin{vmatrix} 1 & -2 \\ 5 & 3 \end{vmatrix} - 3 \cdot \begin{vmatrix} -2 & 1 \\ 5 & 3 \end{vmatrix} + 5 \cdot \begin{vmatrix} -2 & 1 \\ 1 & -2 \end{vmatrix}$$

$$= 1(3 - (-10)) - 3(-6 - 5) + 5(4 - 1)$$

$$= 13 + 33 + 15 = 61$$

$$D_x = \begin{vmatrix} 4 & -2 & 1 \\ 3 & 1 & -2 \\ -8 & 5 & 3 \end{vmatrix} = 4 \cdot \begin{vmatrix} 1 & -2 \\ 5 & 3 \end{vmatrix} - 3 \cdot \begin{vmatrix} -2 & 1 \\ 5 & 3 \end{vmatrix} + (-8) \cdot \begin{vmatrix} -2 & 1 \\ 1 & -2 \end{vmatrix}$$

$$= 4(3 - (-10)) - 3(-6 - 5) + (-8)(4 - 1)$$

$$= 52 + 33 - 24 = 61$$

$$D_y = \begin{vmatrix} 1 & 4 & 1 \\ 3 & 3 & -2 \\ 5 & -8 & 3 \end{vmatrix} = 1 \cdot \begin{vmatrix} 3 & -2 \\ -8 & 3 \end{vmatrix} - 3 \cdot \begin{vmatrix} 4 & 1 \\ -8 & 3 \end{vmatrix} + 5 \cdot \begin{vmatrix} 4 & 1 \\ 3 & -2 \end{vmatrix}$$

$$= 1(9 - 16) - 3(12 - (-8)) + 5(-8 - 3)$$

$$= -7 - 60 - 55 = -122$$

$$D_z = \begin{vmatrix} 1 & -2 & 4 \\ 3 & 1 & 3 \\ 5 & 5 & -8 \end{vmatrix} = 1 \cdot \begin{vmatrix} 1 & 3 \\ 5 & -8 \end{vmatrix} - 3 \cdot \begin{vmatrix} -2 & 4 \\ 5 & -8 \end{vmatrix} + 5 \cdot \begin{vmatrix} -2 & 4 \\ 1 & 3 \end{vmatrix}$$

$$= 1(-8 - 15) - 3(16 - 20) + 5(-6 - 4)$$

$$= -23 + 12 - 50 = -61$$

From these determinants, we calculate the solution:

$$x = \frac{D_x}{D} = \frac{61}{61} = 1 \quad y = \frac{D_y}{D} = \frac{-122}{61} = -2 \quad z = \frac{D_z}{D} = \frac{-61}{61} = -1$$

The ordered triple solution is $(1, -2, -1)$. Check this solution by verifying that it satisfies each equation of the system.   □

E   Exercise Set   MyMathLab®

Evaluate. See Example 1.

1. $\begin{vmatrix} 3 & 5 \\ -1 & 7 \end{vmatrix}$ **2.** $\begin{vmatrix} -5 & 1 \\ 0 & -4 \end{vmatrix}$

3. $\begin{vmatrix} 9 & -2 \\ 4 & -3 \end{vmatrix}$ **4.** $\begin{vmatrix} 4 & 0 \\ 9 & 8 \end{vmatrix}$

5. $\begin{vmatrix} -2 & 9 \\ 4 & -18 \end{vmatrix}$ **6.** $\begin{vmatrix} -40 & 8 \\ 70 & -14 \end{vmatrix}$

Use Cramer's rule, if possible, to solve each system of linear equations. See Examples 2 and 3.

7. $\begin{cases} 2y - 4 = 0 \\ x + 2y = 5 \end{cases}$ **8.** $\begin{cases} 4x - y = 5 \\ 3x - 3 = 0 \end{cases}$

9. $\begin{cases} 3x + y = 1 \\ 2y = 2 - 6x \end{cases}$ **10.** $\begin{cases} y = 2x - 5 \\ 8x - 4y = 20 \end{cases}$

11. $\begin{cases} 5x - 2y = 27 \\ -3x + 5y = 18 \end{cases}$ **12.** $\begin{cases} 4x - y = 9 \\ 2x + 3y = -27 \end{cases}$

Appendix E

Evaluate. See Example 4.

13. $\begin{vmatrix} 2 & 1 & 0 \\ 0 & 5 & -3 \\ 4 & 0 & 2 \end{vmatrix}$

14. $\begin{vmatrix} -6 & 4 & 2 \\ 1 & 0 & 5 \\ 0 & 3 & 1 \end{vmatrix}$

15. $\begin{vmatrix} 4 & -6 & 0 \\ -2 & 3 & 0 \\ 4 & -6 & 1 \end{vmatrix}$

16. $\begin{vmatrix} 5 & 2 & 1 \\ 3 & -6 & 0 \\ -2 & 8 & 0 \end{vmatrix}$

17. $\begin{vmatrix} 3 & 6 & -3 \\ -1 & -2 & 3 \\ 4 & -1 & 6 \end{vmatrix}$

18. $\begin{vmatrix} 2 & -2 & 1 \\ 4 & 1 & 3 \\ 3 & 1 & 2 \end{vmatrix}$

Use Cramer's rule, if possible, to solve each system of linear equations. See Example 5.

19. $\begin{cases} 3x \quad\quad + z = -1 \\ -x - 3y + z = 7 \\ \quad\quad 3y + z = 5 \end{cases}$

20. $\begin{cases} \quad\quad 4y - 3z = -2 \\ 8x - 4y \quad\quad = 4 \\ -8x + 4y + z = -2 \end{cases}$

21. $\begin{cases} x + y + z = 8 \\ 2x - y - z = 10 \\ x - 2y + 3z = 22 \end{cases}$

22. $\begin{cases} 5x + y + 3z = 1 \\ x - y - 3z = -7 \\ -x + y \quad\quad = 1 \end{cases}$

MIXED PRACTICE

Evaluate.

23. $\begin{vmatrix} 10 & -1 \\ -4 & 2 \end{vmatrix}$

24. $\begin{vmatrix} -6 & 2 \\ 5 & -1 \end{vmatrix}$

25. $\begin{vmatrix} 1 & 0 & 4 \\ 1 & -1 & 2 \\ 3 & 2 & 1 \end{vmatrix}$

26. $\begin{vmatrix} 0 & 1 & 2 \\ 3 & -1 & 2 \\ 3 & 2 & -2 \end{vmatrix}$

27. $\begin{vmatrix} \frac{3}{4} & \frac{5}{2} \\ -\frac{1}{6} & \frac{7}{3} \end{vmatrix}$

28. $\begin{vmatrix} \frac{5}{7} & \frac{1}{3} \\ \frac{6}{7} & \frac{2}{3} \end{vmatrix}$

29. $\begin{vmatrix} 4 & -2 & 2 \\ 6 & -1 & 3 \\ 2 & 1 & 1 \end{vmatrix}$

30. $\begin{vmatrix} 1 & 5 & 0 \\ 7 & 9 & -4 \\ 3 & 2 & -2 \end{vmatrix}$

31. $\begin{vmatrix} -2 & 5 & 4 \\ 5 & -1 & 3 \\ 4 & 1 & 2 \end{vmatrix}$

32. $\begin{vmatrix} 5 & -2 & 4 \\ -1 & 5 & 3 \\ 1 & 4 & 2 \end{vmatrix}$

Use Cramer's rule, if possible, to solve each system of linear equations.

33. $\begin{cases} 2x - 5y = 4 \\ x + 2y = -7 \end{cases}$

34. $\begin{cases} 3x - y = 2 \\ -5x + 2y = 0 \end{cases}$

35. $\begin{cases} 4x + 2y = 5 \\ 2x + y = -1 \end{cases}$

36. $\begin{cases} 3x + 6y = 15 \\ 2x + 4y = 3 \end{cases}$

37. $\begin{cases} 2x + 2y + z = 1 \\ -x + y + 2z = 3 \\ x + 2y + 4z = 0 \end{cases}$

38. $\begin{cases} 2x - 3y + z = 5 \\ x + y + z = 0 \\ 4x + 2y + 4z = 4 \end{cases}$

39. $\begin{cases} \frac{2}{3}x - \frac{3}{4}y = -1 \\ -\frac{1}{6}x + \frac{3}{4}y = \frac{5}{2} \end{cases}$

40. $\begin{cases} \frac{1}{2}x - \frac{1}{3}y = -3 \\ \frac{1}{8}x + \frac{1}{6}y = 0 \end{cases}$

41. $\begin{cases} 0.7x - 0.2y = -1.6 \\ 0.2x - y = -1.4 \end{cases}$

42. $\begin{cases} -0.7x + 0.6y = 1.3 \\ 0.5x - 0.3y = -0.8 \end{cases}$

43. $\begin{cases} -2x + 4y - 2z = 6 \\ x - 2y + z = -3 \\ 3x - 6y + 3z = -9 \end{cases}$

44. $\begin{cases} -x - y + 3z = 2 \\ 4x + 4y - 12z = -8 \\ -3x - 3y + 9z = 6 \end{cases}$

45. $\begin{cases} x - 2y + z = -5 \\ 3y + 2z = 4 \\ 3x - y = -2 \end{cases}$

46. $\begin{cases} 4x + 5y = 10 \\ 3y + 2z = -6 \\ x + y + z = 3 \end{cases}$

CONCEPT EXTENSIONS

Find the value of x such that each is a true statement.

47. $\begin{vmatrix} 1 & x \\ 2 & 7 \end{vmatrix} = -3$

48. $\begin{vmatrix} 6 & 1 \\ -2 & x \end{vmatrix} = 26$

49. If all the elements in a single row of a square matrix are zero, to what does the determinant evaluate? Explain your answer.

50. If all the elements in a single column of a square matrix are 0, to what does the determinant evaluate? Explain your answer.

51. Suppose you are interested in finding the determinant of a 4×4 matrix. Study the pattern shown in the array of signs for a 3×3 matrix. Use the pattern to expand the array of signs for use with a 4×4 matrix.

52. Why would expanding by minors of the second row be a good choice for the determinant $\begin{vmatrix} 3 & 4 & -2 \\ 5 & 0 & 0 \\ 6 & -3 & 7 \end{vmatrix}$?

Find the value of each determinant. To evaluate a 4×4 determinant, select any row or column and expand by the minors. The array of signs for a 4×4 determinant is the same as for a 3×3 determinant except expanded.

53. $\begin{vmatrix} 5 & 0 & 0 & 0 \\ 0 & 4 & 2 & -1 \\ 1 & 3 & -2 & 0 \\ 0 & -3 & 1 & 2 \end{vmatrix}$

54. $\begin{vmatrix} 1 & 7 & 0 & -1 \\ 1 & 3 & -2 & 0 \\ 1 & 0 & -1 & 2 \\ 0 & -6 & 2 & 4 \end{vmatrix}$

55. $\begin{vmatrix} 4 & 0 & 2 & 5 \\ 0 & 3 & -1 & 1 \\ 0 & 0 & 2 & 0 \\ 0 & 0 & 0 & 1 \end{vmatrix}$

56. $\begin{vmatrix} 2 & 0 & -1 & 4 \\ 6 & 0 & 4 & 1 \\ 2 & 4 & 3 & -1 \\ 4 & 0 & 5 & -4 \end{vmatrix}$

Appendix F

Mean, Median, and Mode

It is sometimes desirable to be able to describe a set of data, or a set of numbers, by a single "middle" number. Three such **measures of central tendency** are the mean, the median, and the mode.

The most common measure of central tendency is the mean (sometimes called the arithmetic mean or the average). The **mean** of a set of data items, denoted by $\bar{x}$, is the sum of the items divided by the number of items.

EXAMPLE 1   Seven students in a psychology class conducted an experiment on mazes. Each student was given a pencil and asked to successfully complete the same maze. The timed results are below.

Student	Ann	Thanh	Carlos	Jesse	Melinda	Ramzi	Dayni
Time (Seconds)	13.2	11.8	10.7	16.2	15.9	13.8	18.5

a. Who completed the maze in the shortest time? Who completed the maze in the longest time?

b. Find the mean.

c. How many students took longer than the mean time? How many students took shorter than the mean time?

Solution

a. Carlos completed the maze in 10.7 seconds, the shortest time. Dayni completed the maze in 18.5 seconds, the longest time.

b. To find the mean, $\bar{x}$, find the sum of the data items and divide by 7, the number of items.

$$\bar{x} = \frac{13.2 + 11.8 + 10.7 + 16.2 + 15.9 + 13.8 + 18.5}{7} = \frac{100.1}{7} = 14.3$$

c. Three students, Jesse, Melinda, and Dayni, had times longer than the mean time. Four students, Ann, Thanh, Carlos, and Ramzi, had times shorter than the mean time. □

Two other measures of central tendency are the median and the mode.

The **median** of an ordered set of numbers is the middle number. If the number of items is even, the median is the mean of the two middle numbers. The **mode** of a set of numbers is the number that occurs most often. It is possible for a data set to have no mode or more than one mode.

EXAMPLE 2   Find the median and the mode of the following list of numbers. These numbers were high temperatures for fourteen consecutive days in a city in Montana.

$$76, 80, 85, 86, 89, 87, 82, 77, 76, 79, 82, 89, 89, 92$$

(Continued on next page)

Solution

First, write the numbers in order.

76, 76, 77, 79, 80, 82, 82, 85, 86, 87, 89, 89, 89, 92

two middle numbers   mode

Since there is an even number of items, the median is the mean of the two middle numbers.

$$\text{median} = \frac{82 + 85}{2} = 83.5$$

The mode is 89, since 89 occurs most often.

F Exercise Set

MyMathLab®

For each of the following data sets, find the mean, the median, and the mode. If necessary, round the mean to one decimal place.

1. 21, 28, 16, 42, 38

2. 42, 35, 36, 40, 50

3. 7.6, 8.2, 8.2, 9.6, 5.7, 9.1

4. 4.9, 7.1, 6.8, 6.8, 5.3, 4.9

5. 0.2, 0.3, 0.5, 0.6, 0.6, 0.9, 0.2, 0.7, 1.1

6. 0.6, 0.6, 0.8, 0.4, 0.5, 0.3, 0.7, 0.8, 0.1

7. 231, 543, 601, 293, 588, 109, 334, 268

8. 451, 356, 478, 776, 892, 500, 467, 780

The eight tallest buildings in the United States are listed below. Use this table for Exercises 9 through 12.

Building	Height (feet)
Willis Tower, Chicago, IL	1454
Empire State, New York, NY	1250
Amoco, Chicago, IL	1136
John Hancock Center, Chicago, IL	1127
First Interstate World Center, Los Angeles, CA	1107
Chrysler, New York, NY	1046
NationsBank Tower, Atlanta, GA	1023
Texas Commerce Tower, Houston, TX	1002

9. Find the mean height for the five tallest buildings.
10. Find the median height for the five tallest buildings.
11. Find the median height for the eight tallest buildings.
12. Find the mean height for the eight tallest buildings.

During an experiment, the following times (in seconds) were recorded: 7.8, 6.9, 7.5, 4.7, 6.9, 7.0.

13. Find the mean. Round to the nearest tenth.
14. Find the median.
15. Find the mode.

In a mathematics class, the following test scores were recorded for a student: 86, 95, 91, 74, 77, 85.

16. Find the mean. Round to the nearest hundredth.
17. Find the median.
18. Find the mode.

The following pulse rates were recorded for a group of fifteen students: 78, 80, 66, 68, 71, 64, 82, 71, 70, 65, 70, 75, 77, 86, 72.

19. Find the mean.
20. Find the median.
21. Find the mode.
22. How many rates were higher than the mean?
23. How many rates were lower than the mean?
24. Have each student in your algebra class take his/her pulse rate. Record the data and find the mean, the median, and the mode.

Find the missing numbers in each list of numbers. (These numbers are not necessarily in numerical order.)

25. __, __, 16, 18, __
The mode is 21.   The mean is 20.

26. __, __, __, __, 40
The mode is 35.   The median is 37.   The mean is 38.

Appendix G

Review of Angles, Lines, and Special Triangles

The word **geometry** is formed from the Greek words **geo,** meaning earth, and **metron,** meaning measure. Geometry literally means to measure the earth.

This section contains a review of some basic geometric ideas. It will be assumed that fundamental ideas of geometry such as point, line, ray, and angle are known. In this appendix, the notation $\angle 1$ is read "angle 1" and the notation $m\angle 1$ is read "the measure of angle 1."

We first review types of angles.

Angles

A **right angle** is an angle whose measure is 90°. A right angle can be indicated by a square drawn at the vertex of the angle, as shown below.

An angle whose measure is more than 0° but less than 90° is called an **acute angle.**

An angle whose measure is greater than 90° but less than 180° is called an **obtuse angle.**

An angle whose measure is 180° is called a **straight angle.**

Two angles are said to be **complementary** if the sum of their measures is 90°. Each angle is called the **complement** of the other.

Two angles are said to be **supplementary** if the sum of their measures is 180°. Each angle is called the **supplement** of the other.

Acute angle   Right angle   Obtuse angle   Straight angle

Complementary angles
$m\angle 1 + m\angle 2 = 90°$

Supplementary angles
$m\angle 3 + m\angle 4 = 180°$

EXAMPLE 1   If an angle measures 28°, find its complement.

Solution   Two angles are complementary if the sum of their measures is 90°. The complement of a 28° angle is an angle whose measure is $90° - 28° = 62°$. To check, notice that $28° + 62° = 90°$.

Plane is an undefined term that we will describe. A plane can be thought of as a flat surface with infinite length and width, but no thickness. A plane is two dimensional.

The arrows in the following diagram indicate that a plane extends indefinitely and has no boundaries.

Figures that lie on a plane are called **plane figures.** Lines that lie in the same plane are called **coplanar.**

Lines

Two lines are **parallel** if they lie in the same plane but never meet.

Intersecting lines meet or cross in one point.

Two lines that form right angles when they intersect are said to be **perpendicular.**

Parallel lines   Intersecting lines   Intersecting lines that are perpendicular

---

Two intersecting lines form **vertical angles.** Angles 1 and 3 are vertical angles. Also, angles 2 and 4 are vertical angles. It can be shown that **vertical angles have equal measures.**

$m\angle 1 = m\angle 3$
$m\angle 2 = m\angle 4$

Adjacent angles have the same vertex and share a side. Angles 1 and 2 are adjacent angles. Other pairs of adjacent angles are angles 2 and 3, angles 3 and 4, and angles 4 and 1.

A **transversal** is a line that intersects two or more lines in the same plane. Line l is a transversal that intersects lines m and n. The eight angles formed are numbered and certain pairs of these angles are given special names.

Corresponding angles: $\angle 1$ and $\angle 5$, $\angle 3$ and $\angle 7$, $\angle 2$ and $\angle 6$, and $\angle 4$ and $\angle 8$.

Exterior angles: $\angle 1$, $\angle 2$, $\angle 7$, and $\angle 8$.

Interior angles: $\angle 3$, $\angle 4$, $\angle 5$, and $\angle 6$.

Alternate interior angles: $\angle 3$ and $\angle 6$, $\angle 4$ and $\angle 5$.

These angles and parallel lines are related in the following manner.

Parallel Lines Cut by a Transversal

1. If two parallel lines are cut by a transversal, then
   a. corresponding angles are equal and
   b. alternate interior angles are equal.
2. If corresponding angles formed by two lines and a transversal are equal, then the lines are parallel.
3. If alternate interior angles formed by two lines and a transversal are equal, then the lines are parallel.

EXAMPLE 2   Given that lines m and n are parallel and that the measure of angle 1 is 100°, find the measures of angles 2, 3, and 4.

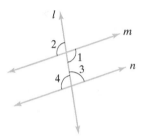

Solution $m\angle 2 = 100°$, since angles 1 and 2 are vertical angles.

$m\angle 4 = 100°$, since angles 1 and 4 are alternate interior angles.

$m\angle 3 = 180° - 100° = 80°$, since angles 4 and 3 are supplementary angles. ☐

A **polygon** is the union of three or more coplanar line segments that intersect each other only at each end point, with each end point shared by exactly two segments.

A **triangle** is a polygon with three sides. The sum of the measures of the three angles of a triangle is 180°. In the following figure, $m\angle 1 + m\angle 2 + m\angle 3 = 180°$.

EXAMPLE 3   Find the measure of the third angle of the triangle shown.

Solution   The sum of the measures of the angles of a triangle is 180°. Since one angle measures 45° and the other angle measures 95°, the third angle measures $180° - 45° - 95° = 40°$. ☐

Two triangles are **congruent** if they have the same size and the same shape. In congruent triangles, the measures of corresponding angles are equal and the lengths of corresponding sides are equal. The following triangles are congruent.

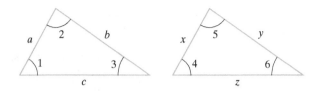

Corresponding angles are equal: $m\angle1 = m\angle4, m\angle2 = m\angle5$, and $m\angle3 = m\angle6$. Also, lengths of corresponding sides are equal: $a = x$, $b = y$, and $c = z$.

Any one of the following may be used to determine whether two triangles are congruent.

Congruent Triangles

1. If the measures of two angles of a triangle equal the measures of two angles of another triangle and the lengths of the sides between each pair of angles are equal, the triangles are congruent.

$$m\angle1 = m\angle3$$
$$m\angle2 = m\angle4$$
and
$$a = x$$

2. If the lengths of the three sides of a triangle equal the lengths of corresponding sides of another triangle, the triangles are congruent.

$$a = x$$
$$b = y$$
and
$$c = z$$

3. If the lengths of two sides of a triangle equal the lengths of corresponding sides of another triangle, and the measures of the angles between each pair of sides are equal, the triangles are congruent.

$$a = x$$
$$b = y$$
and
$$m\angle1 = m\angle2$$

Two triangles are **similar** if they have the same shape. In similar triangles, the measures of corresponding angles are equal and corresponding sides are in proportion. The following triangles are similar. (All similar triangles drawn in this appendix will be oriented the same.)

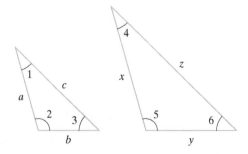

Corresponding angles are equal: $m\angle1 = m\angle4$, $m\angle2 = m\angle5$, and $m\angle3 = m\angle6$.

Also, corresponding sides are proportional: $\dfrac{a}{x} = \dfrac{b}{y} = \dfrac{c}{z}$.

Any one of the following may be used to determine whether two triangles are similar.

Similar Triangles

1. If the measures of two angles of a triangle equal the measures of two angles of another triangle, the triangles are similar.

$$m\angle 1 = m\angle 2$$
and
$$m\angle 3 = m\angle 4$$

2. If three sides of one triangle are proportional to three sides of another triangle, the triangles are similar.

$$\frac{a}{x} = \frac{b}{y} = \frac{c}{z}$$

3. If two sides of a triangle are proportional to two sides of another triangle and the measures of the included angles are equal, the triangles are similar.

$$m\angle 1 = m\angle 2$$
and
$$\frac{a}{x} = \frac{b}{y}$$

EXAMPLE 4   Given that the following triangles are similar, find the missing length x.

Solution   Since the triangles are similar, corresponding sides are in proportion. Thus, $\frac{2}{3} = \frac{10}{x}$. To solve this equation for x, we multiply both sides by the LCD, $3x$.

$$3x\left(\frac{2}{3}\right) = 3x\left(\frac{10}{x}\right)$$
$$2x = 30$$
$$x = 15$$

The missing length is 15 units.

A **right triangle** contains a right angle. The side opposite the right angle is called the **hypotenuse**, and the other two sides are called the **legs.** The **Pythagorean theorem** gives a formula that relates the lengths of the three sides of a right triangle.

The Pythagorean Theorem

If a and b are the lengths of the legs of a right triangle, and c is the length of the hypotenuse, then $a^2 + b^2 = c^2$.

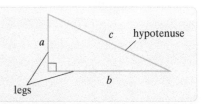

EXAMPLE 5 Find the length of the hypotenuse of a right triangle whose legs have lengths of 3 centimeters and 4 centimeters.

3 centimeters

4 centimeters

Solution Because we have a right triangle, we use the Pythagorean theorem. The legs are 3 centimeters and 4 centimeters, so let $a = 3$ and $b = 4$ in the formula.

$$a^2 + b^2 = c^2$$
$$3^2 + 4^2 = c^2$$
$$9 + 16 = c^2$$
$$25 = c^2$$

Since c represents a length, we assume that c is positive. Thus, if c^2 is 25, c must be 5. The hypotenuse has a length of 5 centimeters. $\square$

 G **Exercise Set** MyMathLab®

Find the complement of each angle. See Example 1.

1. $19°$
2. $65°$
3. $70.8°$
4. $45\frac{2}{3}°$
5. $11\frac{1}{4}°$
6. $19.6°$

Find the supplement of each angle.

7. $150°$
8. $90°$
9. $30.2°$
10. $81.9°$
11. $79\frac{1}{2}°$
12. $165\frac{8}{9}°$

13. If lines m and n are parallel, find the measures of angles 1 through 7. See Example 2.

14. If lines m and n are parallel, find the measures of angles 1 through 5. See Example 2.

In each of the following, the measures of two angles of a triangle are given. Find the measure of the third angle. See Example 3.

15. $11°, 79°$
16. $8°, 102°$
17. $25°, 65°$
18. $44°, 19°$
19. $30°, 60°$
20. $67°, 23°$

In each of the following, the measure of one angle of a right triangle is given. Find the measures of the other two angles.

21. $45°$
22. $60°$
23. $17°$
24. $30°$
25. $39\frac{3}{4}°$
26. $72.6°$

Given that each of the following pairs of triangles is similar, find the missing lengths. See Example 4.

27.

28.

29.

30.

Use the Pythagorean theorem to find the missing lengths in the right triangles. See Example 5.

31.

32.

33.

34.

Contents of Student Resources

Student Resources

Study Skills Builders

Attitude and Study Tips

Study Skills Builder 1

Have You Decided to Complete This Course Successfully?

Ask yourself if one of your current goals is to complete this course successfully.

If it is not a goal of yours, ask yourself why. One common reason is fear of failure. Amazingly enough, fear of failure alone can be strong enough to keep many of us from doing our best in any endeavor.

Another common reason is that you simply haven't taken the time to think about or write down your goals for this course. To help accomplish this, answer the following questions.

Exercises

1. Write down your goal(s) for this course.

2. Now list steps you will take to make sure your goal(s) in Exercise 1 are accomplished.

3. Rate your commitment to this course with a number between 1 and 5. Use the diagram below to help.

High Commitment		Average Commitment	Not Committed at All	
5	4	3	2	1

4. If you have rated your personal commitment level (from the exercise above) as a 1, 2, or 3, list the reasons why this is so. Then determine whether it is possible to increase your commitment level to a 4 or 5.

Good luck, and don't forget that a positive attitude will make a big difference.

Study Skills Builder 2

Tips for Studying for an Exam

To prepare for an exam, try the following study techniques:

- Start the study process days before your exam.
- Make sure that you are up to date on your assignments.
- If there is a topic that you are unsure of, use one of the many resources that are available to you. For example,
  See your instructor.
  View a lecture video on the topic.
  Visit a learning resource center on campus.
  Read the textbook material and examples on the topic.
- Reread your notes and carefully review the Chapter Highlights at the end of any chapter.
- Work the review exercises at the end of the chapter.
- Find a quiet place to take the Chapter Test found at the end of the chapter. Do not use any resources when taking this sample test. This way, you will have a clear indication of how prepared you are for your exam. Check your answers and use the Chapter Test Prep Videos to make sure that you correct any missed exercises.

Good luck, and keep a positive attitude.

Exercises

Let's see how you did on your last exam.

1. How many days before your last exam did you start studying for that exam?

2. Were you up to date on your assignments at that time or did you need to catch up on assignments?

3. List the most helpful text supplement (if you used one).

4. List the most helpful campus supplement (if you used one).

5. List your process for preparing for a mathematics test.

6. Was this process helpful? In other words, were you satisfied with your performance on your exam?

7. If not, what changes can you make in your process that will make it more helpful to you?

Study Skills Builder 3

What to Do the Day of an Exam

Your first exam may be soon. On the day of an exam, don't forget to try the following:

- Allow yourself plenty of time to arrive.
- Read the directions on the test carefully.
- Read each problem carefully as you take your test. Make sure that you answer the question asked.
- Watch your time and pace yourself so that you may attempt each problem on your test.
- Check your work and answers.
- **_Do not turn your test in early._** If you have extra time, spend it double-checking your work.

Good luck!

Exercises

Answer the following questions based on your most recent mathematics exam, whenever that was.

1. How soon before class did you arrive?
2. Did you read the directions on the test carefully?
3. Did you make sure you answered the question asked for each problem on the exam?
4. Were you able to attempt each problem on your exam?
5. If your answer to Exercise 4 is no, list reasons why.
6. Did you have extra time on your exam?
7. If your answer to Exercise 6 is yes, describe how you spent that extra time.

Study Skills Builder 4

Are You Satisfied with Your Performance on a Particular Quiz or Exam?

If not, don't forget to analyze your quiz or exam and look for common errors. Were most of your errors a result of:

- *Carelessness?* Did you turn in your quiz or exam before the allotted time expired? If so, resolve to use any extra time to check your work.
- *Running out of time?* Answer the questions you are sure of first. Then attempt the questions you are unsure of and delay checking your work until all questions have been answered.
- *Not understanding a concept?* If so, review that concept and correct your work so that you make sure you understand it before the next quiz or the final exam.
- *Test conditions?* When studying for a quiz or exam, make sure you place yourself in conditions similar to test conditions. For example, before your next quiz or exam, take a sample test without the aid of your notes or text.

(For a sample test, see your instructor or use the Chapter Test at the end of each chapter.)

Exercises

1. Have you corrected all your previous quizzes and exams?
2. List any errors you have found common to two or more of your graded papers.
3. Is one of your common errors not understanding a concept? If so, are you making sure you understand all the concepts for the next quiz or exam?
4. Is one of your common errors making careless mistakes? If so, are you now taking all the time allotted to check over your work so that you can minimize the number of careless mistakes?
5. Are you satisfied with your grades thus far on quizzes and tests?
6. If your answer to Exercise 5 is no, are there any more suggestions you can make to your instructor or yourself to help? If so, list them here and share these with your instructor.

Study Skills Builder 5

How Are You Doing?

If you haven't done so yet, take a few moments to think about how you are doing in this course. Are you working toward your goal of successfully completing this course? Is your performance on homework, quizzes, and tests satisfactory? If not, you might want to see your instructor to see whether he/she has any suggestions on how you can improve your performance. Reread Section 1.1 for ideas on places to get help with your mathematics course.

Exercises

Answer the following.

1. List any textbook supplements you are using to help you through this course.
2. List any campus resources you are using to help you through this course.
3. Write a short paragraph describing how you are doing in your mathematics course.
4. If improvement is needed, list ways that you can work toward improving your situation as described in Exercise 3.

Study Skills Builder 6

Are You Preparing for Your Final Exam?

To prepare for your final exam, try the following study techniques:

- Review the material that you will be responsible for on your exam. This includes material from your textbook, your notebook, and any handouts from your instructor.
- Review any formulas that you may need to memorize.
- Check to see if your instructor or mathematics department will be conducting a final exam review.
- Check with your instructor to see whether final exams from previous semesters/quarters are available to students for review.

- Use your previously taken exams as a practice final exam. To do so, rewrite the test questions in mixed order on blank sheets of paper. This will help you prepare for exam conditions.
- If you are unsure of a few concepts, see your instructor or visit a learning lab for assistance. Also, view the video segment of any troublesome sections.
- If you need further exercises to work, try the Cumulative Reviews at the end of the chapters.

Once again, good luck! I hope you are enjoying this textbook and your mathematics course.

Organizing Your Work

Study Skills Builder 7

Learning New Terms

Many of the terms used in this text may be new to you. It will be helpful to make a list of new mathematical terms and symbols as you encounter them and to review them frequently. Placing these new terms (including page references) on 3×5 index cards might help you later when you're preparing for a quiz.

Exercises

1. Name one way you might place a word and its definition on a 3×5 card.
2. How do new terms stand out in this text so that they can be found?

Study Skills Builder 8

Are You Organized?

Have you ever had trouble finding a completed assignment? When it's time to study for a test, are your notes neat and organized? Have you ever had trouble reading your own mathematics handwriting? (Be honest—I have.)

When any of these things happen, it's time to get organized. Here are a few suggestions:

- Write your notes and complete your homework assignments in a notebook with pockets (spiral or ring binder).
- Take class notes in this notebook, and then follow the notes with your completed homework assignment.
- When you receive graded papers or handouts, place them in the notebook pocket so that you will not lose them.
- Mark (possibly with an exclamation point) any note(s) that seem extra important to you.
- Mark (possibly with a question mark) any notes or homework that you are having trouble with.

- See your instructor or a math tutor to help you with the concepts or exercises that you are having trouble understanding.
- If you are having trouble reading your own handwriting, *slow down* and write your mathematics work clearly!

Exercises

1. Have you been completing your assignments on time?
2. Have you been correcting any exercises you may be having difficulty with?
3. If you are having trouble with a mathematical concept or correcting any homework exercises, have you visited your instructor, a tutor, or your campus math lab?
4. Are you taking lecture notes in your mathematics course? (By the way, these notes should include worked-out examples solved by your instructor.)
5. Is your mathematics course material (handouts, graded papers, lecture notes) organized?
6. If your answer to Exercise 5 is no, take a moment to review your course material. List at least two ways that you might organize it better.

Study Skills Builder 9

Organizing a Notebook

It's never too late to get organized. If you need ideas about organizing a notebook for your mathematics course, try some of these:

- Use a spiral or ring binder notebook with pockets and use it for mathematics only.
- Start each page by writing the book's section number you are working on at the top.
- When your instructor is lecturing, take notes. *Always* include any examples your instructor works for you.
- Place your worked-out homework exercises in your notebook immediately after the lecture notes from that section. This way, a section's worth of material is together.
- Homework exercises: Attempt and check all assigned homework.
- Place graded quizzes in the pockets of your notebook or a special section of your binder.

Exercises

Check your notebook organization by answering the following questions.

1. Do you have a spiral or ring binder notebook for your mathematics course only?
2. Have you ever had to flip through several sheets of notes and work in your mathematics notebook to determine what section's work you are in?
3. Are you now writing the textbook's section number at the top of each notebook page?
4. Have you ever lost or had trouble finding a graded quiz or test?
5. Are you now placing all your graded work in a dedicated place in your notebook?
6. Are you attempting all of your homework and placing all of your work in your notebook?
7. Are you checking and correcting your homework in your notebook? If not, why not?
8. Are you writing in your notebook the examples your instructor works for you in class?

Study Skills Builder 10

How Are Your Homework Assignments Going?

It is very important in mathematics to keep up with homework. Why? Many concepts build on each other. Often your understanding of a day's concepts depends on an understanding of the previous day's material.

Remember that completing your homework assignment involves a lot more than attempting a few of the problems assigned.

To complete a homework assignment, remember these four things:

- Attempt all of it.
- Check it.
- Correct it.
- If needed, ask questions about it.

Exercises

Take a moment to review your completed homework assignments. Answer the questions below based on this review.

1. Approximate the fraction of your homework you have attempted.

2. Approximate the fraction of your homework you have checked (if possible).

3. If you are able to check your homework, have you corrected it when errors have been found?

4. When working homework, if you do not understand a concept, what do you do?

MyMathLab and MathXL

Study Skills Builder 11

Tips for Turning in Your Homework on Time

It is very important to keep up with your mathematics homework assignments. Why? Many concepts in mathematics build upon each other.

Remember these four tips to help ensure that your work is completed on time:

- Know the assignments and due dates set by your instructor.
- Do not wait until the last minute to submit your homework.
- Set a goal to submit your homework 6–8 hours before the scheduled due date in case you have unexpected technology trouble.
- Schedule enough time to complete each assignment.

Following these tips will also help you avoid losing points for late or missed assignments.

Exercises

Take a moment to consider your work on your homework assignments to date and answer the following questions:

1. What percentage of your assignments have you turned in on time?

2. Why might it be a good idea to submit your homework 6–8 hours before the scheduled deadline?

3. If you have missed submitting any homework by the due date, list some of the reasons this occurred.

4. What steps do you plan to take in the future to ensure that your homework is submitted on time?

Study Skills Builder 12
Tips for Doing Your Homework Online

Practice is one of the main keys to success in any mathematics course. Did you know that MyMathLab/MathXL provides you with **immediate feedback** for each exercise? If you are incorrect, you are given hints to work the exercise correctly. You have **unlimited practice opportunities** and can rework any exercises you have trouble with until you master them, and submit homework assignments unlimited times before the deadline.

Remember these success tips when doing your homework online:

- Attempt all assigned exercises.
- Write down (neatly) your step-by-step work for each exercise before entering your answer.
- Use the immediate feedback provided by the program to help you check and correct your work for each exercise.
- Rework any exercises you have trouble with until you master them.
- Work through your homework assignment as many times as necessary until you are satisfied.

Exercises

Take a moment to think about your homework assignments to date and answer the following:

1. Have you attempted all assigned exercises?
2. Of the exercises attempted, have you also written out your work before entering your answer so that you can check it?
3. Are you familiar with how to enter answers using the MathXL player so that you avoid answer entry–type errors?
4. List some ways the immediate feedback and practice supports have helped you with your homework. If you have not used these supports, how do you plan to use them with the given success tips on your next assignment?

Study Skills Builder 13
Organizing Your Work

Have you ever used any readily available paper (such as the back of a flyer, another course assignment, Post-it notes, etc.) to work out homework exercises before entering the answer in MathXL? To save time, have you ever entered answers directly into MathXL without working the exercises on paper? When it's time to study, have you ever been unable to find your completed work or read and follow your own mathematics handwriting?

When any of these things happen, it's time to get organized. Here are some suggestions:

- Write your step-by-step work for each homework exercise (neatly) on lined, loose-leaf paper and keep this in a 3-ring binder.
- Refer to your step-by-step work when you receive feedback that your answer is incorrect in MathXL. Double-check against the steps and hints provided by the program and correct your work accordingly.
- Keep your written homework with your class notes for that section.
- Identify any exercises you are having trouble with and ask questions about them.
- Keep all graded quizzes and tests in this binder as well to study later.

If you follow these suggestions, you and your instructor or tutor will be able to follow your steps and correct any mistakes. You will have a written copy of your work to refer to later to ask questions and study for tests.

Exercises

1. Why is it important to write out your step-by-step work to homework exercises and keep a hard copy of all work submitted online?
2. If you have gotten an incorrect answer, are you able to follow your steps and find your error?
3. If you were asked today to review your previous homework assignments and first test, could you find them? If not, list some ways you might organize your work better.

Study Skills Builder 14

Getting Help with Your Homework Assignments

Many helpful resources are available to you through MathXL to help you work through any homework exercises you may have trouble with. It is important for you to know what these resources are and when and how to use them.

Let's review these features, found in the homework exercises:

- **Help Me Solve This**—provides step-by-step help for the exercise you are working. You must work an additional exercise of the same type (without this help) before you can get credit for having worked it correctly.

- **View an Example**—allows you to view a correctly worked exercise similar to the one you are having trouble with. You can go back to your original exercise and work it on your own.

- **E-Book**—allows you to read examples from your text and find similar exercises.

- **Video****—your text author, Elayn Martin-Gay, works an exercise similar to the one you need help with. **Not all exercises have an accompanying video clip.

- **Ask My Instructor**—allows you to email your instructor for help with an exercise.

Exercises

1. How does the "Help Me Solve This" feature work?

2. If the "View an Example" feature is used, is it necessary to work an additional problem before continuing the assignment?

3. When might be a good time to use the "Video" feature? Do all exercises have an accompanying video clip?

4. Which of the features above have you used? List those you found the most helpful to you.

5. If you haven't used the features discussed, list those you plan to try on your next homework assignment.

Study Skills Builder 15

Tips for Preparing for an Exam

Did you know that you can rework your previous homework assignments in MyMathLab and MathXL? This is a great way to prepare for tests. To do this, open a previous homework assignment and click "similar exercise." This will generate new exercises similar to the homework you have submitted. You can then rework the exercises and assignments until you feel confident that you understand them.

To prepare for an exam, follow these tips:

- Review your written work for your previous homework assignments along with your class notes.

- Identify any exercises or topics that you have questions on or have difficulty understanding.

- Rework your previous assignments in MyMathLab and MathXL until you fully understand them and can do them without help.

- Get help for any topics you feel unsure of or for which you have questions.

Exercises

1. Are your current homework assignments up to date and is your written work for them organized in a binder or notebook? If the answer is no, it's time to get organized. For tips on this, see Study Skills Builder 13—Organizing Your Work.

2. How many days in advance of an exam do you usually start studying?

3. List some ways you think that practicing previous homework assignments can help you prepare for your test.

4. List two or three resources you can use to get help for any topics you are unsure of or have questions on.

Good luck!

Study Skills Builder 16

How Well Do You Know the Resources Available to You in MyMathLab?

How Well Do You Know the Resources
Available to You in MyMathLab?

Many helpful resources are available to you in MyMathLab. Let's take a moment to locate and explore a few of them now. Go into your MyMathLab course and visit the multimedia library, tools for success, and E-book.

Let's see what you found.

Exercises

1. List the resources available to you in the Multimedia Library.

2. List the resources available to you in the Tools for Success folder.

3. Where did you find the English/Spanish Audio Glossary?

4. Can you view videos from the E-book?

5. Did you find any resources you did not know about? If so, which ones?

6. Which resources have you used most often or found most helpful?

Additional Help Inside and Outside Your Textbook

Additional Help Inside and Outside Your Textbook

Study Skills Builder 17

How Well Do You Know Your Textbook?

How Well Do You Know Your Textbook?

The following questions will help determine whether you are familiar with your textbook. For additional information, see Section 1.1 in this text.

1. What does the ▶ icon mean?

2. What does the ＼ icon mean?

3. What does the △ icon mean?

4. Where can you find a review for each chapter? What answers to this review can be found in the back of your text?

5. Each chapter contains an overview of the chapter along with examples. What is this feature called?

6. Each chapter contains a review of vocabulary. What is this feature called?

7. Practice exercises are contained in this text. What are they and how can they be used?

8. This text contains a student section in the back entitled Student Resources. List the contents of this section and how they might be helpful.

9. What exercise answers are available in this text? Where are they located?

Study Skills Builder 18

Are You Familiar with Your Textbook Supplements?

Below is a review of some of the student supplements available for additional study. Check to see whether you are using the ones most helpful to you.

- Chapter Test Prep Videos. These videos provide video clip solutions to the Chapter Test exercises in this text. You will find this extremely useful when studying for tests or exams.

- Interactive DVD Lecture Series. These are keyed to each section of the text. The material is presented by me, Elayn Martin-Gay, and I have placed a ⊙ by the exercises in the text that I have worked on the video.

- The *Student Solutions Manual*. This contains worked-out solutions to odd-numbered exercises as well as every exercise in the Integrated Reviews, Chapter Reviews, Chapter Tests, and Cumulative Reviews and every Practice exercise.

- Pearson Tutor Center. Mathematics questions may be phoned, faxed, or emailed to this center.

- MyMathLab is a text-specific online course. MathXL is an online homework, tutorial, and assessment system. Take a moment to determine whether these are available to you.

As usual, your instructor is your best source of information.

Exercises

Let's see how you are doing with textbook supplements.

1. Name one way the Lecture Videos can be helpful to you.

2. Name one way the Chapter Test Prep Video can help you prepare for a chapter test.

3. List any textbook supplements that you have found useful.

4. Have you located and visited a learning resource lab located on your campus?

5. List the textbook supplements that are currently housed in your campus's learning resource lab.

Study Skills Builder 19

Are You Getting All the Mathematics Help That You Need?

Remember that, in addition to your instructor, there are many places to get help with your mathematics course. For example:

- This text has an accompanying video lesson by the author for every section. There are also worked-out video solutions by the author to every Chapter Test exercise.

- The back of the book contains answers to odd-numbered exercises.

- A *Student Solutions Manual* is available that contains worked-out solutions to odd-numbered exercises as well as solutions to every exercise in the Integrated Reviews, Chapter Reviews, Chapter Tests, and Cumulative Reviews and every Practice exercise.

- Don't forget to check with your instructor for other local resources available to you, such as a tutor center.

Exercises

1. List items you find helpful in the text and all student supplements to this text.

2. List all the campus help that is available to you for this course.

3. List any help (besides the textbook) from Exercises 1 and 2 above that you are using.

4. List any help (besides the textbook) that you feel you should try.

5. Write a goal for yourself that includes trying everything you listed in Exercise 4 during the next week.

The Bigger Picture—Study Guide Outline

Simplifying Expressions and Solving Equations and Inequalities

I. Simplifying Expressions

  A. Real Numbers

    1. Add: (Sec. 1.5)

$$-1.7 + (-0.21) = -1.91$$

      Adding like signs.
Add absolute values. Attach common sign.

$$-7 + 3 = -4$$

      Adding different signs.
Subtract absolute values. Attach the sign of the number with the larger absolute value.

    2. Subtract: Add the first number to the opposite of the second number. (Sec. 1.6)

$$17 - 25 = 17 + (-25) = -8$$

    3. Multiply or divide: Multiply or divide the two numbers as usual. If the signs are the same, the answer is positive. If the signs are different, the answer is negative. (Sec. 1.7)

$$-10 \cdot 3 = -30, \qquad -81 \div (-3) = 27$$

  B. Exponents (Secs. 5.1 and 5.5)

$$x^7 \cdot x^5 = x^{12};\ (x^7)^5 = x^{35};\ \frac{x^7}{x^5} = x^2;\ x^0 = 1;\ 8^{-2} = \frac{1}{8^2} = \frac{1}{64}$$

  C. Polynomials

    1. Add: Combine like terms. (Sec. 5.2)

$$(3y^2 + 6y + 7) + (9y^2 - 11y - 15) = 3y^2 + 6y + 7 + 9y^2 - 11y - 15$$
$$= 12y^2 - 5y - 8$$

    2. Subtract: Change the sign of the terms of the polynomial being subtracted, then add. (Sec. 5.2)

$$(3y^2 + 6y + 7) - (9y^2 - 11y - 15) = 3y^2 + 6y + 7 - 9y^2 + 11y + 15$$
$$= -6y^2 + 17y + 22$$

    3. Multiply: Multiply each term of one polynomial by each term of the other polynomial. (Secs. 5.3 and 5.4)

$$(x + 5)(2x^2 - 3x + 4) = x(2x^2 - 3x + 4) + 5(2x^2 - 3x + 4)$$
$$= 2x^3 - 3x^2 + 4x + 10x^2 - 15x + 20$$
$$= 2x^3 + 7x^2 - 11x + 20$$

    4. Divide: (Sec. 5.6)

      a. To divide by a monomial, divide each term of the polynomial by the monomial.

$$\frac{8x^2 + 2x - 6}{2x} = \frac{8x^2}{2x} + \frac{2x}{2x} - \frac{6}{2x} = 4x + 1 - \frac{3}{x}$$

b. To divide by a polynomial other than a monomial, use long division.

$$2x + 5 \overline{\smash{\big)}\ 2x^2 - 7x + 10}\ \ \ x - 6 + \dfrac{40}{2x+5}$$

$$\underline{2x^2 + 5x}$$
$$-12x + 10$$
$$\underline{+12x + 30}$$
$$40$$

D. Factoring Polynomials
See the Chapter 6 Integrated Review for steps.

$$3x^4 - 78x^2 + 75 = 3(x^4 - 26x^2 + 25) \quad \text{Factor out GCF—always first step.}$$
$$= 3(x^2 - 25)(x^2 - 1) \quad \text{Factor trinomial.}$$
$$= 3(x + 5)(x - 5)(x + 1)(x - 1) \quad \text{Factor further—each difference of squares.}$$

E. Rational Expressions
1. **Simplify:** Factor the numerator and denominator. Then divide out factors of 1 by dividing out common factors in the numerator and denominator. (Sec. 7.1)

$$\frac{x^2 - 9}{7x^2 - 21x} = \frac{(x + 3)(x - 3)}{7x(x - 3)} = \frac{x + 3}{7x}$$

2. **Multiply:** Multiply numerators, then multiply denominators. (Sec. 7.2)

$$\frac{5z}{2z^2 - 9z - 18} \cdot \frac{22z + 33}{10z} = \frac{5 \cdot z}{(2z + 3)(z - 6)} \cdot \frac{11(2z + 3)}{2 \cdot 5 \cdot z} = \frac{11}{2(z - 6)}$$

3. **Divide:** First fraction times the reciprocal of the second fraction. (Sec. 7.2)

$$\frac{14}{x + 5} \div \frac{x + 1}{2} = \frac{14}{x + 5} \cdot \frac{2}{x + 1} = \frac{28}{(x + 5)(x + 1)}$$

4. **Add or subtract:** Must have same denominator. If not, find the LCD and write each fraction as an equivalent fraction with the LCD as denominator. (Sec. 7.4)

$$\frac{9}{10} - \frac{x + 1}{x + 5} = \frac{9(x + 5)}{10(x + 5)} - \frac{10(x + 1)}{10(x + 5)}$$
$$= \frac{9x + 45 - 10x - 10}{10(x + 5)} = \frac{-x + 35}{10(x + 5)}$$

F. Radicals
1. **Simplify square roots:** If possible, factor the radicand so that one factor is a perfect square. Then use the product rule and simplify. (Sec. 10.3)

$$\sqrt{75} = \sqrt{25 \cdot 3} = \sqrt{25} \cdot \sqrt{3} = 5\sqrt{3}$$

2. **Add or subtract:** Only like radicals (same index and radicand) can be added or subtracted. (Sec. 10.4)

$$8\sqrt{10} - \sqrt{40} + \sqrt{5} = 8\sqrt{10} - 2\sqrt{10} + \sqrt{5} = 6\sqrt{10} + \sqrt{5}$$

3. **Multiply or divide:** $\sqrt{a} \cdot \sqrt{b} = \sqrt{ab}; \dfrac{\sqrt{a}}{\sqrt{b}} = \sqrt{\dfrac{a}{b}}$. (Sec. 10.4)

$$\sqrt{11} \cdot \sqrt{3} = \sqrt{33}; \dfrac{\sqrt{140}}{\sqrt{7}} = \sqrt{\dfrac{140}{7}} = \sqrt{20} = \sqrt{4 \cdot 5} = 2\sqrt{5}$$

4. **Rationalizing the denominator:** (Sec. 10.5)
   a. If denominator is one term,

$$\frac{5}{\sqrt{11}} = \frac{5 \cdot \sqrt{11}}{\sqrt{11} \cdot \sqrt{11}} = \frac{5\sqrt{11}}{11}$$

b. If denominator is two terms, multiply by 1 in the form of $\dfrac{\text{conjugate of denominator}}{\text{conjugate of denominator}}$.

$$\frac{13}{3 + \sqrt{2}} = \frac{13}{3 + \sqrt{2}} \cdot \frac{3 - \sqrt{2}}{3 - \sqrt{2}} = \frac{13(3 - \sqrt{2})}{9 - 2} = \frac{13(3 - \sqrt{2})}{7}$$

II. Solving Equations

A. Linear Equations: (Sec. 2.3)

$$5(x - 2) = \frac{4(2x + 1)}{3}$$

$$3 \cdot 5(x - 2) = \cancel{3} \cdot \frac{4(2x + 1)}{\cancel{3}}$$

$$15x - 30 = 8x + 4$$

$$7x = 34$$

$$x = \frac{34}{7}$$

B. Quadratic and Higher-Degree Equations (Secs. 6.6, 11.1, 11.2, 11.3)

$2x^2 - 7x = 9$	$2x^2 + x - 2 = 0$
$2x^2 - 7x - 9 = 0$	$a = 2, \; b = 1, \; c = -2$
$(2x - 9)(x + 1) = 0$	
$2x - 9 = 0 \quad$ or $\quad x + 1 = 0$	$x = \dfrac{-1 \pm \sqrt{1^2 - 4(2)(-2)}}{2 \cdot 2}$
$x = \dfrac{9}{2} \quad$ or $\quad x = -1$	$x = \dfrac{-1 \pm \sqrt{17}}{4}$

C. Equations with Rational Expressions (Sec. 7.5)

$$\frac{7}{x - 1} + \frac{3}{x + 1} = \frac{x + 3}{x^2 - 1}$$

$$\cancel{(x - 1)}(x + 1) \cdot \frac{7}{\cancel{x - 1}} + (x - 1)\cancel{(x + 1)} \cdot \frac{3}{\cancel{x + 1}}$$

$$= \cancel{(x - 1)}\cancel{(x + 1)} \cdot \frac{x + 3}{\cancel{(x - 1)}\cancel{(x + 1)}}$$

$$7(x + 1) + 3(x - 1) = x + 3$$

$$7x + 7 + 3x - 3 = x + 3$$

$$9x = -1$$

$$x = -\frac{1}{9}$$

D. Proportions: An equation with two ratios equal. Set cross products equal, then solve. Make sure the proposed solution does not make the denominator 0. (Sec. 7.6)

$$\frac{5}{x} = \frac{9}{2x - 3}$$

$$5(2x - 3) = 9 \cdot x \qquad \text{Set cross products equal.}$$

$$10x - 15 = 9x \qquad \text{Multiply.}$$

$$x = 15 \qquad \text{Write equation with variable terms on one side and constants on the other.}$$

E. Absolute Value Equations (Sec. 9.2)

$$|3x - 1| = 8$$

$3x - 1 = 8$ or $3x - 1 = -8$

$3x = 9$ or $3x = -7$

$x = 3$ or $x = -\dfrac{7}{3}$

$$|x - 5| = |x + 1|$$

$x - 5 = x + 1$ or $x - 5 = -(x + 1)$

$-5 = 1$ or $x - 5 = -x - 1$

No solution or $2x = 4$

$x = 2$

F. Equations with Radicals (Sec. 10.6)

$$\sqrt{5x + 10} - 2 = x$$
$$\sqrt{5x + 10} = x + 2$$
$$(\sqrt{5x + 10})^2 = (x + 2)^2$$
$$5x + 10 = x^2 + 4x + 4$$
$$0 = x^2 - x - 6$$
$$0 = (x - 3)(x + 2)$$

$x - 3 = 0$ or $x + 2 = 0$

$x = 3$ or $x = -2$

Both solutions check.

G. Exponential Equations (Secs. 12.3, 12.8)

$$9^x = 27^{x+1}$$
$$(3^2)^x = (3^3)^{x+1}$$
$$3^{2x} = 3^{3x+3}$$
$$2x = 3x + 3$$
$$-3 = x$$

$$5^x = 7$$
$$\log 5^x = \log 7$$
$$x \log 5 = \log 7$$
$$x = \frac{\log 7}{\log 5}$$

H. Logarithmic Equations (Sec. 12.8)

$$\log 7 + \log(x + 3) = \log 5$$
$$\log 7(x + 3) = \log 5$$
$$7(x + 3) = 5$$
$$7x + 21 = 5$$
$$7x = -16$$
$$x = -\frac{16}{7}$$

III. Solving Inequalities

A. Linear Inequalities (Sec. 2.8)

$$-3(x + 2) \geq 6$$
$$-3x - 6 \geq 6$$
$$-3x \geq 12$$
$$\frac{-3x}{-3} \leq \frac{12}{-3}$$
$$x \leq -4 \quad \text{or} \quad (-\infty, -4]$$

B. Compound Inequalities (Sec. 9.1)

$x \leq 3$ *and* $x < -7$

$x \leq 3$

$x < -7$

and

$(-\infty, -7)$

$x \leq 3$ *or* $x < -7$

$x \leq 3$

$x < -7$

or

$(-\infty, 3]$

C. Absolute Value Inequalities (Sec. 9.3)

$|x - 5| - 8 < -2$

$|x - 5| < 6$

$-6 < x - 5 < 6$

$-1 < x < 11$

$(-1, 11)$

$|2x + 1| \geq 17$

$2x + 1 \geq 17$ or $2x + 1 \leq -17$

$2x \geq 16$ or $2x \leq -18$

$x \geq 8$ or $x \leq -9$

$(-\infty, -9] \cup [8, \infty)$

D. Nonlinear Inequalities (Sec. 11.4)

$x^2 - x < 6$

$x^2 - x - 6 < 0$

$(x - 3)(x + 2) < 0$

$(-2, 3)$

$\dfrac{x - 5}{x + 1} \geq 0$

$(-\infty, -1) \cup [5, \infty)$

Evaluate.

1. $6[5 + 2(3 - 8) - 3]$

2. -3^4

3. 4^{-3}

4. $\dfrac{1}{2} - \dfrac{5}{6}$

Perform the indicated operations and simplify if possible.

5. $5x^3 + x^2 + 5x - 2 - (8x^3 - 4x^2 + x - 7)$

6. $(4x - 2)^2$

7. $(3x + 7)(x^2 + 5x + 2)$

Factor.

8. $y^2 - 8y - 48$

9. $9x^3 + 39x^2 + 12x$

10. $180 - 5x^2$

11. $3a^2 + 3ab - 7a - 7b$

12. $8y^3 - 64$

Simplify. Write answer with positive exponents only.

13. $\left(\dfrac{x^2 y^3}{x^3 y^{-4}}\right)^2$

Solve each equation or inequality. Write inequality answers using interval notation.

14. $-4(a + 1) - 3a = -7(2a - 3)$

15. $3x - 5 \geq 7x + 3$

16. $x(x + 6) = 7$

Graph the following.

17. $5x - 7y = 10$

18. $x - 3 = 0$

Find the slope of each line.

19. Through $(6, -5)$ and $(-1, 2)$

20. $-3x + y = 5$

Write equations of the following lines. Write each equation in standard form.

21. Through $(2, -5)$ and $(1, 3)$

22. Through $(-5, -1)$ and parallel to $x = 7$

Solve each system of equations.

23. $\begin{cases} \dfrac{1}{2}x + 2y = -\dfrac{15}{4} \\ 4x = -y \end{cases}$

24. $\begin{cases} 4x - 6y = 7 \\ -2x + 3y = 0 \end{cases}$

25. Divide by long division: $\dfrac{27x^3 - 8}{3x + 2}$

Answer the questions about functions.

26. If $h(x) = x^3 - x$, find
   a. $h(-1)$
   b. $h(0)$
   c. $h(4)$

27. Identify the *x*- and *y*-intercepts. Then find the domain and range of the function graphed.

Solve each application.

28. Some states have a single area code for the entire state. Two such states have area codes where one is double the other. If the sum of these integers is 1203, find the two area codes.

29. Two trains leave Los Angeles simultaneously traveling on the same track in opposite directions at speeds of 50 and 64 mph. How long will it take before they are 285 miles apart?

30. Find the amount of a 12% saline solution a lab assistant should add to 80 cc (cubic centimeters) of a 22% saline solution in order to have a 16% solution.

31. Find the domain of the rational function

$$g(x) = \frac{9x^2 - 9}{x^2 + 4x + 3}.$$

Perform the indicated operations and simplify if possible.

32. $\dfrac{15x}{2x + 5} - \dfrac{6 - 4x}{2x + 5}$

33. $\dfrac{x^2 - 9}{x^2 - 3x} \div \dfrac{xy + 5x + 3y + 15}{2x + 10}$

34. $\dfrac{5a}{a^2 - a - 6} - \dfrac{2}{a - 3}$

35. $\dfrac{5 - \dfrac{1}{y^2}}{\dfrac{1}{y} + \dfrac{2}{y^2}}$

Solve each equation.

36. $\dfrac{4}{y} - \dfrac{5}{3} = -\dfrac{1}{5}$

37. $\dfrac{5}{y+1} = \dfrac{4}{y+2}$

38. $\dfrac{a}{a-3} = \dfrac{3}{a-3} - \dfrac{3}{2}$

Solve.

39. One number plus five times its reciprocal is equal to six. Find the number.

Simplify. If needed, write answers with positive exponents only.

40. $\sqrt{216}$

41. $\left(\dfrac{1}{125}\right)^{-1/3}$

42. $\left(\dfrac{64c^{4/3}}{a^{-2/3}b^{5/6}}\right)^{1/2}$

Perform the indicated operations and simplify if possible.

43. $\sqrt{125x^3} - 3\sqrt{20x^3}$

44. $(\sqrt{5}+5)(\sqrt{5}-5)$

Solve each equation or inequality. Write inequality solutions using interval notation.

45. $|6x-5|-3 = -2$

46. $-3 < 2(x-3) \le 4$

47. $|3x+1| > 5$

48. $y^2 - 3y = 5$

49. $x = \sqrt{x-2}+2$

50. $2x^2 - 7x > 15$

Graph the following.

51. $y > -4x$

52. $g(x) = -|x+2|-1$. Also, find the domain and range of this function.

53. $h(x) = x^2 - 4x + 4$. Label the vertex and any intercepts.

54. $f(x) = \begin{cases} -\dfrac{1}{2}x & \text{if } x \le 0 \\ 2x-3 & \text{if } x > 0 \end{cases}$. Also, find the domain and range of this function.

Write equations of the following lines. Write each equation using function notation.

55. Through $(4,-2)$ and $(6,-3)$

56. Through $(-1,2)$ and perpendicular to $3x - y = 4$

Find the distance or midpoint.

57. Find the distance between the points $(-6,3)$ and $(-8,-7)$.

58. Find the midpoint of the line segment whose endpoints are $(-2,-5)$ and $(-6,12)$.

Rationalize each denominator. Assume that variables represent positive numbers.

59. $\sqrt{\dfrac{9}{y}}$

60. $\dfrac{4-\sqrt{x}}{4+2\sqrt{x}}$

Solve.

61. Suppose that W is inversely proportional to V. If $W = 20$ when $V = 12$, find W when $V = 15$.

62. Given the diagram shown, approximate to the nearest foot how many feet of walking distance a person saves by cutting across the lawn instead of walking on the sidewalk.

63. A stone is thrown upward from a bridge. The stone's height in feet, $s(t)$, above the water t seconds after the stone is thrown is a function given by the equation

$$s(t) = -16t^2 + 32t + 256$$

a. Find the maximum height of the stone.

b. Find the time it takes the stone to hit the water. Round the answer to two decimal places.

COMPLEX NUMBERS: CHAPTER 10

Perform the indicated operation and simplify. Write the result in the form $a + bi$.

64. $-\sqrt{-8}$

65. $(12-6i)-(12-3i)$

66. $(4+3i)^2$

67. $\dfrac{1+4i}{1-i}$

INVERSE, EXPONENTIAL, AND LOGARITHMIC FUNCTIONS: CHAPTER 12

68. If $g(x) = x - 7$ and $h(x) = x^2 - 6x + 5$, find $(g \circ h)(x)$.

69. Determine whether $f(x) = 6 - 2x$ is a one-to-one function. If it is, find its inverse.

70. Use properties of logarithms to write the expression as a single logarithm.

$$\log_5 x + 3\log_5 x - \log_5(x + 1)$$

Solve. Give exact solutions.

71. $8^{x-1} = \dfrac{1}{64}$

72. $3^{2x+5} = 4$ Give an exact solution and a 4-decimal-place approximation.

73. $\log_8(3x - 2) = 2$

74. $\log_4(x + 1) - \log_4(x - 2) = 3$

75. $\ln\sqrt{e} = x$

76. Graph $y = \left(\dfrac{1}{2}\right)^x + 1$

77. The prairie dog population of the Grand Forks area now stands at 57,000 animals. If the population is growing at a rate of 2.6% annually, how many prairie dogs will there be in that area 5 years from now?

CONIC SECTIONS: CHAPTER 13

Sketch the graph of each equation.

78. $x^2 - y^2 = 36$

79. $16x^2 + 9y^2 = 144$

80. $x^2 + y^2 + 6x = 16$

81. Solve the system: $\begin{cases} x^2 + y^2 = 26 \\ x^2 - 2y^2 = 23 \end{cases}$

SEQUENCES, SERIES, AND THE BINOMIAL THEOREM: CHAPTER 14

82. Find the first five terms of the sequence $a_n = \dfrac{(-1)^n}{n + 4}$.

83. Find the partial sum S_5 of the sequence $a_n = 5(2)^{n-1}$.

84. Find S_∞ of the sequence $\dfrac{3}{2}, -\dfrac{3}{4}, \dfrac{3}{8}, \ldots$

85. Find $\displaystyle\sum_{i=1}^{4} i(i - 2)$

86. Expand: $(2x + y)^5$

Answers to Selected Exercises

CHAPTER 2 EQUATIONS, INEQUALITIES, AND PROBLEM SOLVING

Section 2.3
Practice Exercises

1. 3   **2.** $\frac{21}{13}$ **3.** -15 **4.** 3   **5.** 0   **6.** no solution   **7.** all real numbers

Graphing Calculator Explorations 2.3

1. solution   **3.** not a solution   **5.** solution

Vocabulary, Readiness & Video Check 2.3

1. equation   **3.** expression   **5.** expression   **7.** equation   **9.** 3; distributive property, addition property of equality, multiplication property of equality   **11.** The number of decimal places in each number helps you determine what power of 10 you can multiply through by so you are no longer dealing with decimals.

Exercise Set 2.3

1. -6 **3.** 3   **5.** 1   **7.** $\frac{3}{2}$ **9.** 0   **11.** -1 **13.** 4   **15.** -4 **17.** -3 **19.** 2   **21.** 50   **23.** 1   **25.** $\frac{7}{3}$ **27.** 0.2

29. all real numbers   **31.** no solution   **33.** no solution   **35.** all real numbers   **37.** 18   **39.** $\frac{19}{9}$ **41.** $\frac{14}{3}$ **43.** 13   **45.** 4

47. all real numbers   **49.** $-\frac{3}{5}$ **51.** -5 **53.** 10   **55.** no solution   **57.** 3   **59.** -17 **61.** -4 **63.** 3   **65.** all real numbers

67. $-8 - x$ **69.** $-3 + 2x$ **71.** $9(x + 20)$ **73.** $(6x - 8)$ m   **75. a.** all real numbers   **b.** answers may vary   **c.** answers may vary
77. A   **79.** B   **81.** C   **83.** answers may vary   **85. a.** $x + x + x + 2x + 2x = 28$ **b.** $x = 4$ **c.** $x = 4$ cm; $2x = 8$ cm   **87.** answers

may vary   **89.** 15.3   **91.** -0.2 **93.** $-\frac{7}{8}$ **95.** no solution

Integrated Review

1. 6   **2.** -17 **3.** 12   **4.** -26 **5.** -3 **6.** -1 **7.** $\frac{27}{2}$ **8.** $\frac{25}{2}$ **9.** 8   **10.** -64 **11.** 2   **12.** -3 **13.** no solution

14. no solution   **15.** -2 **16.** -2 **17.** $-\frac{5}{6}$ **18.** $\frac{1}{6}$ **19.** 1   **20.** 6   **21.** 4   **22.** 1   **23.** $\frac{9}{5}$ **24.** $-\frac{6}{5}$ **25.** all real numbers

26. all real numbers   **27.** 0   **28.** -1.6 **29.** $\frac{4}{19}$ **30.** $-\frac{5}{19}$ **31.** $\frac{7}{2}$ **32.** $-\frac{1}{4}$ **33.** 2   **34.** 2   **35.** no solution   **36.** no solution

37. $\frac{7}{6}$ **38.** $\frac{1}{15}$

Section 2.4
Practice Exercises

1. 9   **2.** 2   **3.** 9 in. and 36 in.   **4.** 29 Republican and 20 Democratic governors   **5.** $25°, 75°, 80°$ **6.** $46, 48, 50$

Vocabulary, Readiness & Video Check 2.4

1. $2x; 2x - 31$ **3.** $x + 5; 2(x + 5)$ **5.** $20 - y; \frac{20 - y}{3}$ or $(20 - y) \div 3$ **7.** in the statement of the application   **9.** That the 3 angle measures are consecutive even integers and that they sum to $180°$.

Exercise Set 2.4

1. $6x + 1 = 5x; -1$ **3.** $3x - 6 = 2x + 8; 14$ **5.** $2(x - 8) = 3(x + 3); -25$ **7.** $2(-2 + x) = x - \frac{1}{2}; \frac{7}{2}$ **9.** 3 in.; 6 in.; 16 in.

11. 1st piece: 5 in.; 2nd piece: 10 in.; 3rd piece: 25 in.   **13.** 7837 screens; 31,710; In 2010, 7837 screens were 3D.   **15.** 1st angle: 37.5°;
2nd angle: 37.5°; 3rd angle: 105°   **17.** $3x + 3$ **19.** $x + 2; x + 4; 2x + 4$ **21.** $x + 1; x + 2; x + 3; 4x + 6$ **23.** $x + 2; x + 4; 2x + 6$

25. 234, 235   **27.** Belgium: 32; France: 33; Spain: 34   **29.** Sahara: 3,500,000 sq mi; Gobi: 500,000 sq mi   **31.** 5 ft, 12 ft   **33.** $\frac{5}{4}$

35. Botswana: 32,000,000 carats; Angola: 8,000,000 carats   **37.** $58°, 60°, 62°$ **39.** South Korea: 14; Russia: 15; Austria: 16   **41.** -16 **43.** $43°, 137°$

45. 1   **47.** $\frac{3}{2}$ **49.** Maglev: 361 mph; TGV: 357.2 mph   **51.** $\frac{5}{2}$ **53.** California: 58; Montana: 56   **55.** $111°$ **57.** 1st piece: 3 ft; 2nd piece:

12 ft; 3rd piece: 15 ft   **59.** Eagles: *Their Greatest Hits, 1971–1975*   **61.** *Thriller*: $27 million; *The Wall*: $23 million   **63.** answers may vary
65. 34   **67.** 225π **69.** 15 ft by 24 ft   **71.** 5400 chirps per hour; 129,600 chirps per day; 47,304,000 chirps per year   **73.** answers may vary
75. answers may vary   **77.** c

Section 2.5
Practice Exercises

1. 116 sec or 1 min 56 sec   **2.** 9 ft   **3.** 46.4°F   **4.** length: 28 in.; width: 5 in.   **5.** $r = \frac{I}{Pt}$ **6.** $s = \frac{H - 10a}{5a}$ **7.** $d = \frac{N - F}{n - 1}$

8. $B = \frac{2A - ab}{a}$

Vocabulary, Readiness & Video Check 2.5

1. relationships **3.** To show that the process of solving this equation for x—dividing both sides by 5, the coefficient of x—is the same process used to solve a formula for a specific variable. Treat whatever is multiplied by that specific variable as the coefficient—the coefficient is all the factors except that specific variable.

Exercise Set 2.5

1. $h = 3$ **3.** $h = 3$ **5.** $h = 20$ **7.** $c = 12$ **9.** $r \approx 2.5$ **11.** $T = 3$ **13.** $h \approx 15$ **15.** $h = \dfrac{f}{5g}$ **17.** $w = \dfrac{V}{lh}$ **19.** $y = 7 - 3x$

21. $R = \dfrac{A - P}{PT}$ **23.** $A = \dfrac{3V}{h}$ **25.** $a = P - b - c$ **27.** $h = \dfrac{S - 2\pi r^2}{2\pi r}$ **29.** 120 ft **31. a.** area: 103.5 sq ft; perimeter: 41 ft

b. baseboard: perimeter; carpet: area **33. a.** area: 480 sq in.; perimeter: 120 in. **b.** frame: perimeter; glass: area **35.** $-10°C$ **37.** length: 78 ft; width: 52 ft **39.** 18 ft, 36 ft, 48 ft **41.** 55.2 mph **43.** 96 piranhas **45.** 61.5°F **47.** 60 chirps per minute **49.** increases **51.** 2 bags **53.** one 16-in. pizza **55.** $x = 6$ m, $2.5x = 15$ m **57.** 22 hr **59.** 13 in. **61.** 2.25 hr **63.** 12,090 ft **65.** 50°C **67.** 332.6°F

69. 449 cu in. **71.** 0.32 **73.** 2.00 or 2 **75.** 17% **77.** 720% **79.** multiplies the volume by 8; answers may vary **81.** $53\dfrac{1}{3}$

83. $V = G(N - R)$ **85.** $= \dfrac{\blacksquare - \blacktriangle}{\blacksquare}$ **87.** 500 sec or $8\dfrac{1}{3}$ min **89.** 608.33 ft **91.** 4.42 min **93.** $35\dfrac{11}{17}$ mph

CHAPTER 3 GRAPHING

Section 3.2

Practice Exercises

1. a. yes **b.** no **c.** yes **d.** yes **2.** **3.** **4.** **5.**

6. **7.** The graph of $y = -2x + 3$ is the same as the graph of $y = -2x$ except that the graph of $y = -2x + 3$ is moved 3 units upward.

8. a. **b.** We predict 725 thousand computer software application engineers in the year 2020.

Graphing Calculator Explorations 3.2

1. **3.** **5.**

Vocabulary, Readiness & Video Check 3.2

1. In the definition, x and y both have an understood power of 1. Example 3 shows an equation where y has a power of 2, so it is not a linear equation in two variables. **3.** An infinite number of points make up the line and each point corresponds to an ordered pair that is a solution of the linear equation in two variables.

Exercise Set 3.2

1. yes **3.** yes **5.** no **7.** yes **9.**

x	y
6	0
4	−2
5	−1

11.

x	y
1	−4
0	0
−1	4

13.

x	y
0	0
6	2
−3	−1

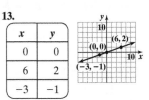

15.

x	y
0	3
1	−1
2	−5

17.

19.

21.

23.

25.

27.

29.

31.

33.

35.

37.

39.

41.

43.

45.

47. c **49.** d **51. a.** $(8, 31)$ **b.** In 2008, there were 31 million joggers. **c.** 40 million joggers **53. a.** $(8, 207.6)$ **b.** In 2008, there were 207.6 million people with driver's licenses. **c.** 225.2 million **55.** $(4, −1)$ **57.** 3; −3 **59.** 0; 0 **61.** $y = x + 5$

63. $2x + 3y = 6$

65. $x + y = 12$; $y = 9$ cm **67.** answers may vary **69.** 0; 1; 1; 4; 4

Section 3.3
Practice Exercises

1. x-intercept: $(−4, 0)$
y-intercept: $(0, −6)$

2. x-intercepts: $(−2, 0), (2, 0)$
y-intercept: $(0, −3)$

3. x-intercept: $(0, 0)$
y-intercept: $(0, 0)$

4. x-intercept: none
y-intercept: $(0, 3)$

5. x-intercepts: $(−1, 0), (5, 0)$
y-intercepts: $(0, 2), (0, −2)$

6.

7.

8.

9.

10.

Graphing Calculator Explorations 3.3

1. $x = 3.78y$

3. $3x + 7y = 21$

5. $−2.2x + 6.8y = 15.5$

Vocabulary, Readiness & Video Check 3.3

1. linear **3.** horizontal **5.** y-intercept **7.** $y; x$ **9.** Because x-intercepts lie on the x-axis; because y-intercepts lie on the y-axis.
11. For a horizontal line, the coefficient of x will be 0 and the coefficient of y will be 1; for a vertical line, the coefficient of y will be 0 and the coefficient of x will be 1.

Exercise Set 3.3

1. $(-1, 0); (0, 1)$ **3.** $(-2, 0); (2, 0); (0, -2)$ **5.** $(-2, 0); (1, 0); (3, 0); (0, 3)$ **7.** $(-1, 0); (1, 0); (0, 1); (0, -2)$ **9.** infinite **11.** 0

13. **15.** **17.** **19.** **21.** **23.**

25. **27.** **29.** **31.** **33.** **35.**

37. **39.** **41.** **43.** **45.** **47.**

49. C **51.** E **53.** B **55.** $\dfrac{3}{2}$ **57.** 6 **59.** $-\dfrac{6}{5}$ **61.** false **63.** true **65.** $(0, 200)$; no chairs and 200 desks are manufactured,
67. 300 chairs **69. a.** $(62, 0)$ **b.** 62 years after 2002, 0 people will attend the movies at the theater. **c.** answers may very **71.** $x = 1$
73. answers may vary **75.** answers may vary

Section 3.4
Practice Exercises

1. -1 **2.** $\dfrac{1}{3}$ **3.** $m = \dfrac{2}{3}$; y-intercept: $(0, -2)$ **4.** $m = 6$; y-intercept: $(0, -5)$ **5.** $m = -\dfrac{5}{2}$; y-intercept: $(0, 4)$ **6.** $m = 0$

7. slope is undefined **8. a.** perpendicular **b.** neither **c.** parallel **9.** 25% **10.** $m = \dfrac{0.75 \text{ dollar}}{1 \text{ pound}}$; The Wash-n-Fold charges \$0.75 per pound of laundry.

Graphing Calculator Explorations 3.4

1. **3.**

Vocabulary, Readiness & Video Check 3.4

1. slope **3.** 0 **5.** positive **7.** $y; x$ **9.** solve the equation for y; the slope is the coefficient of x. **11.** slope-intercept form; this form makes the slope easy to see, and you need to compare slopes to determine if two lines are parallel or perpendicular.

Exercise Set 3.4

1. -1 **3.** undefined **5.** $-\dfrac{2}{3}$ **7.** 0 **9.** $m = -\dfrac{4}{3}$ **11.** undefined slope **13.** $m = \dfrac{5}{2}$ **15.** negative **17.** undefined **19.** upward

21. horizontal **23.** line 1 **25.** line 2 **27.** D **29.** B **31.** E **33.** undefined slope **35.** $m = 0$ **37.** undefined slope

39. $m = 0$ **41.** $m = 5$ **43.** $m = -0.3$ **45.** $m = -2$ **47.** $m = \dfrac{2}{3}$ **49.** undefined slope **51.** $m = \dfrac{1}{2}$ **53.** $m = 0$ **55.** $m = -\dfrac{3}{4}$

57. $m = 4$ **59. a.** 1 **b.** -1 **61. a.** $\dfrac{9}{11}$ **b.** $-\dfrac{11}{9}$ **63.** neither **65.** neither **67.** parallel **69.** perpendicular **71.** $\dfrac{3}{5}$ **73.** 12.5%

75. 40% **77.** 37%; 35% **79.** $m = \dfrac{1}{1}$ or 1; Every 1 year, there are 1 million more U.S. households with televisions. **81.** $m = 0.47$; It costs \$0.47 per 1 mile to own and operate a compact car. **83.** $y = 2x - 14$ **85.** $y = -6x - 11$ **87.** $m = \dfrac{1}{2}$ **89.** answers may vary **91.** 2005 to 2006

93. 2000; 28.5 mi per gallon   **95.** from 2008 to 2009   **97.** $x = 6$ **99. a.** $(2007, 2207); (2010, 2333)$ **b.** 42   **c.** For the years 2007 through 2010, the number of heart transplants increased at a rate of 42 per year.   **101.** The slope through $(-3, 0)$ and $(1, 1)$ is $\frac{1}{4}$. The slope through $(-3, 0)$ and $(-4, 4)$ is -4. The product of the slopes is -1, so the sides are perpendicular.   **103.** -0.25 **105.** 0.875 **107.** The line becomes steeper.

Integrated Review

1. $m = 2$ **2.** $m = 0$ **3.** $m = -\frac{2}{3}$ **4.** undefined slope   **5.**   **6.** $x + y = 3$ **7.**

8.   **9.**   **10.**   **11.**   **12.**

13. parallel   **14.** neither   **15. a.** $(0, 587)$ **b.** In 2000, there were 587 thousand bridges on public roads.   **c.** 1.7   **d.** For the years 2000 through 2009, the number of bridges on public roads increased at a rate of 1.7 thousand per year.   **16. a.** $(9, 26.6)$ **b.** In 2009, the revenue for online advertising was \$26.6 billion.

Section 3.5
Practice Exercises

1.   **2.**   **3.** $y = \frac{1}{2}x + 7$ **4.** $4x - y = 5$ **5.** $5x + 4y = 19$ **6.** $x = 3$ **7.** $y = 3$

8. a. $y = -1500x + 195{,}000$ **b.** \$105,000

Graphing Calculator Explorations 3.5

1.   **3.**   **5.**

Vocabulary, Readiness & Video Check 3.5

1. slope-intercept; $m; b$ **3.** y-intercept; fraction   **5.** Write the equation with x- and y- terms on one side of the equal sign and a constant on the other side.   **7.** Example 6: $y = -3$; Example 7: $x = -2$

Exercise Set 3.5

1.   **3.**   **5.**   **7.**   **9.**   **11.**

13. $y = 5x + 3$ **15.** $y = -4x - \frac{1}{6}$ **17.** $y = \frac{2}{3}x$ **19.** $y = -8$ **21.** $y = -\frac{1}{5}x + \frac{1}{9}$ **23.** $-6x + y = -10$ **25.** $8x + y = -13$

27. $3x - 2y = 27$ **29.** $x + 2y = -3$ **31.** $2x - y = 4$ **33.** $8x - y = -11$ **35.** $4x - 3y = -1$ **37.** $8x + 13y = 0$ **39.** $x = 0$

41. $y = 3$ **43.** $x = -\frac{7}{3}$ **45.** $y = 2$ **47.** $y = 5$ **49.** $x = 6$ **51.** $y = -\frac{1}{2}x + \frac{5}{3}$ **53.** $y = -x + 17$ **55.** $x = -\frac{3}{4}$

57. $y = x + 16$ **59.** $y = -5x + 7$ **61.** $y = 7$ **63.** $y = \frac{3}{2}x$ **65.** $y = -3$ **67.** $y = -\frac{4}{7}x - \frac{18}{7}$ **69. a.** $s = 32t$ **b.** 128 ft/sec

71. a. $y = -33x + 356$ **b.** 92 thousand gasoline-electric hybrids   **73. a.** $y = 0.6x + 85$ **b.** 93.4 persons per sq mi   **75. a.** $y = -1.75x + 60$ **b.** 32 million   **77. a.** $S = -1000p + 13{,}000$ **b.** 9500 Fun Noodles   **79.** -1 **81.** 5   **83.** no   **85.** yes   **87.** point-slope   **89.** slope-intercept   **91.** horizontal   **93.** answers may vary   **95. a.** $3x - y = -5$ **b.** $x + 3y = 5$ **97. a.** $3x + 2y = -1$ **b.** $2x - 3y = 21$

CHAPTER 4 SOLVING SYSTEMS OF LINEAR EQUATIONS

Section 4.1
Practice Exercises

1. no **2.** yes **3.** $(8, 5)$ **4.** $(-3, -5)$ **5.** no solution; inconsistent system; $\{\ \}$ or $\varnothing$

6. infinite number of solutions; consistent system, $\{(x, y) \mid 3x + 4y = 12\}$ or $\{(x, y) \mid 9x + 12y = 36\}$ **7.** one solution **8.** no solution

Graphing Calculator Explorations 4.1

1. $(0.37, 0.23)$ **3.** $(0.03, -1.89)$

Vocabulary, Readiness & Video Check 4.1

1. dependent **3.** consistent **5.** inconsistent **7.** The ordered pair must satisfy all equations of the system in order to be a solution of the system, so we must check that the ordered pair is a solution of both equations. **9.** Writing the equations of a system in slope-intercept form lets you see their slope and y-intercept. Different slopes mean one solution; same slope with different y-intercepts means no solution; same slope with same y-intercept means infinite number of solutions.

Exercise Set 4.1

1. one solution, $(-1, 3)$ **3.** infinite number of solutions **5. a.** no **b.** yes **7. a.** yes **b.** no **9. a.** yes **b.** yes **11. a.** no **b.** no

13. **15.** **17.** **19.** **21.** **23.**

25. no solution **27.** **29.** **31.** no solution; $\{\ \}$ or $\varnothing$ **33.** infinite number of solutions;
$$\{(x, y) \mid y - 3x = -2\} \text{ or}$$
$$\{(x, y) \mid 6x - 2y = 4\}$$

35. **37.** **39.** **41.** infinite number of solutions; **43.** intersecting, one solution
$$\{(x, y) \mid 6x - y = 4\}$$
$$\text{or } \left\{(x, y) \mid \frac{1}{2}y = -2 + 3x\right\}$$

45. parallel; no solution **47.** identical lines; infinite number of solutions **49.** intersecting; one solution **51.** intersecting; one solution

53. identical lines; infinite number of solutions **55.** parallel; no solution **57.** 2 **59.** $-\dfrac{2}{5}$ **61.** 2

63. answers may vary; possible answer **65.** answers may vary; possible answer **67.** answers may vary **69.** 1988–1989; 2001–2002

71. 2003, 2004, 2005, 2006, 2007 **73.** answers may vary **75. a.** $(4, 9)$ **b.** **c.** yes **77.** answers may vary

Section 4.2
Practice Exercises

1. $(8, 7)$ **2.** $(-3, -6)$ **3.** $\left(4, \dfrac{2}{3}\right)$ **4.** $(-3, 2)$ **5.** infinite number of solutions; $\left\{(x, y)\,\middle|\,\dfrac{1}{4}x - y = 2\right\}$ or $\{(x, y)\,|\,x = 4y + 8\}$
6. no solution; $\{\ \}$ or $\varnothing$

Vocabulary, Readiness & Video Check 4.2

1. $(1, 4)$ **3.** infinite number of solutions **5.** $(0, 0)$ **7.** You solved one equation for a variable. Now be sure to substitute this expression for the variable into the *other* equation.

Exercise Set 4.2

1. $(2, 1)$ **3.** $(-3, 9)$ **5.** $(2, 7)$ **7.** $\left(-\dfrac{1}{5}, \dfrac{43}{5}\right)$ **9.** $(2, -1)$ **11.** $(-2, 4)$ **13.** $(4, 2)$ **15.** $(-2, -1)$ **17.** no solution; $\{\ \}$ or $\varnothing$

19. $(3, -1)$ **21.** $(3, 5)$ **23.** $\left(\dfrac{2}{3}, -\dfrac{1}{3}\right)$ **25.** $(-1, -4)$ **27.** $(-6, 2)$ **29.** $(2, 1)$ **31.** no solution; $\{\ \}$ or $\varnothing$ **33.** infinite number of

solutions; $\left\{(x, y)\,\middle|\,\dfrac{1}{3}x - y = 2\right\}$ or $\{(x, y)\,|\,x - 3y = 6\}$ **35.** $\left(\dfrac{1}{2}, 2\right)$ **37.** $(1, -3)$ **39.** $-6x - 4y = -12$ **41.** $-12x + 3y = 9$ **43.** $5n$
45. $-15b$ **47.** answers may vary **49.** no; answers may vary **51.** c; answers may vary **53. a.** $(13, 492)$ **b.** In $1970 + 13 = 1983$,
the number of men and women receiving bachelor's degrees was the same. **c.** answers may vary **55.** $(-2.6, 1.3)$
57. $(3.28, 2.11)$

Section 4.3
Practice Exercises

1. $(5, 3)$ **2.** $(3, -4)$ **3.** no solution; $\{\ \}$ or $\varnothing$ **4.** infinite number of solutions; $\{(x, y)\,|\,4x - 3y = 5\}$ or $\{(x, y)\,|\,-8x + 6y = -10\}$
5. $(2, 2)$ **6.** $\left(-\dfrac{8}{5}, \dfrac{6}{5}\right)$

Vocabulary, Readiness & Video Check 4.3

1. false **3.** true **5.** The multiplication property of equality; be sure to multiply *both* sides of the equation by the number chosen.

Exercise Set 4.3

1. $(1, 2)$ **3.** $(2, -3)$ **5.** $(-2, -5)$ **7.** $(5, -2)$ **9.** $(-7, 5)$ **11.** $(6, 0)$ **13.** no solution; $\{\ \}$ or $\varnothing$ **15.** infinite number of solutions;
$\{(x, y)\,|\,-x + 5y = -1\}$ or $\{(x, y)\,|\,3x - 15y = 3\}$ **17.** $\left(2, -\dfrac{1}{2}\right)$ **19.** $(-2, 0)$ **21.** $(1, -1)$ **23.** no solution; $\{\ \}$ or $\varnothing$ **25.** $\left(\dfrac{12}{11}, -\dfrac{4}{11}\right)$

27. $\left(\dfrac{3}{2}, 3\right)$ **29.** infinite number of solutions; $\left\{(x, y)\,\middle|\,\dfrac{10}{3}x + 4y = -4\right\}$ or $\{(x, y)\,|\,5x + 6y = -6\}$ **31.** $(1, 6)$ **33.** $\left(-\dfrac{1}{2}, -2\right)$ **35.** infinite

number of solutions; $\left\{(x, y)\,\middle|\,\dfrac{x}{3} - y = 2\right\}$ or $\left\{(x, y)\,\middle|\,-\dfrac{x}{2} + \dfrac{3y}{2} = -3\right\}$ **37.** $\left(-\dfrac{2}{3}, \dfrac{2}{5}\right)$ **39.** $(2, 4)$ **41.** $(-0.5, 2.5)$ **43.** $(2, 5)$

45. $(-3, 2)$ **47.** $(0, 3)$ **49.** $(5, 7)$ **51.** $\left(\dfrac{1}{3}, 1\right)$ **53.** infinite number of solutions; $\left\{(x, y)\,\middle|\,\dfrac{x + 2}{2} = \dfrac{y + 11}{3}\right\}$ or $\left\{(x, y)\,\middle|\,\dfrac{x}{2} = \left(\dfrac{2y + 16}{6}\right)\right\}$
55. $(-8.9, 10.6)$ **57.** $2x + 6 = x - 3$ **59.** $20 - 3x = 2$ **61.** $4(n + 6) = 2n$ **63.** $2; 6x - 2y = -24$ **65.** b; answers may vary
67. answers may vary **69. a.** $b = 15$ **b.** any real number except 15 **71.** $(-4.2, 9.6)$ **73. a.** $(7, 22)$ **b.** In 2015 $(2008 + 7)$, the percent of
workers age 25–34 and the percent of workers age 55 and older will be the same. **c.** 22% of the workforce for each of these age groups.

Integrated Review

1. $(2, 5)$ **2.** $(4, 2)$ **3.** $(5, -2)$ **4.** $(6, -14)$ **5.** $(-3, 2)$ **6.** $(-4, 3)$ **7.** $(0, 3)$ **8.** $(-2, 4)$ **9.** $(5, 7)$ **10.** $(-3, -23)$
11. $\left(\dfrac{1}{3}, 1\right)$ **12.** $\left(-\dfrac{1}{4}, 2\right)$ **13.** no solution; $\{\ \}$ or $\varnothing$ **14.** infinite number of solutions; $\{(x, y)\,|\,-x + 2y = 3\}$ or $\{(x, y)\,|\,3x - 6y = -9\}$
15. $(0.5, 3.5)$ **16.** $(-0.75, 1.25)$ **17.** infinite number of solutions; $\{(x, y)\,|\,x = 3y - 7\}$ or $\{(x, y)\,|\,2x - 6y = -14\}$ **18.** no solution; $\{\ \}$ or $\varnothing$
19. $(7, -3)$ **20.** $(-1, -3)$ **21.** answers may vary **22.** answers may vary

CHAPTER 6 FACTORING POLYNOMIALS

Section 6.1
Practice Exercises

1. a. 6 **b.** 1 **c.** 4 **2. a.** y^4 **b.** x **3. a.** $5y^2$ **b.** x^2 **c.** a^2b^2 **4. a.** $4(t + 3)$ **b.** $y^4(y^4 + 1)$ **5.** $8b^2(-b^4 + 2b^2 - 1)$ or
$-8b^2(b^4 - 2b^2 + 1)$ **6.** $5x(x^3 - 4)$ **7.** $\dfrac{1}{9}z^3(5z^2 + z - 2)$ **8.** $4ab^3(2ab - 5a^2 + 3)$ **9.** $(y - 2)(8 + x)$ **10.** $(p + q)(7xy^3 - 1)$
11. $(x + 3)(y + 4)$ **12.** $(5x - 3)(8x^2 + 3)$ **13.** $(2x + 3y)(y - 1)$ **14.** $(7a + 5)(a^2 + 1)$ **15.** $(y - 3)(4x - 5)$ **16.** cannot be
factored by grouping **17.** $3(x - a)(y - 2a)$

Vocabulary, Readiness & Video Check 6.1

1. factors   **3.** least   **5.** false   **7.** The GCF of a list of numbers is the largest number that is a factor of all numbers in the list.   **9.** When factoring out a GCF, the number of terms in the other factor should have the same number of terms as your original polynomial.

Exercise Set 6.1

1. 4   **3.** 6   **5.** 1   **7.** y^2 **9.** z^7 **11.** xy^2 **13.** 7   **15.** $4y^3$ **17.** $5x^2$ **19.** $3x^3$ **21.** $9x^2y$ **23.** $10a^6b$ **25.** $3(a+2)$
27. $15(2x-1)$ **29.** $x^2(x+5)$ **31.** $2y^3(3y+1)$ **33.** $4(x-2y+1)$ **35.** $3x(2x^2-3x+4)$ **37.** $a^2b^2(a^5b^4-a+b^3-1)$
39. $4(2x^5+4x^4-5x^3+3)$ **41.** $\frac{1}{3}x(x^3+2x^2-4x^4+1)$ **43.** $(x^2+2)(y+3)$ **45.** $(y+4)(z-3)$ **47.** $(z^2-6)(r+1)$
49. $-2(x+7)$ **51.** $-x^5(2-x^2)$ **53.** $-3a^2(2a^2-3a+1)$ **55.** $(x+2)(x^2+5)$ **57.** $(x+3)(5+y)$ **59.** $(3x-2)(2x^2+5)$
61. $(5m^2+6n)(m+1)$ **63.** $(y-4)(2+x)$ **65.** $(2x-1)(x^2+4)$ **67.** not factorable by grouping   **69.** $(x-2y)(4x-3)$
71. $(5q-4p)(q-1)$ **73.** $x(x^2+1)(2x+5)$ **75.** $2(2y-7)(3x^2-1)$ **77.** $2x(16y-9x)$ **79.** $(x+2)(y-3)$ **81.** $7xy(2x^2+x-1)$
83. $(4x-1)(7x^2+3)$ **85.** $-8x^8y^5(5y+2x)$ **87.** $3(2a+3b^2)(a+b)$ **89.** $x^2+7x+10$ **91.** b^2-3b-4 **93.** 2, 6   **95.** $-1, -8$
97. $-2, 5$ **99.** b   **101.** factored   **103.** not factored   **105.** answers may vary   **107.** answers may vary   **109. a.** 1200 million
b. 1120 million   **c.** $-20(x^2-15x-6)$ **111.** $12x^3-2x; 2x(6x^2-1)$ **113.** (n^3-6)units   **115.** $(x^n+2)(x^n+3)$
117. $(3x^n-5)(x^n+7)$

Section 6.2
Practice Exercises

1. $(x+2)(x+3)$ **2.** $(x-10)(x-7)$ **3.** $(x+7)(x-2)$ **4.** $(p-9)(p+7)$ **5.** prime polynomial   **6.** $(x+3y)(x+4y)$
7. $(x^2+12)(x^2+1)$ **8.** $(x-6)(x-8)$ **9.** $4(x-3)(x-3)$ **10.** $3y^2(y-7)(y+1)$

Vocabulary, Readiness & Video Check 6.2

1. true   **3.** false   **5.** $+5$ **7.** -3 **9.** $+2$ **11.** 15 is positive, so its factors would have to either be both positive or both negative. Since the factors need to sum to -8, both factors must be negative.

Exercise Set 6.2

1. $(x+6)(x+1)$ **3.** $(y-9)(y-1)$ **5.** $(x-3)(x-3)$ or $(x-3)^2$ **7.** $(x-6)(x+3)$ **9.** $(x+10)(x-7)$ **11.** prime
13. $(x+5y)(x+3y)$ **15.** $(a^2-5)(a^2+3)$ **17.** $(m+13)(m+1)$ **19.** $(t-2)(t+12)$ **21.** $(a-2b)(a-8b)$ **23.** $2(z+8)(z+2)$
25. $2x(x-5)(x-4)$ **27.** $(x-4y)(x+y)$ **29.** $(x+12)(x+3)$ **31.** $(x-2)(x+1)$ **33.** $(r-12)(r-4)$ **35.** $(x+2y)(x-y)$
37. $3(x+5)(x-2)$ **39.** $3(x-18)(x-2)$ **41.** $(x-24)(x+6)$ **43.** prime   **45.** $(x-5)(x-3)$ **47.** $6x(x+4)(x+5)$
49. $4y(x^2+x-3)$ **51.** $(x-7)(x+3)$ **53.** $(x+5y)(x+2y)$ **55.** $2(t+8)(t+4)$ **57.** $x(x-6)(x+4)$ **59.** $2t^3(t-4)(t-3)$
61. $5xy(x-8y)(x+3y)$ **63.** $3(m-9)(m-6)$ **65.** $-1(x-11)(x-1)$ **67.** $\frac{1}{2}(y-11)(y+2)$ **69.** $x(xy-4)(xy+5)$
71. $2x^2+11x+5$ **73.** $15y^2-17y+4$ **75.** $9a^2+23ab-12b^2$ **77.** $x^2+5x-24$ **79.** answers may vary
81. $2x^2+28x+66; 2(x+3)(x+11)$ **83.** $-16(t-5)(t+1)$ **85.** $\left(x+\frac{1}{4}\right)\left(x+\frac{1}{4}\right)$ or $\left(x+\frac{1}{4}\right)^2$ **87.** $(x+1)(z-10)(z+7)$
89. $(x^n+10)(x^n-2)$ **91.** 5; 8; 9   **93.** 3; 4   **95.** 8; 16   **97.** 6; 26

Section 6.3
Practice Exercises

1. $(2x+5)(x+3)$ **2.** $(5x-4)(3x-2)$ **3.** $(4x-1)(x+3)$ **4.** $(7x-y)(3x+2y)$ **5.** $(2x^2-7)(x^2+1)$ **6.** $x(3x+2)(x+5)$
7. $-1(4x-3)(2x+1)$ **8.** $(x+7)^2$ **9.** $(2x+9y)(2x+y)$ **10.** $(6n^2-1)^2$ **11.** $3x(2x-7)^2$

Vocabulary, Readiness & Video Check 6.3

1. perfect square trinomial   **3.** perfect square trinomial   **5.** d   **7.** Consider the factors of the first and last terms and the signs of the trinomial. Continue to check by multiplying until you get the middle term of the trinomial.   **9.** The first and last terms are squares, a^2 and b^2, and the middle term is $2 \cdot a \cdot b$ or $-2 \cdot a \cdot b$.

Exercise Set 6.3

1. $x+4$ **3.** $10x-1$ **5.** $5x-2$ **7.** $(2x+3)(x+5)$ **9.** $(y-1)(8y-9)$ **11.** $(2x+1)(x-5)$ **13.** $(4r-1)(5r+8)$
15. $(10x+1)(x+3)$ **17.** prime   **19.** $(3x-5y)(2x-y)$ **21.** $(3m-5)(5m+3)$ **23.** $x(3x+2)(4x+1)$ **25.** $3(7b+5)(b-3)$
27. $(3z+4)(4z-3)$ **29.** $2y^2(3x-10)(x+3)$ **31.** $(2x-7)(2x+3)$ **33.** $-1(x-6)(x+4)$ **35.** $x(4x+3)(x-3)$
37. $(4x-9)(6x-1)$ **39.** $(x+11)^2$ **41.** $(x-8)^2$ **43.** $(4a-3)^2$ **45.** $(x^2+2)^2$ **47.** $2(n-7)^2$ **49.** $(4y+5)^2$
51. $(2x+11)(x-9)$ **53.** $(8x+3)(3x+4)$ **55.** $(3a+b)(a+3b)$ **57.** $(x-4)(x-5)$ **59.** $(p+6q)^2$ **61.** $(xy-5)^2$
63. $b(8a-3)(5a+3)$ **65.** $2x(3x+2)(5x+3)$ **67.** $2y(3y+5)(y-3)$ **69.** $5x^2(2x-y)(x+3y)$ **71.** $-1(2x-5)(7x-2)$
73. $p^2(4p-5)^2$ **75.** $(3x-2)(x+1)$ **77.** $(4x+9y)(2x-3y)$ **79.** prime   **81.** $(3x-4y)^2$ **83.** $(6x-7)(3x+2)$
85. $(7t+1)(t-4)$ **87.** $(7p+1)(7p-2)$ **89.** $m(m+9)^2$ **91.** prime   **93.** $a(6a^2+b^2)(a^2+6b^2)$ **95.** x^2-4 **97.** a^3+27
99. $25-34$ **101.** answers may vary   **103.** no   **105.** answers may vary   **107.** $4x^2+21x+5; (4x+1)(x+5)$ **109.** $\left(2x+\frac{1}{2}\right)^2$
111. $(y-1)^2(4x^2+10x+25)$ **113.** 8   **115.** $a^2+2ab+b^2$ **117.** 2; 14   **119.** 2   **121.** $-3xy^2(4x-5)(x+1)$
123. $(y-1)^2(2x+5)^2$ **125.** $(3x^n+2)(x^n+5)$ **127.** answers may vary

Section 6.4
Practice Exercises
1. $(5x + 1)(x + 12)$ **2.** $(4x - 5)(3x - 1)$ **3.** $2(5x + 1)(3x - 2)$ **4.** $5m^2(8m - 7)(m + 1)$ **5.** $(4x + 3)^2$

Vocabulary, Readiness & Video Check 6.4
1. a   **3.** b   **5.** This gives us a four-term polynomial, which may be factored by grouping.

Exercise Set 6.4
1. $(x + 3)(x + 2)$ **3.** $(y + 8)(y - 2)$ **5.** $(8x - 5)(x - 3)$ **7.** $(5x^2 - 3)(x^2 + 5)$ **9. a.** $9, 2$ **b.** $9x + 2x$ **c.** $(3x + 1)(2x + 3)$
11. a. $-20, -3$ **b.** $-20x - 3x$ **c.** $(3x - 4)(5x - 1)$ **13.** $(3y + 2)(7y + 1)$ **15.** $(7x - 11)(x + 1)$ **17.** $(5x - 2)(2x - 1)$
19. $(2x - 5)(x - 1)$ **21.** $(2x + 3)^2$ **23.** $(2x + 3)(2x - 7)$ **25.** $(5x - 4)(2x - 3)$ **27.** $x(2x + 3)(x + 5)$
29. $2(8y - 9)(y - 1)$ **31.** $(2x - 3)(3x - 2)$ **33.** $3(3a + 2)(6a - 5)$ **35.** $a(4a + 1)(5a + 8)$ **37.** $3x(4x + 3)(x - 3)$
39. $y(3x + y)(x + y)$ **41.** prime   **43.** $5(x + 5y)^2$ **45.** $6(a + b)(4a - 5b)$ **47.** $p^2(15p + q)(p + 2q)$ **49.** $2(9a^2 - 2)^2$
51. $(7 + x)(5 + x)$ or $(x + 7)(x + 5)$ **53.** $(6 - 5x)(1 - x)$ or $(5x - 6)(x - 1)$ **55.** $x^2 - 4$ **57.** $y^2 + 8y + 16$ **59.** $81z^2 - 25$
61. $x^3 - 27$ **63.** $10x^2 + 45x + 45; 5(2x + 3)(x + 3)$ **65.** $(x^n + 2)(x^n + 3)$ **67.** $(3x^n - 5)(x^n + 7)$ **69.** answers may vary

Section 6.5
Practice Exercises
1. $(x + 9)(x - 9)$ **2. a.** $(3x - 1)(3x + 1)$ **b.** $(6a - 7b)(6a + 7b)$ **c.** $\left(p + \dfrac{5}{6}\right)\left(p - \dfrac{5}{6}\right)$ **3.** $(p^2 - q^5)(p^2 + q^5)$
4. a. $(z^2 + 9)(z + 3)(z - 3)$ **b.** prime polynomial   **5.** $y(6y + 5)(6y - 5)$ **6.** $5(4y^2 + 1)(2y + 1)(2y - 1)$
7. $-1(3x + 10)(3x - 10)$ or $(10 + 3x)(10 - 3x)$ **8.** $(x + 4)(x^2 - 4x + 16)$ **9.** $(x - 5)(x^2 + 5x + 25)$ **10.** $(3y + 1)(9y^2 - 3y + 1)$
11. $4(2x - 5y)(4x^2 + 10xy + 25y^2)$

Graphing Calculator Explorations 6.5

	$x^2 - 2x + 1$	$x^2 - 2x - 1$	$(x - 1)^2$
$x = 5$	16	14	16
$x = -3$	16	14	16
$x = 2.7$	2.89	0.89	2.89
$x = -12.1$	171.61	169.61	171.61
$x = 0$	1	-1	1

Vocabulary, Readiness & Video Check 6.5
1. difference of two cubes   **3.** sum of two cubes   **5.** $(7x)^2$ **7.** $(2y)^3$ **9.** In order to recognize the binomial as a difference of squares and also to identify the terms to use in the special factoring formula.   **11.** First rewrite the original binomial with terms writtten as cubes. Answers will then vary depending on your interpretation.

Exercise Set 6.5
1. $(x + 2)(x - 2)$ **3.** $(9p + 1)(9p - 1)$ **5.** $(5y - 3)(5y + 3)$ **7.** $(11m + 10n)(11m - 10n)$ **9.** $(xy - 1)(xy + 1)$
11. $\left(x - \dfrac{1}{2}\right)\left(x + \dfrac{1}{2}\right)$ **13.** $-1(2r + 1)(2r - 1)$ **15.** prime   **17.** $(-6 + x)(6 + x)$ or $-1(6 + x)(6 - x)$ **19.** $(m^2 + 1)(m + 1)(m - 1)$
21. $(m^2 + n^9)(m^2 - n^9)$ **23.** $(x + 5)(x^2 - 5x + 25)$ **25.** $(2a - 1)(4a^2 + 2a + 1)$ **27.** $(m + 3n)(m^2 - 3mn + 9n^2)$
29. $5(k + 2)(k^2 - 2k + 4)$ **31.** $(xy - 4)(x^2y^2 + 4xy + 16)$ **33.** $2(5r - 4t)(25r^2 + 20rt + 16t^2)$ **35.** $(r + 8)(r - 8)$
37. $(x + 13y)(x - 13y)$ **39.** $(3 - t)(9 + 3t + t^2)$ **41.** $2(3r + 2)(3r - 2)$ **43.** $x(3y + 2)(3y - 2)$ **45.** $8(m + 2)(m^2 - 2m + 4)$
47. $xy(y - 3z)(y + 3z)$ **49.** $4(3x - 4y)(3x + 4y)$ **51.** $9(4 - 3x)(4 + 3x)$ **53.** $(xy - z^2)(x^2y^2 + xyz^2 + z^4)$ **55.** $\left(7 - \dfrac{3}{5}m\right)\left(7 + \dfrac{3}{5}m\right)$
57. $(t + 7)(t^2 - 7t + 49)$ **59.** $n(n^2 + 49)$ **61.** $x^2(x^2 + 9)(x + 3)(x - 3)$ **63.** $pq(8p + 9q)(8p - 9q)$ **65.** $xy^2(27xy + 1)$
67. $a(5a - 4b)(25a^2 + 20ab + 16b^2)$ **69.** $16x^2(x + 2)(x - 2)$ **71.** 6   **73.** -2 **75.** $\dfrac{1}{5}$ **77.** $(x + 2 + y)(x + 2 - y)$
79. $(a + 4)(a - 4)(b - 4)$ **81.** $(x + 3 + 2y)(x + 3 - 2y)$ **83.** $(x^n + 10)(x^n - 10)$ **85.** $(x + 6)$ **87.** answers may vary
89. a. 2560 ft   **b.** 1920 ft   **c.** 13 sec   **d.** $16(13 - t)(13 + t)$ **91. a.** 1456 ft   **b.** 816 ft   **c.** 10 sec   **d.** $16(10 + t)(10 - t)$

Integrated Review
Practice Exercises
1. $(3x - 1)(2x - 3)$ **2.** $(3x + 1)(x - 2)(x + 2)$ **3.** $3(3x - y)(3x + y)$ **4.** $(2a + b)(4a^2 - 2ab + b^2)$ **5.** $6xy^2(5x + 2)(2x - 3)$

Exercise Set

1. $(x + y)^2$ **2.** $(x - y)^2$ **3.** $(a + 12)(a - 1)$ **4.** $(a - 10)(a - 1)$ **5.** $(a + 2)(a - 3)$ **6.** $(a - 1)^2$ **7.** $(x + 1)^2$
8. $(x + 2)(x - 1)$ **9.** $(x + 1)(x + 3)$ **10.** $(x + 3)(x - 2)$ **11.** $(x + 3)(x + 4)$ **12.** $(x + 4)(x - 3)$ **13.** $(x + 4)(x - 1)$
14. $(x - 5)(x - 2)$ **15.** $(x + 5)(x - 3)$ **16.** $(x + 6)(x + 5)$ **17.** $(x - 6)(x + 5)$ **18.** $(x + 8)(x + 3)$ **19.** $2(x + 7)(x - 7)$
20. $3(x + 5)(x - 5)$ **21.** $(x + 3)(x + y)$ **22.** $(y - 7)(3 + x)$ **23.** $(x + 8)(x - 2)$ **24.** $(x - 7)(x + 4)$ **25.** $4x(x + 7)(x - 2)$
26. $6x(x - 5)(x + 4)$ **27.** $2(3x + 4)(2x + 3)$ **28.** $(2a - b)(4a + 5b)$ **29.** $(2a + b)(2a - b)$ **30.** $(4 - 3x)(7 + 2x)$
31. $(5 - 2x)(4 + x)$ **32.** prime   **33.** prime   **34.** $(3y + 5)(2y - 3)$ **35.** $(4x - 5)(x + 1)$ **36.** $y(x + y)(x - y)$ **37.** $4(t^2 + 9)$
38. $(x + 1)(x + y)$ **39.** $(x + 1)(a + 2)$ **40.** $9x(2x^2 - 7x + 1)$ **41.** $4a(3a^2 - 6a + 1)$ **42.** $(x + 16)(x - 2)$ **43.** prime
44. $(4a - 7b)^2$ **45.** $(5p - 7q)^2$ **46.** $(7x + 3y)(x + 3y)$ **47.** $(5 - 2y)(25 + 10y + 4y^2)$ **48.** $(4x + 3)(16x^2 - 12x + 9)$
49. $-(x - 5)(x + 6)$ **50.** $-(x - 2)(x - 4)$ **51.** $(7 - x)(2 + x)$ **52.** $(3 + x)(1 - x)$ **53.** $3x^2y(x + 6)(x - 4)$ **54.** $2xy(x + 5y)(x - y)$
55. $5xy^2(x - 7y)(x - y)$ **56.** $4x^2y(x - 5)(x + 3)$ **57.** $3xy(4x^2 + 81)$ **58.** $2xy^2(3x^2 + 4)$ **59.** $(2 + x)(2 - x)$ **60.** $(3 + y)(3 - y)$
61. $(s + 4)(3r - 1)$ **62.** $(x - 2)(x^2 + 3)$ **63.** $(4x - 3)(x - 2y)$ **64.** $(2x - y)(2x + 7z)$ **65.** $6(x + 2y)(x + y)$
66. $2(x + 4y)(6x - y)$ **67.** $(x + 3)(y + 2)(y - 2)$ **68.** $(y + 3)(y - 3)(x^2 + 3)$ **69.** $(5 + x)(x + y)$ **70.** $(x - y)(7 + y)$
71. $(7t - 1)(2t - 1)$ **72.** prime   **73.** $(3x + 5)(x - 1)$ **74.** $(7x - 2)(x + 3)$ **75.** $(x + 12y)(x - 3y)$ **76.** $(3x - 2y)(x + 4y)$
77. $(1 - 10ab)(1 + 2ab)$ **78.** $(1 + 5ab)(1 - 12ab)$ **79.** $(3 + x)(3 - x)(1 + x)(1 - x)$ **80.** $(3 + x)(3 - x)(2 + x)(2 - x)$
81. $(x + 4)(x - 4)(x^2 + 2)$ **82.** $(x + 5)(x - 5)(x^2 + 3)$ **83.** $(x - 15)(x - 8)$ **84.** $(y + 16)(y + 6)$ **85.** $2x(3x - 2)(x - 4)$
86. $2y(3y + 5)(y - 3)$ **87.** $(3x - 5y)(9x^2 + 15xy + 25y^2)$ **88.** $(6y - z)(36y^2 + 6yz + z^2)$ **89.** $(xy + 2z)(x^2y^2 - 2xyz + 4z^2)$
90. $(3ab + 2)(9a^2b^2 - 6ab + 4)$ **91.** $2xy(1 + 6x)(1 - 6x)$ **92.** $2x(x + 3)(x - 3)$ **93.** $(x + 2)(x - 2)(x + 6)$
94. $(x - 2)(x + 6)(x - 6)$ **95.** $2a^2(3a + 5)$ **96.** $2n(2n - 3)$ **97.** $(a^2 + 2)(a + 2)$ **98.** $(a - b)(1 + x)$ **99.** $(x + 2)(x - 2)(x + 7)$
100. $(a + 3)(a - 3)(a + 5)$ **101.** $(x - y + z)(x - y - z)$ **102.** $(x + 2y + 3)(x + 2y - 3)$ **103.** $(9 + 5x + 1)(9 - 5x - 1)$
104. $(b + 4a + c)(b - 4a - c)$ **105.** answers may vary   **106.** yes; $9(x^2 + 9y^2)$ **107.** a, c   **108.** b, c

Section 6.6
Practice Exercises

1. $-4, 5$ **2.** $-\dfrac{3}{4}, 12$ **3.** $0, \dfrac{6}{7}$ **4.** $-4, 12$ **5.** $\dfrac{4}{3}$ **6.** $-3, \dfrac{2}{3}$ **7.** $-6, 4$ **8.** $-3, 0, 3$ **9.** $\dfrac{2}{3}, \dfrac{3}{2}, 5$ **10.** $-3, 0, 2$
11. The x-intercepts are $(2, 0)$ and $(4, 0)$.

Graphing Calculator Explorations 6.6
1. $-0.9, 2.2$ **3.** no real solution   **5.** $-1.8, 2.8$

Vocabulary, Readiness & Video Check 6.6
1. quadratic   **3.** $3, -5$ **5.** One side of the equation must be a factored polynomial and the other side must be zero.   **7.** To find the x-intercepts of any graph in two variables, we let $y = 0$. Doing this with our quadratic equation gives us an equation $= 0$, which we can solve by factoring.

Exercise Set 6.6

1. $6, 7$ **3.** $2, -1$ **5.** $-9, -17$ **7.** $0, -6$ **9.** $0, 8$ **11.** $-\dfrac{3}{2}, \dfrac{5}{4}$ **13.** $\dfrac{7}{2}, -\dfrac{2}{7}$ **15.** $\dfrac{1}{2}, -\dfrac{1}{3}$ **17.** $-0.2, -1.5$ **19.** $9, 4$ **21.** $-4, 2$
23. $0, 7$ **25.** $8, -4$ **27.** $4, -4$ **29.** $-3, 12$ **31.** $\dfrac{7}{3}, -2$ **33.** $-5, 5$ **35.** $-2, \dfrac{1}{6}$ **37.** $0, 4, 8$ **39.** $\dfrac{3}{4}$ **41.** $-\dfrac{1}{2}, 0, \dfrac{1}{2}$ **43.** $-\dfrac{3}{8}, 0, \dfrac{1}{2}$
45. $-3, 2$ **47.** $-20, 0$ **49.** $\dfrac{17}{2}$ **51.** $-\dfrac{1}{2}, \dfrac{1}{2}$ **53.** $-\dfrac{3}{2}, -\dfrac{1}{2}, 3$ **55.** $-5, 3$ **57.** $-\dfrac{5}{6}, \dfrac{6}{5}$ **59.** $2, -\dfrac{4}{5}$ **61.** $-\dfrac{4}{3}, 5$ **63.** $-4, 3$
65. $\dfrac{8}{3}, -9, 0$ **67.** -7 **69.** $0, \dfrac{3}{2}$ **71.** $0, 1, -1$ **73.** $-6, \dfrac{4}{3}$ **75.** $\dfrac{6}{7}, 1$ **77.** $\left(-\dfrac{4}{3}, 0\right), (1, 0)$ **79.** $(-2, 0), (5, 0)$ **81.** $(-6, 0), \left(\dfrac{1}{2}, 0\right)$
83. e   **85.** b   **87.** c   **89.** $\dfrac{47}{45}$ **91.** $\dfrac{17}{60}$ **93.** $\dfrac{15}{8}$ **95.** $\dfrac{7}{10}$ **97.** didn't write equation in standard form; should be $x = 4$ or $x = -2$
99. answers may vary; for example $(x - 6)(x + 1) = 0$ **101.** answers may vary; for example, $x^2 - 12x + 35 = 0$ **103. a.** $300; 304; 276; 216;$
$124; 0; -156$ **b.** 5 sec   **c.** 304 ft   **d.**   **105.** $0, \dfrac{1}{2}$ **107.** $0, -15$

$y = -16x^2 + 20x + 300$

Section 6.7
Practice Exercises
1. 2 sec   **2.** There are two numbers. They are −4 and 12.   **3.** base: 35 ft; height: 12 ft   **4.** 7 and 8 or −6 and −5   **5.** leg: 8 units; leg: 15 units; hypotenuse: 17 units

Vocabulary, Readiness & Video Check 6.7
1. In applications, the context of the problem needs to be considered. Each exercise resulted in both a positive and a negative solution, and a negative solution is not appropriate for any of the problems.

Exercise Set 6.7
1. width $= x$; length $= x + 4$ **3.** x and $x + 2$ if x is an odd integer   **5.** base $= x$; height $= 4x + 1$ **7.** 11 units   **9.** 15 cm, 13 cm, 70 cm, 22 cm
11. base $= 16$ mi; height $= 6$ mi   **13.** 5 sec   **15.** width $= 5$ cm; length $= 6$ cm   **17.** 54 diagonals   **19.** 10 sides   **21.** −12 or 11   **23.** 14, 15
25. 13 feet   **27.** 5 in.   **29.** 12 mm, 16 mm, 20 mm   **31.** 10 km   **33.** 36 ft   **35.** 9.5 sec   **37.** 20%   **39.** length: 15 mi; width: 8 mi

41. 105 units   **43.** 2 million   **45.** 1.9 million   **47.** 2003   **49.** answers may vary   **51.** $\dfrac{4}{7}$ **53.** $\dfrac{3}{2}$ **55.** $\dfrac{1}{3}$

57. slow boat: 8 mph; fast boat: 15 mph   **59.** 13 and 7   **61.** width: 29 m; length: 35 m   **63.** answers may vary

CHAPTER 7 RATIONAL EXPRESSIONS

Section 7.1
Practice Exercises

1. a. $\{x \mid x \text{ is a real number}\}$ **b.** $\{x \mid x \text{ is a real number and } x \neq -3\}$ **c.** $\{x \mid x \text{ is a real number and } x \neq 2, x \neq 3\}$ **2. a.** $\dfrac{1}{2z - 1}$ **b.** $\dfrac{5x + 3}{6x - 5}$.

3. a. 1   **b.** −1   **4.** $-\dfrac{5(2 + x)}{x + 3}$ **5. a.** $x^2 - 4x + 16$ **b.** $\dfrac{5}{z - 3}$ **6.** $\dfrac{-(x + 3)}{6x - 11}$, $\dfrac{-x - 3}{6x - 11}$, $\dfrac{x + 3}{-(6x - 11)}$, $\dfrac{x + 3}{-6x + 11}$, $\dfrac{x + 3}{11 - 6x}$

7. a. $7.20   **b.** $3.60

Graphing Calculator Explorations 7.1

1. $\{x \mid x \text{ is a real number and } x \neq -2, x \neq 2\}$ **3.** $\left\{x \mid x \text{ is a real number and } x \neq -4, x \neq \dfrac{1}{2}\right\}$

Vocabulary, Readiness & Video Check 7.1

1. rational   **3.** domain   **5.** 1   **7.** $\dfrac{-a}{b}$; $\dfrac{a}{-b}$ **9.** Rational expressions are fractions and are therefore undefined if the denominator is zero; the domain of a rational function is all real numbers except those that make the denominator of the related rational expression equal to 0.
11. You would need to write parentheses around the numerator or denominator if it had more than one term because the negative sign needs to apply to the entire numerator or denominator.

Exercise Set 7.1

1. $\{x \mid x \text{ is a real number}\}$ **3.** $\{t \mid t \text{ is a real number and } t \neq 0\}$ **5.** $\{x \mid x \text{ is a real number and } x \neq 7\}$ **7.** $\left\{x \mid x \text{ is a real number and } x \neq \dfrac{1}{3}\right\}$

9. $\{x \mid x \text{ is a real number and } x \neq -2, x \neq 0, x \neq 1\}$ **11.** $\{x \mid x \text{ is a real number and } x \neq 2, x \neq -2\}$ **13.** $\dfrac{-(x - 10)}{x + 8}$; $\dfrac{-x + 10}{x + 8}$, $\dfrac{x - 10}{-(x + 8)}$, $\dfrac{x - 10}{-x - 8}$

15. $\dfrac{-(5y - 3)}{y - 12}$, $\dfrac{-5y + 3}{y - 12}$, $\dfrac{5y - 3}{-(y - 12)}$, $\dfrac{5y - 3}{-y + 12}$ **17.** 1   **19.** −1   **21.** $\dfrac{1}{4(x + 2)}$ **23.** −5   **25.** $\dfrac{7}{x}$ **27.** $\dfrac{1}{x - 9}$ **29.** $5x + 1$

31. $\dfrac{x^2}{x - 2}$ **33.** $\dfrac{x + 2}{2}$ **35.** $-(x + 2)$ or $-x - 2$ **37.** $\dfrac{11x}{6}$ **39.** $x + y$ **41.** $x^2 - 2x + 4$ **43.** $-x^2 - x - 1$ **45.** $\dfrac{2y + 5}{3y + 4}$

47. $\dfrac{x - 2}{2x^2 + 1}$ **49.** $\dfrac{1}{3x + 5}$ **51.** correct   **53.** correct   **55.** $\dfrac{10}{3}, -8, -\dfrac{7}{3}$ **57.** $-\dfrac{17}{48}, \dfrac{2}{7}, -\dfrac{3}{8}$ **59. a.** $200 million   **b.** $500 million

c. $300 million   **d.** $\{x \mid x \text{ is a real number}\}$ **61.** 400 mg   **63.** $C = 78.125$; medium   **65.** 59.6%   **67.** $\dfrac{3}{11}$ **69.** $\dfrac{4}{3}$ **71.** $\dfrac{117}{40}$

73. correct   **75.** incorrect; $\dfrac{1 + 2}{1 + 3} = \dfrac{3}{4}$ **77.** no   **79.** yes; 1   **81.** yes; −1   **83.** no; answers may vary   **85.** answers may vary

87. $0, \frac{20}{9}, \frac{60}{7}, 20, \frac{140}{3}, 180, 380, 1980;$

89.

$y = \frac{x^2 - 16}{x - 4}$

91.

$y = \frac{x^2 - 6x + 8}{x - 2}$

Section 7.2
Practice Exercises

1. a. $\frac{12a}{5b^2}$ **b.** $-\frac{2q}{3}$ **2.** $\frac{3}{x + 1}$ **3.** $-\frac{3x - 5}{2x(x + 2)}$ **4.** $\frac{b^2}{8a^2}$ **5.** $\frac{3(x - 5)}{4}$ **6.** $\frac{2}{x(x - 3)}$ **7.** 1 **8. a.** $\frac{(y + 9)^2}{16x^2}$ **b.** $\frac{1}{4x}$

c. $-\frac{7(x - 2)}{x + 4}$ **9.** 2 sq ft **10.** 504 sq in. **11.** 549,000 sq ft **12.** 70.0 miles per hour

Vocabulary, Readiness & Video Check 7.2

1. reciprocals **3.** $\frac{a \cdot d}{b \cdot c}$ or $\frac{ad}{bc}$ **5.** $\frac{6}{7}$ **7.** fractions; reciprocal **9.** The units in the unit fraction consist of $\frac{\text{units converting to}}{\text{original units}}$.

Exercise Set 7.2

1. $\frac{21}{4y}$ **3.** x^4 **5.** $-\frac{b^2}{6}$ **7.** $\frac{x^2}{10}$ **9.** $\frac{1}{3}$ **11.** $\frac{m + n}{m - n}$ **13.** $\frac{x + 5}{x}$ **15.** $\frac{(x + 2)(x - 3)}{(x - 4)(x + 4)}$ **17.** $\frac{2x^4}{3}$ **19.** $\frac{12}{y^6}$ **21.** $x(x + 4)$

23. $\frac{3(x + 1)}{x^3(x - 1)}$ **25.** $m^2 - n^2$ **27.** $-\frac{x + 2}{x - 3}$ **29.** $\frac{x + 2}{x - 3}$ **31.** $\frac{5}{6}$ **33.** $\frac{3x}{8}$ **35.** $\frac{3}{2}$ **37.** $\frac{3x + 4y}{2(x + 2y)}$ **39.** $\frac{2(x + 2)}{x - 2}$

41. $-\frac{y(x + 2)}{4}$ **43.** $\frac{(a + 5)(a + 3)}{(a + 2)(a + 1)}$ **45.** $\frac{5}{x}$ **47.** $\frac{2(n - 8)}{3n - 1}$ **49.** $4x^3(x - 3)$ **51.** $\frac{(a + b)^2}{a - b}$ **53.** $\frac{3x + 5}{x^2 + 4}$ **55.** $\frac{4}{x - 2}$

57. $\frac{a - b}{6(a^2 + ab + b^2)}$ **59.** 1440 **61.** 5 **63.** 81 **65.** 73 **67.** 56.7 **69.** 1,201,500 sq ft **71.** 244.9 miles/hour **73.** 1

75. $-\frac{10}{9}$ **77.** $-\frac{1}{5}$ **79.**

81. true **83.** false; $\frac{x^2 + 3x}{20}$ **85.** $\frac{2}{9(x - 5)}$ sq ft **87.** $\frac{x}{2}$ **89.** $\frac{5a(2a + b)(3a - 2b)}{b^2(a - b)(a + 2b)}$

91. answers may vary

Section 7.3
Practice Exercises

1. $\frac{2a}{b}$ **2.** 1 **3.** $4x - 5$ **4. a.** 42 **b.** $45y^3$ **5. a.** $(y - 5)(y - 4)$ **b.** $a(a + 2)$ **6.** $3(2x - 1)^2$ **7.** $(x + 4)(x - 4)(x + 1)$

8. $3 - x$ or $x - 3$ **9. a.** $\frac{21x^2y}{35xy^2}$ **b.** $\frac{18x}{8x + 14}$ **10.** $\frac{3x - 6}{(x - 2)(x + 3)(x - 5)}$

Vocabulary, Readiness & Video Check 7.3

1. $\frac{9}{11}$ **3.** $\frac{a + c}{b}$ **5.** $\frac{5 - (6 + x)}{x}$ **7.** We factor denominators into the smallest factors—including coefficients—so we can determine the most number of times each unique factor occurs in any one denominator for the LCD.

Exercise Set 7.3

1. $\frac{a + 9}{13}$ **3.** $\frac{3m}{n}$ **5.** 4 **7.** $\frac{y + 10}{3 + y}$ **9.** $5x + 3$ **11.** $\frac{4}{a + 5}$ **13.** $\frac{1}{x - 6}$ **15.** $\frac{5x + 7}{x - 3}$ **17.** $x + 5$ **19.** 3 **21.** $4x^3$

23. $8x(x + 2)$ **25.** $(x + 3)(x - 2)$ **27.** $3(x + 6)$ **29.** $5(x - 6)^2$ **31.** $6(x + 1)^2$ **33.** $x - 8$ or $8 - x$ **35.** $(x - 1)(x + 4)(x + 3)$

37. $(3x + 1)(x + 1)(x - 1)(2x + 1)$ **39.** $2x^2(x + 4)(x - 4)$ **41.** $\frac{6x}{4x^2}$ **43.** $\frac{24b^2}{12ab^2}$ **45.** $\frac{9y}{2y(x + 3)}$ **47.** $\frac{9ab + 2b}{5b(a + 2)}$

49. $\frac{x^2 + x}{x(x + 4)(x + 2)(x + 1)}$ **51.** $\frac{18y - 2}{30x^2 - 60}$ **53.** $2x$ **55.** $\frac{x + 3}{2x - 1}$ **57.** $x + 1$ **59.** $\frac{1}{x^2 - 8}$ **61.** $\frac{6(4x + 1)}{x(2x + 1)}$ **63.** $\frac{29}{21}$ **65.** $-\frac{7}{12}$

67. $\frac{7}{30}$ **69.** d **71.** answers may vary **73.** c **75.** b **77.** $-\frac{5}{x - 2}$ **79.** $\frac{7 + x}{x - 2}$ **81.** $\frac{20}{x - 2}$ m **83.** answers may vary

85. 95,304 Earth days **87.** answers may vary **89.** answers may vary

Section 7.4
Practice Exercises

1. a. 0   **b.** $\dfrac{21a + 10}{24a^2}$ **2.** $\dfrac{6}{x - 5}$ **3.** $\dfrac{13y + 3}{5y(y + 1)}$ **4.** $\dfrac{13}{x - 5}$ **5.** $\dfrac{3b + 6}{b + 3}$ or $\dfrac{3(b + 2)}{b + 3}$ **6.** $\dfrac{10 - 3x^2}{2x(2x + 3)}$ **7.** $\dfrac{x(5x + 6)}{(x + 4)(x + 3)(x - 3)}$

Vocabulary, Readiness & Video Check 7.4

1. d   **3.** a   **5.** The problem adds two rational expressions with denominators that are opposites of each other. Recognizing this special case can save you time and effort. If you recognize that one denominator is -1 times the other denominator, you may save time.

Exercise Set 7.4

1. $\dfrac{5}{x}$ **3.** $\dfrac{75a - 6b^2}{5b}$ **5.** $\dfrac{6x + 5}{2x^2}$ **7.** $\dfrac{11}{x + 1}$ **9.** $\dfrac{x - 6}{(x - 2)(x + 2)}$ **11.** $\dfrac{35x - 6}{4x(x - 2)}$ **13.** $-\dfrac{2}{x - 3}$ **15.** 0   **17.** $-\dfrac{1}{x^2 - 1}$

19. $\dfrac{5 + 2x}{x}$ **21.** $\dfrac{6x - 7}{x - 2}$ **23.** $-\dfrac{y + 4}{y + 3}$ **25.** $\dfrac{-5x + 14}{4x}$ or $-\dfrac{5x - 14}{4x}$ **27.** 2   **29.** $\dfrac{9x^4 - 4x^2}{21}$ **31.** $\dfrac{x + 2}{(x + 3)^2}$ **33.** $\dfrac{9b - 4}{5b(b - 1)}$

35. $\dfrac{2 + m}{m}$ **37.** $\dfrac{x^2 + 3x}{(x - 7)(x - 2)}$ or $\dfrac{x(x + 3)}{(x - 7)(x - 2)}$ **39.** $\dfrac{10}{1 - 2x}$ **41.** $\dfrac{15x - 1}{(x + 1)^2(x - 1)}$ **43.** $\dfrac{x^2 - 3x - 2}{(x - 1)^2(x + 1)}$ **45.** $\dfrac{a + 2}{2(a + 3)}$

47. $\dfrac{y(2y + 1)}{(2y + 3)^2}$ **49.** $\dfrac{x - 10}{2(x - 2)}$ **51.** $\dfrac{2x + 21}{(x + 3)^2}$ **53.** $\dfrac{-5x + 23}{(x - 2)(x - 3)}$ **55.** $\dfrac{7}{2(m - 10)}$ **57.** $\dfrac{2x^2 - 2x - 46}{(x + 1)(x - 6)(x - 5)}$ or $\dfrac{2(x^2 - x - 23)}{(x + 1)(x - 6)(x - 5)}$

59. $\dfrac{n + 4}{4n(n - 1)(n - 2)}$ **61.** 10   **63.** 2   **65.** $\dfrac{25a}{9(a - 2)}$ **67.** $\dfrac{x + 4}{(x - 2)(x - 1)}$ **69.** $x = \dfrac{2}{3}$ **71.** $x = -\dfrac{1}{2}, x = 1$ **73.** $x = -\dfrac{15}{2}$

75. $\dfrac{6x^2 - 5x - 3}{x(x + 1)(x - 1)}$ **77.** $\dfrac{4x^2 - 15x + 6}{(x - 2)^2(x + 2)(x - 3)}$ **79.** $\dfrac{-2x^2 + 14x + 55}{(x + 2)(x + 7)(x + 3)}$ **81.** $\dfrac{2x - 16}{(x + 4)(x - 4)}$ in.   **83.** $\dfrac{P - G}{P}$ **85.** answers may vary

87. $\left(\dfrac{90x - 40}{x}\right)^{\circ}$ **89.** answers may vary

Section 7.5
Practice Exercises

1. -2 **2.** 13   **3.** $-1, 7$ **4.** $-\dfrac{19}{2}$ **5.** 3   **6.** -8 **7.** $b = \dfrac{ax}{a - x}$

Graphing Calculator Explorations 7.5

1.   **3.**

Vocabulary, Readiness & Video Check 7.5

1. c   **3.** b   **5.** a   **7.** These equations are solved in very different ways, so you need to determine the next correct move to make. For a linear equation, you first "move" variable terms on one side and numbers on the other; for a quadratic equation, you first set the equation equal to 0.
9. the steps for solving an equation containing rational expressions; as if it's the only variable in the equation

Exercise Set 7.5

1. 30   **3.** 0   **5.** -2 **7.** $-5, 2$ **9.** 5   **11.** 3   **13.** 1   **15.** 5   **17.** no solution   **19.** 4   **21.** -8 **23.** $6, -4$ **25.** 1

27. $3, -4$ **29.** -3 **31.** 0   **33.** -2 **35.** $8, -2$ **37.** no solution   **39.** 3   **41.** $-11, 1$ **43.** $I = \dfrac{E}{R}$ **45.** $B = \dfrac{2U - TE}{T}$

47. $w = \dfrac{Bh^2}{705}$ **49.** $G = \dfrac{V}{N - R}$ **51.** $r = \dfrac{C}{2\pi}$ **53.** $x = \dfrac{3y}{3 + y}$ **55.** $\dfrac{1}{x}$ **57.** $\dfrac{1}{x} + \dfrac{1}{2}$ **59.** $\dfrac{1}{3}$ **61.** $(2, 0), (0, -2)$

63. $(-4, 0), (-2, 0), (3, 0), (0, 4)$ **65.** answers may vary   **67.** $\dfrac{5x + 9}{9x}$ **69.** no solution   **71.** $100^{\circ}, 80^{\circ}$ **73.** $22.5^{\circ}, 67.5^{\circ}$ **75.** $\dfrac{17}{4}$

Integrated Review

1. expression; $\dfrac{3 + 2x}{3x}$ **2.** expression; $\dfrac{18 + 5a}{6a}$ **3.** equation; 3   **4.** equation; 18   **5.** expression; $\dfrac{x + 1}{x(x - 1)}$ **6.** expression; $\dfrac{3(x + 1)}{x(x - 3)}$

7. equation; no solution   **8.** equation; 1   **9.** expression; 10   **10.** expression; $\dfrac{z}{3(9z - 5)}$ **11.** expression; $\dfrac{5x + 7}{x - 3}$ **12.** expression; $\dfrac{7p + 5}{2p + 7}$

13. equation; 23   **14.** equation; 5   **15.** expression; $\dfrac{25a}{9(a - 2)}$ **16.** expression; $\dfrac{4x + 5}{(x + 1)(x - 1)}$ **17.** expression; $\dfrac{3x^2 + 5x + 3}{(3x - 1)^2}$

18. expression; $\dfrac{2x^2 - 3x - 1}{(2x - 5)^2}$ **19.** expression; $\dfrac{4x - 37}{5x}$ **20.** expression; $\dfrac{29x - 23}{3x}$ **21.** equation; $\dfrac{8}{5}$ **22.** equation; $-\dfrac{7}{3}$

23. answers may vary   **24.** answers may vary

Section 7.6
Practice Exercises

1. 99   **2.** $\dfrac{13}{3}$ **3.** \$9.03   **4.** 6   **5.** 15   **6.** $1\dfrac{5}{7}$ hr   **7.** bus: 45 mph; car: 60 mph

Vocabulary, Readiness & Video Check 7.6

1. c   **3.** $\dfrac{1}{x};\dfrac{1}{x} - 3$ **5.** $z + 5;\dfrac{1}{z + 5}$ **7.** $2y;\dfrac{11}{2y}$ **9.** No. Proportions are actually equations containing rational expressions, so they can also

be solved by using the steps to solve those equations.   **11.** divided by, quotient   **13.** $\dfrac{325}{x + 7} = \dfrac{290}{x}$

Exercise Set 7.6

1. 4   **3.** $\dfrac{50}{9}$ **5.** -3 **7.** $\dfrac{14}{9}$ **9.** 123 lb   **11.** 165 cal   **13.** $y = 21.25$ **15.** $y = 5\dfrac{5}{7}$ ft   **17.** 2   **19.** -3 **21.** $2\dfrac{2}{9}$ hr

23. $1\dfrac{1}{2}$ min   **25.** trip to park rate: r; to park time: $\dfrac{12}{r}$; return trip rate: r; return time: $\dfrac{18}{r} = \dfrac{12}{r} + 1; r = 6$ mph   **27.** 1st portion: 10 mph; cooldown: 8 mph

29. 360 sq ft   **31.** 2   **33.** \$108.00   **35.** 20 mph   **37.** $y = 37\dfrac{1}{2}$ ft   **39.** 41 mph; 51 mph   **41.** 5   **43.** 217 mph   **45.** 9 gal   **47.** 8 mph

49. 2.2 mph; 3.3 mph   **51.** 3 hr   **53.** $26\dfrac{2}{3}$ ft   **55.** 216 nuts   **57.** $666\dfrac{2}{3}$ mi   **59.** 20 hr   **61.** car: 70 mph; motorcycle: 60 mph   **63.** $5\dfrac{1}{4}$ hr

65. 8   **67.** first car: 64 mph; second car: 50 mph   **69.** 510 mph   **71.** $x = 5$ **73.** $x = 13.5$ **75.** $-\dfrac{4}{3}$; downward   **77.** $\dfrac{11}{4}$; upward

79. undefined slope; vertical   **81.** 40,200 megawatts   **83.** 22,510,000 people   **85.** yes   **87.** first pump: 28 min; second pump: 84 min

89. none; answers may vary   **91.** answers may vary   **93.** $R = \dfrac{D}{T}$

CHAPTER 8 MORE ON FUNCTIONS AND GRAPHS

Section 8.1
Practice Exercises

1.

2.

3. $f(x) = -4x - 3$ **4.** $f(x) = -\dfrac{2}{3}x + \dfrac{4}{3}$ **5.** $f(x) = -2$ **6.** $3x + 4y = 12$

7. $f(x) = \dfrac{4}{3}x - \dfrac{41}{3}$

Graphing Calculator Explorations 8.1

1. $y = \dfrac{x}{3.5}$

3. $y = -\dfrac{5.78}{2.31}x + \dfrac{10.98}{2.31}$

5. $y = |x| + 3.78$

7. $y = 5.6x^2 + 7.7x + 1.5$

Vocabulary, Readiness & Video Check 8.1

1. linear   **3.** $m = -4$, y-intercept: $(0, 12)$ **5.** $m = 5$, y-intercept: $(0, 0)$ **7.** parallel   **9.** neither   **11.** $f(x) = mx + b$, or slope-intercept form   **13.** if one of the two points given is the y-intercept

Exercise Set 8.1

1. $f(x) = -2x$

3. $f(x) = -2x + 3$

5. $f(x) = \frac{1}{2}x$

7. $f(x) = \frac{1}{2}x - 4$

9. C   **11.** D   **13.** $f(x) = -x + 1$

15. $f(x) = 2x + \frac{3}{4}$ **17.** $f(x) = \frac{2}{7}x$ **19.** $f(x) = 3x - 1$ **21.** $f(x) = -2x - 1$ **23.** $f(x) = \frac{1}{2}x + 5$ **25.** $f(x) = -\frac{9}{10}x - \frac{27}{10}$

27. $f(x) = 3x - 6$ **29.** $f(x) = -2x + 1$ **31.** $f(x) = -\frac{1}{2}x - 5$ **33.** $f(x) = \frac{1}{3}x - 7$ **35.** $f(x) = -\frac{3}{8}x + \frac{5}{8}$ **37.** $f(x) = -4$

39. $f(x) = 5$ **41.** $f(x) = 4x - 4$ **43.** $f(x) = -3x + 1$ **45.** $f(x) = -\frac{3}{2}x - 6$ **47.** $2x - y = -7$ **49.** $f(x) = -x + 7$

51. $f(x) = -\frac{1}{2}x + 11$ **53.** $2x + 7y = -42$ **55.** $4x + 3y = -20$ **57.** $f(x) = -10$ **59.** $x + 2y = 2$ **61.** $f(x) = 12$

63. $8x - y = 47$ **65.** $x = 5$ **67.** $f(x) = -\frac{3}{8}x - \frac{29}{4}$ **69.** 28.4; In 2009, about 28.4% of students took at least one online course.   **71.** 54.22;

In 2016, we predict that 54.22% of students will take at least one online course.   **73.** answers may vary   **75.** $f(x) = -2x + 3$ **77.** $f(x) = \frac{2}{3}x + \frac{7}{3}$

79. a. $y = 32x$ **b.** 128 ft per sec   **81. a.** $y = -250x + 3500$ **b.** 1625 Frisbees   **83. a.** $y = 58.1x + 2619$ **b.** 2851.4 thousand
85. a. $y = -4820x + 297{,}000$ **b.** $258,440   **87.** $-4x + y = 4$ **89.** $2x + y = -23$ **91.** $3x - 2y = -13$ **93.** answers may vary

Section 8.2
Practice Exercises
1. a. -3 **b.** -2 **c.** 3   **d.** 1   **e.** -1 and 3   **f.** -3 **2.** 17 million or 17,000,000 students   **3.** 5.8 million or 5,800,000 students

4. a. 11   **b.** $\frac{1}{4}$ **c.** -8 **d.** not a real number   **e.** 10   **5.** $f(x) = 2x^2$ **6.** $f(x) = -|x|$ **7.** $f(x) = \sqrt{x} + 1$

Graphing Calculator Explorations 8.2
1.   **3.**   **5.**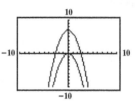

Vocabulary, Readiness & Video Check 8.2
1. V-shaped   **3.** $(-2, 1.7)$ **5.** Using function notation, the replacement value for x and the resulting $f(x)$ or y-value corresponds to an ordered pair (x, y) solution to the function   **7.** not; shape

Exercise Set 8.2
1. 0   **3.** -4 **5.** 3   **7.** $(1, -10)$ **9.** $(4, 56)$ **11.** $f(-1) = -2$ **13.** $g(2) = 0$ **15.** $-4, 0$ **17.** 3   **19.** 7   **21.** $-\frac{2}{3}$ **23.** 8

25. 9   **27.** not a real number   **29.** $f(x) = x^2 + 3$ **31.** $h(x) = |x| - 2$ **33.** $g(x) = 2x^2$ **35.** $f(x) = 5x - 1$

37. $f(x) = \sqrt{x} + 1$ **39.** $g(x) = -2|x|$ **41.** $h(x) = \sqrt{x} + 2$

43. a. answers may vary; between 5 and 6 million or 5,250,000 students   **b.** 5.25 million   **45.** $15.54 billion   **47.** 25π sq cm   **49.** 2744 cu in.   **51.** 166.38 cm   **53.** 163.2 mg

55. infinite number   **57.** -5 **59.** $-\frac{1}{10}$

61. b   **63.** c   **65.** 1997   **67.** answers may vary

69. $y = x^2 - 4x + 7$ **71.** $f(x) = [x]$

Integrated Review

1. $m = 3; (0, -5)$ **2.** $m = \dfrac{5}{2}; \left(0, -\dfrac{7}{2}\right)$ **3.** parallel **4.** perpendicular **5.** $f(x) = -x + 7$ **6.** $f(x) = -\dfrac{3}{8}x - \dfrac{29}{4}$ **7.** $f(x) = 3x - 2$

8. $f(x) = -\dfrac{5}{4}x + 4$ **9.** $f(x) = \dfrac{1}{4}x - \dfrac{7}{2}$ **10.** $f(x) = -\dfrac{5}{2}x - \dfrac{5}{2}$

11. linear **12.** linear **13.** not linear **14.** not linear **15.** not linear **16.** not linear

17. not linear **18.** not linear **19.** linear **20.** linear **21.** not linear **22.** not linear

23. linear **24.** linear **25.** linear **26.** linear

CHAPTER 9 INEQUALITIES AND ABSOLUTE VALUE

Section 9.1
Practice Exercises

1. $\{1, 3\}$ **2.** $(-\infty, 2)$ **3.** $\{ \}$ or $\varnothing$ **4.** $(-4, 2)$ **5.** $[-6, 8]$ **6.** $\{1, 2, 3, 4, 5, 6, 7, 9\}$ **7.** $\left(-\infty, \dfrac{3}{8}\right] \cup [3, \infty)$ **8.** $(-\infty, \infty)$

Vocabulary, Readiness & Video Check 9.1
1. compound **3.** or **5.** $\cup$ **7.** and **9.** or

Exercise Set 9.1
1. $\{2, 3, 4, 5, 6, 7\}$ **3.** $\{4, 6\}$ **5.** $\{\ldots, -2, -1, 0, 1, \ldots\}$ **7.** $\{5, 7\}$ **9.** $\{x \mid x \text{ is an odd integer or } x = 2 \text{ or } x = 4\}$ **11.** $\{2, 4\}$

13. ◄———(———)———► $(-3, 1)$ **15.** ◄———|———► $\varnothing$ **17.** ◄———)———► $(-\infty, -1)$ **19.** $[6, \infty)$ **21.** $(-\infty, -3]$ **23.** $(4, 10)$

25. $(11, 17)$ **27.** $[1, 4]$ **29.** $\left[-3, \dfrac{3}{2}\right]$ **31.** $\left[-\dfrac{7}{3}, 7\right]$ **33.** ◄———)———► $(-\infty, 5)$ **35.** ◄———]——[——► $(-\infty, -4] \cup [1, \infty)$

37. ◄———|———► $(-\infty, \infty)$ **39.** $[2, \infty)$ **41.** $(-\infty, -4) \cup (-2, \infty)$ **43.** $(-\infty, \infty)$ **45.** $\left(-\dfrac{1}{2}, \dfrac{2}{3}\right)$ **47.** $(-\infty, \infty)$ **49.** $\left[\dfrac{3}{2}, 6\right]$ **51.** $\left(\dfrac{5}{4}, \dfrac{11}{4}\right)$

53. $\varnothing$ **55.** $\left(-\infty, -\dfrac{56}{5}\right) \cup \left(\dfrac{5}{3}, \infty\right)$ **57.** $\left(-5, \dfrac{5}{2}\right)$ **59.** $\left(0, \dfrac{14}{3}\right)$ **61.** $(-\infty, -3]$ **63.** $(-\infty, 1] \cup \left(\dfrac{29}{7}, \infty\right)$ **65.** $\varnothing$ **67.** $\left[-\dfrac{1}{2}, \dfrac{3}{2}\right)$

69. $\left(-\dfrac{4}{3}, \dfrac{7}{3}\right)$ **71.** $(6, 12)$ **73.** -12 **75.** -4 **77.** $-7, 7$ **79.** 0 **81.** $2004, 2005$ **83.** answers may vary **85.** $(6, \infty)$ **87.** $[3, 7]$

89. $(-\infty, -1)$ **91.** $-20.2° \le F \le 95°$ **93.** $67 \le \text{final score} \le 94$

Section 9.2
Practice Exercises
1. $-3, 3$ **2.** $-1, 4$ **3.** $-80, 70$ **4.** $-2, 2$ **5.** 0 **6.** $\{ \}$ or $\varnothing$ **7.** $\{ \}$ or $\varnothing$ **8.** $-\dfrac{3}{5}, 5$ **9.** 5

Vocabulary, Readiness & Video Check 9.2
1. C **3.** B **5.** D

Exercise Set 9.2
1. $-7, 7$ **3.** $4.2, -4.2$ **5.** $7, -2$ **7.** $8, 4$ **9.** $5, -5$ **11.** $3, -3$ **13.** 0 **15.** $\varnothing$ **17.** $\dfrac{1}{5}$ **19.** $9, -\dfrac{1}{2}$ **21.** $-\dfrac{5}{2}$ **23.** $4, -4$

25. 0 **27.** $\varnothing$ **29.** $0, \dfrac{14}{3}$ **31.** $2, -2$ **33.** $\varnothing$ **35.** $7, -1$ **37.** $\varnothing$ **39.** $\varnothing$ **41.** $-\dfrac{1}{8}$ **43.** $\dfrac{1}{2}, -\dfrac{5}{6}$ **45.** $2, -\dfrac{12}{5}$ **47.** $3, -2$

49. $-8, \dfrac{2}{3}$ **51.** $\varnothing$ **53.** 4 **55.** $13, -8$ **57.** $3, -3$ **59.** $8, -7$ **61.** $2, 3$ **63.** $2, -\dfrac{10}{3}$ **65.** $\dfrac{3}{2}$ **67.** $\varnothing$ **69.** 31% **71.** $32.4°$

73. answers may vary **75.** answers may vary **77.** $\varnothing$ **79.** $|x| = 5$ **81.** answers may vary **83.** $|x - 1| = 5$ **85.** answers may vary
87. $|x| = 6$ **89.** $|x - 2| = |3x - 4|$

Section 9.3
Practice Exercises

1. $(-5, 5)$ 2. $(-4, 2)$ 3. $\left[-\dfrac{2}{3}, 2\right]$ 4. $\{\ \}$ or $\varnothing$ 5. $\{2\}$

6. $(-\infty, -10] \cup [2, \infty)$ 7. $(-\infty, \infty)$ 8. $(-\infty, 0) \cup (12, \infty)$

Vocabulary, Readiness & Video Check 9.3

1. D   3. C   5. A   7. The solution set involves "or" and "or" means "union."

Exercise Set 9.3

1. $[-4, 4]$ 3. $(1, 5)$ 5. $(-5, -1)$ 7. $[-10, 3]$

9. $[-5, 5]$ 11. $\varnothing$ 13. $[0, 12]$ 15. $(-\infty, -3) \cup (3, \infty)$

17. $(-\infty, -24] \cup [4, \infty)$ 19. $(-\infty, -4) \cup (4, \infty)$ 21. $(-\infty, \infty)$

23. $\left(-\infty, \dfrac{2}{3}\right) \cup (2, \infty)$ 25. $\{0\}$ 27. $\left(-\infty, -\dfrac{3}{8}\right) \cup \left(-\dfrac{3}{8}, \infty\right)$ 29. $[-2, 2]$

31. $(-\infty, -1) \cup (1, \infty)$ 33. $(-5, 11)$ 35. $(-\infty, 4) \cup (6, \infty)$ 37. $\varnothing$

39. $(-\infty, \infty)$ 41. $[-2, 9]$ 43. $(-\infty, -11] \cup [1, \infty)$ 45. $(-\infty, 0) \cup (0, \infty)$

47. $(-\infty, \infty)$ 49. $\left[-\dfrac{1}{2}, 1\right]$ 51. $(-\infty, -3) \cup (0, \infty)$ 53. $\varnothing$

55. $\left\{\dfrac{3}{8}\right\}$ 57. $\left(-\dfrac{2}{3}, 0\right)$ 59. $(-\infty, -12) \cup (0, \infty)$ 61. $[-1, 8]$

63. $\left[-\dfrac{23}{8}, \dfrac{17}{8}\right]$ 65. $(-2, 5)$ 67. $5, -2$ 69. $(-\infty, -7] \cup [17, \infty)$ 71. $-\dfrac{9}{4}$ 73. $(-2, 1)$ 75. $2, \dfrac{4}{3}$ 77. $\varnothing$

79. $\dfrac{19}{2}, -\dfrac{17}{2}$ 81. $\left(-\infty, -\dfrac{25}{3}\right) \cup \left(\dfrac{35}{3}, \infty\right)$ 83. 55 million, 97 million, 138 million   85. -1.5 87. 0   89. $|x| < 7$ 91. $|x| \le 5$

93. answers may vary   95. $3.45 < x < 3.55$

Integrated Review

1. $(-5, 7)$ 2. $(-\infty, \infty)$ 3. $1, \dfrac{1}{2}$ 4. $(-3, 2)$ 5. $(-\infty, -1] \cup [1, \infty)$ 6. $-18, -\dfrac{4}{3}$

7. $\left[-\dfrac{2}{3}, 4\right]$ 8. $\varnothing$ 9. $(-\infty, 1]$ 10. $(-\infty, 0]$ 11. $[0, 6]$ 12. $-\dfrac{3}{2}, 1$ 13. B   14. E

15. A   16. C   17. D

Section 9.4
Practice Exercises

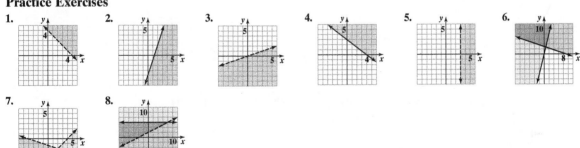

Vocabulary, Readiness & Video Check 9.4

1. linear inequality in two variables   3. false   5. true   7. yes   9. yes   11. We find the boundary line equation by replacing the inequality symbol with $=$. The points on this line are solutions (line is solid) if the inequality is $\ge$ or $\le$; they are not solutions (line is dashed) if the inequality is $>$ or $<$.

Exercise Set 9.4

1. no; yes   **3.** no; no   **5.** no; yes   **7.**

9.   **11.**   **13.**

15.   **17.**   **19.**   **21.**   **23.**

25.   **27.**   **29.**   **31.**   **33.**

35.   **37.**   **39.**   **41.**   **43.** e   **45.** c   **47.** f

49.   **51.**   **53.**   **55.**   **57.**

59.   **61.**   **63.**   **65.**   **67.**

69.   **71.** no solution; { } or ∅   **73.** 25   **75.** −2   **77.** yes   **79.** yes   **81.** $x + y \geq 13$

83. answers may vary   **85.**   **87.** answers may vary   **89. a.** $30x + 0.15y \leq 500$ **b.**

c. answers may vary   **91.** C   **93.** D   **95.**   **97.** answers may vary

CHAPTER 10 RATIONAL EXPONENTS, RADICALS, AND COMPLEX NUMBERS

Section 10.1
Practice Exercises

1. a. 7   **b.** 0   **c.** $\dfrac{4}{9}$ **d.** 0.8   **e.** z^4 **f.** $4b^2$ **g.** -6 **h.** not a real number   **2.** 6.708   **3. a.** -1 **b.** 3   **c.** $\dfrac{3}{4}$ **d.** x^4 **e.** $-$

4. a. 10   **b.** -1 **c.** -9 **d.** not a real number   **e.** $3x^3$ **5. a.** 4   **b.** $|x^7|$ **c.** $|x + 7|$ **d.** -7 **e.** $3x - 5$
f. $7|x|$ **g.** $|x + 8|$ **6. a.** 4   **b.** 2   **c.** 2   **d.** $\sqrt[3]{-9}$ **7.**   **8.**

Vocabulary, Readiness & Video Check 10.1

1. index; radical sign; radicand   **3.** is not   **5.** $[0,\infty)$ **7.** $(16, 4)$ **9.** Divide the index into each exponent in the radicand.   **11.** The square root of a negative number is not a real number, but the cube root of a negative number is a real number.   **13.** For odd roots, there's only one root/answer whether the radicand is positive or negative, so absolute value bars aren't needed.

Exercise Set 10.1

1. 10   **3.** $\dfrac{1}{2}$ **5.** 0.01   **7.** -6 **9.** x^5 **11.** $4y^3$ **13.** 2.646   **15.** 6.164   **17.** 14.142   **19.** 4   **21.** $\dfrac{1}{2}$ **23.** -1 **25.** x^4

27. $-3x^3$ **29.** -2 **31.** not a real number   **33.** -2 **35.** x^4 **37.** $2x^2$ **39.** $9x^2$ **41.** $4x^2$ **43.** 8   **45.** -8 **47.** $2|x|$

49. x **51.** $|x - 5|$ **53.** $|x + 2|$ **55.** -11 **57.** $2x$ **59.** y^6 **61.** $5ab^{10}$ **63.** $-3x^4y^3$ **65.** a^4b **67.** $-2x^2y$ **69.** $\dfrac{5}{7}$

71. $\dfrac{x^{10}}{2y}$ **73.** $-\dfrac{z^7}{3x}$ **75.** $\dfrac{x}{2}$ **77.** $\sqrt{3}$ **79.** -1 **81.** -3 **83.** $\sqrt{7}$

85. $[0,\infty)$;   **87.** $[3,\infty)$; 0, 1, 2, 3   **89.** $(-\infty,\infty)$;   **91.** $(-\infty,\infty)$; 0, 1, -1, 2, -2

93. $-32x^{15}y^{10}$ **95.** $-60x^7y^{10}z^5$ **97.** $\dfrac{x^9y^5}{2}$ **99.** not a real number   **101.** not a real number   **103.** d   **105.** d   **107.** b   **109.** b

111. answers may vary   **113.** 1.69 sq m   **115.** 11,181 m per sec   **117.** answers may vary   **119.**

121.

Section 10.2
Practice Exercises

1. a. 6   **b.** 10   **c.** $\sqrt[3]{x}$ **d.** 1   **e.** -8 **f.** $5x^3$ **g.** $3\sqrt[4]{x}$ **2. a.** 64   **b.** -1 **c.** -27 **d.** $\dfrac{1}{125}$ **e.** $\sqrt[9]{(3x + 2)^5}$

3. a. $\dfrac{1}{27}$ **b.** $\dfrac{1}{16}$ **4. a.** $y^{10/3}$ **b.** $x^{17/20}$ **c.** $\dfrac{1}{9}$ **d.** $b^{2/9}$ **e.** $\dfrac{81}{x^3y^{11/3}}$ **5. a.** $x^{14/15} - x^{13/5}$ **b.** $x + 4x^{1/2} - 12$ **6.** $x^{-1/5}(2 - 7x)$

7. a. $\sqrt[3]{x}$ **b.** $\sqrt{6}$ **c.** $\sqrt[4]{a^2b}$ **8. a.** $\sqrt[12]{x^7}$ **b.** $\sqrt[15]{y^2}$ **c.** $\sqrt[6]{675}$

Vocabulary, Readiness & Video Check 10.2

1. true   **3.** true   **5.** multiply, c   **7.** $-\sqrt[5]{3x}$ **9.** denominator; positive   **11.** Write the radical using an equivalent fractional exponent form, simplify the fraction, then write as a radical again.

Exercise Set 10.2

1. 7   **3.** 3   **5.** $\dfrac{1}{2}$ **7.** 13   **9.** $2\sqrt[3]{m}$ **11.** $3x^2$ **13.** -3 **15.** -2 **17.** 8   **19.** 16   **21.** not a real number   **23.** $\sqrt[5]{(2x)^3}$

25. $\sqrt[3]{(7x + 2)^2}$ **27.** $\dfrac{64}{27}$ **29.** $\dfrac{1}{16}$ **31.** $\dfrac{1}{16}$ **33.** not a real number   **35.** $\dfrac{1}{x^{1/4}}$ **37.** $a^{2/3}$ **39.** $\dfrac{5x^{3/4}}{7}$ **41.** $a^{7/3}$ **43.** x **45.** $3^{5/8}$

47. $y^{1/6}$ **49.** $8u^3$ **51.** $-b$ **53.** $\dfrac{1}{x^2}$ **55.** $27x^{2/3}$ **57.** $\dfrac{y}{z^{1/6}}$ **59.** $\dfrac{1}{x^{7/4}}$ **61.** $y - y^{7/6}$ **63.** $x^{5/3} - 2x^{2/3}$ **65.** $4x^{2/3} - 9$

67. $x^{8/3}(1 + x^{2/3})$ **69.** $x^{1/5}(x^{1/5} - 3)$ **71.** $x^{-1/3}(5 + x)$ **73.** $\sqrt{x}$ **75.** $\sqrt[3]{2}$ **77.** $2\sqrt{x}$ **79.** $\sqrt{xy}$ **81.** $\sqrt[3]{a^2b}$ **83.** $\sqrt{x + 3}$
85. $\sqrt[15]{y^{11}}$ **87.** $\sqrt[12]{b^5}$ **89.** $\sqrt[24]{x^{23}}$ **91.** $\sqrt{a}$ **93.** $\sqrt[6]{432}$ **95.** $\sqrt[15]{343y^5}$ **97.** $\sqrt[6]{125r^3s^2}$ **99.** $25 \cdot 3$ **101.** $16 \cdot 3$ or $4 \cdot 12$

103. $8 \cdot 2$ **105.** $27 \cdot 2$ **107.** A **109.** C **111.** B **113.** 1509 calories **115.** 302.0 million **117.** answers may vary **119.** $a^{1/3}$

121. $x^{1/5}$ **123.** 1.6818 **125.** 5.6645 **127.** $\dfrac{t^{1/2}}{u^{1/2}}$

Section 10.3
Practice Exercises

1. a. $\sqrt{35}$ **b.** $\sqrt{13z}$ **c.** 5 **d.** $\sqrt[3]{15x^2y}$ **e.** $\sqrt{\dfrac{5t}{2m}}$ **2. a.** $\dfrac{6}{7}$ **b.** $\dfrac{\sqrt{z}}{4}$ **c.** $\dfrac{5}{2}$ **d.** $\dfrac{\sqrt[4]{5}}{3x^2}$ **3. a.** $7\sqrt{2}$ **b.** $3\sqrt[3]{2}$

c. $\sqrt{35}$ **d.** $3\sqrt[4]{3}$ **4. a.** $6z^3\sqrt{z}$ **b.** $2pq^2\sqrt[3]{4pq}$ **c.** $2x^3\sqrt[4]{x^3}$ **5. a.** 4 **b.** $\dfrac{7}{3}\sqrt{z}$ **c.** $10xy^2\sqrt[3]{x^2}$ **d.** $6x^2y\sqrt[5]{2y}$

6. $\sqrt{17}$ units ≈ 4.123 units **7.** $\left(\dfrac{13}{2}, -4\right)$

Vocabulary, Readiness & Video Check 10.3

1. midpoint; point **3.** distance **5.** the indexes must be the same **7.** The power must be 1. Any even power is a perfect square and will leave no factor in the radicand; any higher odd power can have an even power factored from it, leaving one factor remaining in the radicand. **9.** average; average

Exercise Set 10.3

1. $\sqrt{14}$ **3.** 2 **5.** $\sqrt[3]{36}$ **7.** $\sqrt{6x}$ **9.** $\sqrt{\dfrac{14}{xy}}$ **11.** $\sqrt[4]{20x^3}$ **13.** $\dfrac{\sqrt{6}}{7}$ **15.** $\dfrac{\sqrt{2}}{7}$ **17.** $\dfrac{\sqrt[4]{x^3}}{2}$ **19.** $\dfrac{\sqrt[3]{4}}{3}$ **21.** $\dfrac{\sqrt[4]{8}}{x^2}$

23. $\dfrac{\sqrt[3]{2x}}{3y^4\sqrt[3]{3}}$ **25.** $\dfrac{x\sqrt{y}}{10}$ **27.** $\dfrac{x\sqrt{5}}{2y}$ **29.** $-\dfrac{z^2\sqrt[3]{z}}{3x}$ **31.** $4\sqrt{2}$ **33.** $4\sqrt[3]{3}$ **35.** $25\sqrt{3}$ **37.** $2\sqrt{6}$ **39.** $10x^2\sqrt{x}$ **41.** $2y^2\sqrt[3]{2y}$

43. $a^2b\sqrt[3]{b^3}$ **45.** $y^2\sqrt{y}$ **47.** $5ab\sqrt{b}$ **49.** $-2x^2\sqrt[5]{y}$ **51.** $x^4\sqrt[3]{50x^2}$ **53.** $-4a^4b^3\sqrt{2b}$ **55.** $3x^3y^4\sqrt{xy}$ **57.** $5r^3s^4$

59. $2x^3y\sqrt[4]{2y}$ **61.** $\sqrt{2}$ **63.** 2 **65.** 10 **67.** x^2y **69.** $24m^2$ **71.** $\dfrac{15x\sqrt{2x}}{2}$ or $\dfrac{15x}{2}\sqrt{2x}$ **73.** $2a^2\sqrt[4]{2}$ **75.** $2xy^2\sqrt[5]{x^2}$ **77.** 5 units

79. $\sqrt{41}$ units ≈ 6.403 units **81.** $\sqrt{10}$ units ≈ 3.162 units **83.** $\sqrt{5}$ units ≈ 2.236 units **85.** $\sqrt{192.58}$ units ≈ 13.877 units **87.** $(4,-2)$

89. $\left(-5, \dfrac{5}{2}\right)$ **91.** $(3,0)$ **93.** $\left(-\dfrac{1}{2}, \dfrac{1}{2}\right)$ **95.** $\left(\sqrt{2}, \dfrac{\sqrt{5}}{2}\right)$ **97.** $(6.2, -6.65)$ **99.** $14x$ **101.** $2x^2 - 7x - 15$ **103.** y^2

105. $-3x - 15$ **107.** $x^2 - 8x + 16$ **109.** true **111.** false **113.** true **115.** $\dfrac{\sqrt[3]{64}}{\sqrt{64}} = \dfrac{4}{8} = \dfrac{1}{2}$ **117.** x^7 **119.** a^3bc^5 **121.** $z^{10}\sqrt[3]{z^2}$

123. $q^2r^5s\sqrt[4]{q^3r^5}$ **125.** 1.6 m **127. a.** 20π sq cm **b.** 211.57 sq ft

Section 10.4
Practice Exercises

1. a. $8\sqrt{17}$ **b.** $-5\sqrt[3]{5z}$ **c.** $3\sqrt{2} + 5\sqrt[3]{2}$ **2. a.** $11\sqrt{6}$ **b.** $-9\sqrt[3]{3}$ **c.** $-2\sqrt{3x}$ **d.** $2\sqrt{10} + 2\sqrt[3]{5}$ **e.** $4x\sqrt[3]{3x}$

3. a. $\dfrac{5\sqrt{7}}{12}$ **b.** $\dfrac{13\sqrt[3]{6y}}{4}$ **4. a.** $2\sqrt{5} + 5\sqrt{3}$ **b.** $2\sqrt{3} + 2\sqrt{2} - \sqrt{30} - 2\sqrt{5}$ **c.** $6z + \sqrt{z} - 12$ **d.** $-6\sqrt{6} + 15$

e. $5x - 9$ **f.** $6\sqrt{x+2} + x + 11$

Vocabulary, Readiness & Video Check 10.4

1. Unlike **3.** Like **5.** $6\sqrt{3}$ **7.** $7\sqrt{x}$ **9.** $8\sqrt[3]{x}$ **11.** Sometimes you can't see that there are like radicals until you simplify, so you may incorrectly think you cannot add or subtract if you don't simplify first.

Exercise Set 10.4

1. $-2\sqrt{2}$ **3.** $10x\sqrt{2x}$ **5.** $17\sqrt{2} - 15\sqrt{5}$ **7.** $-\sqrt[3]{2x}$ **9.** $5b\sqrt{b}$ **11.** $\dfrac{31\sqrt{2}}{15}$ **13.** $\dfrac{\sqrt[3]{11}}{3}$ **15.** $\dfrac{5\sqrt{5x}}{9}$ **17.** $14 + \sqrt{3}$

19. $7 - 3y$ **21.** $6\sqrt{3} - 6\sqrt{2}$ **23.** $-23\sqrt[3]{5}$ **25.** $2a^3b\sqrt{ab}$ **27.** $20y\sqrt{2y}$ **29.** $2y\sqrt[3]{2x}$ **31.** $6\sqrt[3]{11} - 4\sqrt{11}$ **33.** $3x\sqrt[4]{x^3}$

35. $\dfrac{2\sqrt{3}}{3}$ **37.** $\dfrac{5x\sqrt[3]{x}}{7}$ **39.** $\dfrac{5\sqrt{7}}{2x}$ **41.** $\dfrac{\sqrt[3]{2}}{6}$ **43.** $\dfrac{14x\sqrt[3]{2x}}{9}$ **45.** $15\sqrt{3}$ in. **47.** $\sqrt{35} + \sqrt{21}$ **49.** $7 - 2\sqrt{10}$ **51.** $3\sqrt{x} - x\sqrt{3}$

53. $6x - 13\sqrt{x} - 5$ **55.** $\sqrt[3]{a^2} + \sqrt[3]{a} - 20$ **57.** $6\sqrt{2} - 12$ **59.** $2 + 2x\sqrt{3}$ **61.** $-16 - \sqrt{35}$ **63.** $x - y^2$ **65.** $3 + 2x\sqrt{3} + x^2$

67. $23x - 5x\sqrt{15}$ **69.** $2\sqrt[3]{2} - \sqrt[3]{4}$ **71.** $x + 1$ **73.** $x + 24 + 10\sqrt{x-1}$ **75.** $2x + 6 - 2\sqrt{2x+5}$ **77.** $x - 7$ **79.** $\dfrac{7}{x+y}$

81. $2a - 3$ **83.** $\dfrac{-2 + \sqrt{3}}{3}$ **85.** $22\sqrt{5}$ ft; 150 sq ft **87. a.** $2\sqrt{3}$ **b.** 3 **c.** answers may vary **89.** $2\sqrt{6} - 2\sqrt{2} - 2\sqrt{3} + 6$

91. answers may vary

Section 10.5
Practice Exercises

1. a. $\dfrac{5\sqrt{3}}{3}$ **b.** $\dfrac{15\sqrt{x}}{2x}$ **c.** $\dfrac{\sqrt[3]{6}}{3}$ **2.** $\dfrac{\sqrt{15yz}}{5y}$ **3.** $\dfrac{\sqrt[3]{z^2x^2}}{3x^2}$ **4. a.** $\dfrac{5(3\sqrt{5}-2)}{41}$ **b.** $\dfrac{\sqrt{6}+5\sqrt{3}+\sqrt{10}+5\sqrt{5}}{-2}$ **c.** $\dfrac{}{+x-y}$

5. $\dfrac{2}{\sqrt{10}}$ **6.** $\dfrac{5b}{\sqrt[3]{50ab^2}}$ **7.** $\dfrac{x-9}{4(\sqrt{x}+3)}$

Vocabulary, Readiness & Video Check 10.5

1. conjugate **3.** rationalizing the numerator **5.** To write an equivalent expression without a radical in the denominator. **7.** No, except for the fact you're working with numerators, the process is the same.

Exercise Set 10.5

1. $\dfrac{\sqrt{14}}{7}$ **3.** $\dfrac{\sqrt{5}}{5}$ **5.** $\dfrac{2\sqrt{x}}{x}$ **7.** $\dfrac{4\sqrt[3]{9}}{3}$ **9.** $\dfrac{3\sqrt{2x}}{4x}$ **11.** $\dfrac{3\sqrt[3]{2x}}{2x}$ **13.** $\dfrac{3\sqrt{3a}}{a}$ **15.** $\dfrac{3\sqrt[3]{4}}{2}$ **17.** $\dfrac{2\sqrt{21}}{7}$ **19.** $\dfrac{\sqrt{10xy}}{5y}$ **21.** $\dfrac{\sqrt[3]{75}}{5}$

23. $\dfrac{\sqrt{6x}}{10}$ **25.** $\dfrac{\sqrt{3z}}{6z}$ **27.** $\dfrac{\sqrt[3]{6xy^2}}{3x}$ **29.** $\dfrac{3\sqrt[4]{2}}{2}$ **31.** $\dfrac{2\sqrt[4]{9x}}{3x^2}$ **33.** $\dfrac{5\sqrt[5]{4ab^4}}{2ab^3}$ **35.** $\sqrt{2}-x$ **37.** $5+\sqrt{a}$ **39.** $-7\sqrt{5}-8\sqrt{x}$

41. $-2(2+\sqrt{7})$ **43.** $\dfrac{7(3+\sqrt{x})}{9-x}$ **45.** $-5+2\sqrt{6}$ **47.** $\dfrac{2a+2\sqrt{a}+\sqrt{ab}+\sqrt{b}}{4a-b}$ **49.** $-\dfrac{8(1-\sqrt{10})}{9}$ **51.** $\dfrac{x-\sqrt{xy}}{x-y}$

53. $\dfrac{5+3\sqrt{2}}{7}$ **55.** $\dfrac{5}{\sqrt{15}}$ **57.** $\dfrac{6}{\sqrt{10}}$ **59.** $\dfrac{2x}{7\sqrt{x}}$ **61.** $\dfrac{5y}{\sqrt[3]{100xy}}$ **63.** $\dfrac{2}{\sqrt{10}}$ **65.** $\dfrac{2x}{11\sqrt{2x}}$ **67.** $\dfrac{7}{2\sqrt[3]{49}}$ **69.** $\dfrac{3x^2}{10\sqrt[3]{9x}}$ **71.** $\dfrac{6x^2y^3}{\sqrt{6z}}$

73. $\dfrac{-7}{12+6\sqrt{11}}$ **75.** $\dfrac{3}{10+5\sqrt{7}}$ **77.** $\dfrac{x-9}{x-3\sqrt{x}}$ **79.** $\dfrac{1}{3+2\sqrt{2}}$ **81.** $\dfrac{x-1}{x-2\sqrt{x}+1}$ **83.** 5 **85.** $-\dfrac{1}{2},6$ **87.** $2,6$ **89.** $r=\dfrac{\sqrt{A\pi}}{2\pi}$

91. a. $\dfrac{y\sqrt{15xy}}{6x^2}$ **b.** $\dfrac{y\sqrt{15xy}}{6x^2}$ **c.** answers may vary **93.** $\sqrt[3]{25}$ **95.** answers may vary **97.** answers may vary

Integrated Review

1. 9 **2.** -2 **3.** $\dfrac{1}{2}$ **4.** x^3 **5.** y^3 **6.** $2y^5$ **7.** $-2y$ **8.** $3b^3$ **9.** 6 **10.** $\sqrt[5]{3y}$ **11.** $\dfrac{1}{16}$ **12.** $\sqrt[5]{(x+1)^3}$ **13.** y

14. $16x^{1/2}$ **15.** $x^{5/4}$ **16.** $4^{11/15}$ **17.** $2x^2$ **18.** $\sqrt[4]{a^3b^2}$ **19.** $\sqrt[4]{x^3}$ **20.** $\sqrt[6]{500}$ **21.** $2\sqrt{10}$ **22.** $2xy^2\sqrt[4]{x^3y^2}$ **23.** $3x\sqrt[3]{2x}$

24. $-2b^2\sqrt[5]{2}$ **25.** $\sqrt{5x}$ **26.** $4x$ **27.** $7y^2\sqrt{y}$ **28.** $2a^2\sqrt[4]{3}$ **29.** $2\sqrt{5}-5\sqrt{3}+5\sqrt{7}$ **30.** $y\sqrt[3]{2y}$ **31.** $\sqrt{15}-\sqrt{6}$ **32.** $10+2\sqrt{21}$

33. $4x^2-5$ **34.** $x+2-2\sqrt{x+1}$ **35.** $\dfrac{\sqrt{21}}{3}$ **36.** $\dfrac{5\sqrt[3]{4x}}{2x}$ **37.** $\dfrac{13-3\sqrt{21}}{5}$ **38.** $\dfrac{7}{\sqrt{21}}$ **39.** $\dfrac{3y}{\sqrt[3]{33y^2}}$ **40.** $\dfrac{x-4}{x+2\sqrt{x}}$

Section 10.6
Practice Exercises

1. 18 **2.** $\dfrac{1}{4},\dfrac{3}{4}$ **3.** 10 **4.** 9 **5.** $\dfrac{3}{25}$ **6.** $6\sqrt{3}$ meters **7.** $\sqrt{193}$ in. ≈ 13.89 in.

Graphing Calculator Explorations 10.6

1. 3.19 **3.** $\varnothing$ **5.** 3.23

Vocabulary, Readiness & Video Check 10.6

1. extraneous solution **3.** $x^2-10x+25$ **5.** Applying the power rule can result in an equation with more solutions than the original equation, so you need to check all proposed solutions in the original equation. **7.** Our answer is either a positive square root of a value or a negative square root of a value. We're looking for a length, which must be positive, so our answer must be the positive square root.

Exercise Set 10.6

1. 8 **3.** 7 **5.** $\varnothing$ **7.** 7 **9.** 6 **11.** $-\dfrac{9}{2}$ **13.** 29 **15.** 4 **17.** -4 **19.** $\varnothing$ **21.** 7 **23.** 9 **25.** 50 **27.** $\varnothing$

29. $\dfrac{15}{4}$ **31.** 13 **33.** 5 **35.** -12 **37.** 9 **39.** -3 **41.** 1 **43.** 1 **45.** $\dfrac{1}{2}$ **47.** $0,4$ **49.** $\dfrac{37}{4}$ **51.** $3\sqrt{5}$ ft

53. $2\sqrt{10}$ m **55.** $2\sqrt{131}$ m ≈ 22.9 m **57.** $\sqrt{100.84}$ mm ≈ 10.0 mm **59.** 17 ft **61.** 13 ft **63.** 14,657,415 sq mi **65.** 100 ft

67. 100 **69.** $\dfrac{\pi}{2}$ sec ≈ 1.57 sec **71.** 12.97 ft **73.** answers may vary **75.** $15\sqrt{3}$ sq mi ≈ 25.98 sq mi **77.** answers may vary

79. 0.51 km **81.** function **83.** function **85.** not a function **87.** $\dfrac{x}{4x+3}$ **89.** $-\dfrac{4z+2}{3z}$

91. $\sqrt{5x-1}+4=7$ **93.** 1 **95. a.–b.** answers may vary **97.** $-1,0,8,9$ **99.** $-1,4$
$$\sqrt{5x-1}=3$$
$$(\sqrt{5x-1})^2=3^2$$
$$5x-1=9$$
$$5x=10$$
$$x=2$$

Section 10.7

Practice Exercises

1. a. $2i$ **b.** $i\sqrt{7}$ **c.** $-3i\sqrt{2}$ **2. a.** $-\sqrt{30}$ **b.** -3 **c.** $25i$ **d.** $3i$ **3. a.** $-1-4i$ **b.** $-3+5i$ **c.** $3-2i$ **4. a.** $20+0i$

b. $-5+10i$ **c.** $15+16i$ **d.** $8-6i$ **e.** $85+0i$ **5. a.** $\dfrac{11}{10}-\dfrac{7i}{10}$ **b.** $0-\dfrac{5i}{2}$ **6. a.** i **b.** 1 **c.** -1 **d.** 1

Vocabulary, Readiness & Video Check 10.7

1. complex **3.** -1 **5.** real **7.** The product rule for radicals; you need to first simplify each separate radical and have nonnegative radicands before applying the product rule. **9.** the fact that $i^2 = -1$ **11.** $i, i^2 = -1, i^3 = -i, i^4 = 1$

Exercise Set 10.7

1. $9i$ **3.** $i\sqrt{7}$ **5.** -4 **7.** $8i$ **9.** $2i\sqrt{6}$ **11.** $-6i$ **13.** $24i\sqrt{7}$ **15.** $-3\sqrt{6}+0i$ **17.** $-\sqrt{14}$ **19.** $-5\sqrt{2}$ **21.** $4i$ **23.** $i\sqrt{3}$
25. $2\sqrt{2}$ **27.** $6-4i$ **29.** $-2+6i$ **31.** $-2-4i$ **33.** $-40+0i$ **35.** $18+12i$ **37.** $7+0i$ **39.** $12-16i$ **41.** $0-4i$
43. $\dfrac{28}{25}-\dfrac{21}{25}i$ **45.** $4+i$ **47.** $\dfrac{17}{13}+\dfrac{7}{13}i$ **49.** $63+0i$ **51.** $2-i$ **53.** $27+3i$ **55.** $-\dfrac{5}{2}-2i$ **57.** $18+13i$ **59.** $20+0i$

61. $10+0i$ **63.** $2+0i$ **65.** $-5+\dfrac{16}{3}i$ **67.** $17+144i$ **69.** $\dfrac{3}{5}-\dfrac{1}{5}i$ **71.** $5-10i$ **73.** $\dfrac{1}{5}-\dfrac{8}{5}i$ **75.** $8-i$ **77.** $7+0i$

79. $12-16i$ **81.** 1 **83.** i **85.** $-i$ **87.** -1 **89.** -64 **91.** $-243i$ **93.** $40°$ **95.** $x^2 - 5x - 2 - \dfrac{6}{x-1}$ **97.** 5 people

99. 14 people **101.** 16.7% **103.** $-1-i$ **105.** $0+0i$ **107.** $2+3i$ **109.** $2+i\sqrt{2}$ **111.** $\dfrac{1}{2}-\dfrac{\sqrt{3}}{2}i$ **113.** answers may vary
115. $6-3i\sqrt{3}$ **117.** yes

CHAPTER 11 QUADRATIC EQUATIONS AND FUNCTIONS

Section 11.1

Practice Exercises

1. $-4\sqrt{2}, 4\sqrt{2}$ **2.** $-\sqrt{10}, \sqrt{10}$ **3.** $-3-2\sqrt{5}, -3+2\sqrt{5}$ **4.** $\dfrac{2+3i}{5}, \dfrac{2-3i}{5}$ or $\dfrac{2}{5} \pm \dfrac{3}{5}i$ **5.** $-2-\sqrt{7}, -2+\sqrt{7}$

6. $\dfrac{3-\sqrt{5}}{2}, \dfrac{3+\sqrt{5}}{2}$ **7.** $\dfrac{6-\sqrt{33}}{3}, \dfrac{6+\sqrt{33}}{3}$ **8.** $\dfrac{5-i\sqrt{31}}{4}, \dfrac{5+i\sqrt{31}}{4}$ or $\dfrac{5}{4} \pm \dfrac{\sqrt{31}}{4}i$ **9.** 6%

Graphing Calculator Explorations 11.1

1. $-1.27, 6.27$ **3.** $-1.10, 0.90$ **5.** no real solutions

Vocabulary, Readiness & Video Check 11.1

1. $\pm\sqrt{b}$ **3.** completing the square **5.** 9 **7.** We need a quantity squared by itself on one side of the equation. The only quantity squared is x, so we need to divide both sides by 2 before applying the square root property. **9.** We're looking for an interest rate so a negative value does not make sense.

Exercise Set 11.1

1. $-4, 4$ **3.** $-\sqrt{7}, \sqrt{7}$ **5.** $-3\sqrt{2}, 3\sqrt{2}$ **7.** $-\sqrt{10}, \sqrt{10}$ **9.** $-8, -2$ **11.** $6-3\sqrt{2}, 6+3\sqrt{2}$ **13.** $\dfrac{3-2\sqrt{2}}{2}, \dfrac{3+2\sqrt{2}}{2}$

15. $-3i, 3i$ **17.** $-\sqrt{6}, \sqrt{6}$ **19.** $-2i\sqrt{2}, 2i\sqrt{2}$ **21.** $\dfrac{1-4i}{3}, \dfrac{1+4i}{3}$ or $\dfrac{1}{3} \pm \dfrac{4}{3}i$ **23.** $-7-\sqrt{5}, -7+\sqrt{5}$ **25.** $-3-2i\sqrt{2}, -3+2i\sqrt{2}$

27. $x^2 + 16x + 64 = (x+8)^2$ **29.** $z^2 - 12z + 36 = (z-6)^2$ **31.** $p^2 + 9p + \dfrac{81}{4} = \left(p+\dfrac{9}{2}\right)^2$ **33.** $x^2 + x + \dfrac{1}{4} = \left(x+\dfrac{1}{2}\right)^2$

35. $-5, -3$ **37.** $-3 - \sqrt{7}, -3 + \sqrt{7}$ **39.** $\dfrac{-1 - \sqrt{5}}{2}, \dfrac{-1 + \sqrt{5}}{2}$ **41.** $-1 - \sqrt{6}, -1 + \sqrt{6}$ **43.** $\dfrac{-1 - \sqrt{29}}{2}, \dfrac{-1 + \sqrt{29}}{2}$

45. $\dfrac{6 - \sqrt{30}}{3}, \dfrac{6 + \sqrt{30}}{3}$ **47.** $\dfrac{3 - \sqrt{11}}{2}, \dfrac{3 + \sqrt{11}}{2}$ **49.** $-4, \dfrac{1}{2}$ **51.** $-4 - \sqrt{15}, -4 + \sqrt{15}$ **53.** $\dfrac{-3 - \sqrt{21}}{3}, \dfrac{-3 + \sqrt{21}}{3}$

55. $-1, \dfrac{5}{2}$ **57.** $-1 - i, -1 + i$ **59.** $3 - \sqrt{17}, 3 + \sqrt{17}$ **61.** $-2 - i\sqrt{2}, -2 + i\sqrt{2}$ **63.** $\dfrac{-15 - 7\sqrt{5}}{10}, \dfrac{-15 + 7\sqrt{5}}{10}$

65. $\dfrac{1 - i\sqrt{47}}{4}, \dfrac{1 + i\sqrt{47}}{4}$ or $\dfrac{1}{4} \pm \dfrac{\sqrt{47}}{4}i$ **67.** $-5 - i\sqrt{3}, -5 + i\sqrt{3}$ **69.** $-4, 1$ **71.** $\dfrac{2 - i\sqrt{2}}{2}, \dfrac{2 + i\sqrt{2}}{2}$ or $1 \pm \dfrac{\sqrt{2}}{2}i$

73. $\dfrac{-3 - \sqrt{69}}{6}, \dfrac{-3 + \sqrt{69}}{6}$ **75.** 20% **77.** 4% **79.** 9.63 sec **81.** 8.29 sec **83.** 15 ft by 15 ft **85.** $10\sqrt{2}$ cm **87.** -1

89. $3 + 2\sqrt{5}$ **91.** $\dfrac{1 - 3\sqrt{2}}{2}$ **93.** $2\sqrt{6}$ **95.** 5 **97.** complex, but not real numbers **99.** real numbers **101.** complex, but not real numbers **103.** $-8x, 8x$ **105.** $-5z, 5z$ **107.** answers may vary **109.** compound; answers may vary **111.** 6 thousand scissors

Section 11.2
Practice Exercises

1. $2, -\dfrac{1}{3}$ **2.** $\dfrac{4 - \sqrt{22}}{3}, \dfrac{4 + \sqrt{22}}{3}$ **3.** $1 - \sqrt{17}, 1 + \sqrt{17}$ **4.** $\dfrac{-1 - i\sqrt{15}}{4}, \dfrac{-1 + i\sqrt{15}}{4}$ or $-\dfrac{1}{4} \pm \dfrac{\sqrt{15}}{4}i$ **5. a.** one real solution
b. two real solutions **c.** two complex, but not real solutions **6.** 6 ft **7.** 2.4 sec

Vocabulary, Readiness & Video Check 11.2

1. $x = \dfrac{-b \pm \sqrt{b^2 - 4ac}}{2a}$ **3.** $-5; -7$ **5.** $1; 0$ **7. a.** Yes, in order to make sure we have correct values for $a, b,$ and c. **b.** No; clearing
fractions makes the work less tedious, but it's not a necessary step. **9.** With applications, we need to make sure we answer the question(s) asked. Here we're asked how much distance is saved, so once the dimensions of the triangle are known, further calculations are needed to answer this question and solve the problem.

Exercise Set 11.2

1. $-6, 1$ **3.** $-\dfrac{3}{5}, 1$ **5.** 3 **7.** $\dfrac{-7 - \sqrt{33}}{2}, \dfrac{-7 + \sqrt{33}}{2}$ **9.** $\dfrac{1 - \sqrt{57}}{8}, \dfrac{1 + \sqrt{57}}{8}$ **11.** $\dfrac{7 - \sqrt{85}}{6}, \dfrac{7 + \sqrt{85}}{6}$ **13.** $1 - \sqrt{3}, 1 + \sqrt{3}$

15. $-\dfrac{3}{2}, 1$ **17.** $\dfrac{3 - \sqrt{11}}{2}, \dfrac{3 + \sqrt{11}}{2}$ **19.** $\dfrac{-5 - \sqrt{17}}{2}, \dfrac{-5 + \sqrt{17}}{2}$ **21.** $\dfrac{5}{2}, 1$ **23.** $-3 - 2i, -3 + 2i$ **25.** $-2 - \sqrt{11}, -2 + \sqrt{11}$

27. $\dfrac{3 - i\sqrt{87}}{8}, \dfrac{3 + i\sqrt{87}}{8}$ or $\dfrac{3}{8} \pm \dfrac{\sqrt{87}}{8}i$ **29.** $\dfrac{3 - \sqrt{29}}{2}, \dfrac{3 + \sqrt{29}}{2}$ **31.** $\dfrac{-5 - i\sqrt{5}}{10}, \dfrac{-5 + i\sqrt{5}}{10}$ or $-\dfrac{1}{2} \pm \dfrac{\sqrt{5}}{10}i$ **33.** $\dfrac{-1 - \sqrt{19}}{6}, \dfrac{-1 + \sqrt{19}}{6}$

35. $\dfrac{-1 - i\sqrt{23}}{4}, \dfrac{-1 + i\sqrt{23}}{4}$ or $-\dfrac{1}{4} \pm \dfrac{\sqrt{23}}{4}i$ **37.** 1 **39.** $3 - \sqrt{5}, 3 + \sqrt{5}$ **41.** two real solutions **43.** one real solution

45. two real solutions **47.** two complex but not real solutions **49.** two real solutions **51.** 14 ft **53.** $\left(2 + 2\sqrt{2}\right)$ cm, $\left(2 + 2\sqrt{2}\right)$ cm,
$\left(4 + 2\sqrt{2}\right)$ cm **55.** width: $\left(-5 + 5\sqrt{17}\right)$ ft; length: $\left(5 + 5\sqrt{17}\right)$ ft **57. a.** $50\sqrt{2}$ m **b.** 5000 sq m **59.** 37.4 ft by 38.5 ft

61. base, $\left(2 + 2\sqrt{43}\right)$ cm; height, $\left(-1 + \sqrt{43}\right)$ cm **63.** 8.9 sec **65.** 2.8 sec **67.** $\dfrac{11}{5}$ **69.** 15 **71.** $(x^2 + 5)(x + 2)(x - 2)$

73. $(z + 3)(z - 3)(z + 2)(z - 2)$ **75.** b **77.** answers may vary **79.** 0.6, 2.4 **81.** Sunday to Monday **83.** Wednesday **85.** 32; yes

87. a. 20,568 students **b.** 2015 **89. a.** 9076 thousand barrels per day **b.** 2007 **c.** 2012 **91.** answers may vary **93.** $\dfrac{\sqrt{3}}{3}$

95. $\dfrac{-\sqrt{2} - i\sqrt{2}}{2}, \dfrac{-\sqrt{2} + i\sqrt{2}}{2}$ or $-\dfrac{\sqrt{2}}{2} \pm \dfrac{\sqrt{2}}{2}i$ **97.** $\dfrac{\sqrt{3} - \sqrt{11}}{4}, \dfrac{\sqrt{3} + \sqrt{11}}{4}$

99. 8.9 sec: 2.8 sec: **101.** two real solutions

Section 11.3
Practice Exercises

1. 8 **2.** $\dfrac{5 \pm \sqrt{137}}{8}$ **3.** $4, -4, 3i, -3i$ **4.** $1, -3$ **5.** $1, 64$ **6.** Katy: $\dfrac{7 + \sqrt{65}}{2} \approx 7.5$ hr; Steve: $\dfrac{9 + \sqrt{65}}{2} \approx 8.5$ hr

7. to Shanghai: 40 km/hr; to Ningbo: 90 km/hr

Vocabulary, Readiness & Video Check 11.3

1. The values we get for the substituted variable are *not* our final answers. Remember to always substitute back to the original variable and solve for it if necessary.

Exercise Set 11.3

1. 2   **3.** 16   **5.** 1, 4   **7.** $3 - \sqrt{7}, 3 + \sqrt{7}$ **9.** $\dfrac{3 - \sqrt{57}}{4}, \dfrac{3 + \sqrt{57}}{4}$ **11.** $\dfrac{1 - \sqrt{29}}{2}, \dfrac{1 + \sqrt{29}}{2}$ **13.** $-2, 2, -2i, 2i$

15. $-\dfrac{1}{2}, \dfrac{1}{2}, -i\sqrt{3}, i\sqrt{3}$ **17.** $-3, 3, -2, 2$ **19.** $125, -8$ **21.** $-\dfrac{4}{5}, 0$ **23.** $-\dfrac{1}{8}, 27$ **25.** $-\dfrac{2}{3}, \dfrac{4}{3}$ **27.** $-\dfrac{1}{125}, \dfrac{1}{8}$ **29.** $-\sqrt{2}, \sqrt{2}, -\sqrt{3}, \sqrt{3}$

31. $\dfrac{-9 - \sqrt{201}}{6}, \dfrac{-9 + \sqrt{201}}{6}$ **33.** 2, 3   **35.** 3   **37.** 27, 125   **39.** $1, -3i, 3i$ **41.** $\dfrac{1}{8}, -8$ **43.** $-\dfrac{1}{2}, \dfrac{1}{3}$ **45.** 4   **47.** -3

49. $-\sqrt{5}, \sqrt{5}, -2i, 2i$ **51.** $-3, \dfrac{3 - 3i\sqrt{3}}{2}, \dfrac{3 + 3i\sqrt{3}}{2}$ or $-3, \dfrac{3}{2} \pm \dfrac{3\sqrt{3}}{2}i$ **53.** 6, 12   **55.** $-\dfrac{1}{3}, \dfrac{1}{3}, -\dfrac{i\sqrt{6}}{3}, \dfrac{i\sqrt{6}}{3}$ **57.** 5   **59.** 55 mph: 66 mph

61. 5 mph, then 4 mph   **63.** inlet pipe: 15.5 hr; hose: 16.5 hr   **65.** 8.5 hr   **67.** 12 or -8 **69. a.** $(x - 6)$ in.   **b.** $300 = (x - 6) \cdot (x - 6) \cdot 3$ **c.** 16 in. by 16 in.   **71.** 22 feet   **73.** $(-\infty, 3]$ **75.** $(-5, \infty)$ **77.** domain: $(-\infty, \infty)$; range: $(-\infty, \infty)$; function   **79.** domain: $(-\infty, \infty)$; range: $[-1, \infty)$; function   **81.** $1, -3i, 3i$ **83.** $-\dfrac{1}{2}, \dfrac{1}{3}$ **85.** $-3, \dfrac{3 - 3i\sqrt{3}}{2}, \dfrac{3 + 3i\sqrt{3}}{2}$ or $-3, \dfrac{3}{2} \pm \dfrac{3\sqrt{3}}{2}i$ **87.** answers may vary

89. a. 11.615 m/sec   **b.** 11.612 m/sec   **c.** 25.925 mph

Integrated Review

1. $-\sqrt{10}, \sqrt{10}$ **2.** $-\sqrt{14}, \sqrt{14}$ **3.** $1 - 2\sqrt{2}, 1 + 2\sqrt{2}$ **4.** $-5 - 2\sqrt{3}, -5 + 2\sqrt{3}$ **5.** $-1 - \sqrt{13}, -1 + \sqrt{13}$ **6.** 1, 11

7. $\dfrac{-3 - \sqrt{69}}{6}, \dfrac{-3 + \sqrt{69}}{6}$ **8.** $\dfrac{-2 - \sqrt{5}}{4}, \dfrac{-2 + \sqrt{5}}{4}$ **9.** $\dfrac{2 - \sqrt{2}}{2}, \dfrac{2 + \sqrt{2}}{2}$ **10.** $-3 - \sqrt{5}, -3 + \sqrt{5}$ **11.** $-2 - i\sqrt{3}, -2 + i\sqrt{3}$

12. $\dfrac{-1 - i\sqrt{11}}{2}, \dfrac{-1 + i\sqrt{11}}{2}$ or $-\dfrac{1}{12} \pm \dfrac{\sqrt{11}}{2}i$ **13.** $\dfrac{-3 - i\sqrt{15}}{2}, \dfrac{-3 + i\sqrt{15}}{2}$ or $-\dfrac{3}{2} \pm \dfrac{\sqrt{15}}{2}i$ **14.** $-3i, 3i$ **15.** $-17, 0$

16. $\dfrac{1 - \sqrt{13}}{4}, \dfrac{1 + \sqrt{13}}{4}$ **17.** $2 - 3\sqrt{3}, 2 + 3\sqrt{3}$ **18.** $2 - \sqrt{3}, 2 + \sqrt{3}$ **19.** $-2, \dfrac{4}{3}$ **20.** $\dfrac{-5 - \sqrt{17}}{4}, \dfrac{-5 + \sqrt{17}}{4}$

21. $1 - \sqrt{6}, 1 + \sqrt{6}$ **22.** $-\sqrt{31}, \sqrt{31}$ **23.** $-\sqrt{11}, \sqrt{11}$ **24.** $-i\sqrt{11}, i\sqrt{11}$ **25.** $-11, 6$ **26.** $\dfrac{-3 - \sqrt{19}}{5}, \dfrac{-3 + \sqrt{19}}{5}$

27. $\dfrac{-3 - \sqrt{17}}{4}, \dfrac{-3 + \sqrt{17}}{4}$ **28.** 4   **29.** $\dfrac{-1 - \sqrt{17}}{8}, \dfrac{-1 + \sqrt{17}}{8}$ **30.** $10\sqrt{2}$ ft ≈ 14.1 ft   **31.** Jack: 9.1 hr; Lucy: 7.1 hr

32. 5 mph during the first part, then 6 mph

Section 11.4
Practice Exercises

1. $(-\infty, -3) \cup (4, \infty)$ **2.** $[0, 8]$ **3.** $(-\infty, -3] \cup [-1, 2]$ **4.** $(-4, 5]$ **5.** $(-\infty, -3) \cup \left(-\dfrac{8}{5}, \infty\right)$

Vocabulary, Readiness & Video Check 11.4

1. $[-7, 3)$ **3.** $(-\infty, 0]$ **5.** $(-\infty, -12) \cup [-10, \infty)$ **7.** We use the solutions to the related equation to divide the number line into regions that either entirely are or entirely are not solution regions; the solutions to the related equation are solutions to the inequality only if the inequality symbol is $\leq$ or $\geq$.

Exercise Set 11.4

1. $(-\infty, -5) \cup (-1, \infty)$ **3.** $[-4, 3]$ **5.** $[2, 5]$ **7.** $\left(-5, -\dfrac{1}{3}\right)$ **9.** $(2, 4) \cup (6, \infty)$ **11.** $(-\infty, -4] \cup [0, 1]$

13. $(-\infty, -3) \cup (-2, 2) \cup (3, \infty)$ **15.** $(-7, 2)$ **17.** $(-1, \infty)$ **19.** $(-\infty, -1] \cup (4, \infty)$ **21.** $(-\infty, 2) \cup \left(\dfrac{11}{4}, \infty\right)$ **23.** $(0, 2] \cup [3, \infty)$

25. $(-\infty, 3)$ **27.** $\left[-\dfrac{5}{4}, \dfrac{3}{2}\right]$ **29.** $(-\infty, 0) \cup (1, \infty)$ **31.** $(-\infty, -4] \cup [4, 6]$ **33.** $\left(-\infty, -\dfrac{2}{3}\right] \cup \left[\dfrac{3}{2}, \infty\right)$ **35.** $\left(-4, -\dfrac{3}{2}\right) \cup \left(\dfrac{3}{2}, \infty\right)$

37. $(-\infty, -5] \cup [-1, 1] \cup [5, \infty)$ **39.** $\left(-\infty, -\dfrac{5}{3}\right) \cup \left(\dfrac{7}{2}, \infty\right)$ **41.** $(0, 10)$ **43.** $(-\infty, -4) \cup [5, \infty)$ **45.** $(-\infty, -6] \cup (-1, 0] \cup (7, \infty)$

47. $(-\infty, 1) \cup (2, \infty)$ **49.** $(-\infty, -8] \cup (-4, \infty)$ **51.** $(-\infty, 0] \cup \left(5, \dfrac{11}{2}\right]$ **53.** $(0, \infty)$ **55.**

57.

$g(x) = |x| + 2$ $f(x) = |x| - 1$

59. $f(x) = x^2 - 3$ **61.** $h(x) = x^2 + 1$ **63.** answers may vary   **65.** $(-\infty, -1) \cup (0, 1)$, or any number less than -1 or between 0 and 1   **67.** x is between 2 and 11   **69.**   **71.**

Section 11.5
Practice Exercises

1.   **2. a.**   **b.**   **3.**   **4. a.**   **b.**

5.   **6.**   **7.**   **8.**

Graphing Calculator Explorations 11.5

1.   **3.**   **5.**

Vocabulary, Readiness & Video Check 11.5

1. quadratic   **3.** upward   **5.** lowest   **7.** $(0,0)$ **9.** $(2,0)$ **11.** $(0,3)$ **13.** $(-1,5)$ **15.** Graphs of the form $f(x) = x^2 + k$ shift up or down the y-axis k units from $y = x^2$; the y-intercept.   **17.** The vertex, (h,k), and the axis of symmetry, $x = h$; the basic shape of $y = x^2$ does not change.   **19.** the coordinates of the vertex, whether the graph opens upward or downward, whether the graph is narrower or wider than $y = x^2$, and the graph's axis of symmetry

Exercise Set 11.5

1.   **3.**   **5.**   **7.**   **9.**   **11.**

13.   **15.**   **17.**   **19.**   **21.**   **23.**

25.   **27.**   **29.**   **31.**   **33.**   **35.**

37.   **39.**   **41.**   **43.**

45.   **47.**   **49.**   **51.**

53.
$y = -2(x - 4)^2 + 5$

55. $x^2 + 8x + 16$ **57.** $z^2 - 16z + 64$ **59.** $y^2 + y + \dfrac{1}{4}$ **61.** $-6, 2$ **63.** $-5 - \sqrt{26}, -5 + \sqrt{26}$

65. $4 - 3\sqrt{2}, 4 + 3\sqrt{2}$ **67.** c **69.** $f(x) = 5(x - 2)^2 + 3$ **71.** $f(x) = 5(x + 3)^2 + 6$

73. **75.** **77.** **79. a.** 119,141 million **b.** 284,953 million

Section 11.6
Practice Exercises

1. **2.** **3.** **4.** $(1, -4)$ **5.** Maximum height 9 feet in $\dfrac{3}{4}$ second

Vocabulary, Readiness & Video Check 11.6

1. (h, k) **3.** We can immediately identify the vertex (h, k), whether the parabola opens upward or downward, and know its axis of symmetry; completing the square. **5.** the vertex

Exercise Set 11.6

1. $0; 1$ **3.** $2; 1$ **5.** $1; 1$ **7.** down **9.** up **11.** $(-4, -9)$ **13.** $(5, 30)$ **15.** $(1, -2)$ **17.** $\left(\dfrac{1}{2}, \dfrac{5}{4}\right)$ **19.** D **21.** B

23. $y = x^2 + 4x - 5$ **25.** **27.** $y = x^2 - 4$ **29.** $y = 4x^2 + 4x - 3$ **31.** $y = \dfrac{1}{2}x^2 + 4x + \dfrac{15}{2}$

33. $y = x^2 - 6x + 5$ **35.** $y = x^2 - 4x + 5$ **37.** $y = 2x^2 + 4x + 5$ **39.** $y = -2x^2 + 12x$ **41.** $y = x^2 + 1$

43. $y = x^2 - 2x - 15$ **45.** $y = -5x^2 + 5x$ **47.** $y = -x^2 + 2x - 12$ **49.** $y = 3x^2 - 12x + 15$ **51.** $y = x^2 + x - 6$

53. $\left(-\dfrac{3}{4}, \dfrac{289}{8}\right)$ $y = -2x^2 - 3x + 35$ **55.** 144 ft **57. a.** 200 bicycles **b.** $12,000 **59.** 30 and 30 **61.** $5, -5$ **63.** length, 20 units; width, 20 units

65. $y = x^2 + 2$ **67.** $y = x + 2$ **69.** $y = (x + 5)^2 + 2$ **71.** $y = 3(x - 4)^2 + 1$ **73.** $y = -(x - 4)^2 + \dfrac{3}{2}$

75. minimum value   **77.** maximum value   **79.** $y = x^2 + 10x + 15$ **81.**   **83.** -0.84 **85.** 1.43

87. a. maximum; answers may vary   **b.** 2035   **c.** 311 million   **89.**   **91.**

CHAPTER 12 EXPONENTIAL AND LOGARITHMIC FUNCTIONS

Section 12.1
Practice Exercises

1. a. $4x + 7$ **b.** $-2x - 3$ **c.** $3x^2 + 11x + 10$ **d.** $\dfrac{x + 2}{3x + 5}$, where $x \neq -\dfrac{5}{3}$ **2. a.** 50; 46   **b.** $9x^2 - 30x + 26$; $3x^2 - 2$
3. a. $x^2 + 6x + 14$ **b.** $x^2 + 8$ **4. a.** $(h \circ g)(x)$ **b.** $(g \circ f)(x)$

Vocabulary, Readiness & Video Check 12.1
1. C   **3.** F   **5.** D   **7.** You can find $(f + g)(x)$ and then find $(f + g)(2)$ or you can find $f(2)$ and $g(2)$ and then add those results.

Exercise Set 12.1

1. a. $3x - 6$ **b.** $-x - 8$ **c.** $2x^2 - 13x - 7$ **d.** $\dfrac{x - 7}{2x + 1}$, where $x \neq -\dfrac{1}{2}$ **3. a.** $x^2 + 5x + 1$ **b.** $x^2 - 5x + 1$ **c.** $5x^3 + 5x$
d. $\dfrac{x^2 + 1}{5x}$, where $x \neq 0$ **5. a.** $\sqrt[3]{x} + x + 5$ **b.** $\sqrt[3]{x} - x - 5$ **c.** $x\sqrt[3]{x} + 5\sqrt[3]{x}$ **d.** $\dfrac{\sqrt[3]{x}}{x + 5}$, where $x \neq -5$
7. a. $5x^2 - 3x$ **b.** $-5x^2 - 3x$ **c.** $-15x^3$ **d.** $-\dfrac{3}{5x}$, where $x \neq 0$ **9.** 42   **11.** -18 **13.** 0
15. $(f \circ g)(x) = 25x^2 + 1$; $(g \circ f)(x) = 5x^2 + 5$ **17.** $(f \circ g)(x) = 2x + 11$; $(g \circ f)(x) = 2x + 4$
19. $(f \circ g)(x) = -8x^3 - 2x - 2$; $(g \circ f)(x) = -2x^3 - 2x + 4$ **21.** $(f \circ g)(x) = |10x - 3|$; $(g \circ f)(x) = 10|x| - 3$
23. $(f \circ g)(x) = \sqrt{-5x + 2}$; $(g \circ f)(x) = -5\sqrt{x} + 2$ **25.** $H(x) = (g \circ h)(x)$ **27.** $F(x) = (h \circ f)(x)$ **29.** $G(x) = (f \circ g)(x)$
31. answers may vary; for example, $g(x) = x + 2$ and $f(x) = x^2$ **33.** answers may vary; for example, $g(x) = x + 5$ and $f(x) = \sqrt{x} + 2$
35. answers may vary; for example, $g(x) = 2x - 3$ and $f(x) = \dfrac{1}{x}$ **37.** $y = x - 2$ **39.** $y = \dfrac{x}{3}$ **41.** $y = -\dfrac{x + 7}{2}$ **43.** 6   **45.** 4
47. 4   **49.** -1 **51.** answers may vary   **53.** $P(x) = R(x) - C(x)$

Section 12.2
Practice Exercises

1. a. one-to-one   **b.** not one-to-one   **c.** not one-to-one   **d.** one-to-one   **e.** not one-to-one   **f.** not one-to-one   **2. a.** no, not one-to-one
b. yes   **c.** yes   **d.** no, not a function   **e.** no, not a function   **3.** $f^{-1} = \{(4, 3), (0, -2), (8, 2), (6, 6)\}$ **4.** $f^{-1}(x) = 6 - x$

5.   **6. a.**   **b.**   **7.** $f(f^{-1}(x)) = f\left(\dfrac{x + 1}{4}\right) = 4\left(\dfrac{x + 1}{4}\right) - 1 = x + 1 - 1 = x$

$f^{-1}(f(x)) = f^{-1}(4x - 1) = \dfrac{(4x - 1) + 1}{4} = \dfrac{4x}{4} = x$

Vocabulary, Readiness & Video Check 12.2
1. $(2, 11)$ **3.** the inverse of f **5.** vertical   **7.** $y = x$ **9.** Every function must have each x-value correspond to only one y-value. A one-to-one function must also have each y-value correspond to only one x-value.   **11.** Yes; by the definition of an inverse function.
13. Once you know some points of the original equation or graph, you can switch the x's and y's of these points to find points that satisfy the inverse and then graph it. You can also check that the two graphs (the original and the inverse) are symmetric about the line $y = x$.

Exercise Set 12.2
1. one-to-one; $f^{-1} = \{(-1, -1), (1, 1), (2, 0), (0, 2)\}$ **3.** one-to-one; $h^{-1} = \{(10, 10)\}$ **5.** one-to-one; $f^{-1} = \{(12, 11), (3, 4), (4, 3), (6, 6)\}$
7. not one-to-one   **9.** one-to-one;

Rank in Population (Input)	1	47	16	25	36	7
State (Output)	CA	AK	IN	LA	NM	OH

11. a. 3   **b.** 1   **13. a.** 1   **b.** -1 **15.** one-to-one   **17.** not one-to-one   **19.** one-to-one   **21.** not one-to-one

23. $f^{-1}(x) = x - 4$ **25.** $f^{-1}(x) = \dfrac{x + 3}{2}$ **27.** $f^{-1}(x) = 2x + 2$ **29.** $f^{-1}(x) = \sqrt[3]{x}$ **31.** $f^{-1}(x) = \dfrac{x - 2}{5}$ **33.** $f^{-1}(x) = 5x + 2$

35. $f^{-1}(x) = x^3$ **37.** $f^{-1}(x) = \dfrac{5 - x}{3x}$

39. $f^{-1}(x) = \sqrt[3]{x} - 2$

41.   **43.**   **45.**   **47.** $(f \circ f^{-1})(x) = x; (f^{-1} \circ f)(x) = x$ **49.** $(f \circ f^{-1})(x) = x; (f^{-1} \circ f)(x) = x$

51. 5   **53.** 8   **55.** $\dfrac{1}{27}$ **57.** 9   **59.** $3^{1/2} \approx 1.73$ **61. a.** $(2, 9)$ **b.** $(9, 2)$

63. a. $\left(-2, \dfrac{1}{4}\right), \left(-1, \dfrac{1}{2}\right), (0, 1), (1, 2), (2, 5)$ **b.** $\left(\dfrac{1}{4}, -2\right), \left(\dfrac{1}{2}, -1\right), (1, 0), (2, 1), (5, 2)$ **c.**   **d.**

65. answers may vary   **67.** $f^{-1}(x) = \dfrac{x - 1}{3};$ **69.** $f^{-1}(x) = x^3 - 1;$

Section 12.3
Practice Exercises

1.   **2.** $f(x) = \left(\dfrac{1}{3}\right)^x$ **3.**   **4. a.** 2   **b.** $\dfrac{4}{3}$ **c.** -4 **5.** \$3950.43   **6. a.** 90.54%   **b.** 60.86%

Graphing Calculator Explorations 12.3

1. 81.98%;   **3.** 22.54%

Vocabulary, Readiness & Video Check 12.3

1. exponential   **3.** yes   **5.** no; none   **7.** $(-\infty, \infty)$ **9.** In a polynomial function, the base is the variable and the exponent is the constant; in an exponential function, the base is the constant and the exponent is the variable.   **11.** $y = 30(0.996)^{101} \approx 20.0\,\text{lb}$

Exercise Set 12.3

1.   **3.**   **5.**   **7.**   **9.**   **11.**

13.   **15.**   **17.** C   **19.** B   **21.** 3   **23.** $\dfrac{3}{4}$ **25.** $\dfrac{8}{5}$ **27.** $-\dfrac{2}{3}$ **29.** 4   **31.** $\dfrac{3}{2}$

33. $-\dfrac{1}{3}$ **35.** -2 **37.** 24.6 lb   **39. a.** 9.7 billion lb   **b.** 12.3 billion lb   **41. a.** 192,927 students   **b.** 463,772 students   **43.** 378.0 million

45. 544,000 mosquitoes   **47.** \$7621.42   **49.** \$4065.59   **51.** 4   **53.** $\varnothing$ **55.** 2, 3   **57.** 3   **59.** -1 **61.** no   **63.** no   **65.** C

67. D   **69.** answers may vary   **71.**   **73.**   **75.** The graphs are the same since $\left(\dfrac{1}{2}\right)^{-x} = 2^x$.

77. 24.55 lb   **79.** 20.09 lb

Section 12.5
Practice Exercises

1. a. $3^4 = 81$ **b.** $5^{-1} = \dfrac{1}{5}$ **c.** $7^{1/2} = \sqrt{7}$ **d.** $13^4 = y$ **2. a.** $\log_4 64 = 3$ **b.** $\log_6 \sqrt[3]{6} = \dfrac{1}{3}$ **c.** $\log_5 \dfrac{1}{125} = -3$ **d.** $\log_\pi z = 7$

3. a. 2   **b.** -3 **c.** $\dfrac{1}{2}$ **4. a.** -2 **b.** 2   **c.** 36   **d.** 0   **e.** 0   **5. a.** 4   **b.** -2 **c.** 5   **d.** 4

6.   **7.**

Vocabulary, Readiness & Video Check 12.5

1. logarithmic   **3.** yes   **5.** no; none   **7.** $(-\infty, \infty)$ **9.** First write the equation as an equivalent exponential equation. Then solve.

Exercise Set 12.5

1. $6^2 = 36$ **3.** $3^{-3} = \dfrac{1}{27}$ **5.** $10^3 = 1000$ **7.** $9^4 = x$ **9.** $\pi^{-2} = \dfrac{1}{\pi^2}$ **11.** $7^{1/2} = \sqrt{7}$ **13.** $0.7^3 = 0.343$ **15.** $3^{-4} = \dfrac{1}{81}$

17. $\log_2 16 = 4$ **19.** $\log_{10} 100 = 2$ **21.** $\log_\pi x = 3$ **23.** $\log_{10} \dfrac{1}{10} = -1$ **25.** $\log_4 \dfrac{1}{16} = -2$ **27.** $\log_5 \sqrt{5} = \dfrac{1}{2}$

29. 3   **31.** -2 **33.** $\dfrac{1}{2}$ **35.** -1 **37.** 0   **39.** 2   **41.** 4   **43.** -3 **45.** 2   **47.** 81   **49.** 7   **51.** -3

53. -3 **55.** 2   **57.** 2   **59.** $\dfrac{27}{64}$ **61.** 10   **63.** 4   **65.** 5   **67.** $\dfrac{1}{49}$ **69.** 3   **71.** 3   **73.** 1   **75.** -1

77.   **79.**   **81.**   **83.**   **85.** 1   **87.** $\dfrac{x-4}{2}$ **89.** $\dfrac{2x+3}{x^2}$ **91.** 3

93. a. $g(2) = 25$ **b.** $(25, 2)$ **c.** $f(25) = 2$ **95.** answers may vary   **97.** $\dfrac{9}{5}$ **99.** 1

101.   **103.** $y = \left(\dfrac{1}{3}\right)^x$ **105.** answers may vary   **107.** 0.0827

Index

Photo Credits

Page 456 Christopher Parypa/Shutterstock

Page 457 Testing/Shutterstock

Page 487 Digital Vision/Thinkstock

Page 501 (top) SVLuma/Shutterstock

Page 501 (bottom) Ffooter/Shutterstock

Page 508 James Steidl/Shutterstock

Chapter 8

Page 510 Light Poet/Shutterstock

Page 520 Longimanus/Shutterstock

Page 526 Image100/Corbis Royalty Free

Page 539 Neil Roy Johnson/Shutterstock

Page 542 Johanna Goodyear/Shutterstock

Chapter 9

Page 551 Oleksiy Mark/Shutterstock

Chapter 10

Page 586 Zinaida/Shutterstock

Page 602 Jerryb8/Dreamstime

Page 611 Jorg Hackemann/Shutterstock

Page 631 Tramper2/Dreamstime

Chapter 11

Page 651 Typhoonski/Dreamstime

Page 658 Stockbyte/Thinkstock

Page 661 Andy Z./Shutterstock

Page 670 (left) Copyright © National Institute for Fusion Science, Japan

Page 670 (right) Tim Hester Photography/Shutterstock

Page 675 EDHAR/Shutterstock

Page 679 Vibrant Image Studio/Shutterstock

Page 680 Phillip Minnis/Shutterstock

Page 705 Daniel Yordanov/Shutterstock

Page 708 Keith10999/Dreamstime

Chapter 12

Page 712 Pryzmat/Dreamstime

Page 736 Blend Images/Shutterstock

Page 765 Franant/Dreamstime

Page 776 (top) George Doyle & Ciaran Griffin/Stockbyte/Thinkstock

Page 776 (bottom) George Doyle & Ciaran Griffin/Stockbyte/Thinkstock

Chapter 13

Page 779 Alex Melnick/Shutterstock

Appendix B

Page 859 Pcruciatti/Dreamstime